INTUITIONISM AND PROOF THEORY

STUDIES IN LOGIC

AND

THE FOUNDATIONS OF MATHEMATICS

NORTH-HOLLAND PUBLISHING COMPANY
AMSTERDAM · LONDON

INTUITIONISM AND PROOF THEORY

PROCEEDINGS OF THE SUMMER CONFERENCE AT BUFFALO N.Y. 1968

Edited by

A. KINO
J. MYHILL
R. E. VESLEY

1970

NORTH-HOLLAND PUBLISHING COMPANY
AMSTERDAM · LONDON

Library of Congress Catalog Card Number 77-97196

International Standard Book Number 7204 2257 4

PUBLISHERS:

NORTH-HOLLAND PUBLISHING COMPANY - AMSTERDAM

NORTH-HOLLAND PUBLISHING COMPANY, LTD. - LONDON

PRINTED IN THE NETHERLANDS

CONTENTS

* Prof. Yessenin-Volpin was invited to give the opening address, and submitted the paper herein printed as I. However he was unfortunately unable to attend, and Prof. Heyting read the paper VI as an opening address.
** Concluding address.

† Bernays was unfortunately unable to attend, and so his paper XXV was read by Howard

INTRODUCTION

This volume contains papers read at the Conference on Intuitionism and Proof Theory held at the State University of New York at Buffalo, New York, in August 1968. The conference was organized by us with the cooperation of the Department of Mathematics at S.U.N.Y., and with financial support provided partly by the National Science Foundation (Social Sciences Division) and partly by S.U.N.Y. We take this opportunity to thank Miss Melstrads of the National Science Foundation, Mr. Blackstone, Director of Summer Sessions at Buffalo, and Mr. Snell, Dean of the Graduate School at Buffalo, for their financial support which made the conference possible; as well as innumerable students and faculty at Buffalo, who helped us in innumerable ways.

The organization of the volume is as follows: Papers VI–XVIII deal with Intuitionism and papers XVII–XXXI with Proof Theory; the two related papers XVII and XVIII of Prawitz and Scarpellini represent the intersection of the two areas. The first five papers, including Yessenin-Volpin's inaugural address, represent various tendencies in constructive mathematics which do not fit squarely into the dichotomy intuitionism-vs.-formalism.

There are some discrepancies between the list of papers contained in this book and those actually read at the Conference. In particular, Takeuti gave a course of ten lectures on proof-theory, and Troelstra ten on intuitionism; the Takeuti lectures will be published in an extended form by North-Holland, and Troelstra's have already been published as vol. 95 in the Springer lecture-note series ("Principles of Intuitionism"). A paper by Gilmore ("Formalization of Naive Set Theory") was withdrawn because the system presented turned out to be inconsistent, and one by Sabbagh ("Extensions Finies de Fragments du Calcul Propositionnel Intuitionniste") because its results were found at the last minute to be properly included in those of McKay, *J. Symb. Logic* **33** (1968) 258–264. Papers by Krasner ("Definitionism") and De Jongh ("Elementary Remarks on Some Concepts and Methods of Intuitionism") were not received in time for inclusion in this volume. A paper by Hull ("Counterexamples in Intuitionistic Analysis") had already been accepted for publication in the Zeitschrift für Mathematische Logik before the conference was held (Z. Math. Logik **15** (1969) 241–246). Kleene's paper ("Formalized Recursive Functionals") was not included because of its length; it has subsequently appeared as number 89 of the Memoirs of the American Mathematical Society (1969). The paper XX of Feferman contains only a part of the material presented at the conference. The rest is contained in a privately circulated manuscript entitled "Ordinals Associated with Theories for one Inductively Defined Set".

Yessenin-Volpin was invited to give the opening address, but unfortunately could not come; he submitted the long paper with which this volume opens, an which stands here as an opening address. At the Conference itself an alternative opening address was read by Heyting (paper VI in this volume). Bernays too was unfortunately unable to come; his paper (paper XXV) was read by Howard.

Akiko Kino
John Myhill
Richard Vesley

SECTION A

NEW DIRECTIONS

THE ULTRA-INTUITIONISTIC CRITICISM AND THE ANTITRADITIONAL PROGRAM FOR FOUNDATIONS OF MATHEMATICS *

A. S. YESSENIN-VOLPIN

1. The aim of this program is to banish faith from the foundations of mathematics, *faith* being defined as any violation of the law of sufficient reason (for sentences). This law is defined as the identification (by definition) of *truth* with the result of a (present or feasible) proof, in spite of the traditional incompleteness theorem, which deals only with a very narrow kinds of proofs (which I call 'formal proofs'). I define *proof* as any fair way of making a sentence incontestable. Of course this explication is related to ethics – the notion *fair* means 'free from any *coercion* and *fraud*' – and to the theory of disputes, indicating the cases in which a sentence is to be considered as incontestable. Of course the methods of traditional mathematical logic are not sufficient for this program: and I have to enlarge the domain of means explicitly studied in logic. I shall work in a domain wherein are to be found only special notions of proof satisfying the mentioned explication. In this domain I shall allow as a means of proof only the strict following of definitions and other rules or principles of using signs. I shall indicate several new logical theories of this kind dealing with modalities, tenses and voices of verbs, with identifications and distinctions, with rules of attention and neglecting, with general principles of semiotics, etc., and with the help of these theories I shall reconstruct arithmetic and prove the consistency of Zermelo-Fraenkel set theory (ZF) with any finite number of inaccessible cardinals. This program has been studied by me in full detail. I don't insist I have eliminated all difficult questions – but I have introduced in my proofs no essentially new hypothesis and even if I *am* using some kind of hypotheses, these are all of a linguistic nature, and are common to all thinkers. I need no hypotheses concerning infinity.

But this program is too large for a short report, and here I shall confine

* Opening address.

myself to the exposition of my ultra-intuitionist criticism and of some main features of the positive program.

2. I begin with a criticism of the following *traditional* assumptions underlying the body of modern mathematics.

T1. The uniqueness (up to isomorphism) of the natural number series;

T2. The existence of the values of primitive *recursive* functions (prf) for every system of arguments for an arbitrary natural number series.

If for each system $x_1, \ldots, x_n$ of arguments in a natural number series N the value of $\varphi(x_1, \ldots, x_n)$ exists in N, I shall call N *closed* with respect to φ.

T3. The principle of mathematical induction from n to n'.

T4. If the axioms of a formal system are true and the rules of inference conserve the truth then each theorem is true.*

T5. The meaningfulness of the relations of identity and distinctness.

I criticize these assumptions above all simply on the ground they are assumptions. Their incontestability has never been established and this is sufficient reason to doubt them. But this radical line of criticism does not help to establish the connections between these assumptions, and I shall examine them more closely as follows.

Above all, proposition T1 uses a quantifier ranging over a domain including natural number series. It is too obscure to place at the beginning of mathematics.

I accept the traditional intuitionistic criticism of Brouwer and go further. I ask: why has such entity as 10^{12} to belong to a natural number series? Nobody has counted up to it (10^{12} seconds constituting more than 20 000 years) and every attempt to construct the 10^{12}-th member of sequence $0, 0', 0'', \ldots$ requires just 10^{12} steps. But the expression '*n* steps' presupposes that *n* is a natural number i.e. a number of a natural number series. So this

* The assumptions T1–T4 have been criticized by many people, e.g. Borel, Frechet, Mannoury, Rieger and van Dantzig doubted T1, or the 'finiteness' of very great numbers like $10^{10^{10}}$ (van Dantzig). Lusin spoke about T1 as a 'poignant problem'. The independence of T2 is a commonplace in the theory of primitive recursive functions; and doubts about the finiteness of $10^{10^{10}}$ lead immediately to a rejection of T2. H. Poincaré in his 'Science et Méthode' (1908) wrote that many people have rejected T3 because they found a vicious circle in its substantiation: he does not name these scientists, but the most plausible conjecture is that they spoke about the circle involving T3 and T4, as discussed in the text below.

But this criticism has never been made in a systematic manner and I never heard of anybody who has criticized T5 or T8.

natural attempt to construct the number 10^{12} in a natural number series involves a vicious circle. This vicious circle is no better than that involved in the impredicative definitions of set theory: and if we have proscribed these definitions we have to proscribe the belief in existence of a natural number 10^{12}, too.

Let us consider the series F of *feasible* numbers, i.e. of those up to which it is possible to count. The number 0 is feasible and if n is feasible then $n < 10^{12}$ and so n' also is feasible. And each feasible number can be obtained from 0 by adding $'$; so F forms a natural number series. But 10^{12} does not belong to F.

Nevertheless the traditional natural number series containing 10^{12} is generally supposed to exist. And if we accept it there are at least two different natural number series.

This is only the beginning of my criticism. I don't really believe in the *existence* of a series containing 10^{12} – I shall prove the *possibility* of such a series – and I shall not need the notion of feasibility or any other empirical notion for my proof of the possibility of distinct natural number series. But for the present let me continue the consideration of F. Since 10 and 12 are feasible numbers, 10^{12} is not such a number and the function a^b is a prf, T2 is violated for F.

This is not strange. The independence of T2 is many times indicated in the literature. The inductive definition of the natural numbers takes no account of the property T2 of a natural number series.

The mathematicians use the following way of constructing natural number sequences: one chooses a number a_0 and defines a_{n+1} in terms of a_n. Here I am interested only in the case $a_{n+1} > a_n$ for all n. I call a natural number series N *regular* if it is closed with respect to a_n for each such sequence a_n considered as a function of n. Of course, the assumption that every natural number series is regular is even stronger than T2: and so it is wrong.

I doubt the possibility of a regular natural number series. This notion depends on arbitrary sequences of numbers: and so it is connected with problems like that of the continuum. It is natural to consider the notion of T-regularity, T being a class of number sequences, and one may expect to obtain a T-regular series for certain concrete T's.

Of course, with the help of T3 (for arbitrary induction properties) one can prove the regularity of every natural number series but this is an argument against the acceptance of T3, at least in its most general form.

I call T4 *the locality principle* for proofs, – because it asserts that the property of a tree-figure of being a proof depends only on the local properties of this figure – more strictly, on the properties of its summits and nodes, the only 'integral' property consisting of the fact that the local properties are satisfied by each summit and node. A similar principle may be formulated for deductions from arbitrary premises in terms of 'truth relative to the premisses'.

It is clear that T4 depends on T3. Vice versa, T4 is used in obtaining $P(m)$ for arbitrary m from $P(0)$ and $\forall n(P(n) \supset P(n'))$. This vicious circle forces me to reject both T3 and T4 in the deepest questions of foundations of mathematics. It is essentially on these grounds that I am not searching for any axiomatic theory in my program.

This rejection of the axiomatic method does not mean the expulsion of the axioms and rules of inference as such. But I find that these rules are not sufficient to obtain a proof. We always need some supplementary 'rules of guarantee'. I shall consider the traditional tree-figures of logical proofs and deductions too, but I shall not consider them as such and I shall call them the *bodies* of proof or deduction or more briefly the *demonstroids* and the *deductoids*. The rule of guarantee requires that a demonstroid or deductoid is to be accompanied by an *establishment of its convincingness* (which I call also the *soul* of the proof or deduction). This establishment must constitute a proof of the fact that for the given demonstroid the applications of rules of inference considered together form a way of leading only to truths (and similarly for deductoids and relative truths, i.e. truths relative to the premises of deductoids). This is a new proof, and occasionally it may consist of a new demonstroid with its own establishment of convincingness. But in order that this procedure stops at some time, one has to have some primitive kind of proofs, independent of demonstroids. I call these proofs the *protodemonstrations*. The use of definitions and certain logical rules from domains deeper than the predicate calculus (modality theory, etc.) are the only means available in protodemonstrations.

The idea of establishment of convincingness is not completely strange even for traditional mathematical logic. Everyone understands that each tree-figure of proof requires a reference to T4. This reference (perhaps supplied by another reference to T3) is generally considered as an establishment of convincingness: and it is so uniform that it is always omitted. But I criticize this establishment of convincingness for its vicious circle (with T3 and T4). So I reject this traditional establishment of convincingness. I consider a special *genetic theory* dealing with these establishments.

3. Now I go further with my criticism of traditional assumptions. I shall consider T5. I recall the series F of feasible numbers. N denotes a natural number series with 10^{12}.

It may seem quite natural to say that some numbers of N are feasible and that the number 10^{12} is not. I said this above myself. But this way of considering the numbers of F leads to the situation that the finite set of numbers $\{0, 1, \ldots, 10^{12}\}$ of N contains an infinite part F. Perhaps it is not absurd but it leads to many difficulties. If somebody looks over this set of N-numbers he exhausts this infinite part, but I prefer to say an infinite process cannot be exhausted. This difficulty disappears if we distinguish between the F-numbers and the N-numbers equivalent to them. But sometimes it will be more convenient to identify these numbers belonging to different series. It is a very common thing; sometimes we identify objects that we distinguish in other cases. The rules of doing so must be established in a rigorous way.

Already Heraclitus pointed out that the notion of identity is not completely clear. But mathematicians prefer to proceed as if Heraclitus had not lived. I cannot continue in this way. The situation when an infinite process can be imbedded in a finite object is an ordinary one in investigations of distinct natural number series, and I shall need an apparatus for the explicit consideration of all identifications used in such cases.

First of all I maintain that the relation of identity or distinctness has no other meaning than that two objects have been identified or distinguished. There are two important kinds of atomic actions: identifications and distinctions. These actions are commonly used according to certain rules and they can be forced by these rules. Actions do not need to possess any meaning but they may have an aim. The rules also can be accepted as a means to achieve some aim. A very common aim of the identification of two objects a and b is to prepare the acceptance of the sentence 'a and b are identical', and similarly with distinctions. I shall consider a general theory of *collations*, i.e. identifications and the distinctions. A more general theory of rules and aims is needed for it.

Generally, one can identify or distinguish any two objects in two arbitrary occurrences of them. But collations play in our arguments a role similar to that of assumptions, and they must be made quite explicit or at least according to explicitly stated rules.

You can identify Fermat's last theorem with the sentence $2\times 2 = 4$. Then, the last sentence being proved, you can say Fermat's theorem is proved too. This is not awkward if you express it quite explicitly: if Fermat's last theorem is identified with the proved sentence $2 \times 2 = 4$, it is proved. If the identification were an ordinary one, it could be not mentioned; though in identification theory all rules of the ordinary identifications are to be mentioned.

Although one can identify any two objects in arbitrary occurrences of them, there are cases of awkward identifications. E.g. such is every identification of a present object with an absent one. If you consider identifications used without explicit mention you have to proscribe these dangerous identifications and you have to require that no two objects are identified before they appear.

Let us consider the series F and N once more. Each F-number will be identified with the equivalent N-number – but this presupposes the appearance of the F-number. So the identifications constitute an infinite process P. This process effectuates an imbedding of F in the finite part $\{0, 1, \ldots, 10^{12}\}$ of N: but this imbedding is infinite and you never can say it is over or that F is imbedded in $\{0, 1, \ldots, 10^{12}\}$.

I refer to as a *Zenonian situation* every case in which the events of an infinite process are to be identified with the parts of a finite object; and this finite object I call the *field of a Zenonian situation.* It is useful to establish a connection of this notion with the Zenonian paradox of the runner: A runner cannot get from the point A to the point B; for if he does then the infinite process of runnings of consecutive halves of this distance is over. But the events of this infinite discrete imaginative process are not necessarily the same as the parts of the real continuous process of running. (The continuous character of the process would be more evident if the running is replaced by the flight of a ball.) They are only identified with them: but the series of these identifications is an infinite process, and it can never be over as Zeno supposes in his argument. A similar criticism explains the paradox of Achilles and the tortoise.

The identification of two composite objects $f(a_1, \ldots, a_n)$ and $g(b_1, \ldots, b_n)$ is often produced as the result of a *structural procedure* of identification. The structures of these objects are supposed to be identified (which presupposes the identification of n in both occurrences). One identifies f with g, a_i with b_i for all $i = 1, \ldots, n$, then one makes the *establishment of exhaustion* (of all $f, g, a_1, b_1, \ldots, a_n, b_n$), and only then does one identify the objects $f(a_1, \ldots, a_n)$ and $g(b_1, \ldots, b_n)$. That is a *structural identification.*

The described Zenonian situation with the field $\{0, 1, \ldots, 10^{12}\}$ is not impossible if one considers the series of identifications as an infinite one.

It is only an infinite imbedding of the infinite process F in the finite field. One may say this means the field is finite in some occurrences and infinite in other ones. I call it the Zenonian situation *in the wider sense.*

But generally one considers a finite composite object in many occurrences of it and one identifies the object in these occurrences and one thinks these identifications may be considered as structural ones. Given the Zenonian situation one cannot carry out the structural identification of its field (with an infinite process imbedded in it) on the ground that the establishment of exhaustion becomes impossible. But if the identifications are not stated in an explicit manner it is impossible to notice the fact; and one talks about the field as if *this impossible structural identification were carried out.* That would be the Zenonian situation *in the narrower sense.* This situation is impossible – though without the analysis of identification one can easily overlook it.

4. Before going further I introduce now some terminological conventions.

The events of a natural number series N I call the N-numbers. If $N_1(0_1, 0_1', \ldots)$ and $N_2(0_2, 0_2', \ldots)$ are two such series, then I call 0_1 and 0_2 *equivalent* and I denote it by $0_1 \simeq 0_2$; if $m \simeq n$ (where $m \in N_1$ and $n \in N_2$) then I permit it to be said* that $m' \simeq n'$ also, and the relation $m \simeq n$ is always to be established in this way. If for each N_1-number m there is an equivalent N_2-number n, I say that N_1 *is not longer than* N_2 and I denote it by $N_1 \preccurlyeq N_2$. If $N_1 \preccurlyeq N_2$ and $N_2 \preccurlyeq N_1$, then I call the series N_1 and N_2 *isomorphic.* If $N_1 \preccurlyeq N_2$ and N_1 is not isomorphic to N_2, I say that N_1 is *shorter* than N_2 – but intuitionistically this does not mean the existence of an N_2-number equivalent to no N_1-number. If $N_1 \preccurlyeq N_2$ and there is an N_2-number q equivalent to no N_1-number, I say that N_1 is *shorter* than q and I denote it by $N_1 \prec q$; in this case I say also that N_1 is *explicitly shorter* than N_2 (or that N_2 is *explicitly longer* than N_1) and I denote it by $N_1 \prec N_2$.

If one tries to establish an isomorphism between two series N_1 and N_2 by considering the pairs $\langle 0_1, 0_2\rangle$, $\langle 0_1', 0_2'\rangle, \ldots$, since the consideration of each pair $\langle m, n\rangle$ presupposes the appearance of m and n one obtains only

* Usually this is expressed by 'if $m \simeq n$ then $m' \simeq n'$'. But such expressions overlook the fact that $m' \simeq n'$ can appear only after $m \simeq n$ has appeared. This negligence may lead to the platonistic representation of a realm of all equivalences of the kind $m \simeq n$. Of course I have to reject this, and I prefer to speak here about the rules governing the appearance of the equivalences rather than speaking of the equivalences themselves without mentioning the rules.

the consideration of the third series of these pairs which is not longer than each of N_1 and N_2 and nothing more.

I find it useful to consider here the analysis of an ordinary supposed justification of T3. Given $P(0)$ and $\forall n(P(n) \supset P(n'))$ one indicates the possibility of obtaining the deductions for $P(0) \supset P(0')$ and $P(0')$, then for $P(0') \supset P(0'')$ and for $P(0'')$ and so on. This justification of T3 uses:

(a). An application of Carnap's Rule

$$\text{(Ca)} \qquad \frac{\ldots P(\boldsymbol{m}) \ldots}{\forall m\, P(m)}$$

where $\boldsymbol{m}$ denotes an arbitrary value of the variable m.

(b). The *hypothesis of potential feasibility* according to which, given a method of construction requiring an arbitrary finite number m of steps, each step being feasible on the supposition that all preceding steps are fulfilled, one considers as feasible the result of this construction.

(c). The localization principle T4 for deductions.

(d). A *principle of parallelism* according to which at the m-th step of the described deduction one obtains just the sentence $P(\boldsymbol{m})$.

(e). The features of the interpretation of signs $\forall$ and $\supset$ used in the justification of the logical steps leading from $P(0)$ and $\forall n(P(n) \supset P(n'))$ to each $P(\boldsymbol{m})$.

(f). The consideration of the truth of $\forall m P(m)$ (relative to $P(0)$ and $\forall n(P(n) \supset P(n')))$ as denoting the deductibility of each $P(\boldsymbol{m})$ (from the premisses just mentioned); this consideration is used in the justification of (a).

(g). The indirect clause of the inductive definition of a natural number (leading to the conclusion that each $\boldsymbol{m}$ can be obtained from 0 by adding ').

I should mention also the fact that the result of the construction used for each $\boldsymbol{m}$ is a deduction figure for $P(\boldsymbol{m})$ (to which T4 is to be applied). I think one can obtain this fact from the definition of a deduction figure, the application of (b) and a kind of argument similar to (d).

5. Now I describe briefly the structure of this antitraditional program:

It contains a *central nucleus* consisting of two theories: the *ontological theory* and the *genetic theory* and a consistency proof for ZF (and some of its extensions) based on these theories. The *ontological theory* deals with the substantiation of the possibility of natural number series and other discrete processes required for this consistency-proof; and the *genetic theory* deals with the notion of proof for sentences related to the events of distinct processes. The genetic theory deals especially with the elaboration of the notion of the establishment of convincingness for given processes called the *studied processes*. Also some fundamental theories called *prototheories* are needed in the central nucleus – these are e.g. collation theory, the modality and tense theories sketched below, and some others. Generally, only protodemonstrations are available as means of proving in the prototheories and even in the ontological and in the genetic theories. Outside the central nucleus I shall have several *extreme directions* of the program concerned with the substantiations of some hypotheses occurring in the theories of the central nucleus. These hypotheses are implicitly contained also in the traditional theories, or in a general platform underlying them; at any rate they have nothing to do with impredicative definitions or other vicious circles occurring in the foundations of all traditional theories. The protodemonstrations are the only available means of proof also in the extreme directions, and the gap between these and the prototheories may be a temporary one. If the foundations of ZF were the only task of the whole program I could say that the main problems of the extreme directions concerned with the substantiations of the mentioned hypotheses are essentially settled today.

6. Now I continue the list of traditional assumptions.

T6. The possibility of neglecting modalities and aims in foundations of mathematics.

T7. The possibility of neglecting tenses, voices and moods of verbs.

T8. The possibility of neglecting the rules of attention and neglecting.

T9. The hypothesis of potential feasibility.

T10. The division of theories into object theories and metatheories.

T11. The postulates of the intuitionistic predicate calculus.

The reasons for my criticism of T6 and T7 are connected with the previous analysis of traditional assumptions.

Evidently when one applies T9 (see (b) above) one confuses the feasibility of construction with the supposition that the construction is fulfilled. E.g. for an arbitrary $\boldsymbol{m}$ one concludes from (b) and (d) above that the deduction of $P(m)$ is feasible – but that does not suffice to obtain the deduction of $P(\boldsymbol{m}')$ with the help of $P(\boldsymbol{m}) \supset P(\boldsymbol{m}')$, for in order to obtain it one has first to obtain the deduction of $P(\boldsymbol{m})$, and that is more than the assertion about its feasibility. Evidently there is a modal principle justifying this transformation of the possible into the real in the foundation of mathematics – I shall call it the *principle of modal fulfilment* and analyse it more closely below. The exact formulation of this principle requires a theory of modalities.

There is another thing which makes modal investigations necessary in the ultra-intuitionistic program. I mentioned the necessity of making explicit the rules of collations; and this requires a systematic treatment of rules and aims, which leads to a development of a theory of modalities.

In virtue of the traditional intuitionistic criticism we have to consider the natural number series not as accomplished totalities but rather as infinite processes. But one cannot speak exactly about any process without using tenses in order to discern the past events from the future ones. For a natural number series, at each stage, its infiniteness belongs to the domain of the future and so one has to expose the rules of transforming the future tense into the present or the past in reasonings. The theory of tenses is closely connected with that of modalities, and in the course of the development of these theories voices and moods must also be taken in consideration.

I introduce *modal characteristics* in the notion of natural number series. I call such series *necessitary*, *real* or *eventual* according to the modality 'necessary', 'factually' or 'possible' with which the future appearance of n' after n is asserted. Similar characteristics are to be used in connection with the notion of closedness of a series with respect to a function φ, with the relation $N_1 \prec N_2$ (according to the modality with which the existence of $q \in N_2$ with $N_1 \prec q$ is asserted) and so on. The notion of finiteness I connect with that of an end (but not with natural numbers) and one can distinguish the modal characteristics of finiteness etc.

The theory of modalities will be closely connected with *semiotics*, i.e. the general theory of signs.

In semiotics I consider the act of *indication* as central. An indication is an action by which its *author shows* to the *addressee* a *point* with the help of a *sign*. There is a *denotational connection* between the sign X and every point x of an indication and I denote this connection by $X \rightarrow x$.

A *language* is a method or system of indications, it is defined by means of constructing signs and by denotational connections.

A *character* or *tactic* is a system of *rules*, i.e. of propositions expressing permissions and demands (see below). If a tactic is expressed in a language I call it a *method*. A *way* is a tactic or a method.

The notion of *connection* is a primitive one. As with all primitive notions, its use is to be described by some way, i.e. by some method or at least by a tactic. There are many tactics for following connections – they correspond in particular to the different kinds of connections. There are *aim* and *denotational connections* and the tactics for following them I call the *tactics* of *attention*. Every other tactic for following connections is subject in a way to a tactic of attention.

To follow a tactic for following connections is to accept such sentences as '*a* is connected with *b*'. Every sentence of this form is always connected to such a tactic χ, and if some rule of χ prevents the acceptance of the sentence '*a* is connected with *b*' I say that '*a* is strange to *b* (relative to χ)'.

If a sign is made by means of a language I call it the *name* of its points in that language and the points I call the *senses* of that name.

Each sign is used with at least one tactic of attention permitting one to notice that sign, and with a tactic of collations permitting one to identify it in its occurrences. I call a sign *clear* if there is an accepted tactic for following denotational connections with it. All points strange to the sign (relative to this tactic) are always to be neglected as its points. So a sign (in particular a name) is always a sign for its non-strange points only. A clear sign I call *definite* if it is necessary that it has just one point. The definiteness of a sign depends on a tactic of collations.

A *class* is an indefinite name; its *elements* are the fixed values of its senses. (There are rules of using these explications. The idea is to identify the class defined by a name with that name; but that is not always convenient. But the use of the word 'class' is always to be connected with an indefinite name. Of course this use of the word 'class' has nothing to do with classical set-theoretical hypotheses on the existence of classes.)

I call *direct* those occurrences of a sign in which the rôle of the sign is confined to its playing a part as a sign for its points, and to the participation in following those tactics of attention and collations which make it a sign. (The *rôle* of an object is defined as a class of aims and obstacles to which the object is attached by a tactic for following connections.) The rule of interchangeability of synonyms is suitable only for direct occurrences of signs. So the interchangeability of the terms 'indefinite name' and 'class' applies to direct occurrences of these terms only, and can be limited by some further rules useful for a text. These rules may be replaced by rules for distinguishing somewhere the senses of the both terms. All this question is a typical example of how closely the senses of different terms may be interconnected. At the first sight even vicious circles must occur in these explications but one can avoid them by distinguishing the senses of the same term in different occurrences, in the hope that the system of explications gives a reduction for these terms attached to their occurrences.

A *collection* is a finished class (i.e. a class whose elements are exhausted, which may be specified by means of collation theory).

There are the following three fundamental semiotical principles:

S1. Given a collection of indications $\{a_0 \to a_1, a_1 \to a_2, \ldots, a_{n-1} \to a_n\}$ in a language L the indication $a_0 \to a_n$ also belongs to L.

It is a rule for restricting languages. It enables us to follow the denotational connections. One uses this rule each time when the sense of word in a new occurrence is to be identified with its sense in a former one.

S2. If the connections $f \to F$, $a_1 \to A_1, \ldots, a_n \to A_n$ belong to a language L, F being an operation applicable to the objects $A_1, \ldots, A_n$, then the notation $f(a_1, \ldots, a_n) \to$ (the result of applying F to $A_1, \ldots, A_n$) also belongs to L; some specifications of the rôle of the order '$a_1, \ldots, a_n$' may be introduced, and '$f(a_1, \ldots, a_n)$' may be replaced by another record which enables one to reconstruct it. (*The principle of structural parallelism.*)

Parameters are indefinite indecomposable names.

S3. When a text is accepted the result of fixing some collection of parameters in it by their admissible values is also to be accepted; but this operation of fixation may require grammatical agreements in the text obtained by the fixation.

I have to draw special attention to the agreements in the verbal tenses. The fixed values may in turn depend on parameters or even be parameters.

7. Now I shall describe the main features of my modality theory.

First of all, it cannot be an axiomatic theory on the grounds of the vicious circle with T3 and T4. Also it must precede other logical theories, in particular that of the applicability of the axiomatic method, i.e. the genetic theory. So all proofs in it must be protodemonstrations.

I divide the modalities into three *categories* (necessary, real and possible) and four groups: *deontic* modalities connected with rules, e.g. permissions and demands, *aim* modalities connected with aims ('possible' means 'possible for an aim' i.e. the aim might be achieved with this means, and 'necessary' means 'needed for some aim'), and the two kinds of *alethic modalities* – the *organic modalities* connected with methods or ways (I can = I am able, I must = I am forced by rules of a way) and the *epistemic modalities* ('perhaps' or 'certainly'). The epistemic possibility of A may be interpreted as the organic possibility of the continuation of reasoning after A is accepted. The epistemic necessity of A means the organic necessity of the acceptance of A forced by rules of a way. For each group there is the modality 'real' used, e.g. in the abstract consideration of an action in connection with rules in order to investigate the lawfulness of the action without any assumption about the alethic reality of the action.

A *situation* is a class of (senses of) sentences. Generally, a situation S *describes* some conditions indicated in a way. The conditions may be described by a situation with different degrees of precision, the degree being sufficient or not according to the aims of the description.

The modalities may apply to the situations and to the propositions – sentences or names of actions. The deontic, aim and organic modalities apply to the names of actions which may be propositions with one verb in the infinitive mood. The epistemic modalities apply to sentences (so the verb stands in the indicative mood).

When a modal operation is applied to a sentence or to a name of action it is always to be accompanied by the name S of one or more situations. (An occasion possible in one situation may not be possible in another, etc.) That is one of the characteristic features of my modality theory. Symbolically the situation index S is to be applied to the sign of the modal operation ($\Diamond$, ! or $\Box$ for organic modalities, denoting respectively organic possibility, reality and necessity; ⟐, †, $\boxdot$ for aim modalities; P, F and O for deontic modalities; and M, R and N for epistemic modalities). So $M_S A$ means 'perhaps, in the situation S, A', etc. If the assertion $M_S A$, $\Diamond_S A$ etc. is accepted for a class Σ of situations S, it is denoted by $M_\Sigma A$, $\Diamond_\Sigma A$ etc. For aim modalities the sign T denoting the aim is to be added: ⟐$^T_S A$ means 'in the situation S it is possible to achieve T by means of A' etc. But if the situation S or the class Σ is fixed in the context one can omit the index S or Σ in formulating the modal proposition. So one omits the class Σ of all situations obtainable in mathematics in the formulation of the hypothesis of potential feasibility.

There are several *degrees* of modalities. Modal words were used in the basic semiotic explications before the notions of class and situation were introduced. In those contexts it was impossible to use systematically the situation sign. That was the *first degree of modalities*. After the notion of situation appears, the *second degree* is obtained.

The theory of deontic modalities is essentially that of tactics or characters. These are systems of rules, a *rule* being a proposition of the form 'In the situation S it is permitted to do A' or 'In the situation S it is required to do

A'; the *proscription* of *A* is defined as the proposition of the form 'In the situation *S* it is required not to do *A*'. The atomic actions *A* for the foundations of mathematics are:

(I). preferences;
(II). acts of establishing or following connections, in particular acts of attention;
(III). collations;
(IV). indications;
(V). acceptances of *propositions*, i.e. sentences, rules and optional propositions expressing aims or sometimes desires or wishes; (the acceptance of a method is considered as the acceptance of all its rules);
(VI). perceptions;
(VII). the acts inverse to (II) and (V) – acts of neglecting and acts of refusal of accepted propositions;
(VIII). the abstention from the acts (I)–(VII).

In some theories related to the ultra-intuitionistic program, e.g. the theory of disputes, new items appear:

(IX). raising and answering questions (considered as actions similar to (V));
(X). addressing another person

and

(XI). including some text in the memory;

the abstentions (VIII) are extended to these new items.

The tactic expressed in a language is called a *method* (see above; now the notions of rule and tactics are specified). Tactics are *means* for aims (as well as materials which are usually considered as obtained by a tactic; in addition to them, the *means* are the rules occurring in tactics, and the actions performed for the achievement of the aims; in particular those fulfilled in the course of following the rules, etc.). By means of tactics new complicated deeds *A* may be introduced; and this leads to the extension of the class of rules.

In a natural way the notion of *following* a tactic is defined. A *discrete process** is the following of a method and I shall say that it is *described* by the method.

* Generally I take the word 'discrete' always to mean 'expressible in a language of words'. *Procedures* are processes which can be accomplished.

To follow a tactic χ generally presupposes another tactic ψ by means of which the actions A indicated by the rules of χ are fulfilled, the situations S are collated, and so on. The tactic ψ is called *external* or *deeper* with respect to χ or to a process described by χ. The actions made in following ψ but not χ are called *automatic* with respect to χ or a process described by χ. By the way, it happens often that a tactic χ or a process described by it uses many external tactics and the notion of automatic action applies to each of them.

All this is very important for my program. The ultra-intuitionistic program introduces tactics of acts (I)–(VII): but these acts envelop the profoundest acts of our thinking underlying the ultra-intuitionistic reasonings too. Even the reading of a text uses the acts (I)–(III) (e.g. one prefers to read from left to the right) and it would be completely impossible to investigate in the program the many tactics of attention and collations used in the beginning of the exposition of it. But this is superfluous. Most of these tactics turn out to be external to the tactics of the deeds we really need to investigate. So one can assume that many actions (I)–(III) are fulfilled automatically, and even apply such traditional expressions as 'the same word as before' etc. Only in certain cases especially indicated by the ultra-intuitionistic criticism shall I have to describe explicitly the rules of the tactics: and this criticism is ruthless enough, for those cases form a class sufficiently large for all important aims. Other cases may be treated with the traditional negligence to the explicitness of these actions which are considered as the automatic ones. However, the investigation of these external tactics are of great importance e.g. for cybernetics – but for the ultra-intuitionistic program it is not an urgent business.

Tactics may be *incomplete* for two reasons: (a) there may be situations for which the rules permit to make each of two or more incompatible actions (I call these situations the *Buridanian ones*) and (b) there may be *unforeseen* situations of which the rules say nothing. For both cases there are general ways of *completing* the tactics (though the completed tactic does not need to become complete). In case (a), generally, it is done by tactics of preference. In case (b) one chooses one of two fundamental preferences: according to the *principle of liberalism* one prefers permissions to proscriptions and according to the *principle of despotism* one prefers proscriptions to permissions. The acceptance of the first principle leads to the *liberal regime* characterized by the rule 'everything not proscribed by (the rules of) a tactic is permitted by the regime' and the acceptance of the second principle leads to the *despotic regime* expressed by the rule 'everything not permitted by the tactic is proscribed by the regime'. One applies the principle of liberalism in cases one seeks for means for the accepted aims. One applies the principle of despotism in cases one tries to achieve aims with the help of accepted means, or to verify the proposed means with the help of accepted criteria.

Definitions are the rules of usage of names. Their usage is always governed by the despotic regime which leads to prohibiting the application of the term introduced by definition in any other sense. All inductive definitions, e.g. that of natural number, contain an 'indirect clause' which is the imposition of the despotic regime on the consideration of an arbitrary object as satisfying the definition.

The theory of methods and ways is a generalization of the traditional theory of algorithms. There are at least four respects in which the former is more general than the latter: (a) the primitive operations of the normal algorithms (the substitution of words) are performed in a way which is not itself considered as an algorithm; (b) the theory of algorithms depends on natural numbers, which are to be obtained in some way; (c) the methods can be applied to objects of a completely general nature; (d) the 'work' of a method or way (i.e. the following of it) may be an undetermined process.

Now I turn to the alethic modalities. A situation is called *real* if each element of it is accepted on the ground of a perception. So the void situation is real. The problem of perception is of course a very deep one (and it is connected with the consideration of active and passive voices) but in the domain of the foundations of mathematics we can restrict our attention to the perception of texts proposed in the exposition of exhaustions and of the atomic acts (I)–(V) and (VII)–(XI) without further analysis. Each real situation is also called *possible.*

The principle of modal fulfilment (pmf). If the situation S is possible and the action or event A is possible in S then the situation $S \cup \{A\}$ (obtained from S by adjoining A to it) is also possible.

This principle holds for all four groups of the modality 'possible' (all occurrences of which in the formulation of the principle have to belong to the same group). Symbolically it may be stated in the form

$$\bigcirc \frac{S \quad A}{S \cup \{A\}}$$

where '$\bigcirc$' denotes one of the modality signs $\Diamond$, $\Diamond^T$, M or P. It may be specified that A stands in the future tense above the bar and in the present-past tense below it, symbolically

$$\bigcirc \frac{S \quad \Delta A}{S \cup \{\nabla A\}}$$

Δ denoting the future tense and ∇ the present-past tense. If $\bigcirc$ is $\Diamond$ or P then A in $\Diamond_S A$ is the name of an action, and can be expressed by a proposition with one verb in the infinitive mood, in the $\Diamond_S A$ or above the bar it stands in the active voice ('it is possible to do A') but in $S \cup \{A\}$ it stands in the passive voice. Below the bar A stands in the indicative mood. If $\bigcirc$ is M, then A in $M_S A$ is the name of an event, and the verb in A stands in the indicative mood both above and below the bar, and the voice is the same in both cases. So this principle contains also the rules for tenses, voices and moods.

The justification of pmf may consist in the definition of a possible situation as such which can be obtained from a real one by a string of applications of pmf. A closer examination shows that in this way pmf is reduced to its simplest case for which it is rather a tautology.

Perhaps a somewhat more explicit formulation of pmf is

$$\bigcirc \diagdown \frac{S \quad \bigcirc_S A}{S \cup \{A\}} \diagup$$

(or still more precisely with ΔA above the bar and ∇A below it etc.). Here one sees distinctly that A stands with the modality 'possible' attached to it above the bar and without this modality below it. That is the essence of the rule explaining its name of 'fulfilment', and it turns out that pmf is a formalization of the 'utilization' of possibilities. However the modality 'possible' does not disappear below the bar, but it is attached to the situation $S \cup \{A\}$ itself. Often one forgets to mention this occurrence of the modality and speaks of the situation $S \cup \{A\}$ as of a real one. So one obtains faith in $S \cup \{A\}$: and that is the general way of accepting-on-faith in the domains of religion and philosophy, and in traditional intuitionist or constructivist mathematics too. Such are the cases when one believes in mathematical 'reality' on the grounds that its objects *can* be obtained by a method. The ultra-intuitionist analysis reestablishes the correct use of modalities.

A deep idea of this program consists of representing the traditional mathematical 'real' situations only as possible ones obtained by iterations of pmf. The consideration of mathematical situations as possible is certainly sufficient for the sake of consistency proofs.

Now I continue the review of my theory of modalities.

If a process D is described by a tactic χ and for a situation S occurring in the course of D the rules of χ demand an action or event A then for the continuation of D in S the fulfilment of A is necessary.

That is the *main principle of necessity*. It is in virtue of this principle that the definitions are observed in the course of a development of a theory and it seems that this principle itself can be based essentially on the definition of the word 'describe'. It is also in virtue of this principle that each move of a bishop in a chess-game necessarily is a move by a diagonal. This principle may seem quite tautological. But a closer examination shows that it depends on an elimination of a double negation. What *really* can be justified is that in the course of a process the rules of a tactic describing it cannot be violated. It is not the same as the 'fact' that the rules are necessarily observed. But generally I neglect the eliminations of double negations occurring in the deepest questions of that program because it is the matter of an extreme direction to deal with them.

If an event e of a process D is over and done with in a situation S of D and d precedes e in D then it is necessary that d is over in S. (*The principle of ordinal necessity*, p.o.n.) The 'being over and done with' is a form of expressing the past tense. So the principle deals with that tense too.

There are also such 'trivial' principles as 'everything necessary is real' and 'everything real is possible'. These are stated only for the two groups of alethic modalities and for possible situations only. (The reason of the impossibility of a situation may be precisely a violation of some trivial principle in it.) For deontic or aim modalities the observance of these principles is the characteristic feature of just or purposeful activities. There are also some relations between organic and epistemic modalities (e.g. that organic necessity implies the epistemic necessity) – these too are stated for possible situations only. Various other connections – the distributivity of conjunction and the equivalence between the impossibility of A and the necessity of not-A – can be established (with some restrictions) for possible situations.

The violation of the main principle of necessity is impossible in each possible situation. (The *principle of negative evidence*, p.n.e.)

For aim modalities I accept, also for possible situations S only:

If the aim T is not achieved in S, in order to achieve it in S it is necessary to apply (a) some sufficient means and (b) each of the necessary means (the *inversion principle*).

Each system of actions is sufficient for the achievement of each of its necessary result.

For the future tense I deal primarily with the tense 'A will have been' which I denote $\Delta_S A$ or simply ΔA if the situation S to which this 'will' refers is clearly indicated in the context. I accept:

(a). If A has been in S it will have been in every situation which is later than S.

(b). If A is necessary in every situation of a class Σ of situations, A is necessary also in each future situation of Σ.

(c). In each possible situation an appearing event is always later than events already entering in the situation, and this order relation will necessarily be observed in every later situation.

Also the rules occurring in pmf and pon are very important for the theory of tenses. The following rule is of a semiotical nature:

(d). In order that a proposition be meaningful it is necessary that its predicate agree in tense with the objects to which it refers. This means e.g. that the phrase 'tomorrow *is* August 12' is meaningless if pronounced August 11; a meaningful phrase is on that date 'tomorrow *will be* August 12'.

(d) is very important for the analysis of deductoids exposed in the ordinary logico-mathematical language having no future tense. A sentence $A(\boldsymbol{m}, \boldsymbol{n})$, containing the names $\boldsymbol{m}$, $\boldsymbol{n}$ of the events m, n of a process, can be meaningful only on the supposition that m and n have already occurred. (It could be otherwise if the predicate in $A(\boldsymbol{m}, \boldsymbol{n})$ stands in a future tense.) The deductoids may contain the rule (Ca) and so the sentences occurring in them constitute an infinite process. The identifications required for the substantiations of the applications of the rules of inference etc. may introduce a Zenonian situation (even in a narrower sense), and therefore it is not evident that the deductoid must possess an establishment of convincingness.

So a sentence $A(\boldsymbol{m}_1, \ldots, \boldsymbol{m}_k)$ may occur in a deductoid only on the supposition that $m_1, \ldots, m_k$ have already occurred. That is the *first genetic principle* for ultra-intuitionistic proofs. The *second genetic principle* is that if $n_1, \ldots, n_p$ are events of the same process I shall say they have all ensued only if a later event n of the process has ensued (cf. p.o.n.). The *third genetic principle* is connected with the inversion principle: e.g. I cannot consider an occurrence of A in B (or even an occurrence of A depending on an occurrence of B) before this occurrence of B is considered as already having occurred. These three genetical principles constitute a *genetic constitution* which is to be observed in the ontological and especially in the genetic theory. (In the ontological theory as well as in prototheories the sentences $A(\boldsymbol{m}, \boldsymbol{n})$ containing the future tense may occur; and then the first genetic principle may be violated. E.g. in the definition of a natural number series there is the location 'n' will be ensued', to which a modality may be attached; the application of pmf to this location belongs to the ontological theory. Cases of such a nature with the future tense are only ones dealt with in the ontological theory.)

8. Now I return to the consideration of the natural number series and the assumptions T8–T11.

First of all, I have considered a series F without 10^{12} but it does not mean a number q has to be so great as 10^{12} in order it could be longer than some natural number series. If a series N contains a 20th event this does not mean that another series M has to contain *its* 20th event also. In the notion of series there is no proviso about this.

So let us consider two necessitary series N_1 and N_2, whose numbers I denote $a_0, a_1, \ldots$ and $b_0, b_1, \ldots$ respectively. Let N_2 contain b_{20} and let N_1 be shorter than b_{20}, which means that there never shall be such entity as a_{20} in N_1. (Later I shall prove the possibility that N_1 does not contain even a_2.) Let $N_1 N_2$ be the series $a_0, b_0, a_1, b_1, \ldots, a_i, b_i, a_{i+1}, \ldots$ obtained from N_1 and N_2 by alternation. It really is a series because if a_i has occurred then $i < 20$ and there is b_i in N_2 and a_{i+1} necessarily will have occurred; if b_i has occurred in $N_1 N_2$ this means that a_i has occurred in N_1 and so a_{i+1} necessarily will have occurred. Now let us consider the task: to find the occurrence of b_{20} in $N_1 N_2$. This task requires only 42 steps each of them being alethically possible when the preceding steps are accomplished. Nevertheless the fulfilment of the task is impossible because if b_{20} is found in $N_1 N_2$ then a_{20} also is found in it, and so a_{20} is in N_1, which contradicts the condition.

I say there is an *obstacle* to the fulfilment of this task, and I call this obstacle the *catching* of this task *on* N_1. Of course catchings may arise also from more complicated alternation, e.g. the task of finding b_{1000} in the series $a_0, b_0, a_1, b_1, b_2, a_2, b_3, b_4, b_5, a_6, b_6, b_7, b_8, b_9, a_7, \ldots$ (the numbers of b's after a_{i+1} is one greater than after a_i) also catches on N_1. Generally catching is (roughly speaking) an obstacle to a task consisting in the fact that its fulfilment requires the exhaustion of an infinite process.

In the case of a Zenonian situation (in the narrower sense) with the field $\{0, 1, \ldots, 10^{12}\}$ of N-numbers the task of the structural identification of that field in its two occurrences catches on the series F of feasible numbers. So every Zenonian situation in the narrower sense is impossible on the grounds of a catching. Conversely, to every catching it is possible to associate a Zenonian situation (e.g. obtained by the identification of b_i's in $N_1 N_2$ and in N_2, the first one's forming the infinite series; this situation is one in the narrower sense if one requires the structural identification of the segment $\{b_0, \ldots, b_{20}\}$ of N_2 in its occurrences before and after this introduction of infinity into it).

The introduction of the notion of obstacle is a most important feature of the ultra-intuitionistic program. Of course the constructivists were also aware of some 'trivial' obstacles for their constructions, such as the absence of necessary means or a vicious circle in a task. But these obstacles always have been the *barriers for a single step* in the fulfilment of the task. The catching is a *new* kind of obstacle arising from the possibility of a finite sequence being longer than an infinite series. Each 'finite' task whose fulfilment is destroyed by a catching I shall call the *field* of this catching.

The possibility of a catching frequently appears in the genetic theory, whose principal aim is to obtain a list of conditions sufficient for a deductoid to possess a semiotic substantiation undamaged by catchings. In this theory catchings are represented by sequences whose members are just the occurrences like those of b_i in $N_1 N_2$; and these sequences are represented by functions φ, whose values are those occurrences and whose arguments are the numbers of a short natural number series on which the occurrences depend. E.g. $b_i = \varphi(a_i)$ where a_i is in N_1 and b_i is in $N_1 N_2$. I call these functions *metafunctions* (because the occurrences of the members of the sequences are traditionally considered as metatheoretical objects). Each catching in the genetic theory may be represented by a metafunction given for an infinite process (containing the arguments of the metafunction) and all of whose values must belong to the field of the catching and be distinct – these are called *unbounded metafunctions*.

9. Now I pass to my criticism of T8. I wish to introduce a new branch of logic – *relevancy theory* – into the foundations of mathematics. It is a theory about how to take something into attention or to neglect it.

These problems appear at each step in our thinking but the traditional logic worries too little about them. Everyone knows the syllogism: all men are mortal, Socrates is a man, therefore Socrates is mortal. But another argument is no worse: All men can die only once, Socrates has died, therefore now Socrates cannot die and Socrates is not mortal. (I suppose that the word 'mortal' refers only to beings who can die.) That is a paradox. Its explanation I see in the fact that the word 'man' had different senses in this text, one time denoting all men – living and dead – and one time denoting only living men. In order to eliminate all paradoxes of this sort one has to specify the way of following the denotational connections. Every way of following connections I call here a *tactic of attention* (but I mean mainly following the aim or denotational connections).

Perhaps one feels the problem of this tactic is strange to the foundations of mathematics, but even if it is so this fact belongs to relevancy theory and one has to prove it, which already requires some acquaintance with this theory. That is already a criticism of T8.

The main rôle of relevancy theory is attached to the fact that one always. may neglect strange objects, i.e. objects strange to the aims of considerations. With some trivial provisos I insist upon the inverse principle: *only* strange objects may be neglected, which I call the *main principle of relevantism*. This means: first prove the strangeness of an object and only then neglect it. This presupposes that the way of establishing or following connections, i.e. the tactic of attention is sufficiently well known.

In traditional mathematical logic one has never argued about tactics of attention and rules of connection and neglection. One could think that the rigid system of definitions makes that superfluous. But the rigidity of this system depends on the notion of natural numbers and so it cannot be more rigid than this notion is. The rejection of T1 is already the rejection of this rigidity: and so the problem of introducing the tactics of attention into consideration becomes a very urgent one.

But the means of traditional theories are not sufficient in order to fix in a unique way the supposed tactic of attention. The existence of consistent but ω-inconsistent systems may be interpreted as revealing this fact even by traditional means.

I shall apply the relevancy theory to the study of metafunctions. Strange objects are neglected and therefore instead of proving the impossibility of a metafunction ρ destroying a construction C I can prove that each such metafunction ρ must be strange. This I prove chiefly with the help of the following *principle of strangeness* which can be established in the relevancy theory:

If an object $\mathfrak{E}$ is indispensable for any consideration of ρ but one considers C without taking $\mathfrak{E}$ into attention then ρ is strange to C.

The importance of this principle is due to the fact that when an ultra-intuitionistic theory T considers two natural number series F and N, $F \prec N$, one always can intentionally introduce the function $\rho(x)$ on F such that $\rho(m)$ is always the N-number equivalent to m and if $F \prec q \in \mathrm{N}$ then this ρ enables one to introduce the Zenonian situation with the field $\hat{q} = \{0, 1, \ldots, q\}$ where all of $0, 1, \ldots, q$ are N-numbers. As explained before one can further consider a catching destroying an appearance Oc_q of q. But this does not mean one has to worry about it because it is possible that Oc_q has nothing to do with T. $\hat{q}$ is one thing which may be really necessary for the study of N but Oc_q may be strange to the theory T or to a part T′ of it in which this question arises. If ρ creates an obstacle for Oc_q but not for the consideration of $\hat{q}$, then one may neglect this obstacle as a strange one provided one is interested only in $\hat{q}$ but not in Oc_q. One can neglect ρ in such cases even if the obstacle created by ρ impedes a construction of $\hat{q}$ considered in connection with Oc_q. Let $\mathfrak{E}$ be the equivalence relation between F- and N-numbers. Although $\mathfrak{E}$ is a typical ultra-intuitionistic object it may happen that in T or a part T′ of it there is no need for the consideration of it: and then one can suppose that T or at least T′ is really being considered, without taking $\mathfrak{E}$ into attention. Let $\hat{q}$ be considered in T or T′ respectively. Then in T (or T′ respectively) ρ is strange to $\hat{q}$ because $\mathfrak{E}$ is indispensable for any consideration of ρ.

Of course there may be cases of much more complicated metafunctions than this ρ. Typical objects $\mathfrak{E}$ are e.g. fixations of parameters. Usually any ultra-intuitionistic consideration T′ depends on some chosen natural number series $N'_1, \ldots, N'_k$ which may be considered as the fixed values of parameters $N_1, \ldots, N_k$ for the series. Then T′ may be considered as the result of assigning these values to these parameters in a more general consideration T. Let $N''_1, \ldots, N''_k$ be another system of values for $N_1, \ldots, N_k$ not mentioned in T′. Then if ρ is a metafunction whose definition uses $N''_1, \ldots, N''_k$ or N''_j-numbers q''_j such that $N'_j \prec q''_j$ $(j = 1, \ldots, k)$ then ρ is strange to T′. The nature of $\mathfrak{E}$ may be completely arbitrary, e.g. $\mathfrak{E}$ may be using of a tactic of attention χ in a situation where there is no given tactic of collations for objects considered with the help of χ. With the help of such a $\mathfrak{E}$ one can prove the strangeness of a metafunction ρ defined in a manner independent of any tactic of collation; and with the help of a suitable $\mathfrak{E}$ one can do the same, if the tactic of collation of ρ essentially differs from that used for the elements of the supposed field of the catching represented by ρ. In such a manner I prove that a sufficiently symmetrical object cannot be a field of catching – this idea is well known in traditional mathematical logic (cf. e.g. Mostowski's proof of the independence of the axiom of choice).

There are some principles of preference for the tactics of attention in connection with obstacles. When one seeks means for the accepted aims one can prefer the attention to a means to the attention to an obstacle for the application of the means. But when one has chosen a means in order to achieve an aim, e.g. when one carries out a construction, one has before all to take into attention every obstacle for the aim. Nevertheless even here the word 'obstacle' cannot refer to any strange obstacle.

The choice of a tactic of attention may depend (and usually does) on the accepted aims. But for the most part this choice is made implicitly and automatically with respect to the considered activity. Even in my own program, the cases in which I explicitly consider the rules of such tactics are comparatively rare (but important).

A natural number series N is defined as a discrete process having an initial event 0 and a unary *leading operation* n' with an evident (external) tactic of collations for its events and a despotic regime imposed on its events. This regime belongs to the tactic of attention which one has to accept in order to follow the notion of an N-number but it does not define this tactic uniquely. In order to see this, I shall consider the construction of a very short natural number series.

Generally for constructing a natural number series N one can take an accomplished event – say, the indication of a void place – as its zero and take the indication of n as the leading operation n'. If one wishes to receive in this way a necessitary series N, one has to accept the rule requiring the indication of n in the situation that n has occurred and is distinguished from all preceding N-numbers. The necessitary series is also a real one. If one wishes to achieve an eventual series, one can accept two permissions (a) and (b) in place of this requirement: (a) it is permitted to indicate n; (b) it is permitted not to do so. In all cases the events, as they appear, are required to be distinguished from all preceding ones; and the fulfilment of this requirement is to be given by a single action with a parameter m for the preceding numbers. Then the sentence $m \neq \boldsymbol{n}$ may be accepted for each value n of the N-numbers and the m's preceding that $\boldsymbol{n}$, and by the fixing of m with $\boldsymbol{m}$ preceding $\boldsymbol{n}$ one can obtain the sentence $\boldsymbol{m} \neq \boldsymbol{n}$ as an accepted one (see S3 above). But N is not fixed till the tactic of attention to its numbers is specified and the notion of N-number remains not clear. Now suppose (by S3) this tactic is fixed in some manner. Then this notion becomes clear though depending on the undefinite value of this fixation. Let this tactic of attention be denoted by χ.

Now I introduce a new tactic τ of attention to the N-numbers. At each stage n of N (i.e. after the appearance of n before the appearance of n') τ permits one to take into attention only n' and the N-numbers $\leqslant n$. (The word 'only' is an abbreviation for the introduction of the despotic regime.) I call τ the *short-sighted* tactic of attention. The series N considered with this tactic τ I denote by N_τ.

At each stage n of N_τ only the N_τ-numbers $\leqslant n'$ are considered as N_τ-numbers and there is no such entity as n'' amongst all possible N-numbers. Evidently N_τ is not closed with respect to the function n''. If $n = 0$ then (at the stage 0) N_τ is to be considered as a series shorter than 2 (the number 2 being taken from another series, perhaps from N). As a matter of fact, after the sentence S_0^τ asserting the appearance of $0'$ in N_τ is accepted, then (at stage $0'$) the name 'N_τ-number' will denote just the entities 0, $0'$ and $0''$ but not $0'''$, and so on. At each stage of every reasoning one has to consider which are the accepted sentences of the form S_n^τ. Here it is useful that the word 'accepted' stands in its passive form.

That is the proof of the possibility of very short natural number series, and this proof is independent of all empirical considerations like that of unfeasibility of the number 10^{12}. Of course it is as yet too vague, because still I have not expounded the ultra-intuitionistic reconstruction of logic; and without this one does not know how to deal with N_τ. I criticize T4 but at present I have not secured even the simple applicability of the postulates of intuitionistic logic. So I have to reconstruct the substantiations of these postulates (see T11) in order to see that the substantiation is independent of the chosen tactic of attention, or at least that the short-sighted tactic is a suitable one for the acceptance of the postulates. This follows essentially from the fact that a tactic of attention has always underlain the consideration of the traditional intuitionistic postulates, a tactic deeper than its substantiation. Its properties have never been studied: and this may be explained by the fact they are almost inessential. The only important thing was that one can follow a chosen tactic and consider it as a fixed one. But the short-sighted tactic for N_τ contains even less requirements of action than the original tactic χ for N and so one can follow it. There can be no obstacle to combining two tactics χ and τ so as to follow the first in considerations of

N-numbers and the second in considerations of N_τ-numbers: and with this combined tactic of attention one can consider the pair of these series. Besides this one has to remark that in purely logical reasonings about the given objects and processes nothing forces us to accept such a sentence as S_0^τ. This fact belongs to the contemplations of voices, and leads immediately to the possibility of consideration of several natural number series at once. Of course, from the series N_τ without 2 one can obtain a series with the arbitrary given number k from another series K but without $k+2$: it suffices to add N_τ to the accomplished beginning $\{0, \ldots, k\}$ of K.

It is useful to remark that the rules of tenses prevent the acceptance of the appearance of $0'$ in N. I can assume that N and N_τ are necessitary. According to the definition of a series 0 has occurred (= is) in N_τ, and $0'$ *will have* been, but there is no rule enabling to obtain from that the sentence that $0'$ *has* been (= is). After $0'$ will have been in N, $0''$ will have been also, but a future relative to another future is not yet a future. So one cannot obtain a sentence about the appearance in N_τ of its future event $0''$.

10. Hitherto I spoke only about destructive critical ideas insofar as the possibility of constructing a sufficiently long natural number series seems to be diminished by this criticism. But the theory of collations leads to a contrary result, it restores the possibility of considering great finished totalities of objects. The operation of *duplication* of a given finished totality $P = \{a_1, \ldots, a_{n_p}\}$ is accomplished in the following way: given one occurrence Oc_p of P, form another one Oc_p' simply by indicating Oc_p once more and distinguishing P and a_i $(i = 1, \ldots, n_p)$ in their old occurrences (through Oc_p) and the new ones (through Oc_p'); then it is sufficient to indicate the pair of indications on Oc_p and on Oc_p' and obtain with the help of S1 the indications on $2n_p$ objects $0a_1, \ldots, 0a_{n_p}, 1a_1, \ldots, 1a_{n_p}$ ($0a_i$ denoting the a_i in its occurrence through Oc_p and $1a_i$ the occurrence of a_i through Oc_p'). So with the help of indications and distinctions one obtains the duplicated totality $2P = 0a_i, \ldots, 0a_{n_p}, 1a_1, \ldots, 1a_{n_p}$. It is then natural to identify $0a_i$ with a_i $(i = 1, \ldots, n_p)$. Starting with $P = \{0\}$ one obtains after 40 steps of duplication a totality with 2^{40} ($> 10^{12}$) members. S1 is used for indications of these members.

This is still not a natural number series with 10^{12}. In order to go further I have to consider a hypothesis related to T9:

The central ontological hypothesis (c.o.h.). Let E be an accomplished procedure (called the *basis* of c.o.h.). Let for each step e of E l_e be a finite procedure feasible if the l_d's are accomplished for all steps d preceding to e in E. (I call l_e the *load* of c.o.h.). Then a procedure E_l is feasible which consists in the reproduction of E with l_e following each step e (before the later steps f of E are accomplished).

C.o.h. is a very strong hypothesis which practically implies all applications of T9. It is a hypothesis to the effect that the applications of pmf may be iterated; and this is the only kind of iteration of pmf allowed in my program.

C.o.h. deals only with the feasibility, i.e. the organic possibility, of l_e and E_l. There is no counterpart of c.o.h. for epistemic possibility in my theory.

C.o.h. asserts only the feasibility of E_l. Feasibility is a kind of possibility – the possibility of a construction – and if one wishes to assert the presence of E_l one has to accompany the application of c.o.h. by that of pmf.

The acceptance of c.o.h. leads to a *third degree* of modalities and the strength of c.o.h. consists in the extension of the old rules to it. But one can show that c.o.h. is not a sufficient means for obtaining an impossible situation from possible ones and so one can justify the applications of c.o.h. in the consistency-proof for ZF. For the leading idea of this proof is, that if ZF were inconsistent then a violation of the main principle of necessity would hold in a possible situation obtained with the help of c.o.h. (This violation would consist e.g. in the fulfilling of an identification of 0 with 0′ in the course of an activity prohibiting this identification.)

There is another principal hypothesis in my program: *All* (non-trivial) *obstacles other than catchings are strange.* This *hypothesis on obstacles* essentially is not new to the foundations of mathematics because in traditional mathematical logic even catchings are considered as strange. With the help of c.o.h. I can essentially show a protodemonstration of this hypothesis. But the detailed justification of c.o.h. and this hypothesis belongs to some extreme directions of the program.

11. In connection with T10 I say that already the introduction of tactics of attention and collations makes the structure of logical theories more complicated than is provided for by T10. Often it is inconvenient to consider the collations used in a text at the same level as the text, and one has to return from the collations to the collated signs. The consideration of aims introduces pragmatics as a part of the semiotics under investigation. I don't exclude the importance of the two levels considered in T10 but I find it insufficient for my aims. I deal essentially with semantical and pragmatic considerations connected with metatheories. (Following Curry I prefer the term 'epitheory' reserving the term 'metatheory' for a well-defined epitheory.) It is hard to answer whether the rules of inference belong to the object theories or to the metatheories in traditional logic. This question becomes still more difficult if one analyzes these rules and studies the means of analysis in a third theory. Certainly the new means do not belong to the object theory but the metatheory then splits. A fortiori it splits when we introduce considerations of an essentially new kind dealing with the establishment of convincingness. The structure of the new program is to be described in terms of methods, tactics and aims rather than in terms of the traditional division into object and metatheories.*

As concerns T11, I say here only that for most of the intuitionistic postulates one can repeat a way of substantiation available in the traditional logic. There are several methods, and the substantiation is always connected with the interpretation chosen for the ordinary logical operations. I have to carry out such a substantiation in order to see that it is compatible with the requirements of my prototheories: relevancy theory, collation theory, and the theories of the modalities, tenses and voices. Here I note that the traditional postulate $\neg A \supset (A \supset B)$ was reduced by A. Heyting to $(A \vee B) \,\&\, \neg A \supset B$. In order to substantiate the latter I use the permission to identify with b 'the member which is distinguished from a of the pair $\{a, b\}$ of distinguished objects'. It is not difficult to see that this permission is compatible with the requirements of collation theory.

In connection with Bernays' axioms $\forall x A(x) \supset A(t)$ and $A(t) \supset \exists x A(x)$ I note that they presuppose the denotational connection $x \rightarrow t$. These connections I call simply 'arrows'. For a single axiom this is merely a trivial remark: but if a great totality of such axioms enters in a deductoid the study of these arrows becomes a large part of the establishment of convincingness.

Consider two of Bernays' axioms $\forall x A(x) \supset A(t(y))$ and $\forall y B(y) \supset B(s(z))$ entering in a deductoid. They are to be accompanied by the arrows $x \rightarrow t(y)$ and $y \rightarrow s(z)$ respectively. The first of these arrows shows that for each value of y $t(y)$ is an admissible value of x, and the second shows the same thing for z, $s(z)$ and y. Then if the variable y is to be identi-

* The notion of 'formalization' is now to be enlarged; 'to formalize' the use of a notion means for me 'to expose a method of using its name'. Perhaps in this deviation from the traditional understanding of formalization by means of a formal system lies the essence of my criticism of T10. (N.B. A method = a system of rules (expressed in a language). Formalization is to be understood as any establishment of a system of rules.)

fied in its occurrences in both axioms it is natural to suppose that $t(s(z))$ should be (for each value of z) an admissible value of x. It is denoted by the arrow $x \rightarrow t(s(z))$ which is also to be inscribed in connection with the deductoid, I say this arrow *refers to* it. If a third Bernays' axiom, say $C(r(w)) \supset \exists z C(z)$, accompanied by the arrow $z \rightarrow r(w)$, occurs in the deductoid, and the variable z is to be identified here with the same variable in its former occurrences, then in the same way the arrow $x \rightarrow t(s(r(w)))$ is to be considered as referring to the deductoid; and this means that (for each value of w) $t(s(r(w)))$ is an admissible value of x. This fact in its general form is justified by means of S1–S3. But it must not be assumed that the composition of functions (with admissible domains and ranges) always leads to a well-defined function. E.g. every natural number series must be closed relative to n' but N_τ is not closed relative to the function n''. So the semantical conditions expressed by arrows may be violated.

One of the principal concerns of the establishment of convincingness is to show the correctness of all arrows referring to the deductoid. There is a strict system of rules governing the notion of an arrow referring to a deductoid. They are in agreement with the requirements of collation theory, e.g. if an arrow $x \rightarrow t$ refers to a deductoid, and t in this occurrence is to be identified with s somewhere in the deductoid then the arrow $x \rightarrow s$ also has to refer to the deductoid. (This arrow $x \rightarrow s$ is called the *identificational arrow*.) Many complications arise from the fact that rule (Ca) (instead of T3) is allowed as a rule of inference. But the main difficulties resulting from the use of (Ca) are connected with catchings. The latter are studied as unbounded metafunctions, and the second principal concern of the establishment of convincingness is to show that every such metafunction is strange to the deductoid. There are several ways to do it, e.g. the method of symmetry, analogous to that used by A. Mostowski in his proof of the independence of the axiom of choice. This method is applicable when one has to show that a symmetrical part of a deductoid cannot be the field of a catching. The underlying idea, that one cannot define a single-valued function taking infinitely many values in a sufficiently symmetrical field, is made more precise by means of the principle of strangeness from relevancy theory.

There is a kind of identification which is dangerous in the sense that it can very easily create a Zenonian situation. Suppose that φ is a function symbol entering in a deductoid (φ denotes a function defined in a studied process and taking its values also in a studied process) and that there is an infinite class of identifications of the values of φ with different parts of a finite object E (e.g. a term or formula entering into the deductoid). Then E becomes the field of a Zenonian situation. I call such identifications *dangerous*; this danger is of great importance, especially in the case when φ is defined on a short natural number series (which is shorter than E), but theoretically even a long series may be cofinal with a very short subsequence of it. From now on I suppose that all deductoids considered are free from dangerous identifications unless the contrary is allowed explicitly.

There is a protodemonstration of the fact that a deductoid without arrows always possesses an establishment of its convincingness.* The same is easily proved for deductoids without the use of (Ca). But this assertion depends on the fact that all deductoids are considered in a form not making use of open formulas; the axioms of Bernays mentioned are to be replaced by their closures.

In order to say more about the form of deductoids I add here that only closed formulas are admitted in them; this affects the list of axioms for quantifiers. So only closed formulas of the type $\forall x A(x) \supset A(t)$ are admitted as axioms and in the arrow $x \to t$ the term t is a constant. But for each application of (Ca) with the premises $P(\boldsymbol{m})$ whose deductoids use an arrow $x \to \varphi(\boldsymbol{m})$ the conclusion $\forall m P(m)$ is accompanied by the arrow $x \to \varphi(m)$ which is said to *absorb* the arrows $x \to \varphi(\boldsymbol{m})$. Thus the closure of a formula $\forall x A(x) \supset A(t(y, z))$ is proved with the help of two applications of (Ca), and is accompanied by the absorbing arrow $x \to t(y, z)$. Each arrow $x \to t$ accompanying a premise of a rule of inference accompanies also its conclusion; and if x occurs in the other premise the arrow accompanies the latter premise too, provided x is identified in both premises. Thus arrows are repeated and I call them in their new occurrences the *induced* arrows. Now the rules for obtaining the *composition* $x \to t(s(z))$ from two arrows $x \to t(y)$ and $y \to s(z)$ (and for the analogous compositions involving terms $t(y, u)$ with two or more variables) are formulated in a syntactically natural manner. (If an arrow is obtained by several acts of forming compositions of $x \to t(y)$ and $y \to s(z)$ etc., then the different applications of these acts are connected to distinct acts of identification of the variable y in the formulas of the deductoid.) If x enters into a formula with the arrow $x \to t$ through a term $\varphi(x)$, it is required that $\varphi(t)$ should be an admissible value of a variable. A special *interpretational* occurrence of $\varphi(t)$ is introduced in such

* Besides the absence of dangerous identifications, this prototheorem presupposes that all applications of (Ca) are of a nature really encountered in my investigations; cf. the second paragraph on page 31 or the third on page 35.

cases. (The word 'term' is replaced by 'termoid' if it is not certain that for each system of values of its variables the term denotes an admissible value of a variable.)

One can reduce even the first principal objective in regards to arrows to the problem of proving the impossibility of non-strange catchings; a fortiori it is true for the second objective introduced especially in connection with catchings. The latter being the only (non-trivial) obstacles, one can say that the establishment of convincingness is the verification of the absence of (non-strange) obstacles for the construction needed in connection with the substantiation of the deductoid.

Recall now the well-known theorem of Bernays and Gödel concerning the expressibility in the ordinary arithmetic of every prf φ. If one analyzes the occurrences of arrows in the proof of this theorem (represented in a form where T3 is excluded in favour of (Ca)), one notices that the correctness of the condition on arrows presupposes that the natural number series is closed relative to φ.

12. The establishment of convincingness of a deductoid consists mainly in considering a class called the *envelope* of the deductoid. The deductoid itself is a finite object: the applications of (Ca) are represented in it by their tasks. (Two tasks of (Ca) are to be identified if for every $\boldsymbol{m}$ they lead to the identified deductoids of the premise $B(\boldsymbol{m})$.) If an application of (Ca) with the premises $B(\boldsymbol{m})$ enters into a deductoid P then the deductoids for the premises $B(\boldsymbol{m})$ are not presupposed to appear before the conclusion $\forall m B(m)$ of that (Ca). This is connected with the fact that the truth of $\forall m B(m)$ is interpreted as the truth, i.e. the feasibility of a proof, for each $B(\boldsymbol{m})$ (cf.(f) on p. 10), but not as its presence. I say that the deductoids for $B(\boldsymbol{m})$ *refer to P* but not *directly* (whereas the task of (Ca) and the formula of P *refer to P directly*). The envelope of P, called eP, consists of all objects referring to P; these are the formulas of P and of deductoids of premises of (Ca) referring to P, the arrows belonging to formulas, the tasks of (Ca) and the applications of the other rules of inference, the interpretational occurrences of termoids and all collations required for these objects as well as the establishments of exhaustion refering directly to their structural procedures. For each process studied, I introduce the corresponding *semantical process*. The events of this are the names obtained for the events of the studied process, according to S2. Each such name appears in the semantical process after its sense has occurred in the process studied; it is called a *semantical event*. These events refer to P and for each reference of a constant termoid t to P the structural identification of t in this occurrence with the synonym of t occurring as a semantical event refers to P. (Structural identifications for two synonyms are defined in a natural manner with the help of identifications for more simple synonyms occurring as their parts.) These *semantical identifications* represent the interpretations of constant terms occurring in the envelope eP. Also for each $\boldsymbol{m}$ of an application of (Ca) a semantical identification of that $\boldsymbol{m}$ in the semantical process and in $B(\boldsymbol{m})$ is required, in order to guarantee the coincidence of the studied process mentioned in connection with different applications of (Ca) related to the process. All objects of the envelope eP are considered as appearing in accordance with the requirements of genetical constitution. This entails that Zenonian situations destroying the feasibility of the tasks of the elements of eP may appear, and one of the requirements of the establishment of convincingness is to guarantee that this will not be the case. The constructions involved in the semiotical justifications of the intuitionistic postulates don't require the appearance of any event except those which have to have occurred in order that the postulate be meaningful (in its reference to P). So these constructions are always feasible on the grounds of c.o.h., and they cannot introduce new Zenonian situations or catchings. On these grounds these constructions are not introduced in eP (but semantical identifications have been included in eP so that this introduction might be possible without any essential change in the feasibility of the other elements of eP).

There are two principal kinds of arrows:

(a_1). those accompanying the Bernays axioms, the absorbing arrows accompanying the conclusions of (Ca) and the identificational arrows;

(a_2). the arrows obtained from the arrows (a_1) by composition.

For (a_2) as well as for (a_1) there are induced occurrences; and compositions are to be made only from arrows belonging to the same occurrence of a formula. The rule for obtaining the identificational arrows is as follows: Let an arrow $x \to t_1$ belong to a formula F and let $Oc_1, \ldots, Oc_n$ be the occurrences of terms $t_1, \ldots, t_n$ such that for each two Oc_i, Oc_{i+1} ($1 \leqslant i < n$) either the identification of t_i and t_{i+1} in these occurrences refers to P or the occurrences Oc_i and Oc_{i+1} are parts of an equality $t_i = t_{i+1}$ (or of a synonym Eq (t_i, t_{i+1}) of such an equality). Then the *identificational* arrow $x \to t_n$ also belongs to the formula F in the same occurrence of the latter. The identificational arrows refer to P. But it is allowed to neglect them if $x \to t_n$ already has an occurrence belonging to the same occurrence of F

or if there is a protodemonstration that the string $Oc_1, \ldots, Oc_n$ is strange to the construction of elements of *eP*. (The equality $t_i = t_{i+1}$ may be proscribed in the construction of these strings if it is certain that it does not express an identification of t_i and t_{i+1}, e.g. when t_i and t_{i+1} are the events of different studied processes.) When it is not clear if an identificational arrow belongs to a formula, I prefer to count it as belonging to it. (Superfluous arrows can only damage the establishment of convincingness.) The rules for identifications related to parts of arrows are formulated in a natural manner.

There is an important requirement called the requirement of *termoidal completeness*. When a task $\tau(\boldsymbol{x})$ of a name $t(\boldsymbol{x})$ of an event of a studied process refers directly to the task of a deductoid (e.g. through a task of (Ca)) for indefinitely many $\boldsymbol{x}$'s, then it is required that there is a functional symbol $t(\boldsymbol{x})$ representing this τ in the (envelope of the) deductoid. It is required that for each of those $\boldsymbol{x}$'s an identification of $t(\boldsymbol{x})$ with $\tau(\boldsymbol{x})$ refers to a deductoid or at least that there should be a string of such identifications uniting $t(\boldsymbol{x})$ with $\tau(\boldsymbol{x})$. This requirement is in accordance with those of collation theory. It guarantees that one cannot prevent the appearance of the absorbing arrow $x \to \varphi(m)$ by replacing the $\varphi(\boldsymbol{m})$ by their synonyms not containing 'φ'.

The tasks of (Ca) may be, generally, of a completely arbitrary nature. But in practice I need for my aims only several simple cases of these tasks requiring no semiotic pathology. (The most difficult of them are connected with the representation of some variants of T3.) If all (Ca) are restricted to these simple cases there is a protodemonstration of the fact that the requirement of the termoidal completeness is fulfilled if the non-absorbed arrows (of type a_1: cf. p. 34) are finite in number. The latter condition I call that *of the finiteness of the arrows*.

For every element Π of *eP* I denote by $\hat{\Pi}$ the finite set of objects preceding Π in order of genetic constitution. (All these objects are to belong to *eP*.)

Now I can say that the establishment of convincingness of a deductoid P consists in three requirements imposed on P and on deductoids P' referring to P.

I. every termoid referring to P shall be a term;

II. the requirement of termoidal completeness;

III. for every Π in eP' each unbounded metafunction whose values belong to $\hat{\Pi}$ is strange to the considered task of P'.

In accordance with S3 the deductoids as well as their establishments of convincingness may depend on various parameters. These may be fixed in an admissible manner through all occurrences of them; the establishment of convincingness remains an establishment thereafter.

There are many reductions of I–III to sufficient conditions of a finitistic type. E.g. I observe for condition I that for the arrows $x \to t(y)$ occurring in deductoids of formulas $\forall n(P(n) \supset P(n'))$, if a variable y occurs in $t(y)$ it does not occur as the left part of an arrow, which saves the envelope from an accumulation of functional symbols in the right parts of arrows obtained by the composition of $x \to t(y)$ with the arrows $y \to s(z)$. Note also that from l arrows of the form $x \to t$ where t is another variable y or y' one cannot obtain an arrow $x \to r$ where r contains more than 2^{2^l} strokes. Of course if K_l is a natural number series such that for each α in it there must be a K_l-number equivalent to $\alpha + 2^{2^l}$ this leads to some simple finitistic conditions sufficient for I. Requirement II is mostly replaced by the condition of finiteness of arrows. The fulfilment of III is guaranteed by a number of conditions dealing with certain symmetries of different parts of deductoids etc.

I mentioned above that the fulfilment of the condition on the arrows can be reduced to the impossibility of some non-strange catchings. Now I can say that the field of those catchings consists of the *numeroids*, i.e. the termoids obtained by c.o.h. as a result of calculation of given termoids; the obstacle is an obstacle to the semantical interpretation of the numeroid and consists in the fact that the parts of the numeroid catch on a semantical process (or on a studied one).

Now I shall describe briefly the semantical interpretation of the usual logical operators preferred by me in connection with T11. $A \supset B$ is interpreted as the presence of a proof of B from A (this proof being of course of a somewhat more simple nature than that wherein the $A \supset B$ occurs; e.g., this proof may depend on a more simple value of a parameter or on a more simple way of fixing it). $\neg A$ is short for $A \supset f$ where f acts like $0 = 0'$. It is important to remark that this concerns only $\neg$ in the usual contexts of mathematical logic, because the appearances of 'not' in the names of (VIII) on p. 16 cannot be reduced to implications. The quantifiers are introduced before the connectives and afterwards, e.g. conjunction is defined as a universal quantifier with a finite range. This provides me with connectives symmetrical from the beginning. (x) is called the *universal* quantifier: $(x)A(x)$ means the presence of a method enabling one to accept $A(\boldsymbol{x})$ for every value $\boldsymbol{x}$ of x that has occurred. $(\mathrm{E}x)$ is called the *particular* quantifier and $(\mathrm{E}x)A(x)$ means that there may occur (with an arbitrary modal characteristic and tense) an x for which $A(x)$ can be accepted. Here the modality of x in both quantifiers is arbitrary, but if it is 'real' these quantifiers become the usual $\forall x$ and $\exists x$ (used in the explication of the connectives). Some tactic of acceptance of sentences is here borne in mind.

It is not difficult to construct a deductoid for two formulas A and $\neg A$ and even to find an establishment of convincingness for each of them in such a manner that if one forms a further deductoid for $A \& \neg A$ one cannot establish its convincingness. More precisely, this impossibility holds only if the structural identification of both A's in $A \& \neg A$ is to be fulfilled. There are cases when this identification leads to a violation of the condition on the arrows, and there are also other cases when this identification causes a Zenonian situation or catching (e.g. with the field A). These are the *apparent contradictions* or *contradictoids* and they don't disturb the program. Some of them arise if one tries to prove with the help of T3 the isomorphism of two different natural number series: after replacing T3 by (Ca) and analyzing the arrows one finds a violation of the condition on the arrows. There are also contradictoids arising from considerations of the ultra-intuitionistic model for ZF (see below). E.g. one can in many ways indicate a set x and choose as A the sentence 'x is finite' (in some set-theoretical meaning of finiteness). Another contradictoid arises if one finds in this model a set y violating the axiom of choice and takes as A the sentence 'y is well-ordered'. (Besides the consistency of ZF I obtain ultra-intuitionistically Cohen's result about the independence of the axiom of choice and the continuum-hypothesis; but not his result about the independence of the continuum-hypothesis from the axiom of choice in ZF.) It is worth noting that contradictoids disappear if one excludes the identification of A in the text of $A \& \neg A$. Then the formula $A \& \neg A$ ceases to express a contradiction. In connection with T11 I must say that conjunctions $A \& B$ may differ according to the possibilities that parts of A and B are or are not collated to one another. If one has a proof of A and another one of $\neg A$ then the collations of different parts of A within the first A belong to the first proof, and those within $\neg A$ to the second; but if one merely combines both proofs one makes by this action no identification of both A's in the theorems A and $\neg A$. On similar grounds it is possible that there are two theorems A and $A \supset B$ such that B is not a theorem.

Sometimes I use the possibility of considering the texts of conjunctions $A_1 \& \ldots \& A_n$ with no identifications of the parts of the different A_j's. This enables me to consider some important parts of deductoids as symmetrical. E.g. in the axioms $A_1 \& \ldots \& A_n \supset A_j$ ($1 \leqslant j \leqslant n$) the identification of both A_j's destroys the symmetry of the conjunction. But if one analyzes the aims of collations one remarks that this identification is unnecessary for establishing the fact that implication is an axiom, provided that one knows that A_j in the right-hand part of it is a member of the conjunction in the left-hand part of it. So one can exclude some of the customary identifications as useless for logical aims and reestablish the symmetry of many parts of deductoids. This symmetry is used in proving that these parts cannot be fields of catchings. It is only one of many similar devices of my program. E.g. I use the fact that in applications of (Ca) there is no need to collate the parts of different premises $P(\boldsymbol{m})$ and $P(\boldsymbol{n})$. Of course the exclusion of the customary identifications leads to a revision of T11. But as I have mentioned I can reestablish the substantiations of the traditional axioms of the intuitionistical predicate calculus.

This belongs to a brief description of my genetic theory. This theory is essentially more complicated than the ontological theory. (That is natural because the notion of a proof must be more complicated than that of a natural number series.)

13. Now I return to a brief discussion of the ontological theory.

Let K_0 be a natural number series containing a number k but not $k+2$ (see above, p. 27). Then K_0 does not contain 2^k.

For each K_0-number p I denote by $\hat{p}$ the totality of all K_0-numbers $\leqslant p$. (I call $\hat{p}$ the *genesis* of the K_0-number p and similarly I call the *genesis* $\hat{z}$ of an event z of an arbitrary discrete process D the totality of all those events which have necessarily occurred provided z has.) For each K_0-number p I consider now the application of c.o.h. with the basis p and the load consisting, for $0 \in \hat{p}$, in the formation of $\{0\}$ (i.e. in the indication of a void place) and for each $i+1 \in \hat{p}$ in the duplicating of the object obtained as the result of the ith load. So for each $i+1 \in \hat{p}$ I obtain the totality of strings $a_0 \ldots a_{i+1}$, where each a_j ($j \leqslant i+1$) is 0 or 1. I apply the tactic of collations which enables one to identify $00 \ldots 0a_j \ldots a_{i+1}$ of the $(i+1)$st load with the $a_j \ldots a_{i+1}$ of the $(i-j)$th load. Now I apply c.o.h. once more with the basis $\hat{p}$ and with the $(i+1)$st load consisting in looking over the strings $a_0 \ldots a_{i+1}$ in their natural lexicographical order. This load is feasible if the ith such load is because the $(i+1)$st load consists in repeating the ith load two times (the first time in the form $a_1 \ldots a_{i+1}$ or $0a_1 \ldots a_{i+1}$ of the strings, and the second time in the form $1a_1 \ldots a_{i+1}$ of the strings with the same ordering of $a_1 \ldots a_{i+1}$); here the step $10\ldots0$ is to follow the step $01\ldots1$, which causes a fold. Then I apply c.o.h. with the basis $\hat{p}$ and the load consisting for each $i+1 \in \hat{p}$ in the repeating of the foregoing $(i+1)$st load without taking the fold into attention (the result of this load being the consideration of the strings $a_0 \ldots a_{i+1}$ as appearing in lexicographical order). Now I consider the class K_0^* of all appearances of such strings $a_0 \ldots a_{i+1}$ with $i+1 \in \hat{p}$ where p is a K_0-number, the strings with different i's being collated according to the tactic described. The operation $x+1$ or x' is introduced for these appearances in the natural manner; and then the class K_0^* becomes a class of events occurring in the course of following a method which defines a natural number series. In the theory of collations I establish that this class K_0^* may be identified with this course itself, i.e. with a natural number series. (At least I show that the class of texts involving those wherein this identification is allowed is sufficiently large to include the texts I need in the central nucleus of my program.)

So given a natural number series K_0 with a K_0-number k such that 2^k does not belong to K_0 I obtain a new natural number series K_0^* containing numbers $\leqslant 2^i$ for each K_0-number i, and no other numbers. (Of course when I say this, I identify the equivalent K_0- and K_0^*-numbers, which is not always allowed.) From the ontological standpoint the fact that K_0^* is a natural number series means nothing but that the appearance of its events can be described by a method of the kind used in the definition of the notion of a natural number series and the fact of the possibility of K_0^* with the indicated property means nothing but the possibility of obtaining by means of c.o.h. the feasibility of each of the events of K_0^*. Further it is evident that if $K_0 \prec q \in K_1$ then $K_0^* \prec 2^q \in K_1^*$. Also (b) K_0^* is closed with respect to the sum-operation $a+b$ defined in a natural way. If $q = 2^k$ then $q \in K_0^* \prec 2^q$, so (c) there is a natural number series K_0^* closed with respect to $a+b$ but *explicitly not closed* with respect to 2^a and (d) one can construct many series $K_0^* \prec K_1^{**} \prec \ldots$ each of them satisfying the property (c).

Now I fix a natural number series L having property (c), e.g. $L = K_0^*$, and I introduce the series $M_0 = K_0^*$, $M_1 = M_0^*, \ldots M_{i+1} = M_i^*, \ldots$ where $i \in L$. For each L-number i the introduction of M_i is made by means of c.o.h. with the basis $\hat{\imath}$ and the load consisting, for $0 \in \hat{\imath}$, in obtaining the introduction of K_0^*, and for each $e+1 \in \hat{\imath}$, in obtaining K^* from the series K obtained in the result of the eth load. (So by c.o.h. the names of these series are feasible and their events are only the points of indications allowed by S1.) Finally I obtain a natural number series M_L whose events are those belonging to some M_i, $i \in L$ with the natural tactic of collations identifying equivalent numbers of different M_i's. Now it is evident that (e) M_L is closed with respect to 2^a and (f) if $L_1 \prec L_2$ then $M_{L_1} \prec M_{L_2}$. Also it is easy to show (g) $L \preccurlyeq M_L$. For the considered series L it is easy to introduce an operation $\varphi(L)$ such that $L \prec \varphi(L)$ and $\varphi(L)$ is closed with respect to $a+b$ (e.g. $\varphi(K_0) = K_0^*$, $\varphi(L) = L^*$ †, $\varphi(M_i) = M_{i+1}$, $\varphi(M_L) = M_{\varphi(L)}$). Let $\overline{M}_L$ be $M_{\varphi(L)}$. Then (e) and (f) hold with M_L replaced by $\overline{M}_L$ and (g) can be strengthened to (g*) $L \prec \overline{M}_L$.

If $m \in M_i^*$, then

$$2^{2^{\cdot^{\cdot^{\cdot^{2m}}}}},$$

where 2 occurs g times belongs to M_{i+g}^* provided $g \in L$. (This follows from $i+g \in L$.) I denote by $2^{(a)}$ the ath *superpower* of 2 defined by the equations $2^{(0)} = 1$, $2^{(a')} = 2^{2^{(a)}}$. If $m = 1$ then the result obtained shows that $a \in L$ entails $2^{(a)} \in M_L$ (and a fortiori $2^{(a)} \in \overline{M}_L$). $q \in K_0^* \prec 2^q$ gives $q \in M_0 \prec 2^q$ and further

$$2^q \in M_1 \prec 2^{2^q} \in M_2 \prec 2^{2^{2^q}} \in M_3 \quad \text{etc.},$$

the number

$$2^{2^{\cdot^{\cdot^{\cdot^{2q}}}}} \quad (\in M_i)$$

with i 2's being obtainable by means of c.o.h.; and $L = K_0^* \prec 2^q$ gives for each $j \in L$

$$M_j \prec 2^{2^{\cdot^{\cdot^{\cdot^{2q}}}}},$$

where 2 occurs 2^q times whence

$$M_L \prec 2^{2^{\cdot^{\cdot^{\cdot^{2q}}}}}$$

with 2^q 2's and $2^q < 2^{(q)}$ gives $M_L \prec 2^{(2^q+q)} < 2^{(2^{q+1})}$. So $M_L \prec 2^{(2^{q+1})}$; but $q \in K_0^* = M_0$ gives $2^{q+1} \in M_2 \subseteq M_L$, so $2^{q+1} \in M_L \prec 2^{(2^{q+1})}$. (In a similar way one can obtain an r such that $r \in \overline{M}_L \prec 2^{(r)}$.) Now the operation M_L over L behaves itself towards $2^{(a)}$ just as K^* does towards 2^a (with M_L in the rôle of K_0^* and 2^{q+1} in the rôle of k); therefore I can repeat the

† Here it is supposed that $L \prec L^*$.

construction used for K_0^* and 2^a and obtain a series closed with respect to $2^{(a)}$ and (with the help of (g^*)) even many such series $N_1, N_2, \ldots$.

One can go further and obtain series closed with respect to the operations $2_i^{(m)}$ defined by $2_4^{(m)} = 2^{(m)}$ and $2_{i+1}^{(0)} = 1$, $2_{i+1}^{(m')} = 2_i^{(2_{i+1}{}^{(m)})}$. One can even replace here the equation $2_{i+1}^{(0)} = 1$ by $2_{i+1}^{(0)} = 2_i^{(1)}$. For each i from a series L one can obtain another series $N_1 \prec N_2 \prec \ldots$ closed with respect to $2_i^{(m)}$. One can even obtain series closed with respect to $2_i^{(m)}$ as a function of two variables i and m. According to a well-known result of R. Peter, for each prf $\varphi(n)$ one can find an i_φ such that $\varphi(m) < 2_{i_\varphi}^{(m)}$; so one can obtain a natural number series N closed with respect to any prf and even many such series $N_0, N_1 \ldots$ (The index i in N_i may belong to any previously constructed series.)

Of course ultra-intuitionistically the notion of prf is to be relativized and generalized. Let prf be defined as in Kleene's book 'Introduction to metamathematics'. Then each prf can be obtained from some initial prf's in a number of applications of two functionals: (a) the schema of composition, and (b) the schema of primitive recursion. This number is now a N-number, N being a parameter. (One of the initial functions also depends on such a parameter; but that is not very essential.) Further one can now consider prf's defined on different series and taking their values in others. To the two mentioned functionals I propose to add still two functionals consisting merely in replacing an argument or value by its equivalent in another series: (c) continuation and (d) restriction. The rôle of these functionals is to replace one series by another in the trivial manner, the resulting function being undefined if one cannot obtain its value in this way. This is the most essential ultra-intuitionistical generalization of the notion of prf; so one obtains the notion of prf defined by means of various natural number series. The notion of partial recursive function remains essentially the same, insofar as it depends on the calculations, where the latter are to be feasible on the ground of c.o.h. It is easy to show that each partial recursive function $\chi(x_1, \ldots x_n)$ is a prf in the sense just introduced. Namely, let $\psi(\mu y[\chi(x_1, \ldots x_n, y) = 0])$ be its traditional Post normal form – by a continuation of the series considered one gets its applicability (i.e. closure with respect to ψ and χ). Now for the operator $\mu y[\chi(x_1, \ldots, x_n, y) = 0]$ I consider its representation in terms of the function τ defined by a single equation $\tau(z', 0, y) = y$ (see Kleene's book § 57). Let N denote the series on which these functions are now considered and $N \prec q \in \overline{N}$. (For the series considered one always can find such an $\overline{N}$ and q.) Let $\bar{\tau}$ be defined on $\bar{N}$ by the equations $\bar{\tau}(z', 0, y) = y$, $\bar{\tau}(0, u, y) = \bar{\tau}(v, u', y) = q$. Then $\mu y[\chi(x_1, \ldots, x_n, y) = 0]$ can be defined on N as the restriction to N of the prf

$$\mu_{y<q} y \, [\bar{\tau}(\prod_{s<y} \chi(x_1, \ldots, x_n, s), \prod_{s \leqq y} \chi(x_1, \ldots, x_n, s), y) = y]$$

and so $\chi(x_1, \ldots, x_n)$ is a prf.

Of course the result obtained before about the possibility of series N closed with respect to every prf is to be understood as referring to prf's defined by means of N-numbers only. Even this notion is now relativized and one can find series $N_1 \prec N_2 \prec \ldots$ with this property. It may be that these prf's on N_2 majorize Ackerman's function on N_1, and so on.

14. But in order to prove the consistency of ZF with k inaccessible cardinals one needs only the $k+2$ series $K \prec N_0 \prec N_1 \prec \ldots \prec N_k$, the N_i's being closed with respect to superpower and the possibility of every N_k-number k' of such $N'_0 \prec N'_i \prec \ldots \prec N'_{k'}$. For the pure system ZF it is sufficient to consider $K \prec N_0$ with possibility of varying N_0 by choosing its values $N_0^1 \prec N_0^2 \prec \ldots \prec N_0^m$ for each N_0-number m. By means of N_0^i I construct a model D^i for the system $\widetilde{\mathrm{ZF}}_i$ equiconsistent with ZF without the axiom of infinity and I have to introduce the latter into D^i *. In this model D^i there is a set m_l of l 'urelemente', and I choose K such that $m \in K$ entails $m+2^{2^l} \in K$. Then I introduce intentionally a Zenonian situation with the help of a 1–1 function defined on K and taking its values in m_l, so that the set m_l becomes infinite. After this I have to verify the axioms of $\widetilde{\mathrm{ZF}}_i$ (in-

* The main differences between $\widetilde{\mathrm{ZF}}_i$ and ZF are the following:

(a). the axiom of extensionality is missing in $\widetilde{\mathrm{ZF}}_i$ and a new functional symbol $q(x)$ with axioms $x \subseteq q(x)$, and $\forall u(u \in x \backsim u \in y) \supset q(x) = q(y)$ is introduced in order to obtain the equiconsistency with ZF;

(b). the logic of $\widetilde{\mathrm{ZF}}_i$ is intuitionistic and all $\exists x$ in axioms are replaced by $\neg \forall x \neg$ (likewise for all disjunctions);

(c). for the atomic formulas $x \in y$ and $x = y$ the law $\neg\neg A \supset A$ is accepted.

(c) enables one to prove the consistency of $\widetilde{\mathrm{ZF}}_i$ with classical logic. But (b) entails that for the set-theoretic functions (and even for those representing prf's in ZF) instead of existence only the double negation of existence is provable in $\widetilde{\mathrm{ZF}}_i$. This explains the fact that the closedness of N_0 with respect to superdegree enables us to construct a model for $\widetilde{\mathrm{ZF}}_i$.

(d). The axiom of infinity is replaced by the introduction of a new alphabet $\alpha, \beta, \ldots$ of variables for the elements of m_l and of the arithmetical signs 0 and $'$ with Peano's axioms $\forall \alpha \alpha' \neq 0$ and $\forall \alpha \forall \beta (\alpha' = \beta' \supset \alpha = \beta)$.

cluding the axiom of infinity) for the resulting model. I construct a deductoid for each of them, and I show that if there were a contradiction C in $\widetilde{\mathrm{ZF}}_i$ containing $\leqslant l$ formulas then by replacing in C the axioms by their deductoids I obtain a deductoid D for a contradiction (not only a contradictoid!*) and an establishment of convincingness for D. Here I use essentially the fact that the sets of the model D^i are symmetrical, and so the main parts of the deductoids may be constructed as symmetrical also: in this way the most disturbing catchings are avoided. (More precisely, for $k = 0$, I construct deductoids in such a way that all objects taking part in it and depending on l are symmetrical. These cases are the most difficult of all.)

Of course all this is but a very short sketch, in which only a very small part of the consistency proof for ZF is indicated. All technical parts of this proof are investigated by me in complete detail and exposed in many manuscripts. The most urgent of them is ready for publication. But the size of all these manuscripts exceeds that of Kleene's book and that prevents me from publishing them quickly. In this most urgent text, the demonstroids are written down, as well as an exact description of the establishment of their convincingness and the chief ideas needed in carrying it out. After this text becomes available to my colleagues I shall be able to answer further questions with a suitable degree of exactness. But all this technically is a very large program and my requirements as to rigour surpass my ability of writing quickly. So many questions will remain and I hope they will be settled in the course of further study. If I have a success even today, it consists in the fact that these questions are essentially deeper than all questions known independently of my program.

Of course, from the ultra-intuitionistic standpoint the traditional axiomatic set theory ZF is but a poor fragment of our thinking.† It is to be supplemented by the theory of modality and the whole domain of research of my prototheories, and this can essentially be done with the help of my method for founding it. But the resulting theory is of course not an axiomatic one.

15. The ultra-intuitionistic program is also an ultra-pedantic one. In order to fulfil its requirements completely it is necessary to construct theories

* More exactly C is considered as a formal proof of $0 = 0'$ in $\widetilde{\mathrm{ZF}}_i$ and D as a demonstroid for $0 = 0'$.

† Also I have to note that ZF is only one way of formalization of Cantor's set theory and therefore its formalization must not close the domain of research in foundations of set theory. E.g. one has to investigate the consistency of Quine's system 'New Foundations'.

about each grammatical category unavoidable in the exposition of this program. That is possible, but still not fulfilled in all detail. So today there are questions answered only intuitively. There is a kind of intuition unavoidable in this research. To this intuition belongs the understanding of aims of each use of a sign or of each other elementary act of thinking. I aspire to describe also this intuition by some methods but then new elementary acts are required and I am forced to indicate some external tactic followed only intuitively. That is unavoidable. But one of the extreme directions of the program consists in reduction of all uses of intuition to the intuitive understanding that the signs used correspond to their aims. I call this direction *pragma-ultra-intuitionism.*

At any rate nobody can dispense with a kind of confidence to his own memory in his study of a theory. Of course, that is true for my program, too. I argue that this kind of confidence is different from faith in the ordinary sense, because it is not used as an argument in a proof or deduction. Nevertheless the *logic of confidence* governing this kind of confidence is required in my program in order to justify confidence in memory too. This logic deals with the transition from '*A* asserts *B*' and 'I believe *A*' to 'I accept *B*', and with many rules of preference of one source of confidence to another one. I recall that the ethical term 'fair' enters in the general explication of 'proof', and I aim to establish an ethical theorem that it is better to accept memory as a source of confidence than to reject it. (If I prefer *A* to *B*, I say *A* is *better* than *B*; this explication shows why I have always to prefer the better; and if sometimes I say I refuse to do it the reason is a play on words based on the presence of several tactics of preference.) The principle of tautology is considered as the best source of confidence.

I introduce the extreme directions in order to state that today all unsolved questions essentially belong to the extreme directions. So in order to show today's state of affairs in my program I can list these extreme directions. They too have been studied by me in part. I can indicate today the following seven directions (in their names I use the abbreviation 'uism' for 'ultra-intuitionism'):

(1). *ultra-ultra-intuitionism* (briefly: uduism) – the construction of the theory of disputes – the logic of confidence and the relevant parts of ethics;

(2). *extra-ultra-intuitionism* (briefly: eduism) or *relevantism* – the substantiation of the hypothesis on obstacles, or its abolishment from our considerations;

(3). *trans-ultra-intuitionism* (briefly: teduism) – the same for c.o.h.;

(4). *pragma-ultra-intuitionism* (briefly: peduism);

(5). *lega-ultra-intuitionism* (briefly: eluism) – the foundations of the primary permissions and the deontic relations between different extreme directions; the relevant parts of ethics;

(6). *nega-ultra-intuitionism* (briefly: neguism) – the substantiation of the principle of the negative evidence;

(7). *bi-nega-ultra-intuitionism* (briefly: bineguism) – the substantiation of the elimination of double negations in the foundations of prototheories. Some questions of the same type are still remaining in the foundations of the genetic theory, but here there is evidence that they can be settled essentially by means of Gödel's imbedding operations. In many cases this elimination requires the consideration of the double negation of a possibility as a new kind of possibility, for which pmf and other modal principles can be proved. Generally to this direction belong only such questions that can be dissolved in the considerations of modalities.

COMPUTABLE ANALYSIS AND DIFFERENTIAL EQUATIONS

OLIVER ABERTH

Computable analysis is an analysis restricted to the field of computable numbers, where a real number is called computable if there is an algorithm for obtaining arbitrarily precise rational approximations. Algorithms are the basis also for the definitions of the functions and sequences of computable analysis, and in every instance of a number, function or sequence, an appropriate defining algorithm is assumed available. This constructive point of view leads the analysis to take on many intuitionistic aspects.

1. Effective methods. A novel feature of this analysis is the wide use that can be made of the concept of 'effective method'. For a given computational problem, it is natural to ask whether there is a constructive method of finding an algorithm defining the computational result if the algorithms defining the input data are known. To put this more precisely requires entering into the details of what constitutes an algorithm. Here we use the terminology of a recent exposition of computable analysis [**1**], where the formal concepts of 'program' or 'programmable function' replace our undefined term 'algorithm'. N_P denotes the 'descriptive integer of the program P', a unique positive integer assigned to the program P.

There is then an effective method of solving a given computational problem if there is a programmable function $F(N_{P_1}, N_{P_2}, \ldots, N_{P_k})$ such that if $N_{P_1}, N_{P_2}, \ldots, N_{P_k}$ are the descriptive integers of programs defining the input numbers, functions, or sequences, then F defines the computational result. (F may have additional arguments besides the ones shown, in accordance with the type of result that F is to define). A computational problem for which such a programmable function F exists is then *effectively soluble*; whenever it can be shown that no such F exists, the problem is *effectively insoluble.*

A simple example of the employment of these concepts is the following computational problem: Given a (computable) number x defined by the programmable function $\alpha(\varepsilon)$ ($\alpha(\varepsilon)$ is a rational approximation for x with error not greater than the rational ε), find a decimal approximation d_k with k decimal digits after the decimal point such that $|d_k - x| \leqslant r \times 10^{-k}$, r a prescribed rational number. r is usually taken as $\frac{1}{2}$, and often there is an additional requirement of the evenness of the last decimal digit when the maximum error of $\frac{1}{2} \times 10^{-k}$ is attained.

Even ignoring the additional requirement, for $r = \frac{1}{2}$ this problem is effectively insoluble, theorem 14 of **[1]** providing an easy proof. Since there is no difficulty here for the special case when x is a rational number p/q, we can show that for $r > \frac{1}{2}$ the problem is effectively soluble: take d_k to be a decimal number closest to $\alpha((r-\frac{1}{2}) \times 10^{-k})$.

An interesting convenient choice for r is $\frac{5}{9} = 0.\dot{5}$. In this case from d_k we may obtain d_j, $1 \leqslant j \leqslant k-1$, by adding $5 \times 10^{-(j+1)}$ to d_k and then dropping all digits beyond the jth decimal place. Similarly, if r equals $5 \times 10^{s-1}/(10^s - 1)$, $1 \leqslant s < k$, then the described process is correct for $1 \leqslant j \leqslant k-s$.

The identification of unreasonable computational problems that is provided by the concept of an effectively insoluble problem may be useful in numerical analysis.

In the remainder of this paper we treat some topics of differential equations from the point of view of computable analysis, to bring out a few differences in comparison with real analysis, and other applications of the concept of effective method.

2. The differential equation $dy/dx = f(x, y)$. Our first theorem is similar to a standard 'existence theorem' of differential equations.

THEOREM 1. *Given the differential equation* $dy/dx = f(x, y)$ *with* $f(x, y)$ *uniformly continuous in a rectangle* $R = \{(x, y): x \in [a, b], y \in [c, d]\}$, *with* $|f(x, y)| \leqslant M$ *and* $|f(x, y_1) - f(x, y_2)| \leqslant L|y_1 - y_2|$ *for points* (x, y), (x, y_1), (x, y_2) *in* R *and positive constants* M, L, *then for any prescribed constant* y_0 *with* (a, y_0), $(b, y_0 \pm M(b-a))$ *in* R, *there is an effective method of finding a uniformly continuous function* $y(x)$, x *in* $[a, b]$, *and its derivative* $y'(x)$, *such that* $y(a) = y_0$, $y'(x) = f(x, y(x))$. *Moreover, this function is unique.*

The usual constructive techniques of Cauchy and Lipschitz may be employed in the proof of this theorem to show the effective method and uniqueness of $y(x)$ (cf. Ince **[4]**, pp. 75–81). The uniform continuity required for $f(x, y)$ cannot be replaced by pointwise continuity.

THEOREM 2. *Under the same hypotheses as in the previous theorem except that the Lipschitz condition is dropped, for any positive integer n there is an effective method of finding a function* $y_n(x)$, *x in* $[a, b]$, *and its derivative* $y_n'(x)$ *such that* $y_n(a) = y_0$, $|y_n'(x)-f(x, y_n(x))| \leqslant 1/n$. *However, there is an* $f(x, y)$ *such that for appropriate* y_0 *there is no effective method of finding a function* $y(x)$ *satisfying* $y'(x) = f(x, y(x))$, $y(a) = y_0$.

PROOF. There is no difficulty in constructing a uniformly continuous function $f_n(x, y)$ such that $|f_n(x, y)-f(x, y)| \leqslant 1/n$ in R and $f_n(x, y)$ satisfies the Lipschitz condition for $L=L_n$. Then by theorem 1 we may find $y_n(x)$ with

$$|y_n(x)-f(x, y_n(x))| = |f_n(x, y_n(x)-f(x, y_n(x))| \leqslant 1/n.$$

To prove the second part of the theorem, consider the function $f(x, y)=\frac{3}{2}y^{\frac{1}{3}}$, with $[a, b] = [0, 1]$. If $y_0 > 0$, $y = (x+|y_0|^{\frac{2}{3}})^{\frac{3}{2}}$ so that $y(1) > 1$, and if $y_0 < 0$, $y = -(x+|y_0|^{\frac{2}{3}})^{\frac{3}{2}}$ so that $y(1) < -1$. That these functions are unique may be shown by applying theorem 1 for an appropriate rectangle R. If $y_0 = 0$ any of the following functions is a solution: $y = 0$ for x in $[0, x_0]$, $y = \pm(x-x_0)^{\frac{3}{2}}$ for x in $[x_0, 1]$, $0 \leqslant x_0 \leqslant 1$.

If there were an effective method of obtaining a solution $y(x; y_0)$ for any y_0 in an interval containing 0 as an interior point, say $[-1, 1]$, then we arrive at a contradiction. Define the programmable function $Q(n)$ as follows: For $n = N_P$, set $y_0 = a_P$ (cf. proof of theorem 21 of [**1**] for the definition of a_P) and decide on one of the following as true: $y(1; a_P) > -\frac{1}{2}$ or $y(1; a_P) < \frac{1}{2}$. In the first case $Q(n) = +1$, in the second $Q(n) = -1$. Thus if $P(N_P)$ is defined, $Q(N_P) = +1$ if $P(N_P) \leqslant 0$ and -1 if $P(N_P) > 0$. But then if N_Q is the descriptive integer of a program realizing Q, whichever value $Q(N_Q)$ assumes leads to a contradiction.

3. Linear differential equations with constant coefficients. To obtain an effective method of solving the equation $y^{(n)}+a_{n-1}y^{(n-1)}+\ldots+a_1y'+$ $+a_0y = 0$, a_i constants, with the initial conditions that $y^{(k)}(0)$ are specified, $k = 0, 1, \ldots, n-1$, a slight change from the usual approach is necessary. If r is a complex root of multiplicity m for the polynomial $t^n+a_{n-1}t^{n-1}+\ldots+$ $+a_0$, then $z^j e^{rz}$, $j = 0, 1, \ldots, m-1$, are m linearly independent complex solutions to the differential equation. We apparently have an effective method of solving our problem: Since a general solution is $\sum_{i=1}^{n} c_i y_i(z)$, y_i a complete set of the above solutions, we may adjust the constants c_i to satisfy the initial conditions and then take the real part as our solution.

However, the method of obtaining the specific solutions y_i is flawed because there is no effective method of determining whether a polynomial with computable number coefficients and degree > 1 has multiple roots, or even the multiplicity of a given root **[2]**. To get around this difficulty, note that if r_1, r_2 are distinct, the divided difference

$$\frac{e^{r_1 z}-e^{r_2 z}}{r_1-r_2}=\sum_{k=1}^{\infty}\frac{z^k}{k!}\sum_{\substack{i_j\geqslant 0\\ i_1+i_2=k-1}} r_1^{i_1} r_2^{i_2}$$

is also a solution. Using this function, $e^{r_1 z}$, and further divided differences, we obtain n linearly independent solutions given by

$$y_s(z)=\sum_{k=s-1}^{\infty}\frac{z^k}{k!}\sum_{\substack{i_j\geqslant 0\\ i_1+\dots+i_s=\\ =k-s+1}} r_1^{i_1} r_2^{i_2}\dots r_s^{i_s},$$

for $s=1, 2, \dots, n$, where the roots $r_1, r_2, \dots, r_n$ need no longer be distinct. These functions can be used to obtain the effective method of solving the differential equation under the initial conditions.

4. A solution to the equation $\Delta u = 0$ with no analogue in real analysis. Since in computable analysis there are functions pointwise continuous over a closed interval but not uniformly continuous there, the possibility arises of finding such functions as solutions to differential equations. This could not occur with the linear differential equation treated in the previous section; a generalization of theorem 1 applies there. However, for Laplace's differential equation

$$0=\Delta u=\frac{\partial^2 u}{\partial x^2}+\frac{\partial^2 u}{\partial y^2}=\frac{1}{r}\frac{\partial}{\partial r}\left(r\frac{\partial u}{\partial r}\right)+\frac{1}{r^2}\frac{\partial^2 u}{\partial \theta^2},$$

we can show that non-uniformly continuous solutions exist.

THEOREM 3. *There is a function $u(r, \theta)$, not identically zero on the unit disc $0 \leqslant r \leqslant 1$ though equal to zero on its circumference, pointwise continuous but not uniformly continuous on the disc, and satisfying the equation $\Delta u = 0$ inside the disc.*

PROOF. We may enumerate those descriptive integers N_P such that $P(2^{-(N_P+2)})$ is defined: $N_1, N_2, \dots$. If the correspondingly defined rational numbers are $r_1, r_2, \dots$, define $g_n(\theta)$ to be a periodic function, with period 2π, such that $g_n(\theta) = 0$ for $|\theta - r_n| \leqslant 2^{-(N_n+1)}$, $g_n(\theta) = 1$ for $|\theta - r_n| \geqslant 2^{-N_n}$ and $-\pi < \theta - r_n \leqslant \pi$, and $g_n(\theta)$ is given by the obvious linear relations for intermediate θ. If $h_n(\theta) = \prod_{k=1}^{n} g_k(\theta)$, then in a period 2π this function is unequal to 1 on intervals whose total length is less than $2\sum_{k=1}^{\infty} 2^{-k} = 2$.

Now if

$$a(k)_n = \frac{1}{\pi}\int_0^{2\pi} h_n(\theta)\cos k\theta\, d\theta, \quad b(k)_n = \frac{1}{\pi}\int_0^{2\pi} h_n(\theta)\sin k\theta\, d\theta,$$

then these sequences are Cauchy and hence have limiting values $a(k)$, $b(k)$. For $r < 1$ we define our desired function by

$$u(r, \theta) = \tfrac{1}{2}a(0) + \sum_{k=1}^{\infty} r^k \left(a(k)\cos k\theta + b(k)\sin k\theta\right).$$

By differentiation of the series, u may be shown to satisfy $\Delta u = 0$ for $r < 1$.

If $u_n(r, \theta)$ is given by

$$u_n(r, \theta) = \tfrac{1}{2}a(0)_n + \sum_{k=1}^{\infty} r^k (a(k)_n \cos k\theta + b(k)_n \sin k\theta), \qquad r \leqslant 1,$$

an alternate form for $u_n(r, \theta)$ is the Poisson integral (cf. **[5]**, pp. 270–277)

$$u_n(r, \theta) = \frac{1}{2\pi}\int_0^{2\pi} h_n(\varphi)\frac{1-r^2}{r^2 - 2r\cos(\theta-\varphi)+1}\, d\varphi, \quad r < 1.$$

For any angle $\theta' = \{\alpha(\varepsilon)\}$, if N_α is a descriptive integer of a program realizing α, $\alpha(2^{-(N_\alpha+2)})$ is defined, so we may find a large enough n, say n_0, such that $h_{n_0}(\theta) = 0$ on an interval containing θ' as an interior point. Employing the Poisson integral, for any positive number e we can show in the usual manner that $0 \leqslant u_{n_0}(r, \theta) \leqslant e$ for (r, θ) inside the unit disc and sufficiently close to the point $(1, \theta)$ on the circumference. The same applies to $u_n(r, \theta)$, $n > n_0$, by comparison of their Poisson integrals with that of $u_{n_0}(x, y)$, and by an easy additional argument also to $u(r, \theta)$. Thus we may set $u(r, \theta)$ equal to 0 on the circumference of the disc and obtain a computable function defined everywhere on the disc.

5. Effective methods and well posed problems. In real analysis, to make the problems of partial differential equations conform more with physical reality, the concept of a well posed problem, where the solution varies continuously with the initial values, is widely employed. Hadamard's famous example of a problem not well posed was that of determining a solution to $\Delta u = 0$ with $u(x, 0)$, $u_y(x, 0)$ prescribed. The functions $u_n(x, y) = (\sinh ny \sin nx)/n^2$ satisfy the initial conditions $u(x, 0) = 0$,

$u_y(x, 0) = (\sin nx)/n$, but as $n \to \infty$, $u_n(x, y)$ does not approach the solution $u(x, y) = 0$ though the initial conditions approach $u(x, 0) = 0$, $u_y(x, 0) = 0$.

In computable analysis the concept of an effectively soluble problem may be used as a substitute for the idea of a well posed problem. For instance, it is not difficult to show that for functions $g(x)$ not unequal to all the functions 0, $(\sin nx)/n$, there is no effective method of finding a function $u(x, y)$ not unequal to all the functions 0, $(\sinh ny \sin nx)/n^2$, with $u(x, 0) = 0$, $u_y(x, 0) = g(x)$.

A formal proof can be given as follows: Take $g(x)$ equal to $|a_P| \sin(x/|a_P|)$. $|a_P|$ is a reciprocal of a positive integer or is 0 according as $P(N_P)$ is or is not defined. If $|a_P| = 0$, $x/|a_P|$ is undefined, but in this case the coefficient $|a_P|$ allows us to take $g(x) = 0$ and obtain a computable function. If there were an effective method of obtaining $u(x, y)$, then since $u(1, |a_P|) > \frac{1}{2}$ if $P(N_P)$ is defined and $u(1, |a_P|) = 0$ if $P(N_P)$ is undefined, we obtain an effective method of determining whether or not $P(N_P)$ is defined, contradicting theorem 13 of **[1]**.

REFERENCES

[1] O. ABERTH, Analysis in the computable number field, *J. Assoc. Comput. Mach.* **15** (1968) 275–299.

[2] O. ABERTH, The concept of effective method applied to computational problems of linear algebra, to appear.

[3] A. HEYTING, *Intuitionism, an introduction*, 2nd revised ed., North-Holland, Amsterdam (1966).

[4] E. L. INCE, *Ordinary differential equations*, Dover (1956).

[5] A. N. TYCHONOV and A. A. SAMARSKI, *Partial differential equations of mathematical physics*, vol. 1, Holden-Day, San Francisco (1964).

MATHEMATICS AS A NUMERICAL LANGUAGE

ERRETT BISHOP

The one point on which constructivists agree is their criticism of classical mathematics. Brouwer's great contribution was to analyze intensively the inadequacies of that system. After Brouwer and Kronecker, we all know a reformation is needed, but disagree about what coursc it should take. Intuitionism, as developed by Brouwer, stresses as basic our intuition of the integers and our intuition of the real numbers; all of mathematics is to be reduced to these two primitive constructs. In my book [**1**] I proposed, in the spirit of Kronecker rather than Brouwer, that the integers are the only irreducible mathematical construct. This is not an arbitrary restriction, but follows from the basic constructivist goal – that mathematics concern itself with the precise description of finitely performable abstract operations. It is an empirical fact that all such operations reduce to operations with the integers. There is no reason mathematics should not concern itself with finitely performable abstract operations of other kinds, in the event that such are ever discovered; our insistence on the primacy of the integers is not absolute.

Thus by 'constructive' I shall mean a mathematics that describes or predicts the results of certain finitely performable, albeit hypothetical, computations within the set of integers. If a word is needed to delimit this special variety of constructivism, I propose the term 'predictive'. From the predictive point of view, Brouwer's intuitionism at first glance contains elements that are extremely dubious; free choice sequences and allied concepts admit no ready numerical interpretation. Moreover, the numerical content of intuitionistic mathematics is diluted by over-reliance on negativistic techniques. The role of negation in predictive mathematics is philosophically secure, if only because there exist negative statements that do have numerical content. Nevertheless, it is remarkable that a systematic effort to avoid negation leads uniformly to better results.

Constructive mathematics is in its infancy. According to some, it is doomed to the role of scavenger. These people conceive of classical mathematics as establishing the grand design and the imaginative insight, leaving the constructivists to add whatever embellishments their credos demand. Although totally wrong, this viewpoint hints at a truth: The most urgent task of the constructivist is to give predictive embodiment to the ideas and techniques of classical mathematics. Classical mathematics is not totally divorced from reality. On the contrary, most of it has a strongly constructive cast. Much of the constructivization of classical mathematics is therefore routine; constructive versions of many standard results are readily at hand. This makes it easy to miss the point, which is *not* to find a constructive version of this or that, or even of every, classical result. The point is not even to find elegant substitutes for whole classical theories. The point rather is to use classical mathematics, at least initially, as a guide. Much will be of little value to the constructivist, much will be constructive per se, and much will raise fundamental questions which classically are trivial or perhaps do not even make sense. The emphasis will be on the discovery of useful and incisive numerical information. It is the incisiveness and scope of the information, not the elegance of the format, that is relevant.

A given classical result may have no, one, or many constructive versions, none necessarily superior to the rest, because different constructive theorems can represent different numerical aspects of the same classical result, all giving different estimates, useful for different ends. In many instances a classical definition, which makes good constructive sense, no longer represents the correct point of view, and so must be replaced. Finding the correct replacement is often a non-trivial challenge, involving considerations which from the classical standpoint would be absurd. I believe that eventually the influence of constructive on classical mathematics will be greater than the influence the other way. Very possibly classical mathematics will cease to exist as an independent discipline. In the meantime, it behooves constructivists to attach their mathematical and philosophical investigations to mathematics as it exists. Contrary practice has led to numerous irrelevancies and misplaced emphasis. Even a quick look shows that much of the constructivist literature lacks the serious intent the subject demands.

In this short paper I want to indicate what to me are some of the important questions of constructive mathematics today. First, I wish to discuss certain mathematical problems, not because of any special interest or difficulty of these particular problems, but as an indication of the sort of work that needs to be done.

The first example is taken from probability theory. (Modern probabilists seem to have little or no interest in the computation or even the computability of the probabilities with which they deal. It is not surprising the subject is blatantly idealistic.) The Birkhoff ergodic theorem asserts that if T is a measure-preserving transformation on a finite measure space and f is an integrable function, then the averages

$$f^n(x) \equiv \frac{1}{n+1}(f(x)+f(Tx)+\ldots+f(T^n x))$$

converge as $n \to \infty$ for almost all x. Constructively this result fails. For a counterexample in the style of Brouwer, take T to be rotation of the unit circle through an angle $2\pi\alpha$, where α is a real number which, for all we know, could be equal to 0, but could, on the other hand, be irrational. On the one hand $\{f^n\}$ would converge a.e. to f, and on the other to the constant function $(2\pi)^{-1}\int f(\theta)d\theta$. Thus a constructive proof of Birkhoff's theorem is out of the question. It is shown in **[1]** that the sequence $\{f^n\}$ in general satisfies certain inequalities (of a type first introduced by Doob for the study of martingales, and called *upcrossing inequalities*), which classically imply the sequence converges a.e. These inequalities, which from the classical point of view constitute a considerable strengthening of Birkhoff's theorem and its principal modern generalizations, would seem to afford a satisfactory constructive version of the ergodic theorem, but this is not so. In the case of a completely general measure-preserving transformation, the upcrossing inequalities are probably satisfactory. In other words, they afford a good *equal-hypothesis* substitute for Birkhoff's theorem. However, we would also like a good *equal-conclusion* substitute for Birkhoff's theorem – that is, usable conditions on T that imply the constructive convergence of the sequence $\{f^n\}$ almost everywhere. This is an important open problem.

The next example is taken from algebra. Recently I was asked whether the Hilbert basis theorem – that a polynomial ring over a Noetherian domain is Noetherian – is constructively valid. The answer is easily seen to be 'yes'. Unfortunately, not even the ring of integers is Noetherian from the constructive point of view (and therefore the Hilbert basis theorem is vacuous). For a counterexample in the style of Brouwer, let $\{n_k\}$ be a sequence of integers, for which we are in doubt as to whether they are all equal to 0. The ideal generated by the integers n_k has no finite basis in the constructive sense. The problem is to find a constructively usable reformulation of the definition of a Noetherian ring, which would include the integers and give constructive substance to the Hilbert basis theorem.

Our third example, from topology, came as a surprise. Elementary algebraic topology should be constructive, but the definition of the singular cohomology groups gives trouble. A singular 1-simplex of the unit circle S^1 is a continuous function ω from the closed unit interval [0, 1] into S^1. Let Ω denote the set of all such ω. A singular 1-cochain c (over the integers $\mathbf{Z}$) can be thought of as a function from Ω to $\mathbf{Z}$. We wish to define constructively a singular 1-cochain that generates the one-dimensional cohomology group of S^1. Such a cochain will in particular be a non-constant integer-valued function c on Ω. Now the set Ω is arcwise connected, in the sense that if ω_1 and ω_2 are any points of Ω, there exists λ: $[0, 1] \to \Omega$ with $\lambda(0) = \omega_1$ and $\lambda(1) = \omega_2$. A result of Brouwer says that every integer-valued function on [0, 1] is constant. A corollary is that every integer-valued function on an arcwise connected set is constant. Thus a non-constant integer-valued function c on Ω would counterexample Brouwer's result. Brouwer's result has not been counterexampled. These considerations indicate the difficulties involved in finding a satisfactory constructive version of singular cohomology theory.

Each of the three problems just discussed requires the development of new concepts appropriate to the constructive point of view. None of them is likely to be given an acceptable solution by the application of a general technique of constructivization. Incisive estimates and apt definitions are not to be expected as consequences of general schemes that translate from classical to constructive mathematics, although translation techniques may have value in special instances, as we shall see later.

The most urgent foundational problem of constructive mathematics concerns the numerical meaning of implication. Constructivists have customarily accepted Brouwer's definitions of the mathematical connectives and quantifiers, implication in particular. According to Brouwer, $P \to Q$ means that the existence of a proof of P necessarily entails the existence of a proof of Q, in other words, there is a method that converts a proof of P into a proof of Q. In **[1]** I gave a variant of this definition, fitted to the predictive point of view: $P \to Q$ means '. . . the validity of the computational facts implicit in the statement P must insure the validity of the computational facts implicit in the statement Q . . .'. There is a discrepancy between even this reformulated definition and the predictive goal, since, as defined, $P \to Q$ is not a priori predictive of the results of certain finitely performable computations within the set of integers. Rather than prematurely attempt to resolve this discrepancy, in **[1]** I decided to let the mathematics be the test, and found that in actual practice there was little difficulty in giving numerical interpretations to statements with implications or even nested implications. Although the numerical meaning of implication is a priori unclear, in each particular instance the meaning is clear. We are at liberty to continue to treat the numerical meaning of implication as being provided by the context, but hopefully there exists a philosophical explanation of the empirical fact that intuitionistic implication in each instance admits a numerical interpretation. Such an explanation requires a deeper analysis of the content of a theorem of constructive mathematics. As a point of departure for such an analysis, I examined a number of theorems and proofs of **[1]**, and came to the following conclusions.

A *complete* mathematical statement – that is, a theorem conjoined with its proof and with all theorems, proofs, and definitions on which it depends, either directly or indirectly – asserts that a given constructively defined function f, from a given constructively defined set S to the integers, vanishes identically. In other words, it asserts $\forall x A(x)$, where A is the decidable predicate $f(x) = 0$ and x ranges over S.

Most theorems, standing by themselves, are incomplete mathematical statements. An *incomplete mathematical statement* concerns certain entities whose constructions are not described in the statement itself. For instance, the prime number theorem

$$\lim_{n\to\infty} \frac{\pi(n)\log n}{n} = 1$$

implicitly refers to a sequence $\{n_k\}$ of positive integers such that

$$\left| \frac{\pi(n)\log n}{n} - 1 \right| \leqslant k^{-1},$$

whenever $n \geqslant n_k$. The integers n_k can be extracted from the proof of the prime number theorem, presuming it is constructive (as it is). In general, an incomplete mathematical statement asserts the existence of an element y of a set T, such that when the rule for constructing y is given the statement becomes complete. In other words an incomplete statement has the form $\exists y P(y)$, where $P(y)$ is a complete statement with parameter y. According to the above, the incomplete statement therefore has the form

$$\exists y \forall x A(x, y) \tag{1}$$

where x runs over a set S, y runs over a set T, and $A(x, y)$ is a decidable predicate for each x in S and y in T.

An incomplete mathematical statement is a consequence of its completion. Nevertheless, it contains additional information – the intent. If the prime number theorem were written in the form

$$\forall n \forall k \left(n \geqslant n_k \rightarrow \left|\frac{\pi(n) \log n}{n} - 1\right| \leqslant k^{-1}\right),$$

and n_k replaced by its explicit definition, we might fail to realize that the primary intent was to construct any sequence $\{n_k\}$ making the statement true. The use of incomplete statements aids the intuition and saves time. Moreover, incomplete statements are structural components of implications. An implication $P \rightarrow Q$, where P and Q are incomplete statements, means something quite different from $P' \rightarrow Q'$, where P' is a completion of P and Q' of Q.

Let us grant that mathematics is concerned with statements of the form (1), and inquire how an implication $P \rightarrow Q$, where P and Q are statements of form (1), is to be interpreted as a statement of form (1). The interpretation we shall develop is due to Gödel [2]. Let P be $\exists y \forall x A(x, y)$ and Q be $\exists v \forall u B(u, v)$, so that $P \rightarrow Q$ is

$$\exists y \forall x\, A(x, y) \rightarrow \exists v \forall u\, B(u, v). \tag{2}$$

Pure thought translates this into

$$\forall y (\forall x\, A(x, y) \rightarrow \exists v \forall u\, B(u, v)). \tag{3}$$

For a given value of y, which we now fix, (3) asserts that in case the statement $A(x, y)$ is true for all x then v can be constructed to have certain properties. The rule for constructing v will consist of a certain finitely describable procedure, some stages of which perhaps assume the truth of $\forall x A(x, y)$. For example, at a certain stage we may need to know that a certain integer d is non-zero, in order to be able to perform a division, and it may be necessary to make use of the hypothesis $\forall x A(x, y)$ to derive the needed inequality $d \neq 0$. In fact, such an occurrence is no obstacle to giving a universally valid definition of v. We simply take v to be some convenient constant in case $d = 0$ (*which* constant does not matter). Such considerations lead us to expect we can extend out original construction, and give a universal construction for an element v of the set in question, with the property that in case $\forall x A(x, y)$ does hold, then v will have the value originally prescribed. In other words, we conjecture that if we can prove the statement

$$\forall x\, A(x, y) \to \exists v \forall u\, B(u, v), \tag{4}$$

we can actually prove the seemingly stronger statement

$$\exists v(\forall x\, A(x, y) \to \forall u\, B(u, v)), \tag{5}$$

which in turn is equivalent to

$$\exists v \forall u(\forall x\, A(x, y) \to B(u, v)). \tag{6}$$

Thus we conjecture that $P \to Q$ is actually equivalent to the seemingly stronger statement

$$\forall y \exists v \forall u(\forall x\, A(x, y) \to B(u, v)). \tag{7}$$

To go deeper, fix values of y, v and u, and consider the statement

$$\forall x\, A(x, y) \to B(u, v) \tag{8}$$

which asserts that the particular decidable statement $B(u, v)$ is a necessary consequence of the totality of decidable statements $A(x, y)$ for all x. Experience indicates that a proof of a statement such as (8) actually deduces the truth of $B(u, v)$ from the truth of finitely many of the statements $A(x, y)$. Moreover, reflection indicates the difficulty of exhibiting an instance of a proof of a statement such as (8) that actually uses infinitely many of the statements $A(x, y)$ to prove the statement $B(u, v)$. Let us therefore conjecture that if we can prove (8) we can actually construct elements $x_1, \ldots, x_n$ such that

$$A(x_1, y) \wedge \ldots \wedge A(x_n, y) \to B(u, v). \tag{9}$$

Now (9) is a finitary statement involving decidable propositions. Therefore the rules of classical logic hold, so that there exists k with $1 \leqslant k \leqslant n$ such that

$$A(x_k, y) \to B(u, v). \tag{10}$$

Thus we conjecture that if we can prove (8) we can prove

$$\exists x(A(x, y) \to B(u, v)). \tag{11}$$

Thus we conjecture that (7) is actually equivalent to the seemingly stronger statement

$$\forall y \exists v \forall u \exists x(A(x, y) \to B(u, v)). \tag{12}$$

Using the axiom of choice, we transform (12) into

$$\exists \bar{v} \exists \bar{x} \forall y \forall u (A(\bar{x}(y, u), y) \rightarrow B(u, \bar{v}(y))). \tag{13}$$

This is our candidate for a numerical version of $P \rightarrow Q$, and these considerations probably explain why intuitionistic implication in actual practice admits of numerical interpretation. Gödel in **[2]** proves for a particular formal system, designed to accommodate large portions of constructive mathematics, that any proof of (2) can be transformed into a proof of (13). Whether or not we wish to commit ourselves to this or any other formal system, Gödel's result strengthens our conjecture that (13) is the proper numerical version of $P \rightarrow Q$, and leads us to define a new type of implication, which I shall call *numerical implication* (or *Gödel implication*). With P and Q as above, $P \rightarrow Q$ is defined to be the statement (13). Since it appears that intuitionistic implication in practice amounts to numerical implication, it would seem that for the philosophical unity of predictive mathematics we should abandon intuitionistic implication and work with numerical implication exclusively. Before we definitely accept such a change, we should check in more detail that numerical implication is actually being used, and, just as important, that our intuitions can adjust to the change. I believe experience will prove that numerical implication is at least as natural and easy to use as intuitionistic implication.

Another important foundational problem is to find a formal system that will efficiently express existing predictive mathematics. I think we should keep the formalism as primitive as possible, starting with a minimal system and enlarging it only if the enlargement serves a genuine mathematical need. In this way the formalism and the mathematics will hopefully interact to the advantage of both. As a point of departure, we take a formal system such as used by Gödel **[2]**. Another version is given in Spector **[6]**, where the relevant system is called Σ_2. It is closely related to the system of Kleene and Vesley **[3]**, with the free-choice type axioms left out.

To give a quick sketch, our system Σ formalizes the theory of functions of certain types. The types are defined inductively as follows. The primitive type is **[0]**, and a function of type **[0]** is an integer. If $\boldsymbol{t}_1, \ldots, \boldsymbol{t}_n$ are types, $\boldsymbol{t} \equiv (\boldsymbol{t}_1, \ldots, \boldsymbol{t}_n)$ is a type, and a function of type $\boldsymbol{t}$ is an n-tuple $(f_1, \ldots, f_n)$, where f_i is of type $\boldsymbol{t}_i$. If $\boldsymbol{t}_1$ and $\boldsymbol{t}_2$ are types, $\boldsymbol{t}_1 \rightarrow \boldsymbol{t}_2$ is a type, and a function of type $\boldsymbol{t}_1 \rightarrow \boldsymbol{t}_2$ is a function from the set of all functions of type $\boldsymbol{t}_1$ into the set of all functions of type $\boldsymbol{t}_2$. The types $\boldsymbol{t}_1 \rightarrow (\boldsymbol{t}_2 \rightarrow \boldsymbol{t}_3)$ and $(\boldsymbol{t}_1, \boldsymbol{t}_2) \rightarrow \boldsymbol{t}_3$ are considered to be the same, and the types $\boldsymbol{t} \rightarrow (\boldsymbol{t}_1, \ldots, \boldsymbol{t}_n)$ and

$(\boldsymbol{t} \to \boldsymbol{t}_1, \ldots, \boldsymbol{t} \to \boldsymbol{t}_n)$ are considered to be the same. The system Σ contains variables of the various types, for functions of the various types. Variables of the various types are combined in meaningful ways to form terms. A variable of type $\boldsymbol{t}$ is also a term of type $\boldsymbol{t}$. If $\mathfrak{u}$ is a term of type $\boldsymbol{t}_1 \to \boldsymbol{t}_2$ and $\mathfrak{v}$ a term of type $\boldsymbol{t}_1$, then $\mathfrak{u}(\mathfrak{v})$ is a term of type $\boldsymbol{t}_2$. The constant 0 is a term of type $[\mathbf{0}]$. For each term $\mathfrak{u}$ of type $[\mathbf{0}]$, the *successor* $\mathfrak{u}'$ of $\mathfrak{u}$ is a term of type $[\mathbf{0}]$. If $\mathfrak{u}$ is a term of type $\boldsymbol{t}$ and $x_1, \ldots, x_n$ are distinct variables of arbitrary types $\boldsymbol{t}_1, \ldots, \boldsymbol{t}_n$, then $\lambda(x_1, \ldots, x_n)\mathfrak{u}$ is a term of type $(\boldsymbol{t}_1, \ldots, \boldsymbol{t}_n) \to \boldsymbol{t}$, to be interpreted as the function whose value at $(f_1, \ldots, f_n)$ is the result of replacing x_i by f_i in $\mathfrak{u}$ $(1 \leqslant i \leqslant n)$. The primitive formulas of Σ are of the form $\mathfrak{u} = \mathfrak{v}$, where $\mathfrak{u}$ and $\mathfrak{v}$ are terms of type $[\mathbf{0}]$. By means of the connectives $\wedge$, $\vee$ and $\to$, and the quantifiers $\exists$ and $\forall$, applied to primitive formulas, arbitrary formulas are obtained. The statement 'not A' is defined to mean '$A \to 0 = 1$.' The axioms and rules of inference include the axioms and rules of the intuitionistic predicate calculus (rules and axioms A1 through A10 and B1 through B4 of [6]), axioms for equality (axioms C1 through C4 of [6]), the induction rule (rule D of [6]), and the axiom of choice for all types (an extension of axiom E of [6]). Also included is an axiom expressing the meaning of the λ-operator. For convenience we might also include axioms for certain functions, as is done in [3].

Our first problem is to interpret sets in the system Σ. To each set A we associate a formula $A'(x, y)$ containing no quantifiers. (Then $A'(x, y)$ is decidable for given values of the free variables x and y.) The set A is defined by taking $x \in A$ to mean $\forall y A'(x, y)$. (Of course, x may stand for a finite sequence $(x_1, \ldots, x_n)$ of variables of various types, and the same is true of y. Note that it would be incorrect to define $x \in A$ by a formula of the type $\exists z\ \forall y A'(x, y, z)$; in such a situation, the value of z is necessary to completely determine an element of A; hence we should write $(x, z) \in A$ rather than $x \in A$, and define it by the formula $\forall y A'(x, y, z)$.) Each set A has a relation of equality, which means we must define $x_1 =_A x_2$ by a formula

$$\exists z \forall y\, A''(x_1, x_2, y, z).$$

Of course $=_A$ must be shown to be an equivalence relation. The special equality $x_1 = x_2$ defined as $\forall y(x_1(y) = x_2(y))$ is called *functional equality*. Whenever the equality relation on a set A is not defined, functional equality will be meant. In general we require the equality relation on any set to be weaker than functional equality. If A' and A'' contain a variable u, in addition to those described above, we have a family of sets indexed by the parameter u. This construction will only be used in the special case of a family of subsets, as described below. If A and B are any sets, defined respectively by formulas A', A'' and B', B'', we define the set $C \equiv F(A, B)$ of all functions from A to B as follows. Write the formula

$$\forall x(x \in A \rightarrow f(x) \in B) \wedge \forall x_1 \forall x_2 (x_1 \in A \wedge x_2 \in A \wedge x_1 =_A x_2 \rightarrow f(x_1) =_B f(x_2))$$

in the form $\exists u \forall v C'(f, u, v)$. Take $(f, u) \in C$ to mean $\forall v C'(f, u, v)$. Similarly take $(f_1, u_1) =_C (f_2, u_2)$ to mean

$$\forall x(x \in A \rightarrow f_1(x) =_B f_2(x)).$$

To define a subset B of a set A, according to **[1]**, we must define an element x of A, perform the construction of an additional function u, and check that certain additional conditions are satisfied. Thus B will be determined by a certain formula B', and $(x, u) \in B$ will mean

$$x \in A \wedge \forall v B'(x, u, v).$$

We take $(x_1, u_1) =_B (x_2, u_2)$ to mean $x_1 =_A x_2$. In case B' contains a variable w in addition to x, u and v, we obtain a family of subsets of A. The union and the intersection of a family of subsets of A are defined in obvious ways. In case B_1 and B_2 are subsets of A, the formula $B_1 \subset B_2$ is defined in an obvious way, and $B_1 = B_2$ is by definition the formula $B_1 \subset B_2 \wedge B_2 \subset B_1$. The statement $B_1 \subset B_2 \wedge B_2 \subset B_3 \rightarrow B_1 \subset B_3$, for instance, is a formula in Σ containing as subformulas the formulas A', A'', B_1', B_2' and B_3'. (This particular statement is of course provable in Σ.)

There is no difficulty in extending the above ideas to complemented sets. (A complemented set, relative to a family $\mathscr{F}$ of real-valued functions on a set A, is an ordered pair (B_1, B_2) of subsets of A such that for all $x \in B_1$ and $y \in B_2$ there exists f in $\mathscr{F}$ with $f(x) \neq f(y)$.) We first run into difficulty with Borel sets. In **[1]** we consider a set A, a family $\mathscr{F}$ of real-valued functions on A, and a family $\mathscr{M}$ of complemented subsets of A relative to $\mathscr{F}$; we define a Borel set generated by $\mathscr{M}$ to be a complemented subset obtainable inductively from the two following techniques of construction:

(1). The elements of $\mathscr{M}$ are Borel sets.

(2). A countable union (or countable intersection) of Borel sets already constructed is a Borel set.

Properties valid for an arbitrary Borel set are often proved by induction, corresponding to the inductive character of the definition just given. The type of induction in question also occurs in Brouwer's definition of the constructive ordinals. These definitions seem not to be formalizable in Σ. To extend the system Σ to subsume the theory of Borel sets, it would be necessary to include the type of induction in question. W. A. Howard tells me he has constructed such an extension. We shall consider this matter no further, since there is another approach, which will be explained later.

It appears that the theory of the standard abstract structures – groups, metric spaces, differentiable manifolds, and so forth, can be developed within Σ. For example, a metric space (X, ρ) can be realized in Σ by the formulas X', X'' determining the set X, by the element (ρ, v) of the set $F(X \times X, \boldsymbol{R}^{0+})$, and by an element w that arises when the formula

$$x \in X \wedge y \in X \wedge \rho(x, y) = 0 \rightarrow x =_X y$$

is translated to the form $\exists w \forall t P(w, t, \rho) = 0$. We shall abbreviate $M \equiv (X', X'', \rho, v, w)$, and introduce the notation $M \in \mathscr{MET}$ to represent the fact that X' and X'' are formulas defining a set X, that ρ is a metric on X, that v and w are the moduli introduced above, and that a certain formula $\forall y \mathscr{M}'(\rho, v, w, y)$, which contains X' and X'' as subformulas and expresses the fact that ρ is a metric on X and v and w are the moduli described, is valid. As a formula of Σ, $M \in \mathscr{MET}$ stands for $\forall y \mathscr{M}'(\rho, v, w, y)$. We might call $\mathscr{MET}$ a *large set* (or a class), as distinguished from the sets already defined (which we sometimes call *small sets*).

Although the metric spaces form a large set, rather than a small set, the compact (metric) spaces can be regarded as a small set, as follows. Let T be the set of totally bounded pseudo-metrics on the integers $\boldsymbol{Z}$. For each ρ in T, let $\boldsymbol{Z}_\rho$ be the completion of $\boldsymbol{Z}$ with respect to ρ. The set of all such completions is the set of all compact spaces.

In the same way, there is a small set of locally compact spaces.

A (small) category C is an analog of a small set. The set X of objects of C is specified by a formula X', and the equality relation on X is taken to be functional equality. Another formula Y' defines the sets Hom (x_1, x_2) of morphisms, so that $z \in$ Hom (x_1, x_2) means $\forall y Y'(x_1, x_2, z, y)$. A third formula gives the equality relations on the sets Hom (x_1, x_2). There is a function e which to each x in X assigns an element (the *identity element*) e_x of Hom (x, x). There is a function which to each $z_1 \in$ Hom (x_1, x_2) and $z_2 \in$ Hom (x_2, x_3) assigns an element (their product) of Hom (x_1, x_3). The usual axioms for a category must be satisfied.

Of course, all metric spaces, or all groups, or all vector spaces over $\boldsymbol{R}$ cannot be regarded as a small category. However, if a suitable cardinality restriction – such as separability or countability – is imposed on the individual objects, many classical categories can be considered as small categories in our sense. Examples are the compact (metric) spaces, the locally compact (metric) spaces, the countable metric spaces, the (separable) Banach spaces, the countable groups, the locally compact (metric) groups, the (metric) differentiable manifolds, and the countably generated vector spaces over $\boldsymbol{R}$. Functors are easily treated, and a suitable framework for homological algebra is thereby provided. For example, one can formalize the definition of the singular homology functor from the small category of locally compact spaces to a certain small category of abelian groups, and presumably derive in Σ the standard properties of singular homology.

Following the procedure we used for defining a large set, we can define a large category. For example, to make $\mathscr{MET}$ into a large category, we must first define the set Hom (M_1, M_2) of morphisms connecting given objects $M_1 \in \mathscr{MET}$ and $M_2 \in \mathscr{MET}$ of $\mathscr{MET}$. Again the membership relation $z \in \text{Hom}\,(M_1, M_2)$ is defined by a formula $\forall y \mathscr{M}''(M_1, M_2, y, z)$, where our notation indicates that $\mathscr{M}''$ is a formula with variables ρ_1, v_1, w_1, ρ_2, v_2, w_2, y, z containing X_1', X_1'', X_2' and X_2'' as subformulas. Another formula will give the equality relation on Hom (M_1, M_2). Again the function e which assigns to each $M \in \mathscr{MET}$ an identity element of Hom (M, M) and the function describing the product of morphisms must be given. The structure of these functions needs further elucidation. They will not be fixed functions of the system Σ, because their types will depend on the types of their arguments, which are not fixed. Presumably their definitions will have the same form independently of type.

Continuing along the above lines, we should have no difficulty in defining functors between large categories. Whether the theory would be useful in constructive mathematics is not clear. On the one hand, it is possible that small categories are adequate for the applications, but it is also possible that something more general than a large category might be needed, to define which we would need to enlarge the system Σ.

Consider a positive measure μ on a compact space X, that is, a non-negative linear functional $f \to \int f d\mu$ on the space $C(X)$ of all continuous real-valued functions on X. We wish to define the measures of certain subsets of X. It would be extremely awkward to attempt to formalize the theory as given in **[1]** in the system Σ, because there is no set of Borel sets and therefore no set of measurable sets in Σ. Thus we must either extend Σ or take another approach. It turns out that a modification of the approach of **[1]** gives a theory that is not only formalizable in Σ but improves the original version. The idea is to define a *partial set* S to be a triple $(f, \{f_j\}, M)$, where $f \in C(X)$, $0 \leqslant f \leqslant 1$, $f_j \in C(X)$ and $0 \leqslant f_j$ for each positive integer j, and M is a positive integer, such that

(a). $\omega(S) \equiv \lim\limits_{j\to\infty} \int f_j \mathrm{d}\mu$ exists,

(b). $f_M > \min\{f, 1-f\}$,

(c). $f_1 \leqslant f_2 \leqslant \ldots$.

Then we define $x \in S$ to mean that there exists $\delta > 0$ with $f(x) > f_m(x)+\delta$ for all positive integers m, and $x \in {\sim} S$ to mean there exists $\delta > 0$ with $1-f(x) > f_m(x)+\delta$ for all m. Consider $x \in S$ and $y \in {\sim} S$. Now either $f_M(x) \geqslant f(x)$ or $f_M(x) \geqslant 1-f(x)$, by (b). Since the former inequality contradicts $x \in S$, we have in fact $f_M(x) \geqslant 1-f(x)$. Hence $1-f(x) < f(x)$. Similarly $f(y) < 1-f(y)$. Hence $x \neq y$. Write $S' \equiv \{x : x \in {\sim} S\}$ and $S'' \equiv \{x : x \in {\sim} S\}$. The ordered pair

$$\alpha(S) \equiv (S', S'')$$

is a complemented set in the sense of **[1]**, which means that if $x \in S'$ and $y \in S''$ then $x \neq y$. The *complement* of S is defined to be the triple ${\sim} S \equiv (1-f, \{f_j\}, M)$. Clearly $\alpha({\sim} S) = (({\sim} S)', ({\sim} S)'') = (S'', S')$, which by definition (see **[1]**) is $-(S', S'') = -\alpha(S)$.

Now if $T \equiv (g, \{g_j\}, N)$ is a second partial set, we define $S < T$ to mean that for each positive integer m there exists a positive integer $\gamma \equiv \gamma(m)$ such that $|f-g| \leqslant f_\gamma - g_m$. Clearly, $S < T$ if and only if ${\sim} S < {\sim} T$. Also $S < U$ whenever $S < T$ and $T < U$, and $x \in T$ whenever $x \in S$ and $S < T$. Hence $S < T$ implies that $\alpha(S) < \alpha(T)$, in the sense that $x \in \alpha(S) \to x \in \alpha(T)$ and $x \in -\alpha(S) \to x \in -\alpha(T)$.

For the partial set S considered above, write $\int S \equiv \int f \mathrm{d}\mu$. For the partial sets S and T given above, $S < T$ implies

$$\left|\int S - \int T\right| = \left|\int f \mathrm{d}\mu - \int g \mathrm{d}\mu\right| \leqslant \int |f-g| \mathrm{d}\mu \leqslant$$

$$\leqslant \int (f_\gamma - g_m) \mathrm{d}\mu \leqslant \int f_\gamma \mathrm{d}\mu \leqslant \omega(S).$$

The *union* $S \vee T$ of the partial sets S and T is

$$S \vee T \equiv (\max\{f, g\}, \{f_j + g_j\}_{j=1}^{\infty}, M+N).$$

It is easily seen that $S \vee T$ is a partial set, with $\omega(S \vee T) = \omega(S)+\omega(T)$. Similarly, $S \wedge T$ is defined to be

$$(\min\{f, g\}, \{f_j+g_j\}_{j=1}^{\infty}, M+N).$$

It is a partial set. We have

$$\sim(S \vee T) = \sim S \wedge \sim T \quad \text{and} \quad \sim(S \wedge T) = \sim S \vee \sim T.$$

If $S_1 < S_2$ and $T_1 < T_2$, then

$$S_1 \vee S_2 < T_1 \vee T_2 \quad \text{and} \quad S_1 \wedge S_2 < T_1 \wedge T_2 .$$

Also

$$\alpha(S \vee T) < \alpha(S) \cup \alpha(T) \quad \text{and} \quad \alpha(S \wedge T) < \alpha(S) \pm \alpha(T).$$

A *measurable set* $S \equiv \{S(n)\}_{n=1}^{\infty}$ is a sequence $S(1) < S(2) < \ldots$ of partial sets, with

$$S(n) \equiv (f(n, \cdot), \{f_j(n, \cdot)\}_{j=1}^{\infty}, M(n)),$$

such that $\lim_{n\to\infty} \omega(S(n)) = 0$. The limit

$$\mu(S) \equiv \lim_{n\to\infty} \int f(n, \cdot)\mathrm{d}\mu,$$

called the *measure* of S, exists. If T is another measurable set, we define $(S \vee T)(n) \equiv S(n) \vee T(n)$ and $(S \wedge T)(n) \equiv S(n) \wedge T(n)$ for each n. Also $(\sim S)(n) \equiv \sim S(n)$. It follows that $S \vee T$, $S \wedge T$ and $\sim S$ are measurable sets, and the usual algebraic laws are valid.

For each measurable set S, we take $x \in S$ to mean $x \in S(n)$ for some n, and $x \in \sim S$ to mean $x \in \sim S(n)$ for all n. Correspondingly we write $\alpha(S) \equiv \bigcup_{n=1}^{\infty} \alpha(S(n))$. Then $\alpha(\sim S) = -\alpha(S)$.

If the measure $\mu(S)$ of the measurable set S is positive, then $\int f(n, \cdot)\mathrm{d}\mu > > \omega(S_n)$ for some n, and a construction similar to that of [1] gives a point $x \in S(n)$. Hence $x \in S$, so that $\alpha(S)$ is non-void.

If $\{S(\cdot, k)\}_{k=1}^{\infty}$ is a sequence of measurable sets, such that

$$C \equiv \lim_{n\to\infty} \mu(S(\cdot, 1) \vee \ldots \vee S(\cdot, k))$$

exists, a somewhat complicated definition basically similar to that given in [1], leads to a measurable set $S \equiv \bigvee_{k=1}^{\infty} S(\cdot, k)$ having the following properties:

(1). $\mu(S) = C$

(2). $\alpha(S) < \bigcup_{k=1}^{\infty} \alpha(S(\cdot, k))$.

An operation $\bigwedge$ is defined similarly. The theory of chapter 6 of [**1**] can be developed in this framework.

To formalize in Σ the notion of an abstract measure space, definition 1 of chapter 7 of [**1**] must be rewritten as follows. A *measure space* is a family $\mathcal{M} \equiv \{A_t\}_{t \in T}$ of complemented subsets of a set X relative to a certain family $\mathcal{F}$ of real-valued functions on X, a map $\mu: T \to \boldsymbol{R}^{0+}$, and an additional structure as follows: The void set $\emptyset$ is an element A_{t_0} of $\mathcal{M}$, and $\mu(t_0) = 0$. If s and t are in T, there exists an element $s \vee t$ of T such that $A_{s \vee t} < A_s \cup A_t$. Similarly, there exist operations $\wedge$ and $\sim$ on T, corresponding to the set-theoretic operations $\cap$ and $-$. The usual algebraic axioms are assumed, such as $\sim (s \vee t) = \sim s \wedge \sim t$. Certain measure-theoretic axioms, such as $\mu(s \vee t) + \mu(s \wedge t) = \mu(s) + \mu(t)$, are also assumed. Finally, there exist operations $\bigvee$ and $\bigwedge$. If, for example, $\{t_n\}$ is a sequence such that $C \equiv \lim_{k \to \infty} \mu(t_1 \vee \ldots \vee t_k)$ exists, then $\bigvee \{t_n\}$ is an element of T with measure C. Certain axioms for $\bigvee$ and $\bigwedge$ are assumed. If T is the family of measurable sets of a compact space relative to a measure μ, and the set-theoretic function $\mu: T \to \boldsymbol{R}^{0+}$ and the associated operations are defined as indicated above, the result is a measure space in the sense just described.

Considerations such as the above indicate that essentially all of the material of [**1**], appropriately modified, can be comfortably formalized in Σ.

Much effort has been expanded in developing formal systems to accommodate Brouwer's theory of free choice sequences and related constructs. I am of the opinion that this is not the appropriate approach to Brouwer's ideas. Presuming we are satisfied with Σ as a vehicle for predictive mathematics, I think we should realize the non-predictive portions of intuitionistic mathematics as part of the metatheory of Σ, rather than trying to incorporate them in some modification of Σ. (Aspects of Brouwer's approach to free choice sequences lead me to think he might have been sympathetic to this point of view.) Now the metatheory of Σ is based on the work of Gödel [**2**], who shows that every function proved in Σ to exist can be constructed (simply by unwinding the existence proof) by means of certain canonical operations. Kreisel [**5**] has shown that every function f, of the type mapping sequences of integers into integers, constructed by means of Gödel's canonical operations, is continuous, in the sense that if ω_0 is any sequence of positive integers there exists a positive integer N such that if ω and ω' are any sequences of integers with $|\omega| \leqslant \omega_0$ and $\omega(n) = \omega'(n)$ for all $n \leqslant N$ then $f(\omega) = f(\omega')$. This can be regarded as the central result of

Brouwer's theory of spreads. Thus we can develop Brouwer's ideas as a metatheory. In particular, Brouwer's result that every $f: \boldsymbol{R} \to \boldsymbol{R}$ is continuous emerges as a meta-theorem, which states that if we construct within Σ a function $f: \boldsymbol{R} \to \boldsymbol{R}$ having a certain property, then we can construct a continuous f having the same property. In fact more is true, the canonical function which is constructed by unwinding the formalized proof of the existence of f is continuous. After these results have been proved as metatheorems, it becomes constructively meaningful to build a new formal system to incorporate the metatheory. This is not attractive at present, since the theory of spreads has found no significant mathematical applications.

In **[1]** I remarked that the constructive theory of Banach algebras, given in chapter 11, was forced and unnatural, and that some metatheory was indicated, to smooth the transition from the constructive to the classical proofs. Although it is too early to speak with assurance, it appears that for the particular application I had in mind the metatheory in question is provided by the numerical (or Gödel) interpretation of implication. The principle result of chapter 11 of **[1]** involves the notion of a partial ideal P of a Banach algebra $\mathfrak{A}$, determined by elements $x_1, \ldots, x_n$ of $\mathfrak{A}$ and a totally bounded subset A of $\mathfrak{A}$, and defined as

$$\begin{aligned} P &\equiv P(x_1, \ldots, x_n; A) \\ &\equiv \{x_1 y_1 + \ldots + x_n y_n : y_i \in A \text{ for } 1 \leqslant i \leqslant n\}. \end{aligned}$$

If $x_1, \ldots, x_n$ generate an ideal I of $\mathfrak{A}$, then the distance of I to the identity e is 1, so that for each A the distance of P to e is at most 1. Thus the statement $S(x_1, \ldots, x_n)$, that $x_1, \ldots x_n$ generate an ideal, can be written

$$\forall A \forall \alpha \operatorname{dist}(P(x_1, \ldots, x_n; A), e) > \alpha,$$

where A ranges over the totally bounded subsets of $\mathfrak{A}$ and α over the positive constants < 1. Now we want to constructivize the result Γ, that if $x_1, \ldots x_n$ generate an ideal I, then for each x in A there exists a complex number z such that $x_1, \ldots, x_n, x - ze$ generate an ideal; in other words, the statement $S(x_1, \ldots, x_n) \to \exists z S(x_1, \ldots, x_n, x - ze)$. A simple and trivial modification of the classical proof of Γ gives a constructive proof of the weaker statement Γ'

$$S(x_1, \ldots, x_n) \to \forall B \forall \beta \exists z \operatorname{dist}(P(x_1, \ldots, x_n, x - ze; B), e) > \beta,$$

where B ranges over the same set as A and β the same set as α. The numerical meaning of Γ' is

$$\forall B \forall \beta \exists z \exists A \exists \alpha' Q,$$

where Q is the statement

$$\operatorname{dist}(P(x_1, \ldots, x_n; A), e) > \alpha \to \operatorname{dist}(P(x_1, \ldots, x_n, x-ze; B), e) > \beta.$$

This is just the constructive substitute for Γ which was proved in **[1]** by extremely tedious considerations.

Certain other results in the theory of Banach algebras, not treated in **[1]**, cannot be constructivized so simply. For example, an unpublished result Ω of the author, first published in [7], states that if γ is a differentiable arc in complex n-space $\boldsymbol{C}^n$, then every continuous function $f: \gamma \to \boldsymbol{C}$ can be uniformly approximated on γ by polynomials in the coordinates $z_1, \ldots, z_n$ of $\boldsymbol{C}^n$. Stolzenberg informs me he has constructivized the classical proof, in case γ is analytic, by no means a simple task. To try to get a cheap constructivization, note that for each k the distance $d_k(f, \gamma)$ of f to the polynomials of degree k, with coefficients bounded in absolute value by k, is computable. (The proof is left to the reader.) Thus our statement Ω has the form

$$\forall f \forall \gamma \forall m \exists k \exists j (j > m \wedge d_k^j(f, \gamma) < m^{-1}),$$

where f ranges over the set of functions from γ to $\boldsymbol{C}$, γ over the differentiable arcs in $\boldsymbol{C}^n$, and $d_k^j(f, \gamma)$ is the jth rational approximation to the real number $d_k(f, \gamma)$. Actually this is an abbreviation of

$$\forall f \forall \gamma \forall m (\forall y\, A(f, \gamma, y) \to \exists k \exists j (j > m \wedge d_k^j(f, \gamma) < m^{-1})),$$

or

$$\forall f \forall \gamma \forall m \exists k \exists j \exists y (A(f, \gamma, y) \to (j > m \wedge d_k^j(f, \gamma) < m^{-1})),$$

where now the variables f, γ, m, k, j and y range over all functions of certain types, and $\forall y\, A(f, \gamma, y)$ is the statement that f and γ actually belong to the above-mentioned sets. Thus our approximation statement Ω is an $\forall\exists$-theorem, which means it can be written in the form $\forall u \exists v P(u, v)$, where P is decidable. Now it is an empirical observation that $\forall\exists$-theorems of classical mathematics tend to be constructively valid, so we suspect there is a metatheorem to that effect. For instance, we might try to prove the metatheorem M that every $\forall\exists$-theorem provable in the system Σ' obtained by adjoining the axiom of the excluded middle to Σ is constructively valid. (Presuming the classical proof of the above theorem Ω can be formalized within Σ', such a metatheorem M would imply that Ω is constructively valid.) Now Spector **[6]** has proved such a metatheorem M. Unfortunately, his proof involves an inductive procedure whose meaning is unclear, and so the question is still open. At least for certain special theories, such a metatheorem could be extremely useful.

The system Σ, with the predictive interpretation of implication, can certainly be presented as a programming language like fortran and algol. As stated before, each theorem T of Σ has the form $\exists x \forall y A(x, y)$, where x is constructed in the proof of Σ. We should be able to write a compiler for the language Σ, so that whenever a proof of such a theorem T is read into our computer, the computer will compile a program to compute the constructed quantity x. What do we mean by a program to compute a given function x of a given type? Without loss of generality, we consider only functions x whose values are finite sequences of integers of a given length n. Our question can be answered by induction. Presumably we know what it means to program the computer to compute a given integer. If x is an n-tuple $(x_1, \ldots, x_n)$ of functions, to program the computer to compute x we program it to compute each of the functions $x_1, \ldots, x_n$. Finally, if x is of type $t \to [0]$, a program to compute x is a program to compute $x(u)$ for an arbitrary argument u of x. Since $x(u)$ is determined by the values of u, the only information the program will need about u is the values of u at certain of its arguments $\gamma_1, \ldots, \gamma_k$, where of course γ_i may be a function of $u(\gamma_1), \ldots, u(\gamma_{i-1})$, and k itself may be determined in the course of the computations. Thus the program for computing x will contain as subprograms the programs for computing $\gamma_1, \ldots, \gamma_k$. The computation of $u(x)$ will request the values $u(\gamma_1), \ldots, u(\gamma_k)$ at certain junctures, which will be supplied by the program for computing u we supply the machine when we request $x(u)$ in conjunction with the programs for computing the γ_i (which are part of the program for computing x). Thus by induction we see what it means to program the computation of a given function x. Of course, the program may call on other programs, or subroutines, representing proofs of theorems referred to in the proof of the given theorem. Definitions may be called as well. Types of functionals will presumably be established by type declarations, as in algol.

As an example, consider the theorem of Koksma **[4]** that the set A of all $\theta > 1$, for which the powers $\{\theta^n\}_{n=1}^{\infty}$ are equidistributed modulo 1, is a full subset of the set of real numbers > 1, which means its complement has measure 0. Jonathan Tennenbaum has asked whether it is possible to explicitly exhibit an element θ of A, in the sense we can compute an arbitrary term of the decimal expansion of θ. The answer hinges on whether Koksma's proof is constructive. It is, except at one point, and that point is easily constructivized. The upshot is that the answer to Tennenbaum's question is 'yes'. Thus, having realized Σ as a programming language, we could feed the formalized constructivized version of Koksma's theorem into the computer, then feed in a positive integer n, and request the machine to output the nth term of the decimal expansion of the fixed θ constructed in the proof. We might have to wait a long time.

It would be interesting to take Σ as the point of departure for a reasonable programming language, and to write a compiler.

ADDED IN PROOF. The author wishes to thank G. Kreisel, J. Myhill, and G. Stolzenberg for correcting inaccuracies in the original draft. Myhill notes that in view of such definitions as that of $(f, u) \in C$, it would be more comfortable to extend Σ by adding as axioms the formulas which specify the numerical interpretation of implication. On further research, I have not been able to find in [5] or elsewhere in Kreisel's work the quoted result, that every f mapping sequence of integers into integers is continuous. Kreisel proves a somewhat weaker result, a form of pointwise continuity. However, the quoted result is valid. The numerical interpretation of statement (2), as given above, is valid only when each of the variables x, y, u, v ranges over a *basic set* – a set for which no computations are necessary to check that an element belongs to the set. In Σ, all variables range over basic sets; in informal mathematics, all statements can presumably be phrased in terms of variables ranging over basic sets.

REFERENCES

[1] E. BISHOP, *Foundations of constructive analysis*, McGraw-Hill, New York (1967).

[2] K. GÖDEL, Über eine bisher noch nicht benützte Erweiterung des finiten Standpunktes, *Dialectica* **12** (1958) 280–287.

[3] S. C. KLEENE and R. VESLEY, *The foundations of intuitionistic mathematics*, North-Holland, Amsterdam (1965).

[4] J. F. KOKSMA, Ein mengentheoretischer Satz über die Gleichverteilung modulo Eins, *Composito Math.* **2** (1935) 250–258.

[5] G. KREISEL, Functionals, ordinals, species, in *Logic, methodology and philosophy of science*, Amsterdam (1968) 145–159.

[6] C. SPECTOR, Provably recursive functionals of analysis, *Proc. Symp. on pure mathematics, Am. Math. Soc., Providence* **5** (1962) 1–27.

[7] STOLZENBERG, G., Uniform approximation on smooth curves, *Acta Math.* **115** (1966) 185–198.

ON THE NOTION OF RANDOMNESS

PER MARTIN-LÖF

This is a contribution to the investigations into the notion of randomness by von Mises, Wald and Church.

For the sake of simplicity, we shall only consider infinite sequences

$$x_1 x_2 \cdots x_n \cdots$$

of the binary digits 0 and 1 obtained by tossing an ideal coin. Adapted to this case, Church's formulation [**1**] of von Mises' definition of randomness may be phrased as follows.

Firstly, it is required that the limit frequency should equal $\frac{1}{2}$,

$$\lim_{n\to\infty} \frac{s_n}{n} = \frac{1}{2},$$

where $s_n = x_1 + x_2 + \ldots + x_n$. Secondly, this is required not only for the original sequence but also for every infinite subsequence

$$x_{n_1} x_{n_2} \cdots$$

obtained by taking a recursive function f, which is defined for all finite binary sequences and takes the values 0 and 1, and selecting one after another those indices n for which $f(x_1 x_2 \ldots x_{n-1}) = 1$.

The sequences satisfying this definition of randomness form a set of probability one with respect to the measure μ which makes all coordinates independently take the values 0 and 1 with probability $\frac{1}{2}$. A recursive sequence is necessarily non random.

A serious defect of this definition was revealed by Ville [**5**]. He showed that there exist sequences which satisfy the definition but nevertheless have the property

$$\frac{s_n}{n} \geqq \frac{1}{2} \quad \text{for all } n,$$

the probability of which clearly equals zero. Thus von Mises' definition appears to a great extent arbitrary. Not even such an intuitively appealing property as the oscillative behaviour of the relative frequencies necessarily holds for sequences which are random in his sense.

The practice in probability theory is rather the following. As soon as we have proved that a certain property, such as the law of large numbers,

$$\lim_{n\to\infty} \frac{s_n}{n} = \frac{1}{2},$$

or the law of the iterated logarithm,

$$\limsup_{n\to\infty} \frac{s_n - \frac{1}{2}n}{\sqrt{n \log \log n}} = \frac{1}{\sqrt{2}},$$

has probability one, we say that this is a *property of randomness*. However, if we try, within the classical mathematical framework, to define a sequence to be random if it possesses all properties of randomness, we are led to a vacuous notion. For all complements of one point sets have probability one, and hence the intersection of all sets of probability one is empty. Thus no sequence would be random.

It is proposed to avoid this paradox, born of the classical conception of the totality of all sets of probability one, by restricting our attention to hyperarithmetical sets or, equivalently, to properties expressible in the constructive infinitary propositional calculus. This may be regarded as a constructive version of the restriction to Borel sets which is usually accepted in probability theory. Actually, the specific Borel sets considered there are always obtained by applying the Borelian operations to recursive sequences of previously defined sets, which means precisely that they are hyperarithmetical.

Our main purpose is to prove the following theorem.

THEOREM 1. *The intersection of all hyperarithmetical sets of measure one is a Σ_1^1 set of measure one.*

PROOF. If one allows non-constructive methods, it is immediately clear that the intersection of all hyperarithmetical sets of measure one also has measure one, for there are not more than countably many such sets. It would be desirable to have a constructive proof of this, but that has to await the constructivization of measure theory applied to Σ_1^1 and Π_1^1 sets in general. We content ourselves by noting that the statement to be proved, namely that the measure of a certain Σ_1^1 set equals one, has the quantifier form Σ_1^1.

Let namely the Σ^1_1 set A be represented by a recursive monotone Suslin scheme,

$$A = \bigcup \bigcap_{l=1}^{\infty} A_{n_1 n_2 \ldots n_l},$$

where the union extends over all choice sequences of natural numbers $n_1 n_2 \ldots n_l \ldots$ and the sets $A_{n_1 n_2 \ldots n_l}$ are decidable. Then the statement $\mu(A) = 1$ may be written in the form

$$\forall k \exists n_1 n_2 \ldots \forall l (\mu(\bigcup_{m_1=1}^{n_1} \ldots \bigcup_{m_l=1}^{n_l} A_{m_1 \ldots m_l}) > 1 - 2^{-k}),$$

which is clearly Σ^1_1.

It remains to show that the intersection of all hyperarithmetical sets of measure one is Σ^1_1. This will be done by representing it in the form

$$\hat{x} \forall e (P(e) \wedge Q(e) \rightarrow R(e, x)).$$

Here P is a Π^1_1 predicate expressing that e is the Gödel number of a hyperarithmetical set. Q is a Π^1_1 predicate such that, if e is the Gödel number of a hyperarithmetical set, then $Q(e)$ expresses that the measure of this set equals one. Finally, R is a Σ^1_1 predicate such that, if e is the Gödel number of a hyperarithmetical set, then $R(e, x)$ expresses that x belongs to this set.

To construct the predicate P it will be convenient to view a hyperarithmetical set as a countable wellfounded tree to each top point of which there is associated an atomic set, that is, a set determined by a condition of the form $x_n = 0$ or $x_n = 1$, and to each branching point of which there is associated one of the signs $\bigcup$ and $\bigcap$. More precisely, we define a branch to be a syntactic expression of the form $Q_0 n_1 Q_1 n_2 \ldots Q_{l-1} n_l Q_l$, where for every $i = 1, 2, \ldots, l$, n_i is a natural number and Q_{i-1} is $\bigcup$ or $\bigcap$, and, finally, Q_l is an atomic set. A hyperarithmetical set may then be defined as a recursively enumerable set of branches which can be obtained by repeated applications of the following two inductive clauses. Firstly, a recursively enumerable set, whose only element is an atomic set, is hyperarithmetical. Secondly, if $A_1, A_2, \ldots, A_n, \ldots$ is a recursive sequence of hyperarithmetical sets, then the recursively enumerable set, consisting of all $\bigcup n Q_0 n_1 \ldots Q_{l-1} n_l Q_l$ such that $Q_0 n_1 \ldots Q_{l-1} n_l Q_l$ belongs to A_n, is hyperarithmetical. Similarly with $\bigcup$ replaced by $\bigcap$.

A hyperarithmetical set satisfies the consistency condition that, if two branches $P_0 m_1 P_1 m_2 \ldots P_{k-1} m_k P_k$ and $Q_0 n_1 Q_1 n_2 \ldots Q_{l-1} n_l Q_l$ belong to it and $m_i = n_i$ for $i = 1, \ldots, j$, then $P_i = Q_i$ for $i = 0, 1, \ldots, j$. In particular, if $j = \min(k, l)$ then $k = l$. Now, it is clear that we can construct a recursive enumeration of all recursively enumerable sets of branches that satisfy this consistency condition. Let $P(e)$ be the proposition that for all choice sequences of natural numbers $n_1 n_2 \ldots$ there exists a branch $Q_0 n_1 Q_1 n_2 \ldots Q_{l-1} n_l Q_l$ which belongs to the set whose Gödel number in this enumeration equals e. Then P is a Π_1^1 predicate and, by the bar theorem, $P(e)$ holds if and only if e is the Gödel number of a hyperarithmetical set.

As for the predicate Q it suffices to remark that the measure of a hyperarithmetical set is a hyperarithmetical number, and, consequently,the statement that a hyperarithmetical set has measure one is hyperarithmetical. Also, this is so uniformly in the set considered. A predicate Q with the property that, if $P(e)$, then $Q(e)$ expresses that the hyperarithmetical set with Gödel number e has measure one, may thus be chosen Π_1^1 or Σ_1^1 just as we please. (Of course, this does not imply that there is a hyperarithmetical Q with the desired property.) We need Q in Π_1^1 form.

A similar argument shows that a predicate R with the property that, if $P(e)$, then $R(e, x)$ expresses that x belongs to the hyperarithmetical set whose Gödel number equals e, may be taken either Π_1^1 or Σ_1^1. We need it only in Σ_1^1 form. The proof is now complete.

It is proposed to call the Σ_1^1 set just constructed the *set of random sequences*. More precisely, it is the set of sequences that possess all hyperarithmetical properties of randomness.

THEOREM 2. *A hyperarithmetical sequence is not random.*

PROOF. If a sequence is hyperarithmetical, then the one point set determined by that sequence is a hyperarithmetical set of probability zero and hence disjoint from the set of random sequences.

THEOREM 3. *The set of random sequences is not hyperarithmetical.*

PROOF. Suppose that it were hyperarithmetical. Being a hyperarithmetical set of positive measure (in fact, measure one) we could then find a hyperarithmetical point in it which contradicts theorem 2. The fact that a hyperarithmetical set and, more generally, a Π_1^1 set of positive measure contains a hyperarithmetical point is proved in Sacks [**4**].

Actually, the set of random sequences is not even Π_1^1, because being Σ_1^1, it would then by Suslin's theorem be hyperarithmetical in contradiction to theorem 3.

It is a simple corollary of theorems 1 and 2 that there exists a Π_1^0 set in the

Baire space N^N which is non-empty although it contains no hyperarithmetical points. To see this it suffices to represent the set of random sequences, which is a Σ_1^1 set in the Cantor space 2^N, as the projection of a Π_1^0 set in $2^N \times N^N$. Since no hyperarithmetical sequence is random, this Π_1^0 set contains no hyperarithmetical points. Now, the set remains Π_1^0 if we consider it as a subset of $N^N \times N^N$ instead, and the latter space may be identified with N^N in the usual way. The first example of a set of this kind, or, equivalently, of a recursive tree which is not wellfounded although all its hyperarithmetical branches are finite, was given by Kleene [**2**].

Since the set of sequences that satisfy Church's form of von Mises' definition of randomness is a hyperarithmetical (even arithmetical) set of measure one, it is strictly more inclusive that the set of random sequences defined here. By the same argument it is seen that the present definition is stronger than the one proposed in Martin-Löf [3], where the elements of a certain Σ_2^0 set of probability one were called random sequences.

Already Wald [**6**] proposed to sharpen von Mises' concept of randomness by defining a sequence to be random if it possesses all properties of probability one which are expressible within a certain formalized logic such as Principia Mathematica. However, just as the set of random sequences defined here has turned out not to be hyperarithmetical, we must expect that Wald's proposal leads to a set which is no longer expressible in the language we started with. And, if this language is Principia Mathematica or set theory as formalized by Zermelo and Fraenkel, it seems doubtful if we can ever get a clear conception of such a set of random sequences.

The main improvement of the present paper as compared with Wald [**6**] is, firstly, the choice of a language, namely the constructive infinitary propositional calculus, which seems particularly well adapted for probability theory, and, secondly, the fact that we have been able to prove that the set of random sequences, although escaping the hyperarithmetical hierarchy, does not escape us completely but belongs to a class of sets, namely the Σ_1^1 sets, which can still be handled constructively, although, naturally enough, this requires abstractions more powerful than those needed on the hyperarithmetical level.

REFERENCES

[**1**] A. Church, On the concept of a random sequence, *Bull. Amer. Math. Soc.* **46** (1940) 130–135.

[**2**] S. C. Kleene, Hierarchies of number theoretic predicates, *Bull. Amer. Math. Soc.* **61** (1955) 193–213.

[3] P. Martin-Löf, The definition of random sequences, *Information and Control* **9** (1966) 602–619.

[4] G. E. Sacks, Measure theoretic uniformity in recursion theory and set theory, to appear (1968).

[5] J. Ville, *Etude critique de la notion de collectif*, Gauthier-Villars, Paris (1939).

[6] A. Wald, Die Widerspruchsfreiheit des Kollektivbegriffes, *Actualités Sci. Indust.* **735** (1938) 79–99.

ABSTRACT QUANTIFICATION THEORY*

RAYMOND M. SMULLYAN

Introduction. An alternative title for this subject might be 'Quantification theory without logical connectives or quantifiers.' The point is that many of the well-known theorems about first order logic can be established as consequences of purely combinatorial lemmas which do not depend in any essential way on the logical connectives or quantifiers. In earlier works ([**4**], [**5**], [**6**], [**7**]) we introduced a uniform 'α, β, γ, δ' categorization for quantification theory such that in both the presentation of the postulates and the treatment of the metatheory the logical connectives and quantifiers never appear explicitly. The starting point for this present investigation is the realization that the mathematically interesting results of first order logic can be derived from certain very general properties of the α's, β's, γ's and δ's without having to go back to their definition. Our central definition is that of a *logical framework* in which we abstract these key properties. The logical frameworks which arise in the concrete contexts of propositional logic and first order logic possess a certain property which we do not postulate in our general definition, viz. that no formula possesses an infinite descending chain of proper subformulas. The interesting thing is that this property (which we refer to as *regularity* or *well-foundedness*) is exploited in some completeness proofs but not it others. As a result, different proofs of the same completeness theorem generalize in our abstract setting to distinct completeness theorems.

This paper is but a brief sketch in which we give the main definitions and statements of theorems, but not the proofs. The proofs should be easy to supply by those readers with a background in quantification theory, particularly by those familiar with the tableau point of view. A complete exposition of this subject is currently in preparation.

* This research was sponsored by the Information Research Division of the Air Force Office of Scientific Research under grant number 43367.

1. Logical frameworks

DEFINITION 1. By a (*classical*) *logical framework* $\mathscr{L}$ we shall mean an ordered sextuple $\langle E, C, D, \varphi, {}^{-}, P\rangle$ of the following items obeying the conditions stated alongside:

(1). E is a well-ordered set whose elements we call the *elements* of the framework.

(2). C is a subset of E whose elements we call *conjunctive* elements.

(3). D is a subset of E whose elements we call *disjunctive* elements. Elements in $C \cup D$ will be called *compound*; elements of E outside $C \cup D$ will be called *atomic*.

(4). φ is a function which assigns to every *compound* element x a finite or denumerable sequence $\langle x_1, x_2, \ldots, x_n, \ldots\rangle$ of elements of E whose terms we call the *components* of x, more specifically, we refer to x_i as the ith component of x. We require that if x be both conjunctive and disjunctive, then x has only one component.

(5). ${}^{-}$ is a function which assigns to each $x \in E$ an element $\bar{x}$ in E called the *conjugate* of x. We require that conjugation obeys the following laws (for all x in E):

(i). $\bar{x} \neq x$;

(ii). the conjugate of $\bar{x}$ is x;

(iii). if x is conjunctive, $\bar{x}$ is disjunctive, and if x is disjunctive, then $\bar{x}$ is conjunctive; (From this it follows that if x is atomic, so is $\bar{x}$.)

(iv). $\varphi(\bar{x})$ has the same number of terms as $\varphi(x)$, and the ith term of $\varphi(\bar{x})$ is the conjugate of the ith term of $\varphi(x)$. (Thus if $\varphi(x) = \langle x_1, x_2, \ldots, x_n, \ldots\rangle$, then $\varphi(\bar{x}) = \langle \bar{x}_1, \bar{x}_2, \ldots, \bar{x}_n, \ldots\rangle$.)

(6). P is a function which assigns to each x a finite set $P(x)$ of positive integers. We say that x *depends* on i if $i \in P(x)$, and otherwise that x is *independent* of i.

This concludes our definition of a logical framework.

We use the symbol α to mean any *conjunctive* element x such that $\varphi(x)$ is finite, β for disjunctive x such that $\varphi(x)$ is finite, γ for any conjunctive x such that $\varphi(x)$ is infinite, δ for any disjunctive x such that $\varphi(x)$ is infinite. We write α_i for the ith component of α and similarly with β. We write $\gamma(i)$ for the ith component of γ, and similarly with δ. Our conjugation laws imply that $\bar{\alpha}$ is some β, and that for any $i \leqslant$ the number of terms of $\varphi(\alpha)$, $(\bar{x})_i = \overline{\alpha_i}$. Likewise for any γ, $\bar{\gamma}$ is some δ, and $\bar{\gamma}(i) = \overline{\gamma(i)}$.

Applications. Take classical first order logic formulated with $\sim$, $\wedge$, $\vee$,

$\supset$, $\forall$, $\exists$ as independent primitives, and formulated with individual variables $v_1, v_2, \ldots, v_n, \ldots$ and individual parameters (constants) $a_1, a_2, \ldots, a_n, \ldots$. All formulas will be assumed closed. Now we introduce two new symbols T and F, and we define a *signed* formula as an expression of the form TX or of the form FX, where X is a formula. In the framework we now construct E is to be the set of signed formulas. Our α's shall be all signed formulas of one of the four forms $T\,X \wedge Y$, $F\,X \vee Y$, $F\,X \supset Y$, $F \sim X$; our β's shall be all elements of one of the forms $T\,X \vee Y$, $F\,X \wedge Y$, $T\,X \supset Y$, $T \sim X$. Our γ's shall be of one of the forms $T\,(\forall v)\Psi(v)$, $F\,(\exists v)\Psi(v)$ (where v is any individual variable), and our δ's shall be elements of one of the forms $T\,(\exists v)\Psi(v)$, $F\,(\forall v)\Psi(v)$. Our function φ shall assign to each α a 2-term sequence $\langle \alpha_1, \alpha_2 \rangle$, to each β a 2-term sequence $\langle \beta_1, \beta_2 \rangle$, to each γ a denumerable sequence $\langle \gamma(1), \gamma(2), \ldots, \gamma(n), \ldots \rangle$, and to each δ a denumerable sequence $\langle \delta(1), \delta(2), \ldots, \delta(n), \ldots \rangle$, where the components α_i, β_i, $\gamma(i)$, $\delta(i)$ are defined by the following tables:

α	α_1	α_2
$T\,X \wedge Y$	$T\,X$	$T\,Y$
$F\,X \vee Y$	$F\,X$	$F\,Y$
$F\,X \supset Y$	$T\,X$	$F\,X$
$F \sim X$	$T\,X$	$T\,X$

β	β_1	β_2
$T\,X \vee Y$	$T\,X$	$T\,Y$
$F\,X \wedge Y$	$F\,X$	$F\,Y$
$T\,X \supset Y$	$F\,X$	$T\,Y$
$T \sim X$	$F\,X$	$F\,X$

γ	$\gamma(i)$
$T\,(\forall v)\Psi(v)$	$T\,\Psi(a_i)$
$F(\exists v)\Psi(v)$	$F\Psi(a_i)$

δ	$\delta(i)$
$T\,(\exists v)\Psi(v)$	$T\psi(a_i)$
$F(\forall v)\Psi(v)$	$F\Psi(a_i)$

We next define the *conjugate* of a signed formula as the result of changing T to F or F to T (thus $\overline{TX} = FX$; $\overline{FX} = TX$). The reader can easily verify that all our conjugation laws of (5) hold. Finally, for any signed formula X we define $P(X)$ to be the set of all positive integers i such that the parameter a_i occurs in X.

We have thus described the framework that arises with classical first order logic. We remark that although we used $\sim$, $\wedge$, $\vee$, $\supset$, $\forall$, $\exists$ as independent primitives, we could just as well have taken any complete subset. One advantage of our uniform treatment is that it does not commit us to any particular choice of primitives. We might also see that our scheme could accommodate joint denial, or Sheffer's stroke function, or converse implication as primitives (but not e.g. the bi-conditional).

Frameworks are also applicable to languages with expressions of *denumerable* length. For languages with expressions of non-denumerable length, we would have to extend the notion of a framework by allowing $\varphi(x)$ to be a possibly non-denumerable sequence. These extended frameworks are studied in Linden [**3**].

2. Regularity and induction. We now return to the purely abstract development of the subject of frameworks. In this section and the next the function P will play no rôle.

By a *descending chain* for x we mean a finite or denumerable sequence whose first term is x and which is such that every other term is a component of the preceding term. We call y a *descendant* of x if y is a term of some descending chain for x. (Our notion of descendant plays the rôle of the usual notion of subformula, or rather of *positive* subformula in the sense used by Roger Lyndon.)

We call x a *regular* element if it has no infinite descending chain. We call x uniformly regular if there is a finite upper bound for the lengths of all chains for x. We define the *degree* of a uniformly regular element x as the smallest k greater than the lengths of all chains for x. *We call* $\mathscr{L}$ *well-founded* or *regular* if all elements of $\mathscr{L}$ are regular, and *uniformly regular* if all elements of $\mathscr{L}$ are uniformly regular.

The framework of ordinary first order logic is regular, in fact uniformly so. The framework of propositional logic with denumerably infinite conjunctions and disjunctions is regular but not uniformly regular.

We define $\mathscr{L}$ to be a *Boolean* framework if for each x, $\varphi(x)$ is a finite sequence (in other words there are no γ's or δ's). We remark that regular Boolean frameworks are automatically uniformly regular (this is a consequence of König's infinity lemma).

Call a property (of elements of E) *inductive* if it holds for all atomic elements, and for any compound element x, if it holds for all components of x, then it also holds for x. The following induction principle is basic:

If a property is inductive, then it holds for all *regular* elements.

3. Semantic notions. We let S be a subset of E.

DEFINITION 2. We say S is *closed downwards* if for every conjunctive element c of S, all components of c are in S, and for any disjunctive element d of S, at least one component of d is in S. We say S is *closed upwards* if the converses hold, i.e. if for every conjunctive c, $c \in S$ providing all components of c are in S, and for any disjunctive d, $d \in S$ providing at least one component of d is in S.

DEFINITION 3. We call S a *Hintikka set* if S is closed downwards and for no atomic element p it is the case that p and $\bar{p}$ are both in S. We call S a *Kalmar set* if S is closed upwards, and for every atomic p at least one of p and $\bar{p}$ is in S.

DEFINITION 4. We call S a *quasi-truth set* if S is both a Hintikka set and a Kalmar set. Equivalently, S is a quasi-truth set if S is closed both upwards and downwards, and if for every *atomic* element p exactly one of p and $\bar{p}$ is in S.

We call S a *truth set* if S is closed both upwards and downwards, and if for every element x exactly one of the pair x, $\bar{x}$ lies in S.

DEFINITION 5. We call x *valid* (in the framework $\mathscr{L}$) if x belongs to all truth sets, and *satisfiable* if x belongs to at least one. We call S (*simultaneously*) *satisfiable* if S is a subset of at least one truth set. (We note that x is valid iff $\bar{x}$ is not satisfiable.)

We call S *quasi-satisfiable* if S is a subset of some quasi-truth set. We call x strictly valid if $\bar{x}$ is not quasi-satisfiable.

DEFINITION 6. By a *basic set* B we mean a set of atomic elements such that for any atomic element p exactly one of the pair p, $\bar{p}$ lies in B.

By induction one easily proves

THEOREM 1. *Suppose M is closed downwards and U is closed upwards and every atomic element of M lies in U. Then every* regular *element of M lies in U.*

COROLLARY 1. *In a regular framework, if two truth sets contain the same atomic elements, then they are identical. Hence also, in a regular framework a basic set can be extended to at most one truth set.*

Duality. Let $\mathscr{L}$ be a framework $\langle E, C, D, \varphi, ^{-}, P\rangle$. By the *conjugate* framework $\bar{\mathscr{L}}$ we shall mean $\langle E, D, C, \varphi, ^{-}, P\rangle$. (Thus conjunctive elements of $\mathscr{L}$ are called disjunctive in $\bar{\mathscr{L}}$ and vice-versa). It is trivial to verify that $\bar{\mathscr{L}}$ is actually a framework.

The following theorem, though trivial, is useful in some subsequent proofs, since it cuts the labor in half.

THEOREM 2. (DUALITY THEOREM). (a). *S is closed downwards in $\mathscr{L}$ iff $E-S$ is closed upwards in $\bar{\mathscr{L}}$;*

(b). *S is a Hintikka set in $\mathscr{L}$ iff $E-S$ is a Kalmar set in $\bar{\mathscr{L}}$;*

(c). *S is a quasi-truth set in $\mathscr{L}$ iff $E-S$ is a quasi-truth set in $\bar{\mathscr{L}}$. Likewise with truth set.*

We next need

THEOREM 3. (a). *If S is a Hintikka set, then for no* regular *element x can x and $\bar{x}$ both be in S.*

(b). *If S is a Kalmar set, then for every* regular *x, at least one of x and $\bar{x}$ lies in S.*

(c). *If S is a quasi-truth set, then for every regular x, exactly one of x and $\bar{x}$ lies in S.*

One proves (a) by induction. Statement (b) can be proved by a dual argument, or better yet, directly from (a) using the duality theorem.

THEOREM 4. (a). *Every maximal Hintikka set is a quasi-truth set.*

(b) *Every minimal Kalmar set is a quasi-truth set.*

Again, one can prove either half by induction and obtain the other half by duality.

Now consider a basic set B. Let $\mathscr{H}_B$ be the union of all Hintikka supersets of B, and let $\mathscr{K}_B$ be the intersection of all Kalmar supersets of B. It is easily verified that $\mathscr{H}_B$ is a maximal Hintikka set and that $\mathscr{K}_B$ is a minimal Kalmar set. Thus theorem 4 yields

THEOREM 5. *$\mathscr{H}_B$ and $\mathscr{K}_B$ are both quasi-truth sets.*

It is trivial to extend any Hintikka set H to a Hintikka set H' which contains a basic subset B (just take all conjugate pairs $(p, \bar{p})$ such that neither p nor $\bar{p}$ occurs in H and add one of them to H). Also $H' \subseteq \mathscr{H}_B$, and $\mathscr{H}_B$ is a quasi-truth set.

Hence we have:

THEOREM 6. (a). *Every Hintikka set is quasi-satisfiable.*

(b). (After Hintikka). *In a regular framework, every Hintikka set is satisfiable.*

Combining earlier theorems, we have

THEOREM 7. (FUNDAMENTAL VALUATION LEMMA). *Any basic set B of a* regular *framework $\mathscr{L}$ can be extended to one and only one truth set S. And for* *any Hintikka superset H of B and any Kalmar superset K of B we have $H \subseteq S \subseteq K$.*

Discussion. The inclusions $H \subseteq S$, $S \subseteq K$ of theorem 7 are quite important. The first one is substantially Hintikka's lemma and underlies completeness proofs of so-called 'cut-free' systems. The second half (which is 'dual' to the first half) underlies Kalmar's completeness proof for propositional logic. Indeed it yields

COROLLARY 2 (After Kalmar). *Let $\mathscr{B}$ be a* regular Boolean *framework and let $\vdash$ be a relation between finite subsets of E and elements of E satisfying the following conditions (for all S, x, y, α, β):*

K_0. *For every $x \in S$, $S \vdash x$.*

K_1 *If for each component α_i of α $S \vdash \alpha_i$, then $S \vdash \alpha$.*

K_2. *If for at least one component β_i of β $S \vdash \beta_i$, then $S \vdash \beta$.*

K_3. *If $S \cup \{x\} \vdash y$ and $S \cup \{\bar{x}\} \vdash y$, then $S \vdash y$.*

Then for any valid element x of $\mathscr{B}$ $\emptyset \vdash x$ (where $\emptyset$ is the empty set).

We remark that the conclusion still holds if we weaken the hypotheses by requiring them to hold only when S contains only *atomic* elements, and by requiring K_3 to hold only when x is an *atomic descendent* of y. This then in an obvious manner provides a complete Gentzen type axiomatization of regular Boolean frameworks (if we replace '$\vdash$' by the Gentzen arrow and look at K_0 as axioms and K_1, K_2, K_3 as inference rules. Rule K_3 is then a sort of 'cut' rule, but it is *analytic* (in the sense of [7]), i.e. proofs obey the subformula principle.

4. Tableaux. By a *tree* $\mathscr{T}$ we shall mean a collection of finite or denumerable sequences (of elements of E) all having the same first term (called the *origin* of $\mathscr{T}$) and such that no sequence is a proper initial segment of any other. We refer to the elements of $\mathscr{T}$ as *branches*. If θ is a finite branch $(x_1, \ldots, x_n)$, then by (θ, y) we mean the sequence $(x_1, \ldots, x_n, y)$. To *extend* a branch θ to (θ, y), we mean the act of deleting θ from $\mathscr{T}$ and putting in its place (θ, y). To *split* or *simultaneously extend* θ to $(\theta, y_1), \ldots, (\theta, y_n)$ is to delete θ from $\mathscr{T}$ and put in its place $(\theta, y_1), \ldots, (\theta, y_n)$.

By an *analytic tableau* for a set S (of elements of E) we mean a tree constructed as follows:

We start the tree by taking any element of S as the origin. Now suppose $\mathscr{T}$ is a tableau for S and θ is any branch. Then we may extend θ by any of the following five operations (and the result is again a tableau for S):

(A). If α is a term of θ, then we may extend θ to (θ, α_i), where α_i is any component of α.

(B). For any term β of θ we may simultaneously extend θ to $(\theta, \beta_i), \ldots, (\theta, \beta_n)$, where $\beta_1, \ldots, \beta_n$ are the components of β.

(C). For any $\gamma \in \theta$ we may extend θ to $(\theta, \gamma(i))$ (for any i).

(D). For any $\delta \in \theta$ we may extend θ to $(\theta, \delta(i))$, providing all terms of θ and all elements of S are independent of i.

(E). We may extend θ to (θ, s) for any element s of S.

A branch of a tableau is called *closed* if it contains some element and its conjugate; otherwise it is called *open*. A tableau is called closed if all its branches are closed.

By a *synthetic* tableau for a set S, we mean a tree constructed using the rules above as well as the following:

(F). For any element x of E, we may simultaneously extend θ to (θ, x) and $(\theta, \bar{x})$.

Rule (F) is the counterpart to Gentzen's cut rule.

Now we define a set S to be *analytically inconsistent* if there is a closed analytic tableau for S, and *synthetically inconsistent* if there is a closed synthetic tableau for S. We define an element x to be analytically (synthetically) *provable* if the unit set $\{\bar{x}\}$ is analytically (respectively synthetically) inconsistent, and by an analytic (synthetic) *proof* of x we respectively mean a closed analytic (synthetic) tableau for $\bar{x}$.

Semantic normality. We have still made no assumptions about the P function. Now it is necessary to do so. We shall call $\mathscr{L}$ *semantically normal* if for every set S, every δ, every i and every j such that all elements of $S \cup \{\delta\}$ are independent of j, if $S \cup \{\delta(i)\}$ is satisfiable (quasi-satisfiable) then $S \cup \{\delta(j)\}$ is satisfiable (quasi-satisfiable respectively).

We henceforth assume $\mathscr{L}$ to be semantically normal. We also henceforth let S be any *denumerable* set (of elements of E) such that there are only finitely many i such that some element of S depends on i.

One easily shows:

THEOREM 8 (Correctness of the Tableau Method). (a). *If S is quasi-satisfiable, S is analytically consistent. If x is analytically provable, x is strictly valid.*

(b). *If S is satisfiable, S is synthetically consistent. If x is synthetically provable, x is valid.*

By the method of *systematic tableaux* (cf. e.g. **[1]**), one proves

LEMMA 1. *If S is analytically consistent, then S is a subset of a Hintikka set.*

The above lemma with Hintikka's lemma gives

THEOREM 9 (ANALYTIC COMPLETENESS THEOREM). If *S is analytically consistent, S is quasi-satisfiable. If x is strictly valid, x is analytically provable.*

Next we define a set M to be *E-complete* if for every $\delta \in M$, there is some i for which $\delta(\mathrm{i}) \in M$. Then one easily shows

LEMMA 2. *If M is both E-complete and a maximal set which is synthetically consistent, then M is a truth set.*

By a Henkin type construction, one can extend a synthetically consistent set to a set M satisfying the hypotheses of the above lemma. Hence we have

THEOREM 10. (SYNTHETIC COMPLETENESS THEOREM). *If S is synthetically consistent, S is satisfiable. Also every valid x is synthetically provable.*

For regular frameworks theorems 9 and 10 say the same thing. For non-regular frameworks, they are distinct theorems which as far as we know are of incomparable strenths.

We now know that analytic consistency is equivalent to quasi-satisfiabilty, and synthetic consistency is equivalent to satisfiability. Since analytic consistency and synthetic consistency are both properties of finite character, we have

THEOREM 11 (COMPACTNESS THEOREMS). *(a). If all finite subsets of S are quasi-satisfiable, then S is quasi-satisfiable.*

(b). *If all finite subsets of S are satisfiable, then S is satisfiable.*

Eliminability. Call an element x *eliminable* if for every finite set S, if $S \cup \{x\}$ and $S \cup \{\bar{x}\}$ are both *analytically* inconsistent, then S is analytically inconsistent. In a regular framework analytic consistency is equivalent to satisfiability, and so every element is eliminable (Gentzen's theorem). If $\mathscr{L}$ is not necessarily regular, the situation is this. Suppose S is analytically consistent. Then S is a subset of some quasi-truth set S^*, and for any *regular* x either $x \in S^*$ or $\bar{x} \in S^*$, hence either $S \cup \{x\}$ or $S \cup \{\bar{x}\}$ is quasi-satisfiable, hence also analytically consistent. We thus have

THEOREM 12. *For any (semantically normal) framework $\mathscr{L}$, every* regular *element x is eliminable.*

Next we observe that the statement 'every x is eliminable' is equivalent to 'analytic consistency = synthetic consistency' which is equivalent to 'quasi-satisfiability = satisfiability' which is equivalent to 'every Hintikka set is satisfiable.' Thus we have the following theorem (which is reminiscent of a result of Schütte for type theory):

THEOREM 13. *For any (normal framework ($\mathscr{L}$) (regular or not), the following two conditions are equivalent:*

(1). *Every element is eliminable.*

(2). *Every Hintikka set is satisfiable.*

Discussion of further results. For semantically normal regular frameworks, virtually all of the results of [5] go through, in particular the completeness of all the Gentzen type systems considered there, the first *symmetric* completeness theorem, and the first system of linear reasoning. For results like the fundamental theorem and Craig's interpolation lemma we require additional properties of our framework to which we now turn.

5. Structurally complete frameworks. The framework of first order logic possesses the following two properties:

C_1. For any x and y there is an α whose set of components is $\{x, y\}$.

C_2. For any x and any positive integer i there is some γ such that $\gamma(i) = x$ and γ is independent of i.

None of our results so far has required these properties! We call $\mathscr{L}$ *structurally complete* if C_1 and C_2 hold.

Concerning C_1, we might impose the stronger requirement C_1^* that for any x and y there is some α such that $\varphi(\alpha)$ is the *sequence* $\langle x, y\rangle$. We remark that the framework of first order logic with primitive propositional connectives $\sim, \wedge, \vee, \supset$ does not have this stronger property, but if we added converse implication as another primitive, the stronger property C_1^* would hold (as the reader can easily verify).

We now write $x \wedge y$ to mean any α whose set of components is $\{x, y\}$, and $(\forall i)x$ to mean any γ independent of i for which $\gamma(i) = x$. We write $x \vee y$ to mean any β whose set of components is $\{x, y\}$, $x \supset y$ for any β whose set of components is $\{\bar{x}, y\}$, and $(\exists i)x$ for any δ independent of i for which $\delta(i) = x$. (Humorously enough, we are restoring the logical connectives and quantifiers, but only in the metalanguage!)

Property C_1 is all we need in order to state and prove the fundamental theorem. For Craig's interpolation lemma we need C_2 as well, and also the following additional facts about the P function: (1). For any α, α depends on i iff some component of α depends on i; (2). For any γ, i and $j \neq i$, $\gamma(i)$ depends on j iff γ depends on j; (3). x depends on i iff $\bar{x}$ depends on i. For such frameworks, the Craig-Lyndon lemma holds, where we now define an interpolation element for $x \supset y$ as an element z such that (i) $x \supset z$ and $z \supset y$ are both valid; (ii). for any i, z depends on i iff both x and y depends on i; (iii) every *atomic* descendent of z is a descendent of both x and y.

6. Structures for intuitionistic logic. We have recently been able to extend our uniform method and its corresponding abstract viewpoint to intuitionistic logic. We give here only an extremely brief sketch in which we are mainly interested in giving the appropriate definitions.

By a *structure* $\mathscr{S}$ we shall mean a triple $\langle \mathscr{L}, E_1, E_2 \rangle$, where $\mathscr{L}$ is a framework satisfying an additional condition to be given later, E_1 is a subset of E whose elements we call *∃-special*, E_2 is a subset of E whose elements we call *permanent*. We call an element *∀-special* if its conjugate is ∃-special. ∃-special and ∀-special elements are collectively called *special*, and elements not called special are called *ordinary*.

In applications to intuitionistic logic, the ∃-special elements are to be signed formulas of one of the three forms $\boldsymbol{F} X \supset Y$, $\boldsymbol{F} \sim X$, $\boldsymbol{F}(\forall x)\Psi(x)$. The permanent elements are to be those formulas signed with $\boldsymbol{T}$.

We refer to $\mathscr{L}$ as the *underlying framework* of $\mathscr{S}$. The additional condition we must impose is that for any element Q which is either some γ or δ and any distinct i and j, if $Q(i)$ depends on j, then Q depends on j.

Models. The following notion of 'model' appears to be the appropriate generalization of Kripke **[2]**.

By a *model* $\mathscr{M}$ for $\mathscr{S}$ we shall mean a quadruple $\langle \mathscr{G}, \mathrm{R}, \vdash, I \rangle$ satisfying conditions I and II below, where $\mathscr{G}$ is a collection of objects called *universes*, R is a reflexive and transitive relation between universes, $\vdash$ is a relation between elements Γ of $\mathscr{G}$ and elements x of E, I is a function assigning to each universe a non-empty set of positive integers whose members we call the integers *available in* Γ. We call Γ_2 an *extension* of Γ_1 if $\Gamma_1 \mathrm{R} \Gamma_2$. We use the notation Γ^* for any extension of Γ. We read "$\Gamma \vdash x$' as 'Γ yields x' or 'Γ forces x'. Now for the conditions.

I (a). For any Γ and x, Γ yields exactly one of x and $\bar{x}$.
(b). If $\Gamma \vdash x$ and x is *permanent*, then for any Γ^*, $\Gamma^* \vdash x$.
(c). If i is available in Γ, then i is available in Γ^*.

II (a). For *ordinary* α, $\Gamma \vdash \alpha$ iff Γ yields all components of α.

For $\exists$-special α, $\Gamma \vdash \alpha$ iff *some* Γ^* yields all components of α.
For $\forall$-special α, $\Gamma \vdash \alpha$ iff *every* Γ^* yields all components of α.

(b). For ordinary γ, $\Gamma \vdash \gamma$ iff for every i available in Γ, $\Gamma \vdash \gamma(i)$.
For $\exists$-special γ, $\Gamma \vdash \gamma$ iff for some Γ^* and all i available in Γ^*, Γ^* yields $\gamma(i)$.
For $\forall$-special γ, $\Gamma \vdash \gamma$ iff for every Γ^* and every i available in Γ^*, Γ^* yields $\gamma(i)$.

Remarks

(1). The conditions on the β's and δ's follow from II and I(a).

(2). Our notion of 'model' derives from Kripke as follows: In Kripke's models, the relation $\vdash$ is between universes and *unsigned* formulas. Let us say that Γ yields $\boldsymbol{T}X$ if $\Gamma \vdash X$, and Γ yields $\boldsymbol{F}X$ if Γ does not yield X. The reader can verify that conditions I and II are then a uniform version of Kripke's conditions.

(3). Our conditions are really more general than needed for intuitionistic logic. The fact is that in the structure of intuitionistic logic there are no $\forall$-special α's nor $\exists$-special γ's.

Realizability. Following Fitting **[1]** we say that Γ *realizes* x if Γ yields x and if every i on which x is dependent is available in Γ. Now x is called *valid* if for every model, each universe of the model realizes it. A set M is called realizable if for at least one model at least one universe of the model realizes all elements of M.

Semantic normality. We call $\mathscr{S}$ *semantically normal* if for every Q which is either some γ or δ and every finite set M (of elements of E), if $M \cup \{Q(i)\}$ is realizable and if no element of $M \cup \{Q\}$ is dependent on j, then $M \cup \{Q(j)\}$ is realizable.

We again assume semantic normality.

Tableaux. In discussing tableaux for a structure $\mathscr{S}$, we need some device permitting us at various stages to declare an element on a branch to be *cancelled* or *inoperative on that branch* (this can be formalized in many different ways). A branch is then understood to be closed if its set of *uncancelled* terms contains some element and its conjugate.

Our classic tableau rules are then modified as follows. Rules A, B, C, D are the same providing the α, β, γ, δ are either ordinary or $\forall$-special. But if they are $\exists$-special, one cancels all non-permanent elements on the branch θ before extending it.

Completeness. Kripke's form of the completeness theorem goes through intact for semantically normal *regular* structures $\mathscr{S}$, i.e. every consistent set is realizable (and hence every valid element is provable). Bifurcations of the completeness theorem for non-regular structures will be the subject of another study.

Concluding remarks. Many theorems of intuitionistic logic (such as the completeness theorem) do not depend in any way on which elements were singled out as 'special'. All theorems about structures (as we have defined them) apply as well to other subsystems of classical logic by simply changing the class of special elements.

REFERENCES

[1] M. FITTING, *Intuitionistic logic model theory and forcing*, thesis, Yeshiva Univ. New York (1968); North-Holland, Amsterdam (1969).

[2] S. KRIPKE, Semantical analysis of intuitionistic logic I, in *Formal systems and recursive functions*, North Holland, Amsterdam (1965).

[3] T. LINDEN, *Tree procedures for infinitary logic*, thesis, Yeshiva Univ. New York. (1968).

[4] R. SMULLYAN, A unifying principle in quantification theory, *Proc. National Acad. Sci.* (1963).

[5] R. SMULLYAN, *First order logic*, Springer Verlag (1968).

[6] R. SMULLYAN, Uniform Gentzen systems, *J. Symb. Logic* **33** (1968) 549–559.

[7] R. SMULLYAN, Analytic cut, *J. Symb. Logic* **33** (1968) 560–564.

SECTION B

TRADITIONAL INTUITIONISM

RECENT PROGRESS IN INTUITIONISTIC ANALYSIS*

A. HEYTING

In this lecture I wish to report about work done by two of my students, continuing partly unpublished work by myself. Part of the results have been published in the thesis of Ashwini Kumar, now in Kanpur, India [**1**] and in that of C. G. Gibson, now in Liverpool [**4**].

1. The Brouwer-Stieltjes integral. Gibson worked on the Brouwer–Stieltjes integral. We cannot restrict ourselves to the case that the non-decreasing function λ which defines the measure is everywhere defined, because it would then be continuous. It is sufficient to suppose λ defined on a dense, discrete subspecies of the real line. As λ is right continuous, its domain can be extended by the limitpoints of decreasing sequences $\langle x_i \rangle$, for which the sequence $\langle \lambda x_i \rangle$ converges. However, the theory is developed for a λ with a dense, discrete domain; it is a theorem that functions with the same maximal extension give rise to equivalent measures. λ must have the infimum 0 and its supremum must be calculable.

Brouwer's theory of measure and integration [**3**] can now be followed; instead of rational intervals *cells* are used; a cell $(a, b]$ is a set $\{x | a < x \not> b\}$, where a and b are in the domain of λ. It proved advantageous to use here the negative order relation: if $a \lessdot b$ is the positive order relation, which involves that there are two different rational numbers between a and b, then $a < b$ means $\neg\neg(a \lessdot b)$. The main advantage of $<$ over $\lessdot$ is that by the use of $<$ the difference of two cells is either a cell or the sum of two cells. It need not be true that every point in the domain of λ is measurable; this is only the case if $\sup_{y<x} \lambda(y)$ is calculable.

The theory can be extended to functions of bounded variation, provided we suppose that the variation is calculable. Every function μ of calculable variation which is continuous on the right, is the difference of two non-decreasing functions. Let $\mathrm{v}(y, x)$ denote the variation of μ over $[y, x]$,

* Opening address.

$\mu'(x) = \sup_{y<x} v(y, x) = v(-\infty, x)$ and $\mu''(x) = \mu'(x) - \mu(x)$, then μ' and μ'' are nondecreasing and continuous on the right.

The converse does not hold: if λ and λ' are right continuous and nondecreasing, then $\lambda - \lambda'$ need not be of calculable variation. Let λ_y be the function defined by $\lambda_y(x) = 0$ for $y < x$, $\lambda_y = 1$ for $y \nless x$. Then $\text{var}(\lambda_y - \lambda_z) = 2$ for $y \# z$ and $\text{var}(\lambda_y - \lambda_z) = 0$ for $y = z$. Thus if $\lambda_y - \lambda_z$ is of calculable variation for all values of y and z, then it is decidable for all y and z whether $y = z$ or $y \# z$. In particular the function f defined by $f(y) = 0$ for $y \# 0$, $f(0) = 1$ would be everywhere defined and consequently continuous. This is contradictory. The result can be expressed by saying that the space of functions of calculable variation is not linear. It is a subset of the linear space of functions of bounded variation.

2. Separable Hilbert space. Other work concerns the theory of separable Hilbert space ([**1**], [**6**], [7], [**8**]). It can be defined as usual by the set of sequences $\langle x_i \rangle$ such that $\sum x_i^2$ converges; only the convergence must be taken positively. The notion of a sequence can here be taken in the sense of an ips. Von Neumann's axioms can be taken over, but must be formulated more precisely [7]. The functions f such that f^2 is Brouwer summable form a Hilbert space B^2; there is no doubt that this result can be extended to Brouwer–Stieltjes summability for a given measure λ, though this has not been proved explicitly.

In the theory of linear functionals difficulties arise with respect to the Riesz representation theorem. $\bigvee h(F(f) = (f, h))$ if and only if conditions (a) and (b) are satisfied:

(a). F has a calculable supremum $||F||$ for unit vectors,

(b). there is a vector f_0 of minimal length such that $|F(f_0)| = ||F||^2$. If $||F|| \# 0$, then there is a unit vector f_1 such that $F(f_1) = ||F||$, and $||F|| f_1 = f_0$ satisfies condition (b).

The separable Hilbert space H cannot be represented by a fan [**2**] but it admits a representation by a spread. Suppose that H is given by sequences $\langle x_i \rangle$ such that $\sum x_i^2$ converges. Let G be the subset of H, consisting of finite sequences of rational complex numbers. G is dense in H. I construct a spread S as follows: Every sequence of natural numbers is an admissible sequence for S. Let $g_1, g_2, \ldots$ be an enumeration of G. The complementary law Γ of S is defined as follows: $\Gamma(\langle k_1 \rangle) = g_{k_1}$. $\Gamma(\langle k_1, \ldots, k_{n-1}, k_n \rangle) = g_l$, where l is the k_n-th number such that

$$|g_l - \Gamma(\langle k_1, \ldots, k_{n-1} \rangle)| < 2^{-n}.$$

Every element $g_{m_1}, g_{m_2}, \ldots$ of S determines a point h of H such that $|h-g_{m_r}| \leqslant 2^{-r}$ for every r. Conversely every point in H is the limit of an element of S.

The spread representation is used in the proof of the following theorem [**1**].

THEOREM. *A linear operator T which is defined all over H, is uniformly continuous on H.*

PROOF. For $h \in H$ we can find a sequence $q = q_1, q_2, \ldots$ in S such that $|q_i - h| < 2^{-i-2}$ for every i. Then, if $|h-h'| < 2^{-n-1}$, we have $|q_i - h'| < 2^{-i}$ for $i \leqslant n$, so there is a sequence q' in S starting with $q_1, \ldots, q_n$ and coinciding with h'. Let $r = r_1, r_2, \ldots$ be a sequence in S that coincides with Th. For a given m, r_m must become known after a finite segment of q, say $q_1, \ldots, q_n$, has been chosen. It follows that r_m is the same for Th' as for Th. We have then

$$|h'-h| < 2^{-n-1} \Rightarrow |Th' - Th| < 2^{-m+1}.$$

This is the case for every full operator T. If T is linear, we have

$$|f| < 2^{-n-1} \Rightarrow |Tf| < 2^{-m+1}$$

for every f, so

$$|h'-h| < 2^{-n-1} \Rightarrow |Th' - Th| < 2^{-m+1}$$

for every h and h'.

A closed linear manifold M in H need not have a calculable dimension. If a finite or denumerably infinite orthonormal basis for M is known, then M is a subspace of H. The orthogonal complement of a linear manifold M is a closed linear manifold $M^{\perp}$. Even if M is a subspace, it is not always possible to write every vector f in the form $f = f_1 + f_2$, where $f_1 \in M, f_2 \in M^{\perp}$. A necessary and sufficient condition for the general possibility of this decomposition is that M is located; this means that the distance of every vector from M is calculable. It is sufficient to know the distance from M of every vector in an orthonormal basis $e_1, e_2, \ldots$ of H. Let $b_1, b_2, \ldots$ be an orthonormal basis for M, where $b_i = \sum_k b_{ik} e_k$. Then an equivalent condition is that $\sum_i b_{ik}^2$ is calculable for every k.

$M \subset M^{\perp\perp}$, but $M^{\perp\perp} = M$ cannot be asserted, even if M is a closed subspace.

Example: M is defined by the basis $b_1, b_2, \ldots$, where $b_i = e_{2i}$ except when the ith-$(i+9)^{\text{th}}$ digits in the decimal expansion of π are all 7; then $b_i = e_1$.

$e_1 \in M^{\perp} \leftrightarrow$ there are no 10 consecutive 7's in π

$e_1 \in M^{\perp\perp} \leftrightarrow$ it is impossible that there are no 10 consecutive 7's in π. Always $M^{\perp\perp\perp} = M^{\perp}$.

The spectrum of a full completely continuous self-adjoint operator, for which the quadratic functional (Af, f) is positive definite, can be determined by the method of Hilbert–Courant, which has the advantage that the characteristic values are calculated one after the other. Let F be any full completely continuous functional, then $m_0 = \sup_{|f|=1} F(f)$ is calculable. Also, if M is a finite-dimensional subspace, then

$$m(M) = \sup_{\substack{f \in M^{\perp} \\ |f|=1}} F(f)$$

is calculable, and so is $m_k = \inf m(M)$ for all k-dimensional subspaces M. The sequence $m_0, m_1, \ldots$ is non-increasing and has the limit 0. If $F(f) = (Af, f)$, then $m_0, m_1, \ldots$ are the characteristic values of A. All this can be proved intuitionistically, but the proofs are more complicated than the classical ones; they use several times the fact that a function defined on a bounded closed located species has a calculable supremum, [**8**].

The characteristic vectors of A need not be calculable, even in a finite-dimensional space.

Example:

$$F(x, y) = x^2 + y^2 + (ax + by)^2; \quad m_0 = 1 + a^2 + b^2, \quad m_1 = 1;$$
$$f_0 = (-b, a), \quad f_1 = (a, b).$$

If no positive lower bound is known for $|a|$, nor for $|b|$, we shall not always be able to calculate the direction of f_0. However (and this is also the case in Hilbert space) if $m_0 \# m_1$, then f_0 can be found such that $Ff_0 = m_0$.

Ashwini Kumar [**1**] has considered full self-adjoint operators, not necessarily completely continuous. His definitions of the resolvent species RS(T), the approximate point spectrum APS(T) and the continuous spectrum CS(T) are positive versions of the classical definitions. For instance, $\lambda \in$ CS(T) if

$$f \# g \Rightarrow (T-\lambda) f \# (T-\lambda)\, g$$

and for every k there is a unit vector h such that $|(T-\lambda)^{-1} h| > 2^k$. RS$(T) \cap$ APS$(T) = \emptyset$, but as might be expected, it cannot be asserted that RS$(T) \cup$ APS$(T) = \boldsymbol{C}$. Instead we have the theorem that RS$(T) \cup$ APS(T) is congruent with $\boldsymbol{C}$; this means that there cannot exist a complex number which cannot belong to RS(T) ∪ APS(T). APS(T) is real; this does not mean that every non-real number is regular. For $z = x+iy$, $y \# 0$, a necessary and sufficient condition for z to be regular is that the species of the points $(f, ((T-x)/y)f)$ in $H \times H$, for f in H, is located in $H \times H$. For self-adjoint operators it is unnecessary to define the spectrum; it can be identified with APS.

The representation of the resolvent by a Brouwer–Stieltjes integral is obtained by a double limit process. First we consider the subspace H_n spanned by the first n basic vectors; let P_n be the projection on H_n and $T_n = P_n T P_n$. T_n can be represented in H_n by a Hermitian matrix (t_{ij}). We can find the characteristic values of this matrix, but not always the characteristic manifolds. To overcome this difficulty, we approximate the t_{ij} by rational numbers t'_{ij} such that the matrix (t'_{ij}) is hermitian and $\sum (t_{ij}-t'_{ij})^2 < 2^{-n}$. The characteristic values of (t'_{ij}) are algebraic numbers, so for any two of them it is decidable whether they are equal or apart, and the corresponding characteristic subspaces can be found. We add to these $H_n^\perp$ with the characteristic value 0. Let T'_n be the operator, determined by (t'_{ij}) on H_n, and 0 on $H_n^\perp$, then

$$((T'_n - z)f, g) = \int_{-\infty}^{+\infty} (\lambda - z)^{-1} \mathrm{d}(E_n(\lambda)f, g),$$

where $E_n(\lambda)$ is defined in the well known manner. A passage to the limit gives

$$((T-z)f, g) = \lim_{n\to\infty} \int_{-\infty}^{+\infty} (\lambda - z)^{-1} \mathrm{d}(E_n(\lambda)f, g).$$

3. Non-separable Hilbert space ([1]). No example of a non-separable Hilbert space is known. The same sort of difficulties because of which the space of functions of calculable variation is not linear occur in the theory of almost periodic functions. cos λx is a.p. if and only if $\lambda = 0$ or $\lambda \# 0$. If $\lambda \# 0$ and $\mu \# 0$, then $\mathrm{e}^{\mathrm{i}\lambda x} + \mathrm{e}^{\mathrm{i}\mu x}$ is a.p. if and only if $\lambda = \mu$ or $\lambda \# \mu$; this follows from $|\mathrm{e}^{\mathrm{i}\lambda x} + \mathrm{e}^{\mathrm{i}\mu x}|^2 = 2 + 2\cos(\lambda - \mu)x$. It follows that a trigonometric series $\sum a_k \mathrm{e}^{\mathrm{i}\lambda_k x}$ can only be a.p. if for every k, l it is decidable whether $\lambda_k = \lambda_l$ or $\lambda_k \# \lambda_l$; the sum of two series which satisfy this condition need not be a.p. The inner product of $\mathrm{e}^{\mathrm{i}\lambda x}$ and $\mathrm{e}^{\mathrm{i}\mu x}$ is

$$\lim_{T\to\infty} \frac{1}{2T} \int_{-T}^{T} \mathrm{e}^{\mathrm{i}(\lambda-\mu)x} \mathrm{d}x = \begin{matrix} 0 & \text{if} & \lambda \# \mu \\ 1 & \text{if} & \lambda = \mu, \end{matrix}$$

so it is only defined in these two cases.

The mean value of an a.p. function f is always calculable, but that of $f(x)e^{-i\lambda x}$ need not be calculable for every λ; moreover, the Fourier exponents need not be calculable.

It seems that a general theory of a.p. functions is unfruitful. The theory can be restricted to Fourier series with mutually apart exponents, but even these do not constitute a Hilbert space.

From the intuitionist point of view it is natural to consider Hilbert space with the binary fan BF as its index set. Every element of H_{BF} is a function f with a domain $D_f \subset \mathrm{BF}$ and a range $\Delta_f \subset \boldsymbol{C}$ (complex numbers), satisfying the following conditions:

1. for every k there is given a finite species Q_k of mutually apart elements of D_f; for every k, $Q_k \subset Q_{k+1}$,
2. for every k and m, $\sum_{a \in Q_{k+m} - Q_k} |f(a)|^2 < 2^{-k}$,
3. If $a \in D_f$ and a is apart from every element of Q_k, then $|f(a)|^2 < 2^{-k}$.

It is clear that $a \in D_f - \bigcup_k Q_k \Rightarrow f(a) = 0$. Thus we may extend D_f to $\bigcup Q_k \cup (\mathrm{BF} - \bigcup Q_k)$ and put $f(a) = 0$ for $a \in \mathrm{BF} - \bigcup Q_k$.

Unfortunately, H_{BF} is not linear, because from $f, g \in H_{\mathrm{BF}}$ it does not follow that $f+g \in H_{\mathrm{BF}}$. In fact, we are not always able to find $Q_k(f+g)$ satisfying the conditions 1, 2, 3 above. Also the inner product (f, g) is not always defined.

REFERENCES

[1] Ashwini Kumar, *Hilbert Spaces in intuitionism*, thesis, Amsterdam (1966). (With a translation in Esperanto and an abridged version in Hindi.)

[2] Ashwini Kumar, *Über katalogisierte Räume*, *Compositio Math.* **21** (1969) 431–456

[3] L. E. J. Brouwer, Begründung der Funktionenlehre anabhängig vom logischen Satz vom ausgeschlossenen Dritten, *Verhandel. Koninkl. Ned. Akad. Wetenschap.* **13** no. 2 (1923).

[4] C. G. Gibson, *The Radon integral in intuitionism*, thesis, Amsterdam (1967).

[5] A. Heyting, Espace de Hilbert et intuitionnisme. Les méthodes formelles en axiomatique, *Colloq. Intern. Centre Natl. Rech. Sci. Paris* (1953) 59–63.

[6] A. Heyting, Note on the Riesz–Fischer theorem, *Koninkl. Ned. Akad. Wetenschap Proc. Ser. A* **54** (1951) = *Indagationes Math.* **13** (1951) 35–40.

[7] A. Heyting, *Intuitionism, an introduction*, 2d ed., Amsterdam (1966).

[8] A. Heyting, Intuïtionistische theorie der Hilbertruimte (unpublished lecture notes).

A THEORY OF CONSTRUCTIONS EQUIVALENT TO ARITHMETIC

NICOLAS D. GOODMAN

A theory of constructions is a type-free and logic-free theory directly about the rules and proofs which underlie constructive mathematics. The idea of such a theory as a basis for mathematics is implicit in many of the intuitionistic writings. For example, in Heyting [**2**], an informal theory of this sort is tacitly used for the interpretation of the logical connectives. The first attempt to formalize such a theory and to use it to give a semantic foundation for intuitionistic logic is in Kreisel [**4**]; the formalization is carried further in Kreisel [**5**]. Our purpose here is to continue this work by describing a theory $\mathscr{T}$ of constructions which is proof-theoretically equivalent to arithmetic. The proof of this equivalence and a discussion of its proof-theoretic applications will be postponed to a later publication.

The results of this paper, in a somewhat different form, are part of the author's doctoral dissertation at Stanford University, written under the direction of Professor Dana Scott. We wish to express here our deep gratitude to Professor Scott for his patience, his sympathetic guidance, and his many stimulating suggestions. We also wish to express our indebtedness to Professor Georg Kreisel for several valuable conversations on the subject of this paper.

1. The definition of intuitionistic implication. The major difference between intuitionistic and classical logic is that the classical mathematician thinks of himself as reasoning about an objective, external domain of entities. Every meaningful assertion about that domain is objectively either true or false. For the intuitionistic mathematician, on the other hand, it does not make sense to talk about the truth of a mathematical proposition independently of the question of whether or not one has a proof of it. Classically, in order to explain the meaning of a proposition it suffices to give the conditions under which it is true. Intuitionistically, one must rather explain what it means to have a proof of the proposition. For example, if we already understand the propositions $\mathfrak{A}$ and $\mathfrak{B}$, then we explain the implication $\mathfrak{A} \to \mathfrak{B}$ by stipulating that a proof of $\mathfrak{A} \to \mathfrak{B}$ is to consist of a method leading from any proof of $\mathfrak{A}$ to a proof of $\mathfrak{B}$, together with a proof that the method always works.

In the next several paragraphs we shall analyze the presuppositions of this definition in an effort to determine what our eventual theory of constructions must look like.

2. Terms. Since the proof of an intuitionistic implication is essentially a function, it is clear that, in addition to terms denoting the proofs themselves, the theory of constructions must contain notations for various operations on proofs. Moreover, since functions can themselves be parts of proofs of complex assertions, it is technically convenient to work in a type-free theory in which rules and proofs are not distinguished. We shall imitate the combinatory logicians and think of a function of two arguments, for example, as a function of one argument whose values are again functions of one argument. We write the result of applying $\mathfrak{a}$ to $\mathfrak{b}$ as $(\mathfrak{a}\mathfrak{b})$ rather than as $\mathfrak{a}(\mathfrak{b})$. Then we omit parentheses by associating to the left, so that $\mathfrak{a}\mathfrak{b}_0 \ldots \mathfrak{b}_{k-1}$, the result of applying $\mathfrak{a}$ to the arguments $\mathfrak{b}_0, \ldots, \mathfrak{b}_{k+1}$, is

$$((\ldots(\mathfrak{a}\mathfrak{b}_0)\ldots)\mathfrak{b}_{k-1}).$$

We treat everything as a function by taking objects which are intuitively not functions to be totally undefined functions.

We may now give a formal definition of our set of *terms*. We suppose given a list $\mathfrak{v}_0, \mathfrak{v}_1, \mathfrak{v}_2, \ldots$ of *variables*. We use x, y, z, u, v, w to denote variables. We also suppose given a set of *constants*. Each variable and each constant is a term. If $\mathfrak{a}$ and $\mathfrak{b}$ are terms, then $(\mathfrak{a}\mathfrak{b})$ is a term. These are the only terms. We use $\mathfrak{a}$, $\mathfrak{b}$, $\mathfrak{c}$, $\mathfrak{d}$, $\mathfrak{e}$, $\mathfrak{f}$, $\mathfrak{g}$, $\mathfrak{h}$ to denote terms. Every term is uniquely of the form $\mathfrak{a}\mathfrak{b}_0 \ldots \mathfrak{b}_{k-1}$, where $\mathfrak{a}$ is a variable or a constant. A term containing no variables is *closed*. We indicate the substitution of $\mathfrak{a}$ for x in an expression by prefixing $[\mathfrak{a}/x]$.

3. The combinators. The correctness of the laws of Heyting's predicate calculus (HPC) should follow directly from the interpretation of the logical connectives. For example, that $\mathfrak{A} \to \mathfrak{A}$ is a correct logical principle follows from the triviality that the identity function, applied to any proof of $\mathfrak{A}$, gives a proof of $\mathfrak{A}$. In order to be able to formalize such arguments in our theory of constructions, we must have at least certain elementary closure conditions on the functions of the theory. The simplest requirement we can make is that they be closed under explicit definition. To that end we adapt Curry's familiar combinators K and S (see Curry and Feys [**1**]). In order to be able to think of the constants K and S as denoting functions, we modify them so as *only to be defined when their arguments are defined*. Specifically, Kxy has the value x, and $Sxyz$ has the value $xz(yz)$, whenever the latter is defined. It is well known that K and S suffice for the treatment of explicit definition. Below we shall often make use of lambda-abstraction, remembering that this notation is eliminable in favor of K and S by the methods of Curry and Feys [**1**].

The theory of constructive functions at the base of our theory of constructions will be very similar to a classical free-variable theory of Gödel numbers of partial recursive functions acting on each other. Indeed, we can make a diagonal argument to see that ours must also be a theory of *partial* functions. This is to be expected, since Church's thesis is not obviously false. Specifically, suppose we have a term $\mathfrak{f}$ with the property that, if x is not zero, then $\mathfrak{f}x$ is zero, and, if x is zero, then $\mathfrak{f}x$ is not zero. Then consider the term

$$(\lambda x.\mathfrak{f}(xx))(\lambda x.\mathfrak{f}(xx)).$$

If this term had a value, then it would have to be a fixed point of the function denoted by $\mathfrak{f}$, which is impossible. Thus the term must be undefined.

To avoid using partial functions, one would have to think of a constructive function as a pair consisting of a rule and a proof that the rule is everywhere defined. But this is a derived notion which should be defined, within the theory of constructions, in terms of the more elementary notions of rule and proof.

4. Intensional identity. Just as in classical recursion theory there is an underlying notion of computation, so we need a notion of *reduction*. Any closed term of our theory is of the form $\mathfrak{a}\mathfrak{b}_0 \ldots \mathfrak{b}_{k-1}$, where $\mathfrak{a}$ is a constant denoting a rule. In order to evaluate this term we must apply the rule denoted by $\mathfrak{a}$ to the arguments, if any, denoted by $\mathfrak{b}_0, \ldots, \mathfrak{b}_{k-1}$. To do that, we must first evaluate the terms $\mathfrak{b}_0, \ldots, \mathfrak{b}_{k-1}$. The result of the application of $\mathfrak{a}$ will, in general, be another term itself requiring evaluation. In this way the intended interpretation of the constants of the theory will induce the relation of reduction on the closed terms. This relation will be deterministic, since we always reduce the arguments first and then carry out the uniquely determined operation required by the rule denoted by $\mathfrak{a}$. A term which cannot be further simplified by this reduction process, and therefore directly denotes a well-determined construction, is *reduced*. Thus a closed term is defined if and only if it reduces to a reduced term. In general, of course, it is undecidable whether or not the reduction process applied to a given term $\mathfrak{c}$ terminates.

Our notation will be so chosen that syntactically distinct reduced terms denote distinct constructions. Thus we may replace the intuitive relation of intensional identity between constructions by the formal relation of intensional identity between closed terms which holds just in case they reduce to the same reduced term. If $\mathfrak{a}$ and $\mathfrak{b}$ are arbitrary terms of our theory, we write $\mathfrak{a} \equiv \mathfrak{b}$ to mean that $\mathfrak{a}$ and $\mathfrak{b}$ are defined and have intensionally identical values, where we think of free variables as ranging over the reduced terms. In particular, an equation $\mathfrak{a} \equiv \mathfrak{a}$ asserts that $\mathfrak{a}$ is defined.

When we come to the axiomatization of our theory $\mathscr{T}$, we shall be careful to give enough axioms that every closed term which is defined can be reduced within $\mathscr{T}$ to a reduced term. Therefore, as we shall show in another paper, the theory itself induces a unique minimal reduction relation on the closed terms which satisfies all the axioms of the theory.

The relation of intensional identity is an undecidable, purely existential relation. If we know that $\mathfrak{a}$ and $\mathfrak{b}$ are defined, however, then it is decidable whether or not they are intensionally equal. We introduce a constant Q representing the predicate of intensional identity.

Since the basic identity relation of our theory is intensional, it makes sense to introduce operators, which we shall call *discriminators*, whose function it is to analyze the structure of the reduced forms of the terms they apply to. Their importance is primarily technical, in that they enable us to formulate certain principles in a more perspicuous way. We shall need three discriminators. The first of these, which we call δ, determines whether or not the reduced form of its argument $\mathfrak{c}$ is of the form $(\mathfrak{a}_1 \mathfrak{a}_2)$. The other two discriminators, δ_1 and δ_2, carry this analysis further. Specifically, in the above case, we take $\delta_i \mathfrak{c} \equiv \mathfrak{a}_i$ for $i = 1, 2$.

5. Pairing. In § 1 we explained that a proof of an implication is a pair consisting of a function and a proof. Thus our theory must contain pairing functions D, D_1, D_2. We let Dxy be the pair consisting of x and y, in that order. Moreover, for $i = 1, 2$, we let $D_i(Dx_1 x_2) \equiv x_i$. If x is not a pair, then we let $D_i x \equiv x$.

For the interpretation of arithmetic, it is convenient to think of every object as a sequence. Specifically, we think of each x as the (eventually constant) sequence

$$D_1 x,\ D_1(D_2 x),\ D_1(D_2(D_2 x)), \ldots.$$

Then, for each natural number n, we can construct a term C_n such that, for any x, $C_n x$ is the nth component of x thought of as a sequence in this way. Also we can construct, for each n, a term ρ_n such that, for any x and y, $\rho_n xy$ is such that

$$C_n(\rho_n xy) \equiv y,$$

and, if $m \neq n$, then

$$C_m(\rho_n xy) \equiv C_m x.$$

Now suppose that we are giving a definition of the logical connectives for a language containing quantifiers and free variables. Then what we must define is not 'y is a proof of $\mathfrak{A}$' but rather 'y is a proof that the sequence x satisfies $\mathfrak{A}$'. Thus to each formula $\mathfrak{A}$ we will assign a term $|\mathfrak{A}|$ such that, intuitively, $|\mathfrak{A}|xy$ has the value *true* if and only if y proves that x satisfies $\mathfrak{A}$. Suppose we already have the terms $|\mathfrak{A}|$ and $|\mathfrak{B}|$. Then, reformulating the definition in § 1, it is clear that we should have

$|\mathfrak{A} \to \mathfrak{B}| = (\lambda xy.D_1 y$ proves that, for any z, if $|\mathfrak{A}|xz$ has the value *true*, then $|\mathfrak{B}|x(D_2 yz)$ has the value *true*).

6. Truth-functions. In a classical truth definition the logical connectives are presupposed, not defined. The definition in § 5, on the other hand, is actually supposed to explain implication. If the definition is not to be circular, then the 'if . . ., then' in the definition must be essentially simpler than the intuitionistic implication being defined. This is achieved by requiring that the proof predicates $|\mathfrak{A}|$ and $|\mathfrak{B}|$ be decidable, so that, even from an intuitionistic point of view, we can make unproblematical use of truth-functional connectives. Let us look at those connectives more closely.

It is convenient, though arbitrary, to let the truth-value T be $(\lambda xy.x)$, and to let the truth-value $\bot$ be $(\lambda xy.y)$.

Looking at the definition of implication in § 5, we observe that, if z is not as a matter of fact a proof that x satisfies $\mathfrak{A}$, then $D_2 yz$ may be undefined, since the function $D_2 y$ is only supposed to apply to arguments which are proofs of the relevant kind. Thus we only want to try to evaluate $D_2 yz$ if $|\mathfrak{A}|xz \equiv \mathsf{T}$. Thus we need a truth-functional implication between partial predicates of one argument which gives the value T if the antecedent has the value $\perp$, even if the consequent is undefined. We explicitly define a function $\supset_1$ of three arguments u, v and z, writing '$u \supset_1 v$' for '$\supset_1 uv$', in such a way that if $uz \equiv \mathsf{T}$, then the function applies v to z, and if $uz \equiv \perp$, then it applies $(\lambda w.\mathsf{T})$ to z. Remembering how we defined T and $\perp$, we put

$$\supset_1 = (\lambda uvz.uzv(\lambda w.\mathsf{T})z).$$

More generally, we put

$$\supset_k = (\lambda uvz_0 \ldots z_{k-1} . uz_0 \ldots z_{k-1} v(\lambda w_0 \ldots w_{k-1} . \mathsf{T})z_0 \ldots z_{k-1}).$$

Similarly, we let

$$\cap_k = (\lambda uvz_0 \ldots z_{k-1} . uz_0 \ldots z_{k-1} v(\lambda w_0 \ldots w_{k-1} . \perp)z_0 \ldots z_{k-1})$$

and

$$\cup_k = (\lambda uvz_0 \ldots z_{k-1} . uz_0 \ldots z_{k-1}(\lambda w_0 \ldots w_{k-1} . \mathsf{T})vz_0 \ldots z_{k-1}).$$

We can now write the definition of implication as follows:

$$|\mathfrak{A} \rightarrow \mathfrak{B}| = (\lambda xy.D_1 y \text{ proves that, for all } z, \quad [(|\mathfrak{A}|x) \supset_1 (\lambda z.|\mathfrak{B}|x(D_2 yz))]z \equiv \mathsf{T}).$$

7. Sequents. Since the relation $\equiv$ is not decidable, the truth-functions are not quite enough to give us all the basic logical apparatus we need. Nevertheless, since we are working with partial functions, and since it is not obvious how to formulate the correct intuitionistic logic of partial predicates, we wish to minimize the logical presuppositions of our theory. The notion we need is that of a *sequent*.

We use Δ and Γ to denote finite *sets* of equations, where an *equation* is an expression of the form $\mathfrak{a} \equiv \mathfrak{b}$. Then a *sequent* is an expression

$$\Delta \vdash \mathfrak{a} \equiv \mathfrak{b}.$$

This sequent is to be interpreted as an intuitionistic implication: if all the equations in Δ hold, then $\mathfrak{a} \equiv \mathfrak{b}$. The formulas of our theory are sequents. Notice that we only assume implication between purely existential assertions and, in particular, we have no iterated implications.

Except for the specification of the remaining constants, this completes the description of the language of our formal system. We postpone writing down any axioms until after we have completed the discussion of the intended meanings of the constants.

8. The proof predicate. Looking at the definition of implication at the end of § 6, we see that if $|\mathfrak{A} \to \mathfrak{B}|xy \equiv \mathsf{T}$, then $D_1 y$ is a proof of an elementary statement in AE form. We shall take such proofs as basic and will not attempt to analyze their internal structure. Thus it is natural to introduce a primitive decidable operator π such that πuv has the value T iff v is a proof that, for all z, $uz \equiv \mathsf{T}$. Then we can write the definition of implication as

$$|\mathfrak{A} \to \mathfrak{B}| = (\lambda xy \,.\, \pi[(|\mathfrak{A}|x) \supset_1 (\lambda z \,.\, |\mathfrak{B}|x(D_2 yz))](D_1 y)).$$

The decidability of the basic proof predicate π seems to conflict with ordinary mathematical experience. After all, we often think we have a proof of an assertion when, as a matter of fact, the argument we have in mind is still confused. We take this fact as evidence not of the undecidability of the proof predicate, but rather of a lack of clarity in the way the putative proof is presented. From an intuitionistic standpoint, the verbal argument we have in mind is at best a rough guide to the construction of the infinite canonical proof which, if fully grasped, could not be misleading. Thus we assume that a clearly given construction always either is or is not a proof of a given assertion.

9. The self-referential paradox. There is an essential impredicativity in our definition of implication. For the assertion that $|\mathfrak{A} \to \mathfrak{B}|xy \equiv \mathsf{T}$ involves quantification over all proofs of $\mathfrak{A}$, including proofs which may themselves have been built up in some way from y. Unless something is done to moderate this impredicativity, it actually leads to paradox. As a first step, we construct a self-referential sentence which asserts of itself that it is unprovable.

Let

$$\mathfrak{g} = (\lambda yz.S(Ky)(Kz)).$$

Then $\mathfrak{g}$ is a total function of two arguments with the property that, if $\mathfrak{g}yzx$ is defined, then

$$\vdash \mathfrak{g}yzx \equiv S(Ky)(Kz)x.$$

Therefore

$$\mathfrak{g}yzx \equiv \mathfrak{g}yzx \vdash \mathfrak{g}yzx \equiv Kyx(Kzx),$$

and so

$$\mathfrak{g}yzx \equiv \mathfrak{g}yzx \vdash \mathfrak{g}yzx \equiv yz.$$

The assertion that w does not prove that

$$\vdash yz \equiv \mathsf{T} \qquad (1)$$

can then be written as

$$\vdash (\pi(\mathfrak{g}yz) \supset_1 (K\bot))w \equiv \mathsf{T}.$$

Let

$$\mathfrak{h} = (\lambda yz.\pi(\pi(\mathfrak{g}yz) \supset_1 (K\bot))(zz)).$$

Then the equation $\mathfrak{h}yz \equiv \mathsf{T}$ asserts that zz is defined and proves that (1) is unprovable. Thus to construct our self-referential assertion it suffices to find a term $\mathfrak{a}$ such that we can prove that $\mathfrak{a}z \equiv \mathfrak{h}\mathfrak{a}z$ whenever either side is defined. We take

$$\mathfrak{a} = (\lambda z.(\lambda y.\mathfrak{h}(yy)z)(\lambda y.\mathfrak{h}(yy)z)).$$

We can explain the lambda-abstraction here in such a way that $\mathfrak{a}$ is defined. Then we have intuitively that

$$\vdash \mathfrak{a}z \equiv \mathsf{T} \tag{2}$$

just in case zz is defined and is a proof that no x is a proof of (2).

Now, if something is proved, it is *a fortiori* true. Hence

$$\pi(\mathfrak{g}\mathfrak{a}z)x \equiv \mathsf{T} \vdash \mathfrak{g}\mathfrak{a}zu \equiv \mathsf{T},$$

and so, as above,

$$\pi(\mathfrak{g}\mathfrak{a}z)x \equiv \mathsf{T} \vdash \mathfrak{a}z \equiv \mathsf{T}.$$

By our choice of $\mathfrak{a}$, therefore,

$$\pi(\mathfrak{g}\mathfrak{a}z)x \equiv \mathsf{T} \vdash \pi(\pi(\mathfrak{g}\mathfrak{a}z) \supset_1 (K\bot))(zz) \equiv \mathsf{T},$$

so that

$$\pi(\mathfrak{g}\mathfrak{a}z)x \equiv \mathsf{T} \vdash (\pi(\mathfrak{g}\mathfrak{a}z) \supset_1 (K\bot))w \equiv \mathsf{T}.$$

Recalling the definition of $\supset_1$, we have

$$\pi(\mathfrak{g}\mathfrak{a}z)x \equiv \mathsf{T} \vdash K\bot w \equiv \mathsf{T}.$$

Therefore, by the decidability of π,

$$\vdash \pi(\mathfrak{g}\mathfrak{a}z)x \equiv \bot. \tag{3}$$

It follows that

$$\vdash (\pi(\mathfrak{g}\mathfrak{a}z) \supset_1 (K\bot))x \equiv \mathsf{T}. \tag{4}$$

Thus we have specified, uniformly in z, a proof of (4) for all x. Hence there must be a function $\mathfrak{f}$ such that, for all z,

$$\vdash \pi(\pi(\mathfrak{g}\mathfrak{a}z) \supset_1 (K\bot))(\mathfrak{f}z) \equiv \mathsf{T}. \tag{5}$$

In particular,

$$\vdash \pi(\pi(\mathfrak{g}\mathfrak{a}\mathfrak{f}) \supset_1 (K\bot))(\mathfrak{f}\mathfrak{f}) \equiv \mathsf{T}.$$

That is, $\vdash \mathfrak{h}\mathfrak{a}\mathfrak{f} \equiv \mathsf{T}$, and so $\vdash \mathfrak{a}\mathfrak{f} \equiv \mathsf{T}$. For any w, therefore,

$$\vdash \mathfrak{g}\mathfrak{a}\mathfrak{f}w \equiv \mathsf{T},$$

and so we can choose $\mathfrak{b}$ with

$$\vdash \pi(\mathfrak{g}\mathfrak{a}\mathfrak{f})\mathfrak{b} \equiv \mathsf{T},$$

which contradicts (3).

A similar argument shows that if the starred theory in Kreisel [**4**] is modified so as to permit arbitrary lambda-abstraction, the resulting theory is inconsistent. This fact was noticed independently by Kreisel and by the author.

10. Stratification of the theory of constructions. There is a fundamental heuristic principle to the effect that clear ideas lead to consistent theories. What we have left vague above is how constructions are built up. The set-theoretic paradoxes are resolved by observing that sets must be sets *of* objects already at hand. Similarly we suggest that proofs must be *about* objects already constructed. Just as in Zermelo set theory there is an implicit cumulative theory of types, so we propose to formulate a theory of constructions involving a cumulative theory of *levels*. At the bottom level we will have constructive rules operating on each other. Among these will be certain basic, purely finitistic rules such as the combinators. We assume that it is decidable whether a construction belongs to this basic level, and as usual with decidable species, we identify the level with the function which gives T or $\bot$ according to whether its argument is or is not an element of the level. We introduce a constant B to denote this basic level. Given any level L, we suppose that we can extend L to a new level containing all the objects of L, all proofs about objects of L, and certain additional constructions to be described below. If $\mathfrak{a}$ denotes L, then we let $E\mathfrak{a}$ denote the extended level. We emphasize that this is not a stratification by logical type, but rather a stratification according to the subject matter of proofs.

Applying an idea of Kreisel, we can think of the stratification slightly differently. If the operator π of constructive universal quantification is itself to be a construction, then this quantification must only be over a domain which has been *grasped* as a totality. But we cannot grasp the whole of the constructive universe, which is always only a potential totality. The only grasped domains which we shall consider here are those which are *maximal* in the sense that they include everything which is immediately understood when their elements are understood. For example, we could think of the species of natural numbers as a grasped domain. This domain is not maximal, however, since implicit in the species of natural numbers is the species of constructive numerical functions, and so on. In this paper we shall always use 'grasped domain' to mean a totality which is decidable, which is grasped as a whole, and which is maximal in this sense. Therefore the grasped domains are just our levels.

We add a new constant G which, applied to any argument x, determines whether or not x is conceived as a grasped domain. Then we will have $\vdash GB \equiv \mathsf{T}$ and

$$Gx \equiv \mathsf{T} \vdash G(Ex) \equiv \mathsf{T}.$$

From the present point of view the operator π of § 8 no longer makes sense, since the only proofs we understand are proofs about the elements of a given grasped domain. Within this new framework, we must think of π as a function of three arguments, where $\pi xyz \equiv \mathsf{T}$ means that x is a grasped domain containing y, and z is a proof that, for all w in that domain, $yw \equiv \mathsf{T}$. Neither πx nor z will be in the domain x, but only in the extended domain Ex. The operator π itself will not be in any grasped domain.

11. The reducibility operator. Suppose we have a grasped domain a. Then we wish a to be as self-contained as possible. Therefore, if we have any rule z, then we suppose that we can find a rule Faz in the domain a with the property that, if x is in a and zx is defined and in a, then

$$\vdash Fazx \equiv zx.$$

We do not care about the values of Faz for arguments x such that x is not in a, such that zx is undefined, or such that zx is defined but not in a.

Suppose z is actually not in the domain a. Then we shall not assume that if $Fazx$ is defined, with x in a, then the value of $Fazx$ is just zx. For, this principle would imply that z is somehow involved in the definition of Faz, contrary to our conception of the levels as built up from below. Instead, we suppose that Fa, applied to z, chooses some rule already present in a which, extensionally, has enough of the right values to serve as a representative for z. The operator Fa cannot use the fact that z is undefined at an argument x without looking at the meaning of z and therefore giving a function as value which is itself of level higher than that of a.

The effect of the reducibility operator F is similar to the effect of an impredicative comprehension principle. Suppose, for example, that we have proved

$$\bigwedge n \bigvee m \mathfrak{A}(n, m), \tag{6}$$

where n and m are numerical. Then that proof gives us a function f such that

$$\bigwedge n \mathfrak{A}(n, fn).$$

The description of f may involve objects of very high level. For example, the proof of (6) may be by *modus ponens*, so that f may depend on understanding the proof of a complex auxiliary proposition. However, since n and m are certainly in the basic domain B, we also have

$$\bigwedge n \mathfrak{A}(n, FBfn),$$

and FBf is itself in B.

The introduction of the reducibility operator F is made necessary by the impredicative character of intuitionistic implication. It seems to us essential to the intuitionistic position that given a fixed assertion $\mathfrak{A}$ about a well-defined domain, there is always an *a priori* upper bound to the complexity of possible proofs of $\mathfrak{A}$. In case $\mathfrak{A}$ is an implication, this principle already guarantees the existence of some sort of reducibility operator.

12. Proofs. Now suppose f is an element of the grasped domain a. Suppose we have a formal proof in our theory of the assertion that, for any x in a, $fx \equiv \mathsf{T}$. Then we let $\not{p}af$ denote an intuitive proof of the assertion. We take $\not{p}af$ to be in the extended domain Ea. Since the formal proof may involve lemmas about objects of higher level, the introduction of the operator $\not{p}$ involves another impredicativity of essentially the same nature as that involved in the introduction of F. Intuitively, $\not{p}af$ denotes an infinite canonical proof of the assertion. This canonical proof depends only on a and f and not on the structure of the formal proof, which can be thought of as an indication of how to construct the infinite intuitive proof $\not{p}af$. If we have no formal proof of the assertion, then, in general, we are not able to construct the intuitive proof, and $\not{p}af$ is undefined.

13. Avoiding the self-referential paradox. We have now completed the description of the language of our theory $\mathscr{T}$ of constructions. The constants we shall use are K, S, D, D_1, D_2, δ, δ_1, δ_2, Q, E, B, G, π, F and $\not{p}$. The set of *terms* is then defined as in § 2. *Sequents* are defined as in § 7.

Before beginning the axiomatization of $\mathscr{T}$, let us consider how the paradox of § 9 is now avoided. There are several ways in which one might hope to reconstruct the argument leading to the contradiction. The most naive proposal might be to choose $\mathfrak{a}$ so that

$$\vdash \mathfrak{a} \equiv (\lambda z.\pi(Ec)(\pi c(\mathfrak{g}\mathfrak{a}z) \supset_1 (K\bot))(zz)),$$

where c is a grasped domain, and where we write 'Ec' rather than 'c' as the scope of the left-most application of π since we can only correctly apply πc to a rule in the domain c. But in this case the step from (4) to (5) is unjustified because $\mathfrak{a}$ itself is only known to be in the domain Ec, not in c.

Alternatively, we might choose $\mathfrak{a}$ so that

$$\vdash \mathfrak{a} \equiv (\lambda z.\pi(Ec)(\pi c(\mathfrak{g}(Fc\mathfrak{a})z) \supset_1 (K\bot))(zz)).$$

But then, at the beginning of the argument, we only obtain

$$\pi c(\mathfrak{g}(Fc\mathfrak{a})z)x \equiv \mathsf{T} \vdash Fc\mathfrak{a}z \equiv \mathsf{T},$$

which is not enough to give

$$\pi c(\mathfrak{g}(Fc\mathfrak{a})z)\, x \equiv \mathsf{T} \vdash \mathfrak{a}z \equiv \mathsf{T}$$

even with the additional premise $\vdash cz \equiv \mathsf{T}$.

14. Axioms about consequence and identity. We begin with the rules of weakening and cut.

I1. If $\Delta \vdash \mathfrak{a} \equiv \mathfrak{b}$, then $\Delta, \mathfrak{c} \equiv \mathfrak{d} \vdash \mathfrak{a} \equiv \mathfrak{b}$.

2. If $\Delta, \mathfrak{a} \equiv \mathfrak{b} \vdash \mathfrak{c} \equiv \mathfrak{d}$ and $\Delta \vdash \mathfrak{a} \equiv \mathfrak{b}$, then $\Delta \vdash \mathfrak{c} \equiv \mathfrak{d}$.

Next we have substitution for free variables, with an additional premise to guarantee that the term being substituted is defined.

I3. If $\Delta \vdash \mathfrak{a} \equiv \mathfrak{b}$, then $\mathfrak{c} \equiv \mathfrak{c}$, $[\mathfrak{c}/x]\Delta \vdash [\mathfrak{c}/x]\mathfrak{a} \equiv [\mathfrak{c}/x]\mathfrak{b}$.

We have reflexivity, symmetry, and substitutivity of intensional identity.

I4. If $\mathfrak{a}$ is a variable or a constant, then $\vdash \mathfrak{a} \equiv \mathfrak{a}$.

5. $\mathfrak{a} \equiv \mathfrak{b} \vdash \mathfrak{b} \equiv \mathfrak{a}$.

6. $[\mathfrak{a}/x]\mathfrak{b} \equiv \mathfrak{c}$, $\mathfrak{d} \equiv \mathfrak{a} \vdash [\mathfrak{d}/x]\mathfrak{b} \equiv \mathfrak{c}$.

We can only apply a function to an argument if both are defined.

I7. $\mathfrak{a}\mathfrak{b} \equiv \mathfrak{a}\mathfrak{b} \vdash \mathfrak{a} \equiv \mathfrak{a}$.

8. $\mathfrak{a}\mathfrak{b} \equiv \mathfrak{a}\mathfrak{b} \vdash \mathfrak{b} \equiv \mathfrak{b}$.

As applications of the rules of I, the following are all provable:

(i). $\mathfrak{a} \equiv \mathfrak{b} \vdash \mathfrak{a} \equiv \mathfrak{b}$.

(ii). $\mathfrak{a} \equiv \mathfrak{b}, \mathfrak{b} \equiv \mathfrak{c} \vdash \mathfrak{a} \equiv \mathfrak{c}$.

(iii). $\mathfrak{a} \equiv \mathfrak{b} \vdash \mathfrak{a} \equiv \mathfrak{a}$.

We do not, in general, have

$$\mathfrak{a} \equiv \mathfrak{b}, \mathfrak{c} \equiv \mathfrak{d} \vdash \mathfrak{a}\mathfrak{c} \equiv \mathfrak{b}\mathfrak{d},$$

since well-defined functions and arguments may lead to undefined function values.

15. Axioms for the combinators and pairing. The basic axioms for K, S, D, D_1 and D_2 are as follows:

II 1. $\vdash Kxy \equiv x$.

2. $Sxyz \equiv Sxyz \vdash Sxyz \equiv xz(yz)$.

3. $xz(yz) \equiv xz(yz) \vdash Sxyz \equiv Sxyz$.

4. $\vdash Sxy \equiv Sxy$.

5. $\vdash D_i(Dx_1x_2) \equiv x_i$.

6. $\vdash D_ix \equiv D_ix$.

We also need axioms asserting that if x is not a pair, then $\vdash D_ix \equiv x$, but we are not yet in a position to formulate them.

The above axioms suffice for the treatment of explicit definition and sequences as in §§ 3, 5, and 6.

16. Axioms for the discriminators. We first wish to assert that the operator δ represents a decidable predicate. Let us formulate what this means in general. We say that a term $\mathfrak{a}$ is a *decidable predicate of n arguments* iff whenever we have

$$\Delta, \mathfrak{a}\mathfrak{b}_0 \ldots \mathfrak{b}_{n-1} \equiv \top \vdash \mathfrak{c} \equiv \mathfrak{d}$$

and

$$\Delta, \mathfrak{a}\mathfrak{b}_0 \ldots \mathfrak{b}_{n-1} \equiv \bot \vdash \mathfrak{c} \equiv \mathfrak{d},$$

we also have

$$\Delta, \mathfrak{b}_0 \equiv \mathfrak{b}_0, \ldots, \mathfrak{b}_{n-1} \equiv \mathfrak{b}_{n-1} \vdash \mathfrak{c} \equiv \mathfrak{d},$$

If $\mathfrak{a}$ is a decidable predicate of n arguments, then

$$\vdash \mathfrak{a}x_0 \ldots x_{n-1} \equiv \mathfrak{a}x_0 \ldots x_{n-1}.$$

III 1. δ is a decidable predicate of one argument.

Next, $\delta_i x$ is defined only if the reduced form of x is composite.

III2. $\delta_i x \equiv \delta_i x \vdash \delta x \equiv T$.

3. $\delta x \equiv T \vdash \delta_i x \equiv \delta_i x$.

No constant is composite.

III4. Suppose $\mathfrak{a}$ is a constant. Then $\vdash \delta\mathfrak{a} \equiv \bot$.

Finally we need an axiom guaranteeing that δ_i has the right values.

III5. Suppose $\mathfrak{a}$ is K, S, D, Q, E, π, F, $\not{p}$, Sy, Dy, πy, Fy or $\not{p}y$. Then

$$\mathfrak{a}x \equiv \mathfrak{a}x \vdash \delta_1(\mathfrak{a}x) \equiv \mathfrak{a}$$

and

$$\mathfrak{a}x \equiv \mathfrak{a}x \vdash \delta_2(\mathfrak{a}x) \equiv x.$$

17. Axioms for the predicate of identity. The constant Q is to represent the decidable predicate of intensional identity.

IV1. Q is a decidable predicate of two arguments.

2. $\vdash Qxx \equiv \mathsf{T}$.

3. $Qxy \equiv \mathsf{T} \vdash x \equiv y$.

4. If $\mathfrak{a}$ and $\mathfrak{b}$ are distinct constants, then $\vdash Q\mathfrak{a}\mathfrak{b} \equiv \bot$.

We are now ready to write down the axioms which assert that D_i has the right values on arguments which are not pairs.

IV5. $\delta x \equiv \bot \vdash D_i x \equiv x$.

6. $\delta(\delta_1 x) \equiv \bot \vdash D_i x \equiv x$.

7. $QD(\delta_1(\delta_1 x)) \equiv \bot \vdash D_i x \equiv x$.

As an example of the application of Q, we observe that it enables us to distinguish pairs from objects which are not pairs without using the discriminators. For x is a pair just in case x is the pair of its components. Thus let

$$P = (\lambda x. Qx(D(D_1 x)(D_2 x))).$$

Then P is a decidable predicate of one argument which is such that, intuitively, $\vdash Px \equiv \mathsf{T}$ if and only if x is a pair.

18. The rule of induction. In order to interpret arithmetic, we need a principle justifying arguments by induction over the natural numbers. In the context of an intensional theory such as ours, it is natural to add a principle of induction on the way in which the reduced terms are built up. This can be formulated as follows:

V. Suppose x does not occur in Δ or $\mathfrak{a}$. Suppose

(i). $\Delta, \delta x \equiv \bot \vdash \mathfrak{a}x \equiv \mathsf{T}$

(ii). $\Delta,\ \mathfrak{a}(\delta_1 x) \equiv \mathsf{T},\ \mathfrak{a}(\delta_2 x) \equiv \mathsf{T} \vdash \mathfrak{a}x \equiv \mathsf{T}$.
Then $\Delta \vdash \mathfrak{a}x \equiv \mathsf{T}$.

Now we assign a numeral $\boldsymbol{n}$ to each natural number n as follows:

(i). $\mathbf{0} = K$.
(ii). $\boldsymbol{n+1} = D\mathbf{0}\boldsymbol{n}$.

A reduced term $\mathfrak{a}$ is a numeral if it is $\mathbf{0}$ or if it is a pair whose first component is $\mathbf{0}$ and whose second component is a numeral. Then, imitating this definition, it is not difficult to construct a closed term N, without using the discriminators, such that:

(i). N is a decidable predicate of one argument;
(ii). for each n we have $\vdash N\boldsymbol{n} \equiv \mathsf{T}$;

and

(iii). the following special rule of induction is derivable: Suppose x does not occur in Δ or $\mathfrak{a}$. Suppose
(a). $\Delta \vdash \mathfrak{a}\mathbf{0} \equiv \mathsf{T}$.
(b). $\Delta, Nx \equiv \mathsf{T},\ \mathfrak{a}x \equiv \mathsf{T} \vdash \mathfrak{a}(D\mathbf{0}x) \equiv \mathsf{T}$.
Then $\Delta,\ Nx \equiv \mathsf{T} \vdash \mathfrak{a}x \equiv \mathsf{T}$.

For each primitive recursive function H we can construct a closed term $\mathfrak{f}_H$ such that, using induction, $\mathfrak{f}_H$ can be proved to satisfy the defining equations for H.

19. Axioms concerning grasped domains

VI1. G is a decidable predicate of one argument.
2. $\vdash GB \equiv \mathsf{T}$.
3. If $G\mathfrak{a} \equiv \mathsf{T}$, then $\vdash G(E\mathfrak{a}) \equiv \mathsf{T}$.

For each natural number p, we define the pth level L_p as follows:

(i). $L_0 = B$.
(ii). $L_{p+1} = EL_p$.

The only reduced terms of the theory $\mathscr{T}$ which denote grasped domains are the terms L_p. This will not, however, necessarily remain true when $\mathscr{T}$ is extended. Thus instead of asserting directly that these are the only grasped domains, we add axioms which assert, for each term of $\mathscr{T}$ which is not an L_p, that it is not a grasped domain.

VI4. Suppose $\mathfrak{a}$ is a constant of $\mathscr{T}$ other than B. Then $\vdash G\mathfrak{a} \equiv \bot$.
5. Suppose $\mathfrak{a}$ is a constant of $\mathscr{T}$ other than E. Then

$$\delta_1 x \equiv \mathfrak{a} \vdash Gx \equiv \bot.$$

6. Suppose $\mathfrak{a}$ is any constant of $\mathcal{T}$. Then

$$\delta_1(\delta_1 x) \equiv \mathfrak{a} \vdash Gx \equiv \bot.$$

The operator E only applies to grasped domains.

VI 7. $Ex \equiv Ex \vdash Gx \equiv \top$.

Any grasped domain is a decidable predicate of one argument.

VI 8. Suppose

(i). $\Delta, \mathfrak{ab} \equiv \top \vdash \mathfrak{c} \equiv \mathfrak{d}$.

(ii). $\Delta, \mathfrak{ab} \equiv \bot \vdash \mathfrak{c} \equiv \mathfrak{d}$.

Then $\Delta, G\mathfrak{a} \equiv \top, \mathfrak{b} \equiv \mathfrak{b} \vdash \mathfrak{c} \equiv \mathfrak{d}$.

Any element of a grasped domain is also an element of the extended domain.

VI 9. $Gx \equiv \top, xy \equiv \top \vdash Exy \equiv \top$.

A grasped domain is closed under any function belonging to that domain.

VI 10. $Gx \equiv \top, xy \equiv \top, xz \equiv \top, \ yz \equiv yz \vdash x(yz) \equiv \top$.

Certain elementary rules belong to the basic domain.

VI 11. Suppose $\mathfrak{a}$ is K, S, D, D_1, D_2 or Q. Then $\vdash B\mathfrak{a} \equiv \top$.

There are other operators which, because of their great generality, belong to no grasped domain.

VI 12. Suppose $\mathfrak{a}$ is $\delta, \delta_1, \delta_2, E, G, \pi, F$ or $\not{p}$. Then

$$Gx \equiv \top \vdash x\mathfrak{a} \equiv \bot.$$

Every level is an element of itself, but not of the previous level.

VI 13. $Gx \equiv \top \vdash xx \equiv \top$.

14. $Gx \equiv \top \vdash x(Ex) \equiv \bot$.

In certain cases one can argue from the level of a reduced term to the level of its components.

VI 15. Suppose $\mathfrak{a}$ is K, S, D, Q, Sy or Dy. Then

$$Gx \equiv \top, \delta_1 z \equiv \mathfrak{a}, xz \equiv \top \vdash x(\delta_2 z) \equiv \top.$$

16. Suppose $\mathfrak{a}$ is S or D. Then

$$Gx \equiv \top, x(\mathfrak{a}yz) \equiv \top \vdash xy \equiv \top.$$

20. Axioms about the reducibility operator. We begin with two axioms about the level of a term of the form $F\mathfrak{a}$.

VII 1. $Gx \equiv \top \vdash x(Fx) \equiv \top$.

2. $Gx \equiv \top, \delta_1 y \equiv F, xy \equiv \top \vdash x(\delta_2 y) \equiv \top$.

Of course, Fx is only defined if x is a grasped domain.

VII 3. $Fx \equiv Fx \vdash Gx \equiv \mathsf{T}$.

Next we have two axioms about the level of terms of the form $F\mathfrak{a}\mathfrak{b}$.

VII 4. $Gx \equiv \mathsf{T} \vdash x(Fxz) \equiv \mathsf{T}$.

5. $Gx \equiv \mathsf{T}, x(Fyz) \equiv \mathsf{T} \vdash xy \equiv \mathsf{T}$.

Finally we have the characteristic axiom about the values of functions of the form $F\mathfrak{a}\mathfrak{b}$.

VII 6. $Gx \equiv \mathsf{T}, xy \equiv \mathsf{T}, x(zy) \equiv \mathsf{T} \vdash Fxzy \equiv zy$.

21. Axioms about proof. Again, we begin with axioms about the levels of certain constructions.

VIII 1. Suppose $\mathfrak{a}$ is π or $\not{p}$. Then

$$Gx \equiv \mathsf{T} \vdash Ex(\mathfrak{a}x) \equiv \mathsf{T}$$

and

$$Gx \equiv \mathsf{T} \vdash x(\mathfrak{a}x) \equiv \bot.$$

2. Suppose $\mathfrak{a}$ is π or $\not{p}$. Then

$$\mathfrak{a}x \equiv \mathfrak{a}x \vdash Gx \equiv \mathsf{T}.$$

3. Suppose $\mathfrak{a}$ is π or $\not{p}$. Then

$$Gx \equiv \mathsf{T}, \mathfrak{a}xz \equiv \mathfrak{a}xz \vdash Ex(\mathfrak{a}xz) \equiv \mathsf{T}$$

and

$$Gx \equiv \mathsf{T}, x(\mathfrak{a}yz) \equiv \mathsf{T} \vdash x(\mathfrak{a}y) \equiv \mathsf{T}.$$

4. Suppose $\mathfrak{a}$ is π or $\not{p}$. Then

$$\mathfrak{a}xz \equiv \mathfrak{a}xz \vdash xz \equiv \mathsf{T}.$$

5. $\pi xzy \equiv \mathsf{T} \vdash Exy \equiv T$.

If $\mathfrak{a}$ is a grasped domain and $\mathfrak{b}$ is an element of that domain, then $\pi\mathfrak{a}\mathfrak{b}$ is a decidable predicate of one argument.

VIII 6. Suppose

(i). $\Delta, \pi\mathfrak{a}\mathfrak{b}\mathfrak{c} \equiv \mathsf{T} \vdash \mathfrak{d} \equiv \mathfrak{e}$.

(ii). $\Delta, \pi\mathfrak{a}\mathfrak{b}\mathfrak{c} \equiv \bot \vdash \mathfrak{d} \equiv \mathfrak{e}$.

Then $\Delta, G\mathfrak{a} \equiv \mathsf{T}, \mathfrak{a}\mathfrak{b} \equiv \mathsf{T}, \mathfrak{c} \equiv \mathfrak{c} \vdash \mathfrak{d} \equiv \mathfrak{e}$.

The *reflection principle* asserts that anything provable is true.

VIII 7. $\pi xzy \equiv \mathsf{T}, xw \equiv \mathsf{T} \vdash zw \equiv \mathsf{T}$.

The *rule of proof* asserts that formal derivations correspond to correct intuitive proofs.

VIII 8. Suppose x does not occur in Δ, $\mathfrak{a}$ or $\mathfrak{b}$. Suppose

$$\Delta,\ \mathfrak{a}x \equiv \top \vdash \mathfrak{b}x \equiv \top.$$

Then

$$\Delta,\ G\mathfrak{a} \equiv \top,\ \mathfrak{a}\mathfrak{b} \equiv \top \vdash \pi\mathfrak{a}\mathfrak{b}(\not{p}\mathfrak{a}\mathfrak{b}) \equiv \top.$$

A proof of the form $\not{p}\mathfrak{a}\mathfrak{b}$ is only a proof of one assertion.

VIII 9. $\pi xz(\not{p}yw) \equiv \top \vdash y \equiv x$.

10. $\pi xz(\not{p}xw) \equiv \top \vdash z \equiv w$.

Finally, we need three axioms asserting that various objects are not proofs.

VIII 11. Suppose $\mathfrak{a}$ is any constant of $\mathscr{T}$. Then

$$Gx \equiv \top,\ xz \equiv \top \vdash \pi xz\mathfrak{a} \equiv \bot.$$

12. Suppose $\mathfrak{a}$ is any constant of $\mathscr{T}$. Then

$$Gx \equiv \top,\ xz \equiv \top,\ \delta_1 y \equiv \mathfrak{a} \vdash \pi xzy \equiv \bot.$$

13. Suppose $\mathfrak{a}$ is any constant of $\mathscr{T}$ other than $\not{p}$. Then

$$Gx \equiv \top,\ xz \equiv \top,\ \delta_1(\delta_1 y) \equiv \mathfrak{a} \vdash \pi xzy \equiv \bot.$$

This completes the description of the theory $\mathscr{T}$ of constructions.

22. The interpretation of arithmetic. We suppose given a formulation of Heyting's arithmetic (HA). We shall not describe this theory, but refer the reader to Kleene [3] as an example. Then, to each formula $\mathfrak{A}$ of HA, we wish to assign a closed term $|\mathfrak{A}|$ of $\mathscr{T}$ such that, for any sequence x and any y, $|\mathfrak{A}|xy \equiv \top$ if and only if y is a proof that x satisfies $\mathfrak{A}$. First, to each term $\mathfrak{t}$ of HA we assign a closed term $|\mathfrak{t}|$ of $\mathscr{T}$ such that, for any sequence x, $|\mathfrak{t}|x$ is the value of $\mathfrak{t}$ at x. The definition is by recursion on the structure of $\mathfrak{t}$:

1. $|\mathfrak{v}_n| = C_n$.
2. $|\mathbf{0}| = (\lambda x.\mathbf{0})$.
3. $|\mathfrak{t}'| = (\lambda x.D\mathbf{0}(|\mathfrak{t}|x))$.
4. Suppose H is a primitive recursive function of k arguments introduced by certain defining equations. Let $\mathfrak{f}_H$ be the term introduced in § 18 to provably satisfy these equations. Then

$$|H(\mathfrak{t}_0, \ldots, \mathfrak{t}_{k-1})| = (\lambda x\,.\,\mathfrak{f}_H(|\mathfrak{t}_0|x)\ldots(|\mathfrak{t}_{k-1}|x)).$$

Now, the level of a term $|\mathfrak{A}|$ will depend on the depth of nesting of quantifiers and implications in $\mathfrak{A}$. Accordingly, to each formula $\mathfrak{A}$ we assign a *depth*, $\mathrm{d}(\mathfrak{A})$, by recursion on $\mathfrak{A}$:

1. $\mathrm{d}(\mathfrak{s} = \mathfrak{t}) = 0$.
2. $\mathrm{d}(\mathfrak{A} \wedge \mathfrak{B}) = \mathrm{d}(\mathfrak{A} \vee \mathfrak{B}) = \max\{\mathrm{d}(\mathfrak{A}), \mathrm{d}(\mathfrak{B})\}$.
3. $\mathrm{d}(\mathfrak{A} \to \mathfrak{B}) = 1 + \max\{\mathrm{d}(\mathfrak{A}), \mathrm{d}(\mathfrak{B})\}$.
4. $\mathrm{d}(\bigvee \boldsymbol{v}_n \mathfrak{A}) = \mathrm{d}(\mathfrak{A})$.
5. $\mathrm{d}(\bigwedge \boldsymbol{v}_n \mathfrak{A}) = 1 + \mathrm{d}(\mathfrak{A})$.

We can now define the term $|\mathfrak{A}|$ by recursion on the structure of $\mathfrak{A}$:

First, y proves that x satisfies an equation $\mathfrak{s} = \mathfrak{t}$ just in case y is of level zero and $|\mathfrak{s}|x \equiv |\mathfrak{t}|x$:

$$|\mathfrak{s} = \mathfrak{t}| = (\lambda xy \,.\, By \cap_0 Q(|\mathfrak{s}|x)(|\mathfrak{t}|x)).$$

The construction y proves that x satisfies $\mathfrak{A} \wedge \mathfrak{B}$ just in case the first component of y proves that x satisfies $\mathfrak{A}$ and the second component of y proves that x satisfies $\mathfrak{B}$:

$$|\mathfrak{A} \wedge \mathfrak{B}| = (\lambda xy \,.\, |\mathfrak{A}|x(D_1 y) \cap_0 |\mathfrak{B}|x(D_2 y)).$$

The construction y proves that x satisfies $\mathfrak{A} \vee \mathfrak{B}$ just in case either y proves that x satisfies $\mathfrak{A}$ or y proves that x satisfies $\mathfrak{B}$:

$$|\mathfrak{A} \vee \mathfrak{B}| = (\lambda xy \,.\, |\mathfrak{A}|xy \cup_0 |\mathfrak{B}|xy).$$

Suppose $p = \mathrm{d}(\mathfrak{A} \to \mathfrak{B})$. Then $\mathrm{d}(\mathfrak{A}) < p$, and so any proof that x satisfies $\mathfrak{A}$ has level $< p$. Therefore, in defining $|\mathfrak{A} \to \mathfrak{B}|$ it suffices to quantify over L_p:

$$|\mathfrak{A} \to \mathfrak{B}| = (\lambda xy \,.\, \pi L_p[(|\mathfrak{A}|x) \supset_1 (\lambda z \,.\, |\mathfrak{B}|x(D_2 yz))](D_1 y)).$$

The construction y proves that x satisfies $\bigvee \boldsymbol{v}_n \mathfrak{A}$ just in case the first component of y is a natural number and the second component of y proves that x, with the first component of y in the nth place, satisfies $\mathfrak{A}$:

$$|\bigvee \boldsymbol{v}_n \mathfrak{A}| = (\lambda xy \,.\, N(D_1 y)) \cap_2 (\lambda xy \,.\, |\mathfrak{A}|(\rho_n x(D_1 y))(D_2 y)).$$

Finally, suppose $\mathrm{d}(\bigwedge \boldsymbol{v}_n \mathfrak{A}) = p$. Then y proves that x satisfies $\bigwedge \boldsymbol{v}_n \mathfrak{A}$ just in case the first component of y proves that, for any natural number z, the second component of y applied to z proves that x, with z in the nth place, satisfies $\mathfrak{A}$:

$$|\bigwedge \boldsymbol{v}_n \mathfrak{A}| = (\lambda xy \,.\, \pi L_p[N \supset_1 (\lambda z \,.\, |\mathfrak{A}|(\rho_n xz)(D_2 yz))](D_1 y)).$$

Observe that the constant zero sequence is represented by **0**. Then our main result about the interpretation of HA is this

THEOREM. *Suppose* $\mathfrak{A}$ *is a sentence of* HA. *Then* $\mathfrak{A}$ *is a theorem of* HA *if and only if there is a term* $\mathfrak{a}$ *such that we have in* $\mathscr{T}$ *that*

$$\vdash |\mathfrak{A}|0\mathfrak{a} \equiv \mathsf{T}.$$

This theorem establishes the consistency of $\mathscr{T}$ relative to HA.

REFERENCES

[1] H. B. Curry and R. Feys, *Combinatory Logic* **1**, North-Holland, Amsterdam (1958).

[2] A. Heyting, Die formalen Regeln der intuitionistischen Logik, *Sitzungsberichte Preuss. Akad. Wiss. Phys. Math. Kl.* (1930) 42–56.

[3] S. C. Kleene, *Introduction to Metamathematics*, Van Nostrand, New York (1952).

[4] G. Kreisel, Foundations of intuitionistic logic, in *Logic, methodology, and the philosophy of science*, eds. E. Nagel, P. Suppes and A. Tarski, Stanford University Press, Stanford (1962) 198–210.

[5] G. Kreisel, Mathematical logic, in *Lectures on modern mathematics* **3**, ed. T. L. Saaty, Wiley, New York (1965) 95–195.

CHURCH'S THESIS: A KIND OF REDUCIBILITY AXIOM FOR CONSTRUCTIVE MATHEMATICS†

G. KREISEL*

The purpose of this lecture is to expand the remark ([**21**] p. 146, 2.76) relating Church's thesis in constructive mathematics to the 'hypothesis' $V = L$ in set theory (which, by [**4**] p. 147, implies a natural form of the axiom of reducibility). Some problems suggested by the remark are solved in the Technical Notes (e.g. I and II) below. Also (and, to me, this is perhaps most important) the body of open problems is coherent, and so there is at least a chance of some decisive results in this area.

Two topics treated here may be of independent interest. A development of the theory of abstract constructions by use of the notion of graspable domain (§ 5) and a connection between Scott's model [**36**] and the theory of lawless sequences (Technical Note III).

Introduction: ***abstract impredicative and*** **(more or less)** ***explicitly defined notions.*** We consider principally:

(i). The abstract notion of arbitrary subset and the power set operation (collecting all subsets of a given set); correspondingly, the notion of constructible set, obtained by iterating the process of collecting (only) those subsets which are definable by means of formulae in the language of set theory, using names for elements of the given set.

(ii). The (abstract) notion of constructive function (with integral arguments and values) as understood in intuitionistic mathematics, and explained in [**5**]; correspondingly, the notion of recursive function, defined by means of recursion equations.

The clause 'more or less (explicitly defined)' is needed because (i) the abstract notion of set (theoretic ordinal) is used for formulating the iteration process and (ii) the notion of constructive function is involved in the mean-

† Concluding address.

* Preparation of this paper was partially supported by grant DA-ARO-31-124-G 985.

ing of the quantifier combination $\forall\exists$ in $\forall n \exists m\, T(e, n, m)$ (for Kleene's T-predicate) used to define the notion of recursion equation. Only for certain segments of the constructible hierarchy and certain subclasses of the class of recursive functions are the relevant definitions independent of the corresponding abstract notions (cf. my other lecture **[26]**).

Undoubtedly the natural way, incidentally corresponding roughly to the historical development, of looking at the two sets of notions, is this:

First we have the abstract notions and their basic properties (axioms), e.g. the axioms of Zermelo, Mahlo, Fraenkel in (i), Heyting's arithmetic and extensions in (ii). These axioms are recognized by inspection or reflection. Afterwards defined notions are introduced. Those mentioned above (happen to) satisfy the axioms originally found for the corresponding abstract notions. This fact was not immediate on inspection, but had to be established by a detailed argument, by Gödel for (i), by Kleene for (ii) using the notion of recursive realizability.[1]

Note in passing that for mathematical practice too the abstract notions are primary. Thus mathematicians speak freely of sets, but get bored or confused by explanations of first order definability, let alone of its iteration. In constructive mathematics, Bishop's book **[1]** owes much of its appeal (and cogency) to the fact that he does not write out recursion equations but works with the primitive notion of constructive function; for more technical points see also **[24]** p. 233. Finally, as a related and more elementary illustration (**[21]** p. 103, l. 42), the natural way of looking at the Euclidean plane is not to introduce coordinates (names for points) at all, let alone algebraic ones for points obtained by explicit constructions; their place is in refinements.

Probably the first natural *logical* problem is to look for properties which distinguish between the abstract and corresponding explicitly defined notions. In set theory this kind of question was suggested by Gödel **[6]** and first carried out (by use of axioms about measurable cardinals) in Scott **[35]**. Another, quite different, attempt is given in a letter (1963) of Myhill quoted in **[28]** (by use of axioms for random reals). From the present point of view it is equally natural to try and refute

$$\forall f \exists e \forall n \exists p [T(e, n, p) \wedge fn = U(p)]$$

(for constructive functions f, numbers e, n, p, Kleene's T and U) which we shall here call *Church's thesis.*[2] One expects to use recondite properties of the basic constructive notions but, if possible, less problematic ones than those used by Scott and Myhill above. (Evidently the project makes sense only if one understands or, as one sometimes says, 'accepts' the basic notions; it would be circular if one thinks of the explicitly defined ones as replacing the others.)

Let me end this introduction with a word on the difficulties of the project. Subjectively, we live at present in a logical tradition which insists on algebraization or arithmetization (in place of the geometric way of looking at things). Not only (as in Euclid's axioms) do we list explicit properties of notions, but we try to list the means of generating the objects studied. As an illustration, contrast the explicit definition of the property of continuity with the (algebraic) restriction to e.g. polynomials built up by addition and multiplication. In its extreme form this tradition requires the kind of explicit description mentioned as a prerequisite of precision itself (cf. **[23]** concerning formal and informal rigour). Whatever its merits or defects the tradition exists and presents a psychological obstacle to the study of abstract notions. For this reason, I give *elementary examples* in § 1 (and consider them basic.)

Objectively, the nature of the abstract notions *is* problematic; indeed this is perhaps their principal interest for the logician (though of course not for the working mathematician). Evidently the analysis of the notions is the ultimate aim of our research. But we should be able to say at the start, at least roughly, what kind of entities these abstract objects are. This is not the place to go into the notion of subset.[3] But what are the constructive functions or rules, and, more generally, the constructive proofs for which we wish to set up a theory? Speaking for myself, I think their usual characterization as mental objects (in contrast to their spatio-temporal or linguistic representations) is inadequate in an essential respect. The rules and proofs are of course involved in the mental (psychological) experience of mathematical activity. But the theories we try to set up are not about this experience as it presents itself to us, they concern its logically significant aspects.

Before mechanically dismissing this distinction as 'vague' or 'circular' (cf. note 4 on p. 143 for a sermon) let us pursue it, and compare our problems with those arising in mechanics, say. The objects considered in this science are not the (material) bodies of physical experience as they present themselves to our senses. To apply mechanics we have to determine the mechanically significant data in an empirical situation (mass of the body rather than, say, its colour, electric charges if there is electric interaction etc.). Indeed, we need the theoretical notions to tell us which data are significant, but we do not have a recipe for stepping from crude physical experience to those data. One last and highly relevant historical point. The notions and laws of mechanics (e.g. the equations for incompressible fluids) were derived from general qualitative experience, not from delicate measurements which, incidentally, can often be stated only in terms of the theoretical notions.

In the last analysis (cf. **[21]**, p. 191, 5.422) the interest in the general theory of constructivity is based on the conviction that the (mental) experience of mathematical activity is susceptible to a similar kind of theory as we have for (familiar) mechanical phenomena. We can't be sure that the conviction is well founded. But it's a sensible idea, and, as we know, sensible physical theories, even when false, have led to interesting formal mathematical problems and results. This certainly seems to carry over to our project.

1. Basic example: constructive (prima facie) non-mechanical rules for number theoretic functions (cf. **[21]**, p. 131, 2.35). We consider a formal system such as Heyting's arithmetic HA which we have recognized to be constructively valid. Thus to each formal derivation (with Gödel number) n corresponds a constructive proof, say $\mathbf{p}_n$. The rule f is given by cases:

Case 1. If n is not a derivation of any closed formula of the form $\exists x\mathfrak{A}$ then $fn = 0$. Otherwise

Case 2.1. $fn = 0$ if $\mathbf{p}_n$ does not provide a *specific* numerical instance satisfying $\mathfrak{A}$, e.g. if $\exists x\mathfrak{A}$ has been inferred from $\forall x\mathfrak{A}$;

Case 2.2. $fn = x+1$ if x is the number verifying $\mathfrak{A}$ which is provided by $\mathbf{p}_n$.

Clearly, no Turing machine will react to this rule as it stands. But let's look at it before calling it vague[4]. As a first test of understanding we show: f is not equivalent to the following (mechanical) rule f' (Recall that $(\mathrm{HA} \vdash \exists x\mathfrak{A}) \Rightarrow \exists x \vdash \mathfrak{A}\boldsymbol{x}$ where $\boldsymbol{x}$ denotes the xth numeral.):

Case 1′. If n is not a derivation (in HA) of any closed formula $\exists x\mathfrak{A}$ then $f'n = 0$. Otherwise

Case 2′. $f'n = x+1$ where $\boldsymbol{x}$ is the argument of $\mathfrak{A}$ in the shortest derivation (in HA) of a formula of the form $\mathfrak{A}\boldsymbol{x}$.

The rules are clearly different since case 2.1 has no analogue here at all. They are not even equivalent. For let $\mathfrak{B}$ and $\mathfrak{C}$ be two closed theorems of HA such that $\mathfrak{C}$ has a much shorter derivation than $\mathfrak{B}$, and let $\mathfrak{A}$ be

$$(x = 0 \wedge \mathfrak{B}) \vee (x = 1 \wedge \mathfrak{C}).$$

Let n consist of a derivation of $\mathfrak{B}$, followed by the inference to $\exists x\mathfrak{A}$. Then $fn = 1$, but $f'n = 2$.

We can go a little farther. Consider an enumeration $\mathfrak{A}_m$ in a system $\boldsymbol{S}$ of arithmetic properties, and let $\mathfrak{R}(m, n, y)$ mean:

$$\text{If } n \text{ is a derivation in } \boldsymbol{S} \text{ of } \exists x\mathfrak{A}_m \text{ then } \mathfrak{A}_m y.$$

If $\boldsymbol{S}$ is constructively valid, we have $\forall m\forall n\exists y\,\mathfrak{R}(m, n, y)$ and hence $\exists h\forall m\forall n\mathfrak{R}(m, n, h(n))$. But in general (in contrast to HA) we cannot expect

$$(\boldsymbol{S} \vdash \exists x\mathfrak{A}_m) \Rightarrow \exists x(\boldsymbol{S} \vdash \mathfrak{A}_m \boldsymbol{x}),$$

for example, if (i) the closed formula $\exists x\mathfrak{A}x$ is constructively valid, (ii) for no numeral $\boldsymbol{x}$ is $\exists x\mathfrak{A}x \to \mathfrak{A}\boldsymbol{x}$ derivable in HA, and (iii) $\boldsymbol{S} = \text{HA} \cup \{\exists x\mathfrak{A}x\}$. In that case the only definition of h that we have goes via $\mathbf{p}_n$; while, for $\boldsymbol{S} = \text{HA}$, our f' above will (at least) be *a* solution of

$$\forall m\forall n\ \mathfrak{R}(m, n, h(n)).$$

REMARK. It is almost banal that we understand non-mechanical rules; on the contrary too detailed, that is 'too' mechanical rules only confuse the human computer. The point of considering the specific rule f above is to have precise questions in a familiar context.

2. Basic example: formal problems. Having understood the rule f, we ask

Problem 1. *Is f equivalent to some mechanical rule?*

Clearly the problem has the same character as any other problem of informal mathematics: we look for minimal assumptions about $\mathbf{p}_n$, as evident as possible, which are sufficient to settle the question. However, if preferred, there is a 'corresponding' purely formal problem.

Recall that each of the following syntactic studies of HA assigns a specific term t, possibly containing free variables (corresponding to case 2.1), to any formal derivation of $\exists x\mathfrak{A}$:

Kleene's various recursive realizability interpretations ([**14**]–[**16**]); Gödel's functional interpretation [**5**]; its variant ([**17**], p. 112, 3.52); Goodman [**8**]; cut elimination by use of infinite proof figures ([**34**] as extended in [**21**], p. 164, 3.332 [5]). Let $f_{\mathscr{I}}$ be the mechanical rule which the interpretation $\mathscr{I}$ assigns to derivations in HA.

Problem 2. *Are the functions $f_{\mathscr{I}}$ for the interpretations $\mathscr{I}$ above, equivalent?* ('Equivalent' either in the sense that the terms assigned to n by the $f_{\mathscr{I}}$ denote definitionally[6] or extensionally equal objects.)

Problem 3. *Which, if any, of the $f_{\mathscr{I}}$ are equivalent to the non-mechanical rule f above?*

Problem 2 belongs to traditional proof theory of intuitionistic arithmetic, a subject very much in need of less crude problems than the hackneyed question: does $\vdash \exists x \mathfrak{A}$ imply $\exists x \vdash \mathfrak{A}x$? *Ad* problem 3, note that $\mathfrak{t}$ assigned by a given $\mathscr{I}$ 'satisfies' $\mathfrak{A}$ in the sense of $\mathscr{I}$, not always for the intended interpretation.

3. Church's thesis: generalities; incompleteness of Heyting's predicate calculus. For systems not containing variables for constructive (number theoretic) functions the axiom on p. 122 is replaced by

$$\forall X\{\forall x \exists y(\langle x, y\rangle \in X) \rightarrow \exists e \forall x \exists z[T(e, x, z) \wedge \langle x, U(z)\rangle \in X]\},$$

and for systems not containing variables X for species, by the schema

$$\forall x \exists y\, \mathfrak{R}(x, y) \rightarrow \exists e \forall x \exists z[T(e, x, z) \wedge \mathfrak{R}(x, U(z))] \qquad (*)$$

for all definable relations $\mathfrak{R}$ not containing free variables (parameters) for incompletely defined objects such as free choice sequences.

Church's rule is, by definition, the inference of the conclusion in (*) when the premise has been derived.

As observed in **[19]** (p. 140, l. 11–14, for $\mathfrak{A}$ of theorem 3, p. 150) Church's thesis implies incompleteness of Heyting's predicate calculus, and this is sharpened in the Technical Note I below.[7] Regarding Church's thesis as neither plausible nor refuted, we can say that the notion of *constructive validity of first order formulae* depends on problematic properties of the basic notion of constructive function; like second order validity (**[23]**, p. 157), and unlike first order validity (cf. p. 144, note 7) in the classical case.

The following question asks for an analogue to Skolem-Loewenheim:

Problem 4. *Is there a definition (in the theory of species of natural numbers or even in arithmetic) of the species of constructively valid formulae in the language of predicate calculus (without having to decide Church's thesis)?*

But Church's thesis would of course imply that the species so defined is not the set of theorems in Heyting's system. (Note that there is no solution of problem 4 by a constructively enumerated species.)

4. Church's thesis and Church's rule; consistency and conservative extension problems. Evidently, given any formal system containing the notation needed for formulating Church's thesis (or its variants in § 3), it makes sense to ask whether the addition of Church's thesis or rule is consistent, or whether the system is closed under the rule[8]; more generally, whether the addition is conservative for suitable classes of formulae (corresponding to **[21]**, p. 106, l. 535, for the addition of $V = L$).

Good candidates for such classes of formulae are usually arithmetic formulae in the fragment ($\neg$, $\wedge$, $\forall$) or $\forall\exists$ formulae. But perhaps the subject is ripe for a more general treatment (possibly simplifying **[15]** a bit):

Problem 5. *Are there simple syntactic conditions (on axioms) which ensure that the axioms, added to intuitionistic predicate calculus, are (i) consistent with Church's thesis or (ii) closed under Church's rule?*

But, for immediate progress, it is probably more useful to indicate particular systems that present open problems.

(a). *Theory of species of natural numbers* (like classical analysis with the comprehension axiom and the axiom of dependent choices, but intuitionistic instead of classical predicate logic). In Technical Note II I give a sketch of a proof of closure under Church's rule (as I conjectured **[21]**, p. 351). We have the following question (but cf. the postscript on p. 147):

Problem 6. *For what classes of formulae (if any, e.g. $\{0=1\}$) is the addition of Church's thesis to the theory of species conservative?*

For a justification of the theory of species see the end of § 5 below. But problem 6 is of interest even for those who (have not thought out the justification, or who simply) are primarily interested in a narrower area of constructive mathematics. Various formal theories of (possibly iterated) inductive definitions or, equivalently, so-called higher number classes can obviously be modelled in the theory of species, and so the consistency of Church's thesis with the latter covers also those systems. (Naturally a separate argument is needed to treat the rule above; cf. end of Note II.)

(b). *Theories of choice sequences.* For a brief summary see Technical Note IV. For all such theories, or better for all notions of choice sequence α considered, we have

$$\neg\, \forall\alpha\exists e\forall x\exists z[T(e, x, a)\wedge \alpha(x) = U(z)].$$

This is natural. For instance, for dice α (or lawless sequences) you don't expect to *prove* that successive values of α will follow a recursive, or for that matter, any law. Nor will the thinking (freely creating) subject α convince himself that his (mathematical) behaviour is subject to such a law!

What is more reasonable to assume, is the consistency of the schema (*)

in § 3 for relations $\mathfrak{R}$ defined by use of quantifiers for choice sequences. The bulk of the theories (cf. Technical Note IV) are reduced to the particular theory IDK in such a way that the consistency of (*) with IDK implies its consistency with those other theories. I have convinced myself that Kleene's original recursive realizability interpretation extends to IDK (§ 1 of **[24]**) by use of the trick **[24]**, p. 235, l. 12. (*Added in proof:* the details are now in **[43]**, 3.7.2.) But there is room for a more complete solution of

Problem 7. *For what class of formulae is the addition of Church's thesis to* IDK *conservative?*[9]

(c). *Kripke's schema.* The schema is *justified* by reference to the 'thinking subject' or, more objectively, to the analysis of mathematics into ω stages (**[23]**, p. 179, l. −7); but it is *stated* in the 'usual' language of intuitionistic analysis. For species X and constructive functions f (not only choice sequences) we have a 'strong' form ($\boldsymbol{KS}^+$)

$$\forall X \exists f \forall n [X(n)] \leftrightarrow \exists m (f(m) = n)]$$

(proved consistent by Scott **[36]**, with various basic axioms, cf. Technical Note IV) and the 'weak' form ($\boldsymbol{KS}^-$)

$$\forall X \exists f \forall n ([\exists m (f(m) = n) \rightarrow X(n)] \wedge [\neg \exists m (f(m) = n) \rightarrow \neg X(n)])$$

(which follows from the axioms **[23]**, p. 159–160). Even ($\boldsymbol{KS}^-$) is inconsistent with Church's axiom $\forall f \exists e \forall n \exists p\ [T(e, n, p) \wedge U(p) = f(n)]$.[10]

However, I do not know the answer to

Problem 8. *For $\mathfrak{R}$ in the (restricted) language of analysis (not containing the primitive $\vdash_n$ of* **[23]**), *is* ($\boldsymbol{KS}$), *together with the axioms of Technical Note IV, consistent with Church's schema, and is the system closed under Church's rule?*

Discussion. The assumptions used in deriving $\boldsymbol{KS}^-$, namely thinking of the body of mathematical evidence as arranged in an ω order, seem arbitrary (though not absurd) if, as in the theory of ordinals, one also thinks of individual proofs as consisting of a transfinite sequence of steps (**[3]**, footnote 8). Therefore the inconsistency of ($\boldsymbol{KS}$) with Church's thesis does not, I think, refute the latter conclusively. In any case it leaves open the question *whether constructive rules f defined without reference to such an hypothetical ω-order of mathematical proofs are equivalent to recursive functions.* We therefore turn now to an area of constructive mathematics which does not assume such an order, yet looks promising, that is, it looks abstract enough not to be *reducible* to mechanical operations.

5. Abstract constructions and proofs. See for reference **[21]**, pp. 125–127 or Troelstra's course at the present conference and Goodman's lecture **[8]**.[11] It is useful to think of the latter as a setlike, of the former as a classlike theory, where constructions correspond to sets, notions to classes (p. 126).[12] For the present purpose it seems slightly more convenient to use the classlike formulation. Let us scrutinize a bit the basic relation:

For some given notion α, the construction (more precisely, judgement) c proves αd for variable d.

For the discussion below it is quite sufficient to consider a particular notion α which we understand. More generally, there is nothing to force us to look at any notion α or any object $\boldsymbol{d}$ except *after* we have convinced ourselves that everything in sight makes sense, provided we have also convinced ourselves that the closure conditions (axioms) explicitly formulated are satisfied. After all, this freedom is one of the principal virtues of quantifier-free systems such as theories of constructions.

The principal issue is this:

If we think of the variable d as ranging over the, so to speak, absolutely unattained universe of all constructions, it seems dubious that there should be any construction (something that we grasp completely) which proves αd, even if we have convinced ourselves that, for any clearly given $\boldsymbol{d}$, α is indeed a well defined notion. (In set theory: even if $x \in y$ makes sense for each pair of well defined x and y, why should we be able to put together, here and now, all x: $x = x$, or x: $x \notin x$?).

On the other hand, if we take some particularly simple notion αd, say $\beta d \rhd \beta d$ (where I use $\rhd$ for truth functional implication and, if one wants to, $\triangle$ and $\triangledown$ for truth functional conjunction and disjunction respectively) we simply have a proof. Whatever else may be in doubt, we have a perfectly clear idea or 'schema' for verifying $\beta d \rhd \beta d$. The kind of judgement involved here plays the same role among proofs as, say, the identity operator plays among functions. It is simply a mindless ritual to chant: for each type we have a different identity operator. (Though, trivially, for each domain D the set of pairs $\{\langle x, x\rangle : x \in D\}$ depends on D.)

The obvious and immediate conclusion is: just as there are some operations which are defined for arbitrary operations (in the non-trivial sense of giving distinct values for 'lots' of arguments, e.g. the identity operator, the composition operator etc.) so there are some notions α which can be proved by constructions to hold for unrestricted d. The definition of other operators depends essentially on a given domain ('essentially' in the sense that the function is made total by a trick of, say, defining its value to be zero outside the given domain; cf. **[21]**, 2.151, pp. 124–125). In the case of notions α, the corresponding restriction concerns the variable d.

Example (cf. **[21]**, p. 126, 2.213). Suppose the variable d does not occur in α, and $\alpha \rhd \beta$ has been formally derived by a derivation p. Now, if this p uses only very elementary principles (of propositional substitutions), by the above we may infer $\alpha \rhd \pi(a_p; d \cdot \beta d)$ in the notation *loc. cit.* In words:

If α then the proof a_p (described by p) establishes β for variable d.

If, however, the formal derivation p itself uses principles such as the reflection principle and β refers to properties of the notion of proof itself, we should only infer, for a given (grasped) domain D:

If α then the proof a_p^D establishes $d \in D \rhd \beta d$, for variable d.

Present development of the theory of constructions is unsymmetric with respect to functions and proofs. Several non-trivial total functions are available (such as pairing and inverse pairing functions in **[21]**, p. 126, l. 6, 7, superseded by Goodman's much more thorough **[8]**[13]), but next to nothing is done by way of analysis of judgements. The device (cf. **[21]**, p. 126, l. – 12) of using the formal derivation p as a name of the proof a_p is a purely formal trick.

Grasped domains and the theory of species of natural numbers. Clearly what is required is an analysis of the kinds of restrictions D (if any) needed for given p, and principles, corresponding to set theoretic existential axioms, for stepping from given D to 'bigger' ones. This matter is wide open. But for orientation (and also for its intrinsic interest) let me consider the particular abstract assumptions sufficient to derive the formal laws of the theory of species [in § 4(a)]. The present discussion supersedes **[21]**, p. 126, 2.215 and **[25]**, p. 429.

We suppose given the graspable species of natural numbers with characteristic function C_N, i.e. $C_N d = 1$ if d is a natural number and $C_N d = 0$ otherwise.

The assumption is that we can grasp the notion of being a species of natural numbers, that is we have a characteristic function C_{N_1} for the property (of d):

d is a construction *involved in the notion of species* (of natural numbers). In words, if we understand the concept of natural number we also understand what a proof or construction implicit in the concept of natural number is (more precisely, normalized, irredundant constructions are meant; otherwise it would be absurd to suppose that we have a grasp of their totality). Thus, in particular

(i). For species c, we have: $C_{N_1}c$ (short for $C_{N_1}c = 1$);
(ii). For species c, and (constructions) p and x,

$$(C_{N_1}c \triangle cpx) \triangleright (C_{N_1}p \triangle C_N x),$$

that is, if c is a species and p proves that x is in the species c, then p is involved in the notion of species (of natural numbers) and x is a natural number;

(iii). We have a *functor* F, associating to $c, c_1, \ldots, c_n$, all satisfying C_{N_1}, a construction d, $d = F(c; c_1, \ldots, c_n)$, such that

$$C_{N_1}d = 1 \quad \text{and} \quad \pi(p; x \,.\, C_{N_1}x \triangleright cxc_1 \ldots c_n) = dp.$$

Thus suppose the species defined by the formula $\mathfrak{A}$ with free variables X, X_i $(1 \leqslant i \leqslant n)$ is determined by the construction c with parameters x, x_i. Then $\forall X \mathfrak{A}$ defines the species d, when X_i has the value c_i.

Comment. The analysis above, like the interpretation of the logical operations intended by Brouwer and fomulated by Heyting, uses notions which are more abstract than those of familiar constructive mathematics ([**21**], p. 119). The analysis has enough coherence and substance to suggest that there is something deflnite to understand here (even if, by note 3, we have not yet done so). But do we want to know about it, not only subjectively, but for getting on with the business of constructive mathematics? Not the possibility of understanding intuitionistic concepts, but their usefulness is the true issue. Dramatic exaggerations would only lead to the kind of let-down which Russell felt after he (or rather, according to his autobiography, after Whitehead) finished *Principia*.

Assuming that the intentions of such an abstract analysis of the principles behind the theory of species of natural numbers have been properly formulated we have

Problem 9. *Is the hypothetical theory of constructions consistent with Church's thesis?*

(Of course, a positive solution of problem 6 does not necessarily ensure one for problem 9.[14])

Finally we have the somewhat related

Problem 10. *Is the set of derivable (variable-free) closed atomic formulae in this hypothetical theory of constructions recursive?*

In particular, for any given (closed) term $\mathfrak{t}$ it should be decidable whether the construction intended by $\mathfrak{t}$ proves a given assertion in the theory of species. And, for the formal theory, it should be recursively decidable whether $\mathfrak{t}$ can be formally shown to have this property.

It should be noted that the 'corresponding' requirement is neither satisfied by Kleene's recursive realizability interpretations **[14]** and **[16]** nor by Gödel's functional interpretation **[5]** of the logical operations. Specifically, recall that to each formula $\mathfrak{A}$ are associated the relations

the number e realizes $\mathfrak{A}$

and

the functional s satisfies $\forall t \mathfrak{A}_0(s, t)$

resp., where $\exists s \forall t \mathfrak{A}_0(s, t)$ is the interpretation of $\mathfrak{A}$ according to **[5]**. Thus, on the interpretations considered, the partial recursive function (with number) e and the functional s are the constructions that 'constitute' the proof of $\mathfrak{A}$ (together with the judgement that these constructions stand in the relation above to $\mathfrak{A}$). But neither of these relations is evidently decidable, and the formal derivability of the corresponding formulae (in the systems considered) is certainly not recursively decidable.

The decidability property mentioned in problem 10 therefore distinguishes (what I conceive to be) the intended intuitionistic interpretation of the logical operations from some other constructively meaningful ones. The property may turn out to be a useful *adequacy condition.*

Discussion (*continuing the comment of p.* 131): The notions here considered need not be analyzed before one can do constructive mathematics. The principal interest here is philosophical: not to confine oneself to what is necessary[15] for (current) practice, but to see what is possible by way of theoretical analysis. And there are surely many who have an interest in the abstract notions, but who, for temperamental or for other reasons, had best wait till the theory is technically more developed. After all there are a lot of other things to do in constructive mathematics; intentionally I chose for my other talk **[26]** a topic at the opposite end of the scale dealing with restricted notions of proof and small ordinals.

TECHNICAL NOTES

Notes I and II arise directly from the project described in the main text. They derive constructively meaningful results from arguments in the literature which were not only prima facie non-constructive but (it is fair to say) seemed to have a purely technical interest. In Note II Spector's important paper **[37]** is used to derive for full classical analysis a result whose interest is independent of the notoriously problematic constructive validity of bar recursion for all finite types (cf. **[25]**, p. 421). Notes III and

IV concern some notions of choice sequence and their formal theories, summarized in the chart at the end of the paper.

I. Non-enumerability of the species of valid formulae of predicate calculus by a recursive function (under Church's thesis). We combine the ideas of [**19**] and of Mostowski [**30**].

Consider any primitive recursive binary tree T. For a suitable formula $\mathfrak{F}_T$ (cf. [**19**]) containing function symbols, the assertion

all constructive paths through T are finite

is equivalent to

$\mathfrak{F}_T$ is (contructively) valid.

The proof of equivalence uses the facts set out in note 7; the result stated holds also if 'finite' is replaced by 'not infinite', and '$\mathfrak{F}_T$' by '$\neg\neg\mathfrak{F}_T$'. $\mathfrak{F}_T$ has the form $\mathfrak{U} \rightarrow \mathfrak{E}$ where $\mathfrak{U}$ is universal and $\mathfrak{E}$ is existential, and so $\neg\neg\mathfrak{F}_T$ has the form $\neg(\mathfrak{U} \wedge \mathfrak{U}_1)$ where $\mathfrak{U}_1$ is universal and equivalent to $\neg\mathfrak{E}$.[16]

Mostowski's general theorem states that the sets of formulae

$\{\mathfrak{A}: \mathfrak{A}$ is true in all r.e. models$\}$

and

$\{\mathfrak{A}: \mathfrak{A}$ is false in some primitive recursive model$\}$

are not arithmetically separable. Inspection shows that, for $\mathfrak{A}$ of the form $\neg(\mathfrak{U} \wedge \mathfrak{U}_1)$ above, the sets above are not separable by an r.e. set, i.e., an r.e. set including $\{\mathfrak{F}_T: \mathfrak{F}_T$ is true in all r.e. models$\}$.

Remark. The abstract recursion theoretic result is this. The sets of primitive recursive trees

$\{T$: all recursive paths are finite$\}$

and

$\{T$: there is an infinite primitive recursive path$\}$

are effectively not separable by an r.e. set.

From this classical result we now get the corresponding intuitionistic result as follows. Given any proposed r.e. separation, say ω_e, we find explicitly T_e and a classical proof of

$T_e \in \omega_e$ and not all recursive paths are finite

or

$T_e \notin \omega_e$ and a particular primitive recursive path p_e is infinite.

Hence, intuitionistically, it is absurd that

(i). $\neg\neg T_e \in \omega_e \rightarrow$ (all weakly recursive paths of T_e are not infinite)

and

(ii). $\neg T_e \in \omega_e \rightarrow$ (p_e is infinite),

where $\{e\}$ is called weakly recursive if $\forall x \neg\neg \exists y T(e, x, y)$. Now (i) implies

$$\neg\neg T_e \in \omega_e \rightarrow \text{(all recursive paths of } T_e \text{ are not infinite).}$$

We now conclude the required result since (ii) implies

$$\text{(all recursive paths in } T_e \text{ are not infinite)} \rightarrow \neg\neg T_e \in \omega_e.$$

For this argument it would not have been sufficient to have a classically recursive, that is intuitionistically weakly recursive, path in place of p_e. So one needs here in an essential way Mostowski's inseparability result in place of the more 'natural' result

$$\{\mathfrak{A}: \mathfrak{A} \text{ is true in all recursive models}\} \text{ is not arithmetic,}$$

while in Mostowski's original formulation, the inseparability property had the role of a refinement.

REMARK. A common misunderstanding is avoided by distinguishing between completeness and soundness on the one hand and faithfulness on the other. For each $\mathfrak{A}$ in the language of predicate calculus, let the formula $\mathfrak{V}(\mathfrak{A})$ of a formal theory of species, say $\mathscr{S}$, define the validity of $\mathfrak{A}$. $\mathscr{S}$ is called *faithful*, provided that, for each $\mathfrak{A}$,

$\mathfrak{A}$ is derivable in Heyting's predicate calculus iff $\mathfrak{V}(\mathfrak{A})$ is derivable in $\mathscr{S}$.

Despite the impossibility of establishing completeness (in any existing system) there are quite elementary formal systems for species or, for that matter, for abstract constructions which are faithful. The situation is completely parallel in the case of classical logic. Let $\mathfrak{V}_{\mathscr{L}}(\mathfrak{A})$, in the language $\mathscr{L}$ of set theory, define classical validity. Now for set theory without the axiom of infinity we have

$\mathfrak{V}_{\mathscr{L}}(\mathfrak{A})$ provable if and only if $\mathfrak{A}$ is derivable in predicate logic,

but not

$\mathfrak{V}_{\mathscr{L}}(\mathfrak{A}) \rightarrow$ ($\mathfrak{A}$ is derivable in predicate logic).

(Take for $\mathfrak{A}$: every ordered set has a least element.) On the other hand soundness is derivable without the axiom of infinity.

II. Theory of species: closure under Church's rule. The present note contains sketches of proofs (but for the theory $\mathscr{S}$ of species without axioms of choice; cf. also the postscript on p. 147).

For each finite subsystem $\mathscr{S}_n$ of the theory $\mathscr{S}$ of species of natural numbers, we can formally prove in the latter

(i). for primitive recursive $\mathfrak{A}(x, y)$, if $\forall x \neg\neg \exists y \mathfrak{A}(x, y)$ can be proved in $\mathscr{S}_n$ then $\forall x \exists y \mathfrak{A}(x, y)$ can be proved in $\mathscr{S}$ (where $\mathfrak{A}$ is a canonical definition of the primitive recursive relation considered),

(ii). for arbitrary $\mathfrak{A}(x, y)$ containing x and y as its only free variables, if $\forall x \exists y \mathfrak{A}(x, y)$ can be proved in $\mathscr{S}_n$ then there is a number $\boldsymbol{e}$ such that

$$\forall x \exists z [T(\boldsymbol{e}, x, z) \wedge \mathfrak{A}(x, U(z))]$$

can be proved in $\mathscr{S}$.

A corollary to (i) is of course, that exactly the same equations can be proved to be recursion equations in full classical analysis and in the theory of species. (It is well known that this class of equations is stable in the sense that it is unchanged by adding the assumption that all sets are constructible.)

To prove (i), we use Spector's paper **[37]**, together with a model of bar recursion of finite type in the theory of species (but using only the comprehension principle). For by **[37]**, if $\forall x \neg\neg \exists y \mathfrak{A}(x, y)$ is proved in the theory of species, there is a term $\mathfrak{t}$ of the theory of bar recursion of finite type such that

$$\mathfrak{A}(x, \mathfrak{t}(x))$$

is derivable in the latter. So all we need is a valuation function in the theory of species for terms $\mathfrak{t}(\boldsymbol{x})$. (All species needed here are explicitly defined. I do not know if **[32]** can be extended to include axioms of choice.)

(ii) follows from (i) together with suitable refinement of work presented in the lecture by Prawitz **[32]** (or Scarpellini **[33]**, whose exposition was however less clear). It is sufficient to formalize the proof of cut elimination (in the sense of Prawitz **[32]**) for systems $\mathscr{S}_n$. Given a derivation of $\forall x \exists y \mathfrak{A}(x, y)$ in $\mathscr{S}_n$ we get derivations in second order logic of

$$\mathfrak{Z}(s, 0) \to \exists y \mathfrak{A}_1(s^m 0, y), \quad m = 0, 1, 2, \ldots,$$

where $\mathfrak{Z}(s, 0)$ is the usual first order axiom for zero and successor, and $\mathfrak{A}_1$

is got from $\mathfrak{A}$ by letting the variables for individuals range over the least species closed under successor. Cut elimination provides, uniformly in n, terms t_n, built up from 0 and s (and possibly variables). Since the reflection principle for $\mathscr{S}_n$ can certainly be proved in $\mathscr{S}$, and since we have an enumeration of t_n primitive recursive in the function which maps proofs of $\mathscr{S}_n$ with cuts into cut free proofs, we get a proof of $\forall x\mathfrak{A}(x, \{e\}(x))$ in $\mathscr{S}$ for suitable $\boldsymbol{e}$.

It remains to note that for finite subsystems of second order logic that is restricted to comprehension axioms of limited logical complexity, Prawitz' proof can be carried out in classical analysis itself. But the statement of cut elimination is of the form $\forall x\exists y\mathfrak{A}(x, y)$ with primitive recursive $\mathfrak{A}$, and so we can apply (i).

It may be observed that a completely analogous argument solves questions 1, 2, 3(ii) on p. 350 of [**44**] positively, and establishes for *classical* analysis the finitist equivalence of cut elimination and 1-consistency of analysis; that is, if ψ maps proofs with cuts into corresponding cut free ones, some σ maps proofs n of $\exists x\mathfrak{A}x$ for primitive recursive $\mathfrak{A}$ into numerical realizations σn of $\mathfrak{A}x$, such that this σ is primitive recursive in ψ, and conversely.

REMARK. There is an amusing parallel between the formally quite different work of Prawitz [**32**] and Scarpellini [**33**]. Both start with a theorem first proved for classical logic and, in the classical context, of very limited use. Prawitz takes cut elimination in the sense of Takeuti, in which the most important properties of usual cut elimination (such as the subformula property) are lacking. Scarpellini takes Gentzen's second consistency proof which, as it stands, merely provides a reduction procedure for derivations of purely numerical formulae. (The existence of *some* reduction procedure is an immediate consequence of consistency, and so the interest of Gentzen's result depends sensitively on the particular reduction and the particular principles used for establishing the termination of the reduction procedure.) In contrast, when applied to a wide class of formal systems based on the rules of Heyting's predicate calculus, the ideas used in the two 'unemployed' proofs mentioned above, establish closure under Church's rule. The rule is genuinely problematic. First, even if the theory of species is seen to be constructive, Church's thesis is certainly not evident (cf. problem 6). Second since the systems are of course incomplete, even if (for the intended interpretation) Church's thesis holds, i.e. formal derivability in $\mathscr{S}$ of $\forall x\exists y\mathfrak{A}(x, y)$

implies the validity of $\exists e \forall x \exists z[T(e, x, z) \wedge \mathfrak{A}(x, U(z))]$, there is no guarantee that the latter can be derived in $\mathcal{S}$ itself (cf. also problem 5).

III. Scott's model [36] and the theory of lawless sequences. (The present Note is not essential to the main topic of this paper; a mild connection with Church's thesis will come up at the end of this Note.) The model, found by Scott some time ago, is natuıally interpreted in terms of the theory of lawless sequences of natural numbers and constructive functions, more precisely, of constructive functions of finite type over the natural numbers (that is, § 1 of [**24**] extended conservatively to finite types, as in [**5**]). The interpretation follows the lines of [**18**] where lawless sequences were first used to extract intuitionistically meaningful results from work on the topological interpretation. From the present point of view Scott's [**36**] provides, to date, by far the most advanced development of any theory of derivatives of lawless sequences, also called 'compounds' ([**24**], p. 244) or 'projections' (by van Dalen and Troelstra [**39**]); cf. Note IV for some general remarks on such derivatives. We now consider Scott's model.

Basic definition. A *real number* (generator) is a pair (a, α) (c.f. [**24**], p. 244, 4.1) where the functions a considered are obtained by composing an arbitrary continuous function (element of K) with a projection into the usual spread σ of convergent sequences of rationals, and so a is a continuous (constructive) function with arguments in N^N and values in σ.

In other words, freely chosen real numbers are regarded as 'projections' of some lawless sequence α by means of a.

With every formula in Scott's language of real numbers [**36**] is associated a formula of [**24**]; and with any formula in the language of functions of real numbers is associated a formula in the language of [**24**] but (as mentioned above) extended by variables for constructive functions of higher type as follows.

Instead of associating an open set $\subset N^N$ with a prime formula $x < y$, one takes the proposition, with parameter α,

$$\exists n \exists m \forall p > m[(a, \alpha)(p) + n^{-1} < (b, \alpha)(p)], \qquad (*)$$

where a and b are associated to the variables x and y respectively, $(a, \alpha)(m)$ being the mth (rational) element of the path in the spread σ defined by (a, α). Note that we use just one parameter α throughout (in contrast to the derivates of [**24**] or the projections of van Dalen and Troelstra [**39**]).

It is then a *theorem* of the theory of lawless sequences that, for given

a and b, the species of α satisfying (*) is the open set $[\![x < y]\!] \subset N^N$, and, for logically compound formulae $\mathfrak{A}$, if $\mathfrak{A}'$ is the formula associated with $\mathfrak{A}$,

$$\{\alpha: \mathfrak{A}'\} = [\![\mathfrak{A}]\!],$$

provided the quantifiers $\forall x$ and $\exists x$ are replaced by $\forall a$ and $\exists a$ respectively.

Finally, if $\mathfrak{A}$ is closed, truth of $\mathfrak{A}$ in Scott's model is formally equivalent to $\forall\alpha\mathfrak{A}'$.

Similarly, for formulae containing variables for functions for real numbers, the application operation is defined in the natural way, and the functions, that is mappings of continuous functions a (in the basic definition) into such a, satisfy the formal axioms of extensionality and comprehension formulated by Scott **[36]**.

Main result. By the elimination of variables for lawless sequences **[24]**, the basic theorems of Scott's paper (such as Kripke's schema or Brouwer's continuity theorem for extensional functions defined on a closed interval of the continuum) *are equivalent to assertions in the language of constructive functions* (and functionals of lowest type).

What is still open is, whether the latter assertions are constructively valid; Scott promises to analyze this matter. But even as it stands his work establishes the consistency of a formal theory of choice sequences including Kripke's schema (cf. the chart in Note IV) for which previously there was no wholly convincing proof. The consistency follows from the fact that the assertions involved (in the language of constructive functions of finite type) are theorems of classical analysis.

It should of course not be assumed that the proofs in Scott's paper **[36]**, as it stands, are all constructive. Further one would expect that essentially different assumptions about constructive functions will be needed to establish (the assertions equivalent to) Brouwer's theorem and Kripke's schemata (in weak or strong form of § 4). The latter is of course of special interest here because it conflicts with Church's thesis.

REMARK. Scott **[36]** points out that he had thought of his model some time ago but did not pursue it until encouraged by experience with boolean valued models (though he does not use any technical results about such models). It should be added that another, perhaps more objective, obstacle had been overcome in the mean time. Until Myhill's critique (cf. **[23]**, p. 173, elaborated in **[31]**) the axiom of choice, for continuous f, was taken in the form

$$\forall x \exists y \mathfrak{A}(x, y) \rightarrow \exists f \forall x \mathfrak{A}(x, fx)$$

without requiring uniqueness on y; see e.g. **[16]** or **[21]**, p. 135, 2.511. (Incidentally this was done despite the fact (**[21]** p. 133 top) that this form fails in the model consisting of what I myself called 'continuous functionals' in **[17]**, cf. also the discussion in Note IV.) The unrestricted form fails in Scott's model **[36]**. To regard the model as anything beyond a formal exercise it was necessary to give an informal analysis of the intended notion of choice sequence to show that the form above not only fails in the model, but fails for the intended notion. The existence of a *continuous* f can be asserted only if y depends extensionally on x, and one (simple) way of ensuring this is to strengthen the hypothesis to $\forall x \exists ! y \mathfrak{A}(x, y)$, when the axiom holds in Scott's model. (Only in the special case of lawless sequences is extensional dependence automatic, cf. **[24]**, p. 238.)

Correction. Though I myself have not had doubts about the legitimacy of the notion of lawless sequences (**[18]**, p. 378, l. 10–12), as recently as January 1964, when I gave the lecture **[21]** (p. 142, bottom), I questioned their usefulness.

IV. Notions of choice sequence and their formal theories. The purpose of this Note is to expand a side remark in § 4(b) by describing (my views on) the role of choice sequences in constructive mathematics.

Contrary to popular first impressions, a little reflection shows that we have a reasonably clear notion of choice sequence; more precisely (as so often, cf. the notion of set in **[27]**, pp. 171–173) we have a crude mixture of notions which have to be separated by distinctions. Further it appears (again as so often) that there are relatively few basic ingredients of the mixture from which the rest can be defined. Several papers in the present Proceedings set out, axiomatically, properties of such basic notions. Personally I believe that the notion of choice sequence is of particular interest in formulating geometric conceptions within constructive mathematics (**[24]**, pp. 246–247, though I have not been able to develop this idea). This last remark suggests the following point of view:

Granted that we understand such notions of choice sequence, we may ask whether they are reducible to notions used more widely in constructive mathematics. This would be the analogue to reducing the (geometric) continuum to set theory, in the sense that (i) it is the only structure satisfying Dedekind's axioms and (ii) there are set theoretically defined structures which satisfy these axioms too. In other words we have sufficient properties of the continuum to characterize it uniquely up to isomorphism (or, equivalently, characterize it as far as any extensional statements about it are concerned). Correspondingly, in the intuitionistic case, as soon as the notion of abstract construction was proposed as an analogue (for constructive mathematics) to the notion of set in usual set theoretic foundations, one of the first questions to consider ([**20**], p. 208, footnote 11) was the reduction of choice sequences, since the latter are not constructions. Only 'reduction' may here have to be understood in a somewhat weaker sense (with respect to statements in a specified language only). The so-called elimination theorems provide precisely this kind of reduction. (Not surprisingly they also have formal applications, in establishing the proof theoretic strengths of systems for choice sequences.)

We now list the principal formal systems with a kind of running commentary.

Formal relations between theories of choice sequences.

$\boldsymbol{H}_1$: elementary analysis [**12**].

$\boldsymbol{H}'$: an isomorphic copy of $\boldsymbol{H}_1$ but without (even) the axioms asserting the existence of pairing functions or closure under primitive recursion; thus $\boldsymbol{H}'$ is satisfied by lawless sequences.

$\boldsymbol{H}_1'$: includes both $\boldsymbol{H}_1$ and $\boldsymbol{H}'$, but also countable axioms of choice $\forall n\exists m$, $\forall n\exists x$.

$\boldsymbol{B}$: theory of constructive functions and Brouwer operations ([**24**], § 1); ($\boldsymbol{B}$ is sometimes called: IDK.)

$\boldsymbol{L}$: theory of lawless sequences, [**24**], § 2.

Kinds of choice sequences

$\boldsymbol{\Sigma}$: closure of choice sequences under mappings of spreads into spreads (cf. [**21**], p. 135, and [**24**] p. 243, footnote 9)

$\boldsymbol{\Gamma}$: closure of choice sequences under arbitrary continuous mappings [**38**]. These two conditions hold respectively when a choice sequence is given

(i). by a spread

and

(ii). as the image of a continuous mapping.

The corresponding further axioms are

$\boldsymbol{S}$: a property of a sequence holds in some spread to which the sequence belongs ([**21**], p. 135).

$\boldsymbol{C}$: a property of a sequence holds for the whole range of some continuous operation (which range contains the given sequence), [**38**].

Closure conditions on choice sequences

$\forall\exists!$: obtained from H_1 by adding the assertion that there exists a continuous 'choice' function if $\mathfrak{A}(\alpha, x)$ is extensional and $\forall\alpha\exists!x\mathfrak{A}(\alpha, x)$.

BI!: bar induction with uniqueness in the premise or, equivalently (cf. [**24**], p. 233, bottom), decidability of the set of secured sequences. This last condition was mentioned in Brouwer's statement of the bar theorem [**3**], but not explicitly used in his own arguments. In fairness to Brouwer it should be said that, in his statement, he did not use the quantifier combination $\forall\alpha\exists x$ but spoke of functions (on choice sequences). But the time honoured condition on a functional relation $\mathfrak{A}$ requires uniqueness $\forall\alpha\exists!x$ and so, as mentioned already, decidability of $\mathfrak{A}$. See also note 40 of [**26**].

$\forall\exists$: corresponding to $\forall\exists!$, but without uniqueness (and $\forall\exists_\sigma$ when adjoined to ***S***).

BI: corresponding to ***BI***! without uniqueness.

Discussion of ***BI*** *and* $\forall\exists$, which (in contrast to ***BI***! and $\forall\exists!$) are not immediately evident and in general not true for many of the clearly analyzed notions of choice sequence: Historically they were almost certainly introduced as the result of an oversight, ignoring (cf. Note III) (i) that obviously only extensional functions could be expected to be continuous and (ii) that, even if $\mathfrak{A}(x, y)$ is extensional and $\forall x\exists y\mathfrak{A}(x, y)$ is valid, there is not necessarily a continuous $f\colon x \mapsto y$ such that $\forall x\mathfrak{A}(x, fx)$.

Illustration (by analogy): Let $\bar{x} = \langle \bar{x}_1, \bar{x}_2 \rangle$, $\bar{y} = \langle \bar{y}_1, \bar{y}_2 \rangle$ range over pairs of r.e. sets. Let $\mathfrak{A}(\bar{x}, \bar{y})$ express

$$\bar{x}_1 \cup \bar{x}_2 = \bar{y}_1 \cup \bar{y}_2;\ \bar{y}_1 \subset \bar{x}_1,\ \bar{y}_2 \subset \bar{x}_2;\ \bar{y}_1 \cap \bar{y}_2 = \emptyset.$$

Then, by Rosser's trick there is a recursive function f from (pairs of) Gödel numbers x of $\bar{x}$ to Gödel numbers y, but no effective (extensional) operation, i.e. no recursive f such that if

$$\bar{x}_1 = \bar{x}_1',\ \bar{x}_2 = \bar{x}_2' \quad \text{then} \quad (\overline{fx})_1 = (\overline{fx'})_1 \quad \text{and} \quad (\overline{fx})_2 = (\overline{fx'})_2.$$

Since in general two wrongs don't make a right, ***BI*** and $\forall\exists$ do not become interesting by simply adding (heavy formal work) to the original oversight that led to their choice. But the systems may have interest for two quite independent reasons. Philosophically, since Troelstra [**38**] has at least made plausible that, under certain restrictions on the possibility of communicating rules, ***BI*** and $\forall\exists$ may be valid after all. Proof theoretically, because the systems considered (and even Kleene's subsystems [**15**] excluding

C) are closed under Church's rule, and so, whatever their interpretation, they may be useful examples in connection with problem 5.

Correction. In my joint paper with Howard **[12]** the significant difference between $\forall\exists$ and $\forall\exists!$ is overlooked. By a fluke the results are not meaningless because only numerical existential quantifiers $\forall f \exists n \mathfrak{A}(f, n)$ occur and the distinction between decidable and undecidable $\mathfrak{A}$ *is* made: by the above this happens to be equivalent to the distinction between $\forall\exists$ and $\forall\exists!$.

All the systems below (except suitable strong forms of Kripke's schema ***KS***) are interpretable in ***B***; in particular all statements in the language of ***B*** which are derivable in any of the systems are also theorems of ***B***.

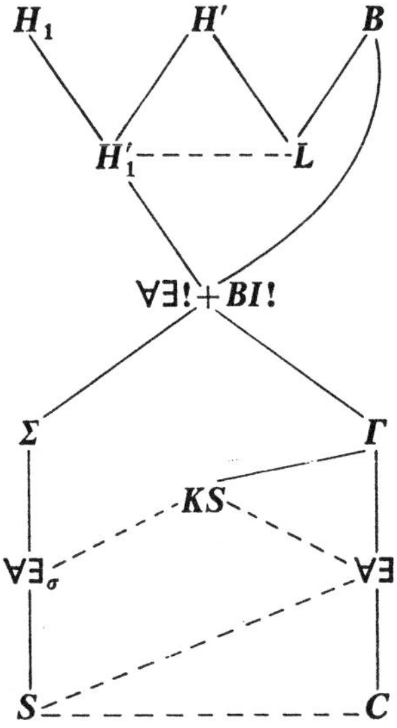

Legend. If a system $\mathscr{S}$ is below $\mathscr{S}'$ and joined to $\mathscr{S}'$ then $\mathscr{S}$ includes $\mathscr{S}'$. A broken line indicates mutual inconsistency (inconsistency of ***S*** and ***C***, by **[38]**, is only known on the basis of certain additional axioms for constructive functions, e.g. Church's thesis).

NOTES

1. More precisely, (i) and (ii) are not exactly parallel. Membership and classical logic are kept fixed in (i), and so relativization to L determines unambiguously the meaning of formulae in the language of set theory. But in (ii), not only the notion of constructive number theoretic function is restricted, but the meaning of the logical particles is altered

somewhat arbitrarily. Specifically, even if one considers the identification 'constructive = recursive', and $R(e, \alpha)$ stands for 'e realizes α', it is arbitrary to put $R(e', \alpha \to \beta) = \forall e[R(e, \alpha) \to R(\{e'\}(e), \beta)]$, that is to interpret $\exists e R(e, \alpha) \to \exists e' R(e', \beta)$ by $\exists e' \forall e[R(e, \alpha) \to R(\{e'\}(e), \beta)]$, unless $R(e, \alpha)$ is assumed to be decidable. The value of e' need not only depend on e, but also on the proof of $R(e, \alpha)$. To make the parallel complete one has to use an abstract theory of constructions as e.g. in Goodman's **[8]** in place of Heyting's arithmetic. Then all prima facie higher type objects are required to be coded by natural numbers, and all functions are taken to be recursive. (This 'reduction' to numbers is essential when Church's thesis is regarded as a reducibility axiom.)

2. Historically the choice of name (e.g. **[10]**, p. 190) is perhaps dubious. Turing's assertion was only that all mechanically realizable functions are recursive. Here we have the *additional* assertion that all instructions defined in terms of constructive notions are mechanically realizable. But historically it is equally dubious whether the distinction was recognized when Church formulated his thesis. Since in the twenties and early thirties the abstract character of intuitionistic concepts was not realized, the concepts finitist and intuitionistic were often identified (e.g. von Neumann **[40]**, p. 7, 1.19 or Herbrand **[9]**, p. 210 and the (somewhat modified) footnote 3 on p. 225), and so probably constructive and mechanical, i.e. formal, rules would have been identified too.

Digression. Besides the two notions of mechanical and constructive rules we have the notion of physically realizable (number theoretic) function, that is realizable according to current physical theory (cf. **[21]**, p. 144, elaborated in **[22]**, § **4**). It seems to be open whether there are (finitely specified) physical systems whose most probable behavior is non-recursive, in the sense that printing the course of values of a (recursive) function, programmed on a computer, is the 'most probable' behaviour of the latter (regarded as a physical system). The theory of partial differential equations gives a negative answer for a general class of systems in classical mechanics. This result is not trivial since we are dealing with the mechanics of continua and Turing machines are discrete mechanisms. For quantum physics our question above seems to be open. It may be remarked (for an earlier discussion see **[29]**) that the celebrated three body problem suggests a more specific question. Given three neighborhoods U_1, U_2, U_3 in phase space (the mass of particles being included) and an integer n can we always determine recursively neighborhoods V_1, V_2, V_3 with the following properties: either $V_i \subset U_i$ $(i = 1, 2, 3)$ and with initial conditions in V_1, V_2, V_3 there is no collision up to time $t—n^{-1}$, or the differences $V_i - U_i$ $(i = 1, 2, 3)$ are $< n^{-1}$ and for some positions in V_1, V_2, V_3 there is a collision before $t+n^{-1}$? As far as I know this problem is open. It would be of interest to examine whether, in case of a negative solution, one could use this situation for an analog computation of a non-recursive function (by repeating collision experiments sufficiently often).

3. Though some understanding of this notion and of the history of its analysis certainly helps in thinking about the theory of species of, say, natural numbers in § **5**. Note however this difference between our understanding of abstract sets and abstract constructions: while possibly our formal theories of constructions are approaching the standard reached in **[41]**, our understanding of their meaning is far short of the analysis of the cumulative hierarchy in **[42]**.

4. So to speak: on a priori grounds. Granted there are ideas which some people thought unambiguous and which on analysis turned out to need distinctions. Why shouldn't there

be other ideas which (perhaps for doctrinaire reasons) people think vague, but which on reflection turn out not to be so? If the man in the street is shown examples of convexity, they strike him as indicating a vague concept, certainly not as one definable in familiar geometric terms. Another (highly relevant) example that is often overlooked (but cf. **[21]**, footnote 14 on p. 122) concerns the identity of proofs; in arguments about priority mathematicians discuss, in patently objective terms, whether two proofs are essentially identical.

5. There are significant variants according to whether $\exists x\mathfrak{A}$ can only be inferred from $\mathfrak{A}(\mathrm{t})$ for some term t, or also from $\mathfrak{A}(\mathrm{t}) \vee \exists x\mathfrak{A}$. For instance, in the latter case one can use primitive recursive proof figures, in the former not generally. *Correction.* In **[21]**, p. 165, 3.3321 the interest of this difference was not properly considered.

6. Problem 2 is strictly formal only for the case of extensional equality, because of the abstract character of the concept of definitional equality between rules, say $[\mathrm{t}]$, denoted by terms t (of some formal system). The intended rule will in general involve a specific but not necessarily mechanical reduction procedure. Evidently a (syntactic) relation $\equiv$ between terms may satisfy given axioms without satisfying

$$\forall \mathrm{t}_1 \forall \mathrm{t}_2 (\mathrm{t}_1 \equiv \mathrm{t}_2 \leftrightarrow [\mathrm{t}_1] = [\mathrm{t}_2]).$$

It seems plausible that some relations $\equiv$ in the literature (cf. e.g. Howard's lecture **[11]**) do correspond to the intended $\{(\mathrm{t}_1, \mathrm{t}_2) : [\mathrm{t}_1] = [\mathrm{t}_2]\}$, though no argument is given. (It seems to me perfectly coherent to reject the notion of definitional equality as simply not being necessary for existing mathematical practice. But something close to the sin of ultimate despair is involved in both rejecting the notion and going through the labour of working out the formal theory of $\equiv$).

7. The evident facts used, though not listed explicitly loc. cit., are:

(i). the intended meaning of completeness, p. 139 (1);

(ii). any species satisfying the axioms $\mathfrak{Z}$ (for the fragment of arithmetic) (pp. 142–143) contains a subspecies (constructively) isomorphic to the natural numbers,

(iii). for species X of natural numbers and constructive number theoretic functions f

$$\forall X[\forall n(X(n) \vee \neg X(n)) \rightarrow \exists f \forall n(f(n) = 0 \leftrightarrow X(n)].$$

(iv). the principle of dependent choices in the form: for species D ('D' for domain) and P of one and two arguments respectively, and functions f with numerical arguments

$$\forall x(Dx \rightarrow \exists y[Dy \wedge P(x, y)]) \rightarrow \forall z(Dz \rightarrow \exists f \forall n[f0 = z \wedge D(fn) \wedge P(fn, fn^+)]).$$

In short, the *connection* between Church's thesis and the notion of constructive validity (though ipso facto not this notion itself) is insensitive to the exact meaning of the basic constructive notions; cf. e.g. **[22]**, p. 254 concerning first order validity in the classical case (which requires 'little' about the notion of set except of course that infinite sets are included).

8. Let us not forget our theme of comparing Church's thesis to $V = L$. Consider the converse: what corresponds to Church's rule in the case of $V = L$? In general, from a proof of $\exists X\mathfrak{A}(X)$ we cannot infer the existence of a constructible X_c say, such that $\mathfrak{A}(X_c)$; we have to restrict $\mathfrak{A}$ to be invariant (for extensions over the constructibles). Using note 1 on p. 142, compare (i) some X_c satisfies $\mathfrak{A}$ *in L* with (ii) the comment to problem 3 on p. 126.

9. The main purpose of the consistency results is to help avoid fruitless lines of research, since our principal interest is the refutation of Church's thesis (as formulated here). Note that consistency results exclude even a 'weak' refutation in the sense of showing the absurdity of a proof, not only a 'strong' one in the sense of exhibiting a counterexample of the kind considered in § 1.

Correction. In contrast to § 1, and despite its title, Kalmar's **[13]** contains no trace of any uniform, mechanical or non-mechanical, procedure which might conflict with Church's thesis (in any of the senses of note 2, p. 143). Note also that **[13]** explicitly insists on using classical logic; a 'conflict' must be established by a counterinstance, and so even the assumptions about the thinking subject which, by Kripke (cf. note 10 below), establish the absurdity of proving Church's thesis, are not enough for Kalmar's purpose. It may fairly be said that **[13]** does not provide a framework within which one might even *begin* to refute Church's thesis.

10. Since Kripke's result is (correctly) attributed to him, but his argument does not seem to be in print, here is a proof of the result. We only need a specific X, say Kleene's $\forall y \neg T(n, n, y)$, X_0 for short. Kleene shows that X_0 is not r.e.. Let us suppose the argument uses the principles of classical first order arithmetic. Writing $\mathfrak{A}(e, m, n)$ for

$$\exists q[T(e, m, q) \wedge U(q) = n],$$

we observe that both $\exists m\mathfrak{A}(e, m, n) \rightarrow X_0(n)$ and $\neg \exists m\mathfrak{A}(e, m, n)$ are (equivalent to) formulae in the fragment $(\neg, \wedge, \rightarrow, \forall)$. Now Kleene shows for variable e

$$\forall m \neg\neg \exists q T(e, m, q) \rightarrow \neg \forall n([\exists m\mathfrak{A}(e, m, n) \rightarrow X_0(n)] \wedge [\neg \exists m\mathfrak{A}(e, m, n) \rightarrow \neg X_0(n)]).$$

Since X_0 (and hence $\neg X_0$) are also in the fragment above, we have a proof in intuitionistic first order arithmetic of Kleene's result, and a fortiori one with the stronger premise $\forall m \exists q T(e, m, q)$.

But this patently contradicts Church's axiom under the assumption (KS^-).

11. *Correction.* I shall refer principally to these formulations and not to my earlier **[20]**. It is true that **[20]** gives a good explicit analysis of the meanings of proposition and species (pp. 201–202), correctly stresses the need for total functions (p. 206, 1–17) in a genuine analysis of implication, and generally gives the primitive notions (p. 205) in terms of which Heyting's explanation of the logical operations can be built up. But the details of the formal language in **[20]** simply do not correspond to the intentions stated. For example, the use of λ-notation and a large number of specific function constants (p. 203, 1.3) side by side is absurd since the point of λ-notation is to define specific functions. But to do this smoothly, the functions have to be partial. Consistency was ensured by a bunch of restrictions, which are bad on two counts. Some merely nullify the familiar use of λ-notation (which ought never to have been introduced at all), others (e.g. p. 204, l. 20) which do have a sensible meaning (for instance, p. 204, l. 20, which applies to notions of proof discussed in my other lecture, where only closure conditions on proofs can be given since the totality of proofs considered is not assumed to be grasped) are not explained.

There is an additional distinction which has so far not been formally necessary, but which is probably important, for example in the explanation of implication (or universal quantification). When we think of the pair (p_1, p_2)

p_1 proves the identity: for variable p, if p proves A then $p_2(p)$ proves B,

p_2 is a genuine function or operation, while p_1 recognizes that p_2 satisfies the condition stated; thus p_1 is a judgement. But similarly, since in general both the arguments p and the values $p_2(p)$ of p_2 are such pairs, say $p = (p', p'')$ and $p_2(p) = (p_2', p_2'')$, should the function p_2'' depend both on p'' and on p' (or only on p'')? It is perhaps significant that in Gödel's interpretation [5] of $\mathfrak{A} \to \exists s \mathfrak{B}$ for purely universal $\mathfrak{A}$ and $\mathfrak{B}$, we have $\exists s(\mathfrak{A} \to \mathfrak{B})$, that is the function s does not depend on the (hypothetical) proof of $\mathfrak{A}$. (It is not unusual that conceptually basic components of a notion are not distinguished in a formal theory; cf. the type or rank of a set in set theory.)

12. It is trivially simple minded to transfer thoughtlessly set theoretic notions to constructive mathematics. But it is equally simple minded to dismiss thoughtful attempts in this direction as 'mere analogies' for the following theoretical reason: Most mathematicians do not have a clear conception of the nature of the objects they are talking about. So if some notion or distinction has a very wide immediate appeal, the chances are that it has a meaning for different conceptions of mathematics. Evidently two provisoes follow: (i) the transfer can be expected to be valid, say in the case of a familiar set theoretic notion, only if the latter is defined in the natural (not in some other, classically, equivalent) way (ii) the notion presents itself naively in mathematics, and does not have an explicit foundational purpose.

13. It should be noted that Goodman's axioms are valid for the very abstract notions of proof and construction here considered, although his own intended notion ('semantics') concerns particularly elementary and explicitly described manipulations.

14. By now the reader will be able to pursue our theme for himself (if he wishes to do so), that is to state the analogue in set theory for $V = L$ corresponding to problems on Church's thesis. Actually, several passages in **[21]** have been intentionally set out to have an obvious analogue for the theme considered, for example, pp. 105–106, 1.52, 1.53, 1.533.

15. To avoid a very common misunderstanding a distinction has to be made which in turn is very much in need of precise analysis. What is 'necessary' for practice?

(a). There is clearly a certain combinatorial element in mathematical reasoning, which is intuitively best reflected by stating implications $\mathfrak{A} \to \mathfrak{B}$ using only the most elementary logical principles even if $\mathfrak{A}$ can be seen to be valid. As people put it, all the 'hard work' or (when we eliminate logical symbols altogether in favour of functions; cf. Bishop's lecture **[2]**) the numerical content may reside in the construction leading from $\mathfrak{A}$ to $\mathfrak{B}$; the nature of the verification of $\mathfrak{A}$ is often quite different. As far as classical mathematics is concerned instead of taking ZF as 'framework', one could stay within predicate logic, and as far as constructive mathematics goes, some quantifier-free theory like Gödel's T **[5]** (perhaps even without induction) is an immediate candidate. Naturally if one takes the (psychological) analysis of 'hard work' seriously the choice of framework is the central issue because it expresses one's view of the nature of the 'hard' part of mathematical activity.

(b). Besides the question of discovering unconditional assertions $\mathfrak{B}$ there is also the problem of making the choice of notions intelligible. It is one thing to point out (correctly), as Bishop does, that Brouwer's assertion concerning the continuity of (extensional) functions does not really affect mathematical practice, in sense (a), if we simply take our functions as given *together* with a modulus of continuity. But it is a separate matter to explain this step by showing that any definition satisfying some abstract condition is bound to provide the additional information; in other words by analyzing (when possible) the most general notion of construction, not merely definitions in some formal system such as Gödel's T [**5**]. Abstract intuitionistic mathematics is concerned with this kind of problem, which of course is not touched in (a) above.

16. As a result of correspondence with Professor Scott it seems desirable to add some comments.

(a). Our results hold for both interpretations (i) and (i′) of validity on p. 139 of [**19**]; the crucial direction in the equivalence is the derivation of '$\neg\neg\mathfrak{F}_T$ is valid'.

(b). Since the domain of the variables (in $\mathfrak{F}_T$) is arbitrary and not a 'detachable' subspecies, the desired result, even in case (*i′*), does not follow directly from early work on consistent formulae with no recursive models (e.g. in footnote 5 on p. 384 of [**18**]), because the domain of these models is assumed to be recursive.

(c). The formula $\mathfrak{U}$ above corresponds in an obvious way to the formula (7) on p. 144 of [**19**]. The delicate case to consider occurs if the species depend on freely chosen objects, say p, as parameters and the elements of D^* are such objects. Q^* corresponds to a path through T. We have, of course, a constructive sequence of operations a_0^*, a_1^*, .. with a_0^*p, a_1^*p, . . . the 'natural numbers' of D^*.

Evidently some properties of (operations on) freely chosen objects have to be used in our deduction. What we need essentially is that $\forall p \neg(\mathfrak{U}^* \wedge \mathfrak{U}_1^*)$ should follow from the corresponding result with p replaced by constructive objects, such as the theorem (for the choice sequences treated in [**21**], p. 136, line 1 or 2, .524 or [**38**]): $(\forall a \neg Aa) \rightarrow (\forall \alpha \neg A\alpha)$ for constructive number theoretic functions a and choice sequences α. The reader who has another notion of choice sequence (and hence of validity) in mind should concentrate on the conjunct

$$\forall n \exists ! m([m = 0 \wedge \mathfrak{Q}^*(a_n^* p)] \vee [m \neq 0 \wedge \neg\, \mathfrak{Q}^*(a_n^* p)])$$

corresponding to $(x)[\mathfrak{Q}(x) \vee \neg\, \mathfrak{Q}(x)]$ in (7) on p. 144 of [**19**]. If, for each n, m depends only on a neighborhood of p, the possible paths corresponding to different p can be constructively enumerated. Hence the assumption that all constructive paths through T are not infinite gives the required conclusion.

POSTSCRIPT

(*to problem 6 and Technical Note II*)

The consistency of Church's schema has now been verified by extending Kleene's original recursive realizability interpretation to the theory of species ([**43**], 3.7.3; further work needed for conservative extension results is analyzed in [**43**], 3.8. Closure under Church's rule can probably be obtained by modifying [**43**], 3.7.3 using Kleene's ($\vdash$ realizability) [**15**], and thus improving Technical Note II). As a result of correspondence with Dr. Troelstra I can now formulate my original doubts about the consistency.

We know of course that the addition of axioms for species to an elementary theory of constructive functions is non-conservative (with respect to the language of the latter); new sets of equations can be proved to define (total) functions. To show that species have 'nothing to do' with functions, we should have to have a set F of evident axioms for functions, such that the addition of the usual axioms for species is conservative. But the nearest approximation to such an F is Kripke's schema in § 4(c) which implies of course that every species is constructively enumerable. But F *is* inconsistent with Church's schema.

REFERENCES

[1] E. Bishop, *Foundations of constructive analysis*, New York (1967).

[2] E. Bishop, Mathematics as a numerical language, these proceedings, 53–71.

[3] L. E. J. Brouwer, Über Definitionsbereiche von Funktionen, *Math. Ann.* **97** (1927) 60–76.

[4] K. Gödel, Russell's mathematical logic, in *The philosophy of Bertrand Russell*, ed. Schilpp, Chicago (1944) 123–153.

[5] K. Gödel, Über eine bisher noch nicht benützte Erweiterung des finiten Standpunktes, *Dialectica* **12** (1958) 280–287.

[6] K. Gödel, What is Cantor's continuum problem? in *Philosophy of mathematics*, ed. Benaceraff and Putnam, Englewood Cliffs (1964) 258–273.

[7] K. Gödel, Remarks before the Princeton bicentennial conference on problems in mathematics, in *The undecidable*, ed. Davis, New York (1964) 84–88.

[8] N. Goodman, A theory of constructions equivalent to arithmetic, these proceedings, 101–120.

[9] J. Herbrand, in *Ecrits logiques*, ed. van Heijenoort, Paris (1968).

[10] A. Heyting, Infinitistic methods from a finitist point of view, in *Infinitistic methods*, Warsaw (1961) 185–192.

[11] W. A. Howard, Assignment of ordinals to terms for primitive recursive functionals of finite type, these proceedings, 443–458.

[12] W. A. Howard and G. Kreisel, Transfinite induction and bar induction of types zero and one, and the role of continuity in intuitionistic analysis, *J. Symb. Logic* **31** (1966) 325–358.

[13] L. Kalmar, An argument against the plausibility of Church's thesis, in *Constructivity in mathematics*, ed. Heyting, Amsterdam (1959) 72–80.

[14] S. C. Kleene, *Introduction to metamathematics*, Princeton (1952).

[15] S. C. Kleene, Formalized recursive functionals and formalized realizability, *Memoirs Am. Math. Soc.* **89** (1969).

[16] S. C. Kleene and R. E. Vesley, *Foundations of intuitionistic mathematics*, Amsterdam (1965).

[17] G. Kreisel, Interpretation of classical analysis by means of constructive functionals of finite type, in *Constructivity in mathematics*, ed. Heyting, Amsterdam (1959) 101–128.

[18] G. KREISEL, A remark on free choice sequences and the topological completeness proofs, *J. Symb. Logic* **23** (1958) 369–387.
[19] G. KREISEL, On weak completeness of intuitionistic predicate logic, *J. Symb. Logic* **27** (1962) 139–158.
[20] G. KREISEL, Foundations of intuitionistic logic, in *Proc. intern. congress logic, methodology and philosophy of science*, 1960, Stanford (1962) 198–210.
[21] G. KREISEL, Mathematical Logic, in *Lectures on modern mathematics, vol. III*, ed. Saaty (1965) 95–195.
[22] G. KREISEL, Mathematical logic: What has it done for the philosophy of mathematics? in *Bertrand Russell: Philosopher of the century*, London (1966) 201–272.
[23] G. KREISEL, Informal rigour and completeness proofs, in *Problems in the philosophy of mathematics*, ed. Lakatos, Amsterdam (1967) 138–171.
[24] G. KREISEL, Lawless sequences of natural numbers, *Compositio* **20** (1968) 222–248.
[25] G. KREISEL, Functions, ordinals, species, in *Logic, methodology and philosophy of science III*, Amsterdam (1968) 145–159.
[26] G. KREISEL, Principles of proof and ordinals implicit in given concepts, these proceedings, 489–516.
[27] G. KREISEL and J. L. KRIVINE, *Elements of mathematical logic*, Amsterdam (1967).
[28] A. H. KRUSE, Some notions of random sequence and their set theoretic foundations, *Z. math. Logik u. Grundl. Math.* **13** (1967) 299–322.
[29] R. M. MONTAGUE, Deterministic theories, in *Decision, values and groups*, ed. Washburne, New York (1962) 325–370.
[30] A. MOSTOWSKI, On recursive models of formalized arithmetic, *Bull. Acad. Polon. Sci.* **5** (1957) 705–710.
[31] J. MYHILL, Notes towards an axiomatization of intuitionistic analysis, *Logique et analyse* **35** (1967) 260–297.
[32] D. PRAWITZ, Some results for intuitionistic logic with second order quantifier rules, these proceedings, 259–269.
[33] B. SCARPELLINI, On cut elimination in intuitionistic systems of analysis, these proceedings, 271–285
[34] K. SCHÜTTE, *Beweistheorie*, Berlin (1960).
[35] D. SCOTT, Measurable cardinals and constructible sets, *Bull. Acad. Polon. Sci.* **9** (1961) 521–524.
[36] D. SCOTT, Extending the topological interpretation to intuitionistic analysis II, these proceedings, pp. 235–255.
[37] C. SPECTOR, Provably recursive functionals of analysis: a consistency proof of analysis by an extension of principles formulated in current intuitionistic mathematics, *Proc. Symp. Pure Math.* **5** (1962) 1–27.
[38] A. S. TROELSTRA, The theory of choice sequences, in *Logic, methodology and philosophy of science III*, Amsterdam (1968) 201–223.
[39] D. VAN DALEN and A. S. TROELSTRA, Projections of lawless sequences, these proceedings, pp. 163–186.
[40] J. VON NEUMAN, Zur Hilbertschen Beweistheorie, *Math. Z.* **26** (1927) 1–46.
[41] E. ZERMELO, Untersuchungen über die Grundlagen der Mengenlehre, *Math. Ann.* **65** (1908) 261–281.

[42] E. Zermelo, Über Grenzzahlen und Mengenbereiche, *Fund. Math.* **16** (1930) 29–47.

[43] G. Kreisel and A. S. Troelstra, Formal systems for some branches of intuitionistic analysis, *Ann. Math. Logic* **1** (3) (1970) 229–387 (announced in [**24**] and [**38**] under the title: A formal system for intuitionistic analysis).

[44] G. Kreisel, A Survey of proof Theory *J. Symb. Logic* **33** (1968) 321–388.

FORMAL SYSTEMS OF INTUITIONISTIC ANALYSIS II: THE THEORY OF SPECIES

JOHN MYHILL

1. Background. In the first paper [**4**] of this series I proposed an axiom system for the 'elementary' part of intuitionistic analysis, i.e. the theory of natural numbers, computable functions and free-choice sequences. The treatment of species in that paper was very sketchy (I merely adjoined comprehension axioms, giving two forms of the system, one predicative and one impredicative). In this second paper I consider the question of axiomatizing higher-type objects more fully. I believe that what I have done is adequate to the uses of higher types in the actual writings of Brouwer.

Unfortunately, it does not seem that a theory suitable for this purpose can be obtained simply by adjoining new axioms to my old system. The reason for this is that the old system was designed to include 'Kripke's schema', with a view to formalizing Brouwer's so-called historical arguments which are being discussed by Professors Troelstra, De Iongh and Van Rootselaar and Mr. Hull at this conference. Let us recall: the schema states that for any proposition $\mathfrak{A}$, possibly containing parameters, we can form a sequence $\tau_{\mathfrak{A}}$ such that $\tau_{\mathfrak{A}}(n) = 1$ or 0 according as $\mathfrak{A}$ has or has not been proved by the nth stage. Thus

$$\tau_{\mathfrak{A}}(n) = 1 \rightarrow \mathfrak{A} \tag{1}$$

and

$$(\forall n)(\tau_{\mathfrak{A}}(n) = 0) \leftrightarrow \neg\, \mathfrak{A}. \tag{2}$$

This schema (explicitly stated by Brouwer, and even with $\leftrightarrow$ instead of $\rightarrow$ in (1)) is used by him e.g. to prove that $\neg(\forall x)(\alpha(x) = 0)$ does not imply $(\exists x)(\alpha(x) \neq 0)$. (For this, consider $\alpha = \tau_{\mathfrak{A} \vee \neg \mathfrak{A}}$ with an undecided $\mathfrak{A}$: then by (2) $\neg(\forall x)(\alpha(x) = 0)$, but no n for which $\alpha(n) \neq 0$ is known.)

In my old system I asserted Kripke's schema in the form

$$(\exists\alpha)\begin{bmatrix}(\forall x)(\alpha(x) = 0 \vee \alpha(x) = 1)\\ \wedge\\ (\exists x)(\alpha(x) = 1) \to \mathfrak{A}\\ \wedge\\ (\forall x)(\alpha(x) = 0) \leftrightarrow \neg\, \mathfrak{A}\end{bmatrix}$$

i.e. we asserted that the $\tau_{\mathfrak{A}}$ of (1)–(2) was a *free-choice* sequence. This got us into trouble with $(\forall\alpha)(\exists\beta)$-continuity, i.e. the assertion that if $(\forall\alpha)(\exists\beta)$ $\mathfrak{B}(\alpha, \beta)$ then the β depends continously on the α. (Here and henceforth α, β, γ denote free-choice sequences). To see why this is so, let $\mathfrak{A}$ be '$(\forall x)$ $(\beta(x) = 0)$' with a free-choice parameter β; then $\neg\,(\beta \equiv 0) \leftrightarrow (\alpha \equiv 0)$ and $\alpha(x) = 1 \to \beta \equiv 0$, so that α cannot possibly be a continuous function of β. This point (the contradiction between Kripke's schema and $(\forall\alpha)(\exists\beta)$-continuity) was I believe first made by me in my 'Logique et Analyse' article, and has been explored at length by Troelstra in one of his lectures.

A makeshift repair was made by me in my Amsterdam paper last year (the first paper of the present series), by substituting the $(\forall\alpha)(\exists n)$-continuity axiom for the $(\forall\alpha)(\exists\beta)$ one. The resulting system, including Kripke's schema, has resisted any attempts to find a contradiction in it and not much analysis appears to be sacrificed. For it is proved in the book of Kleene and Vesley that $(\forall\alpha)(\exists n)$-continuity implies $(\forall\alpha)(\exists!\beta)$-continuity ($\exists!\beta$ = there exists an (extensionally) *unique* β) and it is the latter that is almost always needed in analysis. Further the $\beta = \tau_{(\forall x)(\alpha(x)=0)}$ is conspicuously non-unique, at least on the intersubjective version of intuitionism; different mathematical subjects are evidently free to prove things in different orders.

However, this repair ($(\forall\alpha)(\exists n)$-continuity replacing $(\forall\alpha)(\exists\beta)$-continuity) is not based on a careful philosophical analysis of what it is to be 'given' a free-choice sequence; one finds this out the hard way when one realizes that on a most evident assumption about functionals, the two forms are equivalent.

More precisely: the *axiom of choice* says

$$(\forall\alpha)(\exists\beta)\mathfrak{A}(\alpha, \beta) \to (\exists\Phi)(\forall\alpha)\mathfrak{A}(\alpha, \Phi(\alpha)),$$

at least for $\mathfrak{A}$ with only lawlike parameters. Kripke's schema says

$$(\forall\alpha)(\exists\beta)\begin{bmatrix}\neg\,(\alpha \equiv 0) \leftrightarrow \beta \equiv 0\\ \wedge\\ (\exists x)(\beta(x) = 1) \to (\forall x)(\alpha(x) = 0)\end{bmatrix}$$

for short $(\forall\alpha)(\exists\beta)\mathfrak{B}(\alpha, \beta)$.

By the axiom of choice there is a function Φ for which always

$$\mathfrak{B}(\alpha, \Phi(\alpha)),$$

in fact $\Phi(\alpha)$ is what we called before $\tau_{(\forall x)(\alpha(x)=0)}$. Hence $(\forall\alpha)(\exists!\beta)(\beta = \Phi(\alpha))$; and any such β depends discontinuously on α. Thus $(\forall\alpha)(\exists!\beta)$-continuity is violated and consequently $(\forall\alpha)(\exists n)$-continuity also. Briefly, *we cannot have in the same system Kripke's schema, the axiom of choice and (even weak) continuity* in its unrestricted form. The restriction needed is simply that if $(\forall\alpha)(\exists n)\mathfrak{A}(\alpha, n)$ *and if* $\mathfrak{A}$ *is extensional in* α then n is a continuous function of α. Indeed the classical arguments for continuity make no sense unless only the *values* of α are used in computing n. From this we can infer $(\forall\alpha)(\exists!\beta)$-continuity for extensional contexts. Now $(\forall\alpha)(\exists!\beta)(\beta \equiv\!\!\equiv \tau_{(\forall x)(\alpha(x)=0)})$, but in computing β we use knowledge about α which does not consist simply of its values. So the restriction on continuity is not simply an ad hoc one to avoid contradiction, but one which is evident once we analyse the meaning of the prefix $(\forall\alpha)(\exists!\beta)$. We formalize the requirement that $\mathfrak{A}$ be extensional in α by

$$\mathfrak{Ext}_{\alpha n}\,\mathfrak{A}(\alpha, n) \leftrightarrow (\forall\alpha\beta n)(\alpha \equiv \beta \wedge \mathfrak{A}(\alpha, n) \rightarrow \mathfrak{A}(\beta, n))$$

but here a doubt arises which is not completely resolved. We want $\mathfrak{Ext}_{\alpha n}\,\mathfrak{A}(\alpha, n)$ to mean that n depends only on the values of α, not on any other (intensional) information. The condition $\alpha \equiv \beta \wedge \mathfrak{A}(\alpha, n) \rightarrow \mathfrak{A}(\beta, n)$ is a *necessary* one for extensionality in this sense (if α and β have the same values and $\mathfrak{A}(\alpha, n)$ and n depends only on the values, then $\mathfrak{A}(\beta, n)$); the implication in the opposite direction is not absolutely clear though very plausible, and we shall hopefully undertake its defense (on philosophical grounds) in a later paper of this series. We are indebted to Professor De Iongh for pointing out to us the necessity for such a justification.

There are a few other additions to be made to the original system. Since the functionals Φ are now not necessarily extensional (e.g. if $\Phi\alpha \equiv\!\!\equiv \tau_{(\forall x)(\alpha(x)=0)}$ then $\alpha \equiv \beta$ does not imply $\Phi\alpha \equiv\!\!\equiv \Phi\beta$) we must include axioms for intensional identity $\equiv\!\!\equiv$ as well as extensional identity $\equiv$. There is also a problem about 'lawlike'. The axiom of choice (in all types) should read someting like

$$(\forall\mathfrak{x})(\exists\mathfrak{y})\mathfrak{A}(\mathfrak{x}, \mathfrak{y}) \rightarrow (\exists\Phi)(\forall\mathfrak{x})\mathfrak{A}(\mathfrak{x}, \Phi\mathfrak{x})$$

where Φ is lawlike if $\mathfrak{A}$ has only lawlike parameters. However this yields

$$(\exists\Phi)(\forall\alpha)\begin{bmatrix} (\exists x)(\Phi\alpha)(x) = 1 \rightarrow (\forall x)(\alpha x = 0) \\ \wedge \\ (\forall x)(\Phi\alpha)(x) = 0 \leftrightarrow \neg(\forall x)(\alpha x = 0) \end{bmatrix}$$

with a *lawlike* Φ, which is certainly not true if by 'lawlike' one means 'mathematical'. An ingenious counterexample suggested by Kreisel in his concluding address at this conference indicates that even in the case that $\mathfrak{x}$ and $\mathfrak{y}$ in the axiom of choice are number-variables and only mathematical notions occur in $\mathfrak{A}$, still the Φ may be only 'empirically' and not mathematically lawlike. (This example will be discussed later in the present paper.) Hence we need *both* the notion $\boldsymbol{D}$ of 'lawlike' used in **[4]** *and* a stronger notion $\boldsymbol{M}$ of 'mathematically lawlike' (= Troelstra's 'absolutely lawlike' in **[6]**): the formal treatment of this distinction is the most curious feature of the system proposed here.

2. Formal description of the system. *Signatures* and *levels* are defined by simultaneous recursion as follows (cf. Schütte **[5]** pp. 245 seq.). N (the type of the natural numbers) is a signature and its level is 0. If $n \geqslant 1, \sigma_1, \ldots, \sigma_n$ are signatures, and m is greater than the level of each of $\sigma_1, \ldots, \sigma_n$, then $m(\sigma_1, \ldots, \sigma_n)$ is a signature and its level is m (the type of sets of n-tuples $\langle \mathfrak{x}_1, \ldots, \mathfrak{x}_n \rangle$ with $\mathfrak{x}_i \in \sigma_i$ for $i = 1, \ldots, n$ defined by formulas quantifying only over levels $< m$). If $n \geqslant 1$ and $\sigma_1, \ldots, \sigma_n, \tau$ are signatures, then $(\sigma_1, \ldots, \sigma_n)\tau$ is a signature and its level is greater by 1 than the greatest of the levels of $\sigma_1, \ldots, \sigma_n, \tau$ (the type of functionals having n arguments of types $\sigma_1, \ldots, \sigma_n$ respectively and taking values in type τ). If τ is a signature so is $[\tau]$ (the type of finite sequences of objects of type τ).

If we write $(\sigma_1, \ldots, \sigma_n)$ as a signature we understand it to be $m+1$ $(\sigma_1, \ldots, \sigma_n)$, where m is the highest of the levels of $\sigma_1, \ldots, \sigma_n$.

The *type* of a term is defined recursively as follows. A variable with signature (superscript) σ is of type σ; so is a defined constant with signature σ introduced under RD below. If $\mathfrak{t}_1, \ldots, \mathfrak{t}_n$ are of types $\sigma_1, \ldots, \sigma_n$ respectively and $\mathfrak{s}$ is of type $(\sigma_1, \ldots, \sigma_n)\tau$, then $\mathfrak{s}(\mathfrak{t}_1, \ldots, \mathfrak{t}_n)$ is of type τ. If $\mathfrak{t}$ is of type $[\tau]$ and $\mathfrak{s}$ is of type N, then $\mathfrak{t}[\mathfrak{s}]$ is of type τ.

0 is of type N (zero).

s is of type (N)N (successor).

$\boldsymbol{D}^{(\tau)}$ and $\boldsymbol{M}^{(\tau)}$ are of type (τ). (Here and in some other cases the superscript will be omitted if no confusion can arise. $\boldsymbol{D}^{(\tau)}$ is the species of lawlike object of type τ and $\boldsymbol{M}^{(\tau)}$ is the corresponding species of mathematical (absolutely lawlike) objects.)

$[\ ]^{[\tau]}$ is of type $[\tau]$ (empty sequence of objects of type τ). $\equiv(\sigma_1, \sigma_1)$ is of type (σ_1, σ_1) (intensional identity).

If $\mathfrak{t}$ is of type $[\tau]$ and $\mathfrak{s}$ of type τ, then $\mathfrak{t}*[\mathfrak{s}]$ (the finite sequence obtained by adjoining $\mathfrak{s}$ to the sequence $\mathfrak{t}$) is of type $[\tau]$.

$\boldsymbol{K}^{(((N)N)\tau)}$ is of type $(((N)N)\tau)$ (the species of continuous mappings of (N)N into type τ).

Certain primitive recursive functionals of specified type also appear in the axioms.

Conventions. An italic variable without superscript will be used for type N. Upper case italic variables will be used for species (sometimes the signature will be omitted). Large Greek letters will be used for functionals, i.e. variables of type $(\sigma_1, \ldots, \sigma_n)\tau$, except for N(N) for which we use $\alpha, \beta, \ldots$. Small German letters denote variables or terms of unspecified type; large German letters denote formulas (possibly with free variables).

Formulas are built up from atomic ones of the form $\mathfrak{s}(\mathfrak{t}_1, \ldots, \mathfrak{t}_n)$ where $\mathfrak{s}$ is of type $(\tau_1, \ldots, \tau_n)$ and $\mathfrak{t}_1, \ldots, \mathfrak{t}_n$ are of types $\tau_1, \ldots, \tau_n$ respectively, by connectives and quantifiers of all signatures. [We write $\mathfrak{t}_1 \equiv \mathfrak{t}_2$ for $\equiv (\mathfrak{t}_1, \mathfrak{t}_2)$ and (sometimes) $\mathfrak{t}_1^\tau \in \mathfrak{t}_2^{(\tau)}$ for $\mathfrak{t}_2(\mathfrak{t}_1)$.] In addition if $\mathfrak{A}$ is any formula and $\mathfrak{t}$ a term of type N, then $\vdash_{\mathfrak{t}} \mathfrak{A}$ plays the role of an atomic formula.

The underlying logic is an infinitely many-sorted intuitionistic predicate calculus.

In addition to the usual logical rules, we have:

RD. If $(\exists x^\tau)\mathfrak{A}(x)$ is a theorem ($\mathfrak{A}$ without free variables other than x), one can introduce a term $\mathfrak{t}$ of type τ by the defining postulate $\mathfrak{A}(\mathfrak{t})$. (Notice we do not need to prove uniqueness.) We call the proof of $(\exists x^\tau)\mathfrak{A}(x)$ the *justification* of $\mathfrak{t}$.

The non-logical axioms fall into several groups:

P. *Peano axioms* with variables of type N, with $\equiv$ for the identity relation (sometimes we write $=$ instead in this case) and with induction as a schema.

K. *The inductive definition of* $\boldsymbol{K}^{(((N)N)\tau)}$:

$$\mathfrak{Const}^{(((N)N)\tau)}\Phi \rightarrow \boldsymbol{K}\Phi,$$

$$(\forall n)\boldsymbol{K}(\Phi(n)) \rightarrow \boldsymbol{K}(\Xi\Phi),$$

$$(\forall\Phi)(\mathfrak{Const}\,\Phi \rightarrow \mathfrak{A}(\Phi)) \wedge (\forall\Psi)((\forall n)\mathfrak{A}(\Psi(n)) \rightarrow \mathfrak{A}(\Xi\Psi)) \rightarrow (\forall\Phi)(\boldsymbol{K}\Phi \rightarrow \mathfrak{A}\Phi),$$

where we define $\mathfrak{Const}$ and Ξ (under RD above) by the defining postulates

$$\mathfrak{Const}\,\Phi \leftrightarrow (\forall\chi\chi')(\Phi(\chi) \equiv \Phi(\chi')),$$

$$(\Xi\Phi)(\alpha) \equiv (\Phi(\alpha(0)))(\rho\alpha),$$

where

$$(\rho\alpha)n \equiv \alpha(n+1).$$

Note that our continuous functionals are not necessarily lawlike.

I. *Axioms for* (intensional) *identity and finite sequences*:

$$\mathfrak{x} \equiv \mathfrak{x},$$
$$\mathfrak{A}(\mathfrak{x}) \wedge \mathfrak{x} \equiv \mathfrak{y} \rightarrow \mathfrak{A}(\mathfrak{y}),$$
$$\mathfrak{x} \equiv \mathfrak{y} \vee \neg (\mathfrak{x} \equiv \mathfrak{y}),$$
$$\neg ([\ ]^{[\tau]} \equiv x^{[\tau]} * y^{\tau}),$$
$$x^{[\tau]} \equiv y \leftrightarrow l^{([\tau])\mathrm{N}}(x) \equiv l(y) \wedge (\forall z < l(y))(x(z) \equiv y(z));$$

$l^{([\tau])\mathrm{N}}(x)$ is the *length* of the finite sequence $x^{[\tau]}$ and we postulate the defining equations:

$$l[\ ] \equiv 0,$$
$$lx{*}[y] \equiv sl(x),$$
$$\mathfrak{A}[\ ] \wedge (\forall x^{[\tau]})(\forall y^{\tau})(\mathfrak{A}(x) \rightarrow \mathfrak{A}(x * [y])) \rightarrow (\forall x^{[\tau]})\mathfrak{A}(x),$$
$$n < lx^{[\tau]} \rightarrow x * [y](n) \equiv x(n), \quad x * [y]l(x) \equiv y,$$
$$n \geqslant l(x) \rightarrow x^{[\tau]}(n) \equiv 0^{\tau}$$

(where 0^{τ} is an appropriately chosen zero-object in each type).

$$\tilde{\ }(\Phi^{(\mathrm{N})\tau}, 0) \equiv [\ ]^{\tau}$$
$$\tilde{\ }(\Phi^{(\mathrm{N})\tau}, s(x)) \equiv \tilde{\ }(\Phi x) * [\Phi(x)]$$

(course-of-values functional; henceforth we write $\tilde{\Phi}(x)$ instead of $\tilde{\ }(\Phi, x)$.)

D. *Axioms for* ***D*** *and* ***M***:

$$\boldsymbol{D}\mathfrak{x}_1 \wedge \ldots \wedge \boldsymbol{D}\mathfrak{x}_n \rightarrow \boldsymbol{D}\mathfrak{t} \qquad (n \geqslant 0),$$

where $\mathfrak{x}_1, \ldots, \mathfrak{x}_1, \ldots, \mathfrak{x}_n$ are all the free variables of $\mathfrak{t}$ except the number variables. (Thus a species or functional is lawlike if only lawlike parameters enter into its definition.) Likewise

$$\boldsymbol{M}\mathfrak{x}_1 \wedge \ldots \wedge \boldsymbol{M}\mathfrak{x}_n \rightarrow \boldsymbol{M}\mathfrak{t} \qquad (n \geqslant 0),$$

where $\mathfrak{x}_1, \ldots, \mathfrak{x}_n$ are all the free variables of $\mathfrak{t}$ except the number variables, and *where the sign* $\vdash$ *is not used in the justification of any defined constant occuring in* $\mathfrak{t}$.

$$\boldsymbol{D}\mathfrak{x} \vee \neg \boldsymbol{D}\mathfrak{x},$$
$$\boldsymbol{M}\mathfrak{x} \vee \neg \boldsymbol{M}\mathfrak{x}$$
$$\boldsymbol{M}\mathfrak{x} \rightarrow \boldsymbol{D}\mathfrak{x}.$$

Thus the lawlike objects of any type are a detachable subspecies of that type, and the mathematical objects are a detachable subspecies of the lawlike one.

F. *Axioms of continuity*:

$$(\forall\alpha)(\exists x)(\boldsymbol{D}x \wedge \mathfrak{A}(\alpha, x)) \wedge \mathfrak{Ert}_{\alpha x}\mathfrak{A}(\alpha, x) \rightarrow (\exists\Phi \in \boldsymbol{K})[(\forall\alpha)\mathfrak{A}(\alpha, \Phi\alpha) \wedge (\boldsymbol{D}\mathfrak{x}_1 \wedge \ldots \wedge \boldsymbol{D}\mathfrak{x}_n \rightarrow \boldsymbol{D}\Phi)]$$

where $\mathfrak{x}_1, \ldots, \mathfrak{x}_n$ are all the free variables of $\mathfrak{A}$ except α and x. (One might be tempted to postulate the same thing with $\boldsymbol{M}$ replacing $\boldsymbol{D}$: but the apparent invalidity of the same substitution in the axiom of choice, discussed below in section **3**, makes us hesitant to do this.)

S. *Axioms for species* (comprehension):

$$(\exists S^{m(\sigma_1, \ldots, \sigma_n)})[(\forall x^{\sigma_1}) \ldots (\forall x^{\sigma_n})(S(x_1, \ldots, x_n) \leftrightarrow \mathfrak{A}(x_1, \ldots, x_n)) \wedge (\boldsymbol{D}\mathfrak{y}_1 \wedge \ldots \wedge \boldsymbol{D}\mathfrak{y}_n \rightarrow \boldsymbol{D}S)]$$

where $\mathfrak{y}_1, \ldots, \mathfrak{y}_n$ are all the parameters of $\mathfrak{A}$. Thus a species is lawlike if no non-lawlike parameters occur in its definition. The same clearly holds reading 'mathematical' for 'lawlike', and we postulate

$$(\exists S^{m(\sigma_1, \ldots, \sigma_n)})[(\forall x_1, \ldots, x_n)(S(x_1, \ldots, x_n) \leftrightarrow \mathfrak{A}(x_1, \ldots, x_n)) \wedge (\boldsymbol{M}\mathfrak{y}_1 \wedge \ldots \wedge \boldsymbol{M}\mathfrak{y}_n \rightarrow \boldsymbol{M}S)]$$

where $\mathfrak{y}_1, \ldots, \mathfrak{y}_n$ are as above and where $\mathfrak{A}$ continues neither $\vdash$ nor any constant in whose justification $\vdash$ appears.

Notice that with RD these axioms give us the effect of an abstraction operator.

In the above axioms m is to be any number *greater than* the levels of $\sigma_1, \ldots, \sigma_n$ or any variable occurring bound in $\mathfrak{A}$, and *greater than or equal to* the level of any constant or free variable occurring in $\mathfrak{A}$. (For this purpose $\vdash$ is regarded as having level 0). This gives the ordinary (finite) ramified hierarchy (Schütte, loc. cit.).

C. *Axioms of choice.*

AC.

$$(\forall\mathfrak{x}_1) \ldots (\forall\mathfrak{x}_n)(\exists\mathfrak{y})\mathfrak{A}(\mathfrak{x}_1, \ldots, \mathfrak{x}_n, \mathfrak{y}) \rightarrow (\exists\Phi)[((\forall\mathfrak{x}_1) \ldots (\forall\mathfrak{x}_n)\mathfrak{A}(\mathfrak{x}_1, \ldots, \mathfrak{x}_n, \Phi(\mathfrak{x}_1, \ldots, \mathfrak{x}_n)) \wedge (\boldsymbol{D}\mathfrak{y}_1 \wedge \ldots \wedge \boldsymbol{D}\mathfrak{y}_k \rightarrow \boldsymbol{D}\Phi)],$$

where $\mathfrak{y}_1, \ldots, \mathfrak{y}_k$ are all the free variables of $\mathfrak{A}$ other than $\mathfrak{x}_1, \ldots, \mathfrak{x}_n$, $\mathfrak{y}$

and number variables (notice there is no restriction on $\mathfrak{y}$; notice also that this with RD obviates the need for λ-terms).

DC (Dependent choice).

$$\mathfrak{A}[\ ]^{[\tau]} \wedge (\forall x^{[\tau]})(\mathfrak{A}x \to (\exists y^{\tau})(\mathfrak{A}(x * [y])) \to (\exists \Phi^{(N)\tau})[((\forall n)\mathfrak{A}\tilde{\Phi}(n)) \wedge (\boldsymbol{D}\mathfrak{y}_1 \wedge \ldots \wedge \boldsymbol{D}\mathfrak{y}_k \to \boldsymbol{D}\Phi)]$$

where $\mathfrak{y}_1, \ldots, \mathfrak{y}_k$ are all the free variables of $\mathfrak{A}(x)$ except (number variables and) x itself.

With RD this allows us to make definitions by primitive recursion in all types: hence the system contains all the Dialectica functionals.

J. Axioms for the thinking subject:

$$\vdash_m \mathfrak{A} \vee \neg \vdash_m \mathfrak{A},$$
$$((\exists m) \vdash_m \mathfrak{A}) \leftrightarrow \mathfrak{A}$$
$$\vdash_m \mathfrak{A} \wedge n > m \to \vdash_n \mathfrak{A}.$$

Finally we assert the 'Never-on-Sunday schema', which asserts roughly that unless we have already proved $\mathfrak{A} \vee \neg \mathfrak{A}$, we can say nothing mathematical about the stage at which $\mathfrak{A}$ will be decided.

NOS: $\mathfrak{Ext}(S) \wedge \boldsymbol{M}S \wedge \vdash_n (\tau_{\mathfrak{A}} \in S) \to$

$$\vdash_n \mathfrak{A} \vee \vdash_n \neg \mathfrak{A} \vee (\forall \alpha) \begin{bmatrix} (\forall x)(\alpha(x) \leqslant 1) \\ \wedge \\ (\forall xy)(\alpha(x) = 1 \wedge y > x \to \alpha(y) = 1) \\ \wedge \\ (\forall x \leqslant n)(\alpha(x) = 0) \end{bmatrix} \to \alpha \in S$$

Here $\tau_{\mathfrak{A}}$ is introduced by RD using the axioms for thinking subject and satisfies

$$\tau_{\mathfrak{A}}(x) \leqslant 1,$$
$$\tau_{\mathfrak{A}}(x) = 1 \to (\tau(x+y) = 1),$$
$$\mathfrak{A} \leftrightarrow (\exists x)(\tau_{\mathfrak{A}}(x) = 1).$$

NOS yields as consequences to both Troelstra's

$$\boldsymbol{M}\alpha \wedge \neg \vdash_x \mathfrak{A} \wedge \neg \vdash_x \neg \mathfrak{A} \to \neg \vdash_x (\tau_{\mathfrak{A}} \equiv \alpha),$$

(where we do not see the necessity that $\mathfrak{A}$ contains only lawlike parameters). and the strengthened form of Kripke's schema discussed by Hull in [**1**].

We presume that much more can be said about $\vdash_x$, $\boldsymbol{M}$ and their relationships; for example, there seems no way of proving from what is said here that $\neg(\forall\chi)(\boldsymbol{D}\chi \to \boldsymbol{M}\chi)$. (There is an obvious intuitive argument.) But this is a subject for another paper.

3. Concluding remarks. These remarks concern the particular forms of the axiom of choice (AC and DC) that we used. In both of them we have been more cautious than would appear on the face of it to be warranted: we wish to justify this caution.

Consider first a simple case of AC

$$(\forall x)(\exists y)\mathfrak{A}(x, y) \to (\exists\Phi)(\forall x)[\mathfrak{A}(x, \Phi x) \wedge \boldsymbol{D}\Phi], \tag{1}$$

where $\mathfrak{A}$ contains only *mathematical* parameters and constants. Should we not in this case be allowed to infer $\boldsymbol{M}\Phi$ rather than $\boldsymbol{D}\Phi$? (Notice that by an earlier observation in section 1 of this paper, we cannot do this if $\mathfrak{x}$ and $\mathfrak{y}$ are replaced by free-choice variables.)

Let us consider the usual intuitionistic argument for (1). The hypothesis is proved by exhibiting a *method* for obtaining the y from the x; $\Phi(x)$ is simply the y obtained by that method. There are it seems several possible situations. (I) The method may not use any information about any $\tau_{\mathfrak{B}}$ at all. In that case there is no trouble with (I) and Φ is absolutely lawlike. (II) It may use general properties of the $\tau_{\mathfrak{B}}$ (e.g. Kripke's schema itself or NOS) but still no particular *values* of any $\tau_{\mathfrak{B}}$. This still seems harmless to me; in particular if Church's thesis were refutable on that basis I would think Church's thesis was simply wrong, i.e. that there are uniform methods which are constructive from the point of view of intuitionism and yet non-recursive. (III) Particular values of some $\tau_{\mathfrak{B}}$ are used in computing y from x, and yet they always lead to the same y. If that could be proved, i.e. if $(\forall\mathfrak{x})(\exists! y)$ $\mathfrak{A}(x, y)$, it seems to me that this reduces to II since the particular values of $\tau_{\mathfrak{B}}$ are not used in any essential way, but only its general properties. *This* case of (1) (the $(\forall x)(\exists! y)$-axiom of choice) seems much more justifiable, but of course not as useful as the general form since it only applies to decidable $\mathfrak{A}$. (IV) One or more $\tau_{\mathfrak{B}}$'s appear in $\mathfrak{A}$. Then y can certainly be expected to depend on x in a non-(absolutely) lawlike manner, but that need cause us no concern: the restriction on the $\boldsymbol{D}$-axioms (that no defined constant can be asserted to belong to $\boldsymbol{D}$ if Kripke's schema was used in proving the existence theorem for that constant) prevents the application of (1) since the $\tau_{\mathfrak{B}}$'s count as non-lawlike. (V) There may be no $\tau_{\mathfrak{B}}$'s in $\mathfrak{A}$, nor any notion defined in terms of them, and nevertheless the *particular values* of certain

$\tau_{\mathfrak{B}}$'s could make a difference to the value of the y obtained by the 'method'. It seems highly implausible to me that such a thing could ever happen and yet I cannot prove that it is impossible. Quite probably a detailed philosophical argument could rule it out; but Troelstra has been very scrupulous and refrained from asserting (1) until such an argument is forthcoming.

In his paper **[3]** at this Conference, Kreisel has given a strong argument against (1), not indeed for $\mathfrak{A}$'s written in the notation of this system, but for another $\mathfrak{A}$ which we might quite reasonably wish to add. This $\mathfrak{A}(x, y)$ means: either x is not the Gödel number of a proof (in some particular intuitionistic system) of an existential statement $(\exists z)\mathfrak{B}(z)$, and y is 0; or x is the Gödel number of such a proof *and y is the z yielded by the proof.* Then the hypothesis of (1) is true, and there is certainly a method (namely examination of the proof x) to find the y; but one cannot in general expect a recursive method. For particular intuitionistic systems such methods are sometimes known (cf. Kleene **[2]**) but there seems no justification at all for asserting that given an intuitionistic system (e.g. the present one) we can find (from the proof that it *is* an intuitionistic system) a recursive Φ for this particular $\mathfrak{A}$. Hence we have no reason to assert the conjunction of the two following propositions:

For this particular $\mathfrak{A}$, there exists a Φ which is mathematical (absolutely lawlike) (2)

and

Every mathematical $\Phi \in (\mathrm{N})\mathrm{N}$ is recursive (Church's thesis). (3)

In our system, we assert neither (2) nor (3). But when we reflect on the meaning of 'lawlike' and 'mathematical' Kreisel's argument seems to throw doubt on (2) more than on (3). There certainly does exist a Φ for (1); we can tell someone 'analyse the proof x and find the z yielded by it'. This is a *lawlike* method (certainly it does not depend on any free choices) but it is not a *mechanical* method (it demands understanding and reflection, not only following rules). Nevertheless we could reasonably maintain that the predicate $\mathfrak{A}(x, y)$ *is* a mathematical one rather than an empirical one: hence we cannot in general strengthen $\boldsymbol{D}$ to $\boldsymbol{M}$ in (1). At least no argument has been given why we should.

Our last remark concerns the axiom of dependent choice. One might be inclined to postulate something simpler namely

$$(\forall \mathfrak{x} \in S)(\exists \mathfrak{y} \in T)\mathfrak{A}(\mathfrak{x}, \mathfrak{y}) \rightarrow (\exists \Phi \in (S)T)(\forall \mathfrak{x} \in S)\mathfrak{A}(\mathfrak{x}, \Phi(\mathfrak{x})). \tag{4}$$

That certainly yields DC as a consequence, and at first sight it looks plausible. Why not accept it instead of DC? To avoid the notational complications involved in partially defined functionals $\Phi \in (S)T$, let us consider a weaker form of (4) (but still enough to give (DC). If we succeed in making the weaker form doubtful, we shall have no reason to assert the stronger one either:

$$(\forall \mathfrak{x} \in S)(\exists \mathfrak{y})\mathfrak{A}(\mathfrak{x}, \mathfrak{y}) \rightarrow (\exists T)[(\forall x \in S)(\exists ! y)T(\mathfrak{x}, \mathfrak{y}) \wedge (\forall \mathfrak{x} \in S)(\forall \mathfrak{y})(T(\mathfrak{x}, \mathfrak{y}) \rightarrow \mathfrak{A}(\mathfrak{x}, \mathfrak{y}))] \quad (4')$$

(For *decidable* S, this is a consequence of AC).

The reason one is inclined to believe (4) or (4′) is that at first sight the usual intuitionistic justification of AC seems to go over unchanged. But let us recall that justification, and see where the difference comes about.

If $(\forall \mathfrak{x})(\exists \mathfrak{y})\mathfrak{A}(\mathfrak{x}, \mathfrak{y})$, then by the intuitionistic interpretations of $\exists$ there is a method for finding the $\mathfrak{y}$ from the $\mathfrak{x}$. Then $\Phi(\mathfrak{x})$ in AC is simply the $\mathfrak{y}$ obtained by the method. Likewise in (4′) we are inclined at first to say: T is the species of those pairs $(\mathfrak{x}, \mathfrak{y})$ where $\mathfrak{x} \in S$ and where $\mathfrak{y}$ is obtained from $\mathfrak{x}$ and the proof of $\mathfrak{x} \in S$ by the method which we must have in order to assert $(\forall \mathfrak{x})(\mathfrak{x} \in S \rightarrow (\exists \mathfrak{y})\mathfrak{A}(\mathfrak{x}, \mathfrak{y}))$. But if we analyse this in terms of the theory of constructions, we see that we have made an error.

Let us recall some principles of that theory:

$$\pi \text{ proves } (\forall \mathfrak{x})\mathfrak{A}(\mathfrak{x}) \quad \text{iff} \quad \pi_1 \text{ proves that } (\forall \mathfrak{x})[\pi_2(\mathfrak{x}) \text{ proves } \mathfrak{A}(\mathfrak{x})],$$
$$\pi \text{ proves } \mathfrak{A} \rightarrow \mathfrak{B} \quad \text{iff} \quad \pi_1 \text{ proves that } (\forall \rho)(\rho \text{ proves } \mathfrak{A} \rightarrow \pi_2(\rho) \text{ proves } \mathfrak{B}),$$
$$\pi \text{ proves } (\exists \mathfrak{x})\mathfrak{A}(\mathfrak{x}) \quad \text{iff} \quad \pi_1 \text{ proves } \mathfrak{A}(\pi_2),$$

Applying these principles to (4′) we get

$$\pi \text{ proves } (\forall \mathfrak{x})(\mathfrak{x} \in S \rightarrow (\exists \mathfrak{y})\mathfrak{A}(\mathfrak{x}, \mathfrak{y}))$$
$$\leftrightarrow$$
$$\pi_1 \text{ proves } (\forall \mathfrak{x})(\pi_2(\mathfrak{x}) \text{ proves } (\mathfrak{x} \in S \rightarrow (\exists \mathfrak{y})\mathfrak{A}(\mathfrak{x}, \mathfrak{y})))$$
$$\leftrightarrow$$
$$\pi_1 \text{ proves } (\forall \mathfrak{x})((\pi_2(\mathfrak{x}))_1 \text{ proves } (\forall \rho)(\rho \text{ proves } \mathfrak{x} \in S \rightarrow (\pi_2(\mathfrak{x}))_2(\rho) \text{ proves } (\exists \mathfrak{y})\mathfrak{A}(\mathfrak{x}, \mathfrak{y})))$$
$$\rightarrow$$
$$(\forall \mathfrak{x} \rho)(\rho \text{ proves } \mathfrak{x} \in S \rightarrow \mathfrak{A}(\mathfrak{x}, ((\pi_2(\mathfrak{x}))_2(\rho))_2);$$

i.e. the $\mathfrak{y}$ in (4′) depends not only on the $\mathfrak{x}$ but on the proof that $\mathfrak{x} \in S$: different proofs can be expected to yield different $\mathfrak{y}$'s. (This is particularly clear if S is defined by an existential condition).

On the other hand, the theory of constructions yields a straightforward justification of DC itself.

Assume

$$\mathfrak{A}[\ ]^{[\tau]} \tag{5}$$

then something, say π^*, proves it. Assume also

$$(\forall x^{[\tau]})(\mathfrak{A}x \to (\exists y^{\tau})\mathfrak{A}(x * [y])), \tag{6}$$

then the antecedent of (4′) yields functions φ and ψ such that for all $x^{[\tau]}$

$$\pi \text{ proves } \mathfrak{A}x \to \varphi(\pi, x) \text{ proves } \mathfrak{A}(x*[\psi(\pi, x)]). \tag{7}$$

So

$$\pi^* \text{ proves } \mathfrak{A}[\ ],$$

$$\varphi(\pi^*, [\ ]) \text{ proves } \mathfrak{A}[\psi(\pi^*, [\ ])],$$

$$\varphi(\varphi(\pi^*, [\ ]), \psi(\pi^*, [\ ])) \text{ proves } \mathfrak{A}([\psi(\pi^*, [\ ])]*[\psi(\varphi(\pi^*, [\ ]), \psi(\pi^*, [\ ]))]),$$

and in general if we define by simultaneous recursion

$$\pi_0 = \pi^*,$$

$$\mathfrak{y}_n = \psi(\pi_n, [\mathfrak{y}_0, \ldots, \mathfrak{y}_{n-1}]),$$

$$\pi_{n+1} = \varphi(\pi_n, [\mathfrak{y}_0, \ldots, \mathfrak{y}_{n-1}]),$$

we obtain from (7) that always

$$\pi_n \text{ proves } \mathfrak{A}[\mathfrak{y}_0, \ldots, \mathfrak{y}_{n-1}],$$

and DC is satisfied with Φ taken as $(\lambda x)\mathfrak{y}_x$.

REFERENCES

[1] R. HULL, Counterexamples in intuitionistic analysis using Kripke's schema, *Z. math. Log. u. Grundl. Math.* **15** (1969) 241–246.

[2] S. C. KLEENE, Formalized recursive functionals and formalized realizability, *Memoirs Am. Math. Soc.* **89**.

[3] G. KREISEL, Church's thesis: a kind of reducibility axiom for constructive mathematics, these proceedings 121–149.

[4] J. MYHILL, Formal systems of intuitionistic analysis I, in *Logic, methodology and philosophy of science III*, eds. B. van Rootselaar and J. F. Staal, North-Holland, Amsterdam (1968) 161–178.

[5] K. SCHÜTTE, *Beweistheorie*, Springer (1960).

[6] A. S. TROELSTRA, Principles of intuitionism, *Lecture Notes in Mathematics* **95**, Springer, Berlin (1969).

PROJECTIONS OF LAWLESS SEQUENCES

D. VAN DALEN AND A. S. TROELSTRA

Introduction. Intuitionistically, one may conceive a wide variety of notions of choice sequence (see e.g. [**2**], [3], [**4**] § 10, [**5**]).

Many of these notions are of little use to the construction of a theory of real numbers because of their 'anti-social behaviour' (described in [5]). Nevertheless, they provide us with a nice testing ground for intuitionistic concepts and principles, and also they represent interesting examples of topological spaces.

In this paper we restrict ourselves to so-called anti-social notions of choice sequence; they are supposed to be described within the general framework outlined in [**5**]. Sections 1 and 2 summarize notions, notations and principles from [**5**] which are needed in this paper. For intuitive explanations we must refer to [**5**].

The 'anti-social' behaviour of the notions considered is due to the fact that the so-called restricting conditions (see § 2) do not contain non-lawlike parameters in these cases. This type of behaviour is best illustrated by a result (given in [**5**]) which states that for a wide variety of anti-social notions the concept is not closed under simple continuous operations (like the operator Γ, defined by $\lambda\chi . [\lambda x . 2\chi x]$ where χ is a variable for numerical-valued sequences). More precisely, simple relations like $2\chi = \xi$ are possible only when χ, ξ are both lawlike.

Our aim is to 'approximate' some of these notions by sequences which are obtained by certain lawlike transformations (called *projection operators*) on lawless sequences (of lawlike objects). The resulting sequences are called *projected sequences.*

With each projection operator the question presents itself: to what extent do the projected sequences approximate the intended notion of choice sequence? The matter is subtle (see § 4) but in some respects we obtain satisfactory approximations.

For example, in § 6 we obtain a proof of $\bigwedge \alpha \bigvee ! x$-continuity and $\bigwedge \alpha \bigvee ! a$

continuity for projected sequences which 'approximate' notions of choice sequence with these properties. The results concerning anti-social behaviour are also easily translated for projected sequences.

It turns out however, that the validity of $\bigwedge \alpha \bigvee x$-continuity may depend on the projection chosen for the approximation. This is illustrated by an example given in § 4, where for two projections, both approximating the same notion, $\bigwedge \alpha \bigvee x$-continuity holds in the first case, but is refutable in the second case. From the results in the final section however, it follows that $\bigwedge \alpha \bigvee x$-continuity also holds in the second case with respect to predicates in a suitably restricted language. Further research in this direction seems to be promising.

The motivation behind the study of projections is two-fold. In the first place, lawless sequences are relatively simple, so we may ask for approximations (which in some cases are almost as good as conceptual reductions, as we shall see) of the more complicated notions by the conceptually simpler lawless sequences. In this respect, the elimination of **abstr** (the abstraction-process introduced in [4], [5]) from the derivation of $\bigwedge \alpha \bigvee ! x$-continuity for projected sequences is worth noting (§ 6).

In the second place, because the projected sequences are approximations of certain notions, they may serve the same mathematical purposes as these notions. Thus we reduce the number of notions required in intuitionistic mathematics.

§1. Preliminaries. In this section we introduce some notations and conventions. For intuitive explanations we refer to [5].

1.1. We use boldface capitals $\boldsymbol{A}$, $\boldsymbol{B}$, $\boldsymbol{C}$, $\boldsymbol{D}$, ... for constructive classes (species) of constructive (lawlike) objects. We shall assume these classes to be decidable (in a universal sense), i.e. for a given construction it is decidable whether it is a construction of the given species or not. $\boldsymbol{N}$ is reserved for the class of natural numbers. For elements of $\boldsymbol{N}$ we use the lower case letters k, n, m, x, y, z, u, v, w (with sub- or superscripts if necessary).

We suppose these classes $\boldsymbol{C}, \boldsymbol{D}, \ldots$ to be provided with a decidable definitional (or intensional) equality, usually denoted by $\equiv$ (or more precisely by $\equiv_{\boldsymbol{C}}$, $\equiv_{\boldsymbol{D}}$ etc.). We write $=$ for $\equiv_{\boldsymbol{N}}$.

1.2. Cartesian products are defined as usual (notations: $\boldsymbol{C} \times \boldsymbol{D}$, $\boldsymbol{C}^n$). A *mapping* φ from $\boldsymbol{C}$ into $\boldsymbol{D}$ is any kind of (not necessarily predetermined) method of assigning an element of $\boldsymbol{D}$ to any element of $\boldsymbol{C}$. A mapping φ from $\boldsymbol{C}$ into $\boldsymbol{D}$ is said to be of type $(\boldsymbol{C})\boldsymbol{D}$, or expressed otherwise: $\varphi \in (\boldsymbol{C})\boldsymbol{D}$.

We use the lower case letters a, b, c, d, e, f (with or without sub- or superscripts) as variables for lawlike elements of $(\boldsymbol{N})\boldsymbol{N}$. These functions are thought of as being given by a prescription with a proof that a natural number is assigned to any given natural number. $a \equiv b$ means that prescriptions and proofs for a and b are identical.

1.3. *Sequences* are mappings of type $(\boldsymbol{N})\boldsymbol{C}$ for a suitable $\boldsymbol{C}$. In discussing mappings of type $(\boldsymbol{N})\boldsymbol{C}$ we use $\xi, \chi, \chi', \chi'', \ldots$ as variables for mappings of this type.

A finite (ordered) sequence of elements $p_0, \ldots, p_n$ of $\boldsymbol{C}$ is written as $\langle p_0, \ldots, p_n \rangle$; $\hat{p} \equiv_{\mathrm{Def}} \langle p \rangle$. The equality $\equiv_C$ may be extended to finite sequences of elements of $\boldsymbol{C}$ (i.e. to $\bigcup_n \boldsymbol{C}^n$) by stipulating:

$$\langle p_0, \ldots, p_n \rangle \equiv \langle p'_0, \ldots, p'_m \rangle \equiv_{\mathrm{Def}} n = m \wedge \bigwedge x \leqslant n (p_x \equiv p'_x).$$

Concatenation $*$ is defined by

$$\langle p_0, \ldots, p_n \rangle * \langle p_{n+1}, \ldots, p_{n+m} \rangle \equiv_{\mathrm{Def}} \langle p_0, \ldots, p_{n+m} \rangle.$$

The length of a sequence is defined by

$$\mathrm{lth}\, \langle p_0, \ldots, p_n \rangle = n+1,$$

$$\mathrm{lth}\, \langle\ \rangle = 0.$$

For natural numbers, we may suppose a bi-unique enumeration of all finite sequences of elements of $\boldsymbol{N}$ to be given, such that $\langle\ \rangle$ corresponds to zero. In our terminology we shall not distinguish between sequences and their numbers in such an enumeration.

1.4. $\{\ ,\ \}$ is used as a lawlike pairing function onto $\boldsymbol{N}$ of type $(\boldsymbol{N}^2)\boldsymbol{N}$; j_1, j_2 denote the inverse pairing functions.

In discussing sequences of type $(\boldsymbol{N})\boldsymbol{C}$, we shall use σ, τ as variables for initial segments, i.e. $\sigma, \tau \in \bigcup_n \boldsymbol{C}^n$. We define

$$\bar{\chi}0 \equiv_{\mathrm{Def}} \langle\ \rangle,$$

$$\bar{\chi}x \equiv_{\mathrm{Def}} \langle \chi 0, \ldots, \chi(x-1) \rangle \quad \text{for } x > 0.$$

$$\chi \in \sigma \equiv_{\mathrm{Def}} \bigvee x (\bar{\chi}x \equiv \sigma),$$

$\langle p_0, \ldots, p_{n-1}\rangle * \chi$ is a sequence χ' with

$$\chi' m = p_m \quad \text{if } m < n,$$
$$\chi' m = \chi(m-n) \quad \text{if } m \geqslant n;$$
$$\langle\ \rangle * \chi \equiv_{\text{Def}} \chi.$$

In describing sequences and predicates, λ will be universally used as an abstraction operator.

1.5. (First-level) extensional equality between sequences $\chi, \xi \in (N)C$ is defined by

$$\chi = \xi \equiv_{\text{Def}} \bigwedge x(\chi x \equiv_C \xi x).$$

1.6. Let $\mathfrak{B}$ stand for an arbitrary (not necessarily decidable) species. Then as a selection principle (axiom of choice) we state:

$$\bigwedge p \in \boldsymbol{C} \bigvee q \in \mathfrak{B} A(p, q, \chi, \ldots) \to \bigvee \Psi \in (\boldsymbol{C})\mathfrak{B} \bigwedge p \in \boldsymbol{C} A(p, \Psi p, \chi, \ldots).$$

In case A does not contain non-lawlike parameters, Ψ may be supposed to be lawlike.

Important special cases:

$$\bigwedge x \bigvee y A(x, y) \to \bigvee a \bigwedge x A(x, ax)$$
$$\bigwedge x \bigvee y A(x, y, \chi, \chi' \ldots) \to \bigvee \xi \bigwedge x A(x, \xi x, \chi', \chi' \ldots)$$

and for extensional A, i.e. an A such that

$$A(\ldots, \chi, \ldots) \wedge \bigwedge x(\chi x = \chi' x) \to A(\ldots, \chi', \ldots) \quad (\chi \in (N)N),$$

we have

$$\bigwedge x \bigvee a A(x, a) \to \bigvee b \bigwedge x A(x, \lambda y \,.\, b\{x, y\}),$$
$$\bigwedge x \bigvee \chi A(x, \chi, \chi') \to \bigvee \xi \bigwedge x A(x, \lambda y \,.\, \xi\{x, y\}, \chi').$$

1.7. As a general convention, we assume all non-lawlike parameters of the predicates to be exhibited in formulae.

§2. Lawless and choice sequences

2.1. We consider lawless sequences of type $(N)C$. Lawless sequences of type $(N)N$ are discussed extensively in [**2**].

We shall assume

$$\bigvee p \in \boldsymbol{C} \bigvee q \in \boldsymbol{C}(\neg\, p \equiv_C q). \tag{2.1}$$

$\varepsilon, \eta, \vartheta, \zeta$ will be used as variables for lawless sequences. Intensional equality between lawless sequences is denoted by $\equiv$. The following properties hold for lawless sequences:

$$\bigwedge \sigma \bigvee \varepsilon(\varepsilon \in \sigma), \tag{2.2}$$

$$\varepsilon \equiv \eta \vee \varepsilon \not\equiv \eta, \tag{2.3}$$

$$W(\varepsilon, \varepsilon_0, \ldots, \varepsilon_n) \wedge \not\equiv (\varepsilon, \varepsilon_0, \ldots, \varepsilon_n) \to \bigvee x \bigwedge \eta \in \bar{\varepsilon}x(\not\equiv (\eta, \varepsilon_0, \ldots, \varepsilon_n) \to W(\eta, \varepsilon_0, \ldots, \varepsilon_n)) \tag{2.4}$$

where $\not\equiv (\varepsilon, \varepsilon_0, \ldots, \varepsilon_n)$ is an abbreviation for

$$\varepsilon \not\equiv \varepsilon_0 \wedge \varepsilon \not\equiv \varepsilon_1 \wedge \ldots \wedge \varepsilon \not\equiv \varepsilon_n .$$

From these principles one derives easily

$$\varepsilon \equiv \eta \leftrightarrow \bigwedge x(\varepsilon x \equiv \eta x). \tag{2.5}$$

Hence for lawless sequences $\equiv$ and $=$ coincide.

Let us use Γ for a lawlike continuous operator acting on lawless sequences, with values in N. Continuity of Γ is expressed by

$$\bigwedge \varepsilon \bigvee x \bigvee y \bigwedge \eta \in \bar{\varepsilon}x(\Gamma\eta = y). \tag{2.6}$$

Let Γ^* denote a lawlike operator of type $(\bigcup_n C^n)N$. We shall assume

$$\bigwedge \Gamma \bigvee \Gamma^*[\bigwedge \varepsilon \bigvee x \Gamma^* \bar{\varepsilon}x \neq 0 \wedge \bigwedge \sigma(\Gamma^*\sigma \neq 0 \to \bigvee y \bigwedge \eta \in \sigma(\Gamma\eta = y))]. \tag{2.7}$$

A stronger assumption about Γ^* is the so-called *extension principle*:

$$\bigwedge \Gamma^*(\bigwedge \varepsilon \bigvee x \Gamma^* \bar{\varepsilon}x \neq 0 \to \bigwedge \chi \bigvee x \Gamma^* \bar{\chi}x \neq 0). \tag{2.8}$$

In combination with (2.7), the extension principle asserts that every continuous functional defined on lawless sequences of type $(N)C$ is defined on all sequences of type $(N)C$.

The principle of $\bigwedge \varepsilon \bigvee x$-(extensional) continuity may be expressed as follows:

$$\bigwedge \varepsilon \bigvee x W(\varepsilon, x) \to \bigvee \Gamma \bigwedge \varepsilon W(\varepsilon, \Gamma\varepsilon). \tag{2.9}$$

Analogously for $\bigwedge \varepsilon \bigvee a$-continuity etc. In the case of more variables, (2.9) is to be replaced by

$$\bigwedge \varepsilon_1 \ldots \bigwedge \varepsilon_n(\# (\varepsilon_1, \ldots, \varepsilon_n) \to \bigvee x W(\varepsilon_1, \ldots, \varepsilon_n, x)) \to \bigvee \Gamma_n \bigwedge \varepsilon_1 \ldots \bigwedge \varepsilon_n(\# (\varepsilon_1, \ldots, \varepsilon_n) \to W(\varepsilon_1, \ldots, \varepsilon_n, \Gamma_n\langle \varepsilon_1, \ldots, \varepsilon_n \rangle)),$$

where $\#(\varepsilon_1, \ldots, \varepsilon_n)$ is an abbreviation of $\varepsilon_i \not\equiv \varepsilon_j$ for all $i \neq j$, $1 \leqslant i \leqslant n$, $1 \leqslant j \leqslant n$, and where Γ_n denotes a continuous functional acting on n-tuples of lawless sequences with values in N. We can make assumptions about the Γ_n analogous to (2.7), (2.8).

In the case of lawless sequences of type $(N)N$, we can make one further assumption:

$$\bigwedge \Gamma \bigvee e \in K \bigwedge \varepsilon \bigvee x(\Gamma\varepsilon = e\bar{\varepsilon}x \dot{-} 1) \tag{2.10}$$

(see [4], [2]). Hence with (2.9):

$$\bigwedge \varepsilon \bigvee x\, X(\varepsilon, x) \rightarrow \bigvee e \bigwedge n(en \neq 0 \rightarrow \bigwedge \varepsilon \in n\, W(\varepsilon, en \dot{-} 1)), \tag{2.11}$$

$$\bigwedge \varepsilon \bigvee a\, X(\varepsilon, a) \rightarrow \bigvee e \bigwedge n(en \neq 0 \rightarrow \bigvee b \bigwedge \varepsilon \in n\, W(\varepsilon, b)). \tag{2.12}$$

2.2. Let us consider sequences of type $(N)N \times \boldsymbol{R}$, where $\boldsymbol{R}$ is a class of *lawlike* extensional conditions on sequences of type $(N)N$, i.e.

$$R \in \boldsymbol{R} \wedge \chi = \xi \wedge R\chi \rightarrow R\xi,$$

with $\chi, \xi \in (N)N$. For sequences χ of type $(N)N \times \boldsymbol{R}$ we introduce two projection operators π_0, π_1 by stipulating for $\chi \equiv_{\mathrm{Def}} \langle\langle x_n, R_n\rangle\rangle_n$:

$$\pi_0\chi = \langle x_n\rangle_n, \qquad \pi_0\chi n = x_n,$$

$$\pi_1\chi = \langle R_n\rangle_n, \qquad \pi_1\chi n = R_n.$$

2.3. We shall suppose $\boldsymbol{R} = \bigcup_x \boldsymbol{R}_x$; we also assume a (not necessarily extensional) decidable binary relation $\sqsubset$ on $\boldsymbol{R}$ to be given. Choice sequences ($\alpha, \beta, \gamma, \delta$ are used to indicate choice variables) are sequences of type $(N)N \times \boldsymbol{R}$ which satisfy the following general a priori conditions:

(A) $\bigwedge x(\pi_1\alpha(x+1) \sqsubset \pi_1\alpha x)$, $\bigwedge x(\pi_1\alpha x \in \boldsymbol{R}_x)$, $\bigwedge x(\pi_1\alpha x(\pi_0\alpha))$.

At any stage, an initial segment $\bar{\alpha}x$ and the conditions (A) are given, nothing more.

2.4. For a clear intuitive picture we make some further assumptions:

(B) To every $R \in \boldsymbol{R}$ we may associate in a unique way a condition R^* such that

$$\bigwedge R \in \boldsymbol{R} \bigwedge x(R^*x \vee \neg R^*x),$$

$$\bigwedge R \in \boldsymbol{R} \bigwedge \chi \in (N)N(R\chi \leftrightarrow \bigwedge xR^*\bar{\chi}x).$$

(C) $R \in \boldsymbol{R}_x \wedge R' \in \boldsymbol{R}_{x+1} \wedge R' \sqsubset R \rightarrow$

$$\bigwedge a \bigwedge y(y > x+1 \rightarrow (R'^*\bar{a}y \rightarrow R^*\bar{a}y)).$$

In simple examples, (C) is often fulfilled in virtue of the stronger condition $R \sqsubset R' \to \bigwedge x(R^*x \to R'^*x)$.

(D) $\bigwedge R \in \boldsymbol{R}(R^*0), \quad \bigwedge R \in \boldsymbol{R}_0 \bigvee x(R^*\hat{x})$.

(E) $$\bigwedge a \bigwedge x \bigwedge R \in \boldsymbol{R}_x(\bigwedge y \leqslant (x+1)R^*\bar{a}y \to \bigvee R' \in \boldsymbol{R}_{x+1}(R' \sqsubset R \wedge \bigwedge y \leqslant (x+1)R'^*\bar{a}y)),$$

and

$$\bigwedge a \bigwedge x \bigwedge R \in \boldsymbol{R}_x \bigwedge R' \in \boldsymbol{R}_{x+1}(R' \sqsubset R \wedge \bigwedge y \leqslant (x+1)R^*\bar{a}y \wedge \bigwedge y \leqslant (x+1)R'^*\bar{a}y \to \bigvee zR'^*(\bar{a}(x+1) * \hat{z})).$$

In fact we could have taken a weaker condition for (E):

$$\bigwedge a \bigwedge x \bigwedge R \in \boldsymbol{R}_x(\bigwedge y \leqslant (x+1)R^*\bar{a}y \to \bigvee z \bigvee R' \in \boldsymbol{R}_{x+1}(R' \sqsubset R \wedge \bigwedge y \leqslant (x+1)R'^*\bar{a}y \wedge R'^*(\bar{a}(x+1) * \hat{z}))),$$

but the assumption (E) is fulfilled in the relevant examples, and moreover it simplifies the construction of projections in § 4.

2.5. Some other properties which may be assumed for choice sequences are listed for future reference:

(F) There exists a $U \in \boldsymbol{R}$ such that

$$\bigwedge x(U \in \boldsymbol{R}_x),$$

$$\bigwedge R \in \boldsymbol{R}(R \sqsubset U),$$

$$\bigwedge \chi \in (\boldsymbol{N})\boldsymbol{N}(U\chi \leftrightarrow 0 = 0).$$

(U stands for 'universal condition').

(G) $\bigwedge \alpha \bigwedge x \bigvee a \in \boldsymbol{C} \bigvee \beta(\bar{\alpha}x \equiv \bar{\beta}x \wedge \pi_0\beta = a)$.

(H) $\bigwedge a \in \boldsymbol{C} \bigwedge x \bigvee \beta(\bigwedge y < x(\pi_1\beta y \equiv U) \wedge \pi_0\beta = a)$.

2.6. A sequence $\sigma \equiv \langle\langle x_0, R_0\rangle, \ldots, \langle x_n, R_n\rangle\rangle$ is called *admissible* ($\sigma \in \boldsymbol{A}_{\text{adm}}$) in case

$$\bigwedge u < n(R_u \sqsubset R_{u+1}) \wedge \bigwedge u \leqslant n(R_u \in \boldsymbol{R}_u) \wedge$$

$$R_0^*\langle x_0\rangle \wedge (R_1^*\langle x_0\rangle \wedge R_1^*\langle x_0, x_1\rangle) \wedge \ldots \wedge (R_n^*\langle x_0\rangle \wedge \ldots \wedge R_n^*\langle x_0, \ldots, x_n\rangle).$$

$\langle\ \rangle$ is also called admissible.

As a first principle about choice sequences we have

$$\bigwedge \sigma \in \boldsymbol{A}_{\text{adm}} \bigvee \alpha(\alpha \in \sigma). \tag{2.13}$$

If $\equiv$ denotes intensional equality for choice sequences, we require this equality to be decidable:

$$\alpha \equiv \beta \vee \alpha \not\equiv \beta. \tag{2.14}$$

Let X, Y, Z be used for predicates which are π_0-extensional with respect to choice sequences, i.e.

$$X\alpha \wedge \pi_0 \alpha = \pi_0 \beta \to X\beta.$$

We assume a principle of intensional continuity for choice sequences:

$$X(\alpha, \alpha_0, \ldots, \alpha_n) \wedge \not\equiv (\alpha, \alpha_0, \ldots, \alpha_n) \to \bigvee \sigma[\alpha \in \sigma \wedge \bigwedge \beta \in \sigma(\not\equiv (\beta, \alpha_0, \ldots, \alpha_n) \to X(\beta, \alpha_0, \ldots, \alpha_n))]. \tag{2.15}$$

In many examples of notions of choice sequence

$$\alpha \equiv \beta \leftrightarrow \bigwedge x(\pi_0 \alpha x = \pi_0 \beta x \wedge \pi_1 \alpha x \equiv \pi_1 \beta x).$$

This is always true for example when to every $\bar{\alpha}x$ one can find β, γ, y such that $\bar{\alpha}x \equiv \bar{\beta}x \equiv \bar{\gamma}x$, $\bar{\beta}(x+y) \not\equiv \bar{\gamma}(x+y)$. The proof is given by using (2.15).

2.7. In case (A)–(H) are valid for our notion of choice sequence, we have

$$\bigwedge \alpha \bigvee ! x X(\alpha, x) \to \bigvee e \in K \bigwedge \alpha X(\alpha, e(\pi_0 \alpha)) \tag{2.16}$$

(for K and notation $e(\alpha)$ see [4]) or equivalently

$$\bigwedge \alpha \bigvee ! x X(\alpha, x) \to \bigvee e \in K \bigwedge n(en \neq 0 \to \bigwedge \alpha(\pi_0 \alpha \in n \to X(\alpha, en \dot{-} 1))) \tag{2.17}$$

Similarly

$$\bigwedge \alpha \bigvee ! a X(\alpha, a) \to \bigvee e \in K \bigwedge n(en \neq 0 \to \bigvee a \bigwedge \alpha(\pi_0 \alpha \in n \to X(\alpha, a)) \tag{2.18}$$

($\bigwedge \alpha \bigvee ! a$ is interpreted extensionally: $X(\alpha, a) \wedge X(\alpha, b) \to a = b$).

§3. Examples. Below we indicate some notions of choice sequence by specifying $\sqsubset$ and the $\boldsymbol{R}_x$. As special conditions we introduce

$$N_x \equiv_{\mathrm{Def}} \lambda \chi \,.\, [\bigwedge z \geqslant x(\chi z = 0)],$$

$$B_x \equiv_{\mathrm{Def}} \lambda \chi \,.\, [\bigwedge z \geqslant x(\chi z \leqslant 1)].$$

In case of B_x, B_x^* may be stipulated by:

$$B_x^* \bar{a} y \leftrightarrow 0 = 0 \quad \text{in case } y \leqslant x$$

$$B_x^* \bar{a} y \leftrightarrow a(y-1) \leqslant 1 \quad \text{in case } y > x.$$

Similarly for N_x. Now we list examples (I)–(VI):

(I). $\boldsymbol{R}_x \equiv_{\mathrm{Def}} \{U, N_x\}$. $N_{x+1} \sqsubset N_x$, $N_x \sqsubset U$, $U \sqsubset U$.

(II). $\boldsymbol{R}_x \equiv_{\mathrm{Def}} \{U, N_x, B_x\}$. $N_{x+1} \sqsubset N_x$, $B_{x+1} \sqsubset B_x$, $N_{x+1} \sqsubset B_x$, $N_x \sqsubset U$, $B_x \sqsubset U$, $U \sqsubset U$.

(III). $\boldsymbol{R} \equiv \boldsymbol{R}_x \equiv_{\mathrm{Def}} \{U\} \cup \{R_a\colon a \text{ lawlike}, a \in (\boldsymbol{N})\boldsymbol{N}\}$, where $R_a \equiv_{\mathrm{Def}} \lambda\chi \,.\, \chi = a$. $R_a \sqsubset U$, $R_a \sqsubset R_a$, $U \sqsubset U$.

(IV). $\boldsymbol{R} \equiv \boldsymbol{R}_x \equiv_{\mathrm{Def}} \{U\} \cup \{R_x\colon x \in \boldsymbol{N}\}$, where $R_x \equiv_{\mathrm{Def}} \lambda\chi \,.\, (\chi = \lambda y \,.\, a\{x, y\})$; a is supposed to be a fixed universal function for all primitive recursive functions, i.e. $\langle \lambda y \,.\, a\{x, y\}\rangle_x$ enumerates all primitive recursive functions. $R_x \sqsubset U$, $R_x \sqsubset R_x$, $U \sqsubset U$.

(V). Myhill's notion of choice sequence as discussed in [3] (cf. also [**4**], 10.2 (D)), which was inspired by Brouwer, can be reformulated so as to fit our scheme of description; see § 4.

(VI). Like example (V), but with a restriction to primitive recursive spreadlaws as given by an enumerating function.

§4. Projection operators

4.1. We shall consider an easy example first.

Let $\boldsymbol{R}$ contain a single condition

$$R\chi \leftrightarrow \bigwedge x(\chi x = 0 \vee \chi x = 1).$$

We stipulate $\sqsubset$ by $R \sqsubset R$. R^* is specified by

$$R^*\bar{\chi}(x+1) \equiv \chi x = 0 \vee \chi x = 1.$$

$$R^*0 \equiv 0 = 0.$$

Then we have obtained the lawless sequences with values 0, 1 only.

Now we define Proj on lawless sequences of natural numbers as follows: Let $\alpha = \mathrm{Proj}\,\varepsilon$, ε a lawless element of $(\boldsymbol{N})\boldsymbol{N}$.

$$\pi_0\alpha x = 0 \quad \text{if} \quad \bigwedge y \leqslant x\,(\varepsilon y = 0 \vee \varepsilon y = 1) \wedge \varepsilon x = 0,$$

$$\pi_0\alpha x = 1 \quad \text{if} \quad \bigwedge y \leqslant x\,(\varepsilon y = 0 \vee \varepsilon y = 1) \wedge \varepsilon x = 1,$$

$$\pi_0\alpha x = 1 \quad \text{if} \quad \bigvee y \leqslant x\,(\varepsilon y > 1),$$

$$\pi_1\alpha x \equiv R \quad \text{for all } x.$$

Now this is a bad approximation of our notion of choice sequence, since we clearly have (a denoting any lawlike sequence of $(N)N$):

$$\bigwedge \varepsilon \neg\neg \bigvee a\, (\pi_0 \operatorname{Proj} \varepsilon = a)$$

for as soon as $\varepsilon y > 1$ for some y, Proj ε is lawlike; and for lawless sequences we have $\bigwedge \varepsilon \neg\neg \bigvee x\, (\varepsilon x > 1)$.

$\operatorname{Proj}^* \varepsilon$ defined by $\pi_0 \alpha = \lambda x \,.\, \operatorname{sg}(\varepsilon x)$ and $\pi_1 \alpha x \equiv R$ for all x, is a much more accurate approximation; now we have

$$\bigwedge \varepsilon \bigwedge a \neg (\pi_0 \operatorname{Proj}^* \varepsilon = a).$$

The projection operators we shall consider obey the conditions below which guarantee that a certain minimal degree of faithfulness is obtained:

(i) $\overline{\operatorname{Proj} \varepsilon} n$ is determined from $\bar{\varepsilon} n$.

(ii) If $\overline{\operatorname{Proj} \varepsilon} n * \langle x, R \rangle$ satisfies the general conditions imposed by (A) (is an admissible initial segment for the notion of choice sequence considered), then we can find a p such that for η with $\bar{\eta}(n+1) = \bar{\varepsilon} n * \hat{p}$ we have $\overline{\operatorname{Proj} \eta}(n+1) = \overline{\operatorname{Proj} \varepsilon} n * \langle x, R \rangle$.

One might express these conditions by saying that Proj 'preserves local freedom of choice'.

4.2. Let us discuss example (I). We approximate this notion by a projection of lawless sequences of natural numbers. Let $\alpha = \operatorname{Proj} \varepsilon$,

$$\pi_0 \alpha x = \begin{cases} j_1 \varepsilon x & \text{if } \bigwedge u \leqslant x (j_2 \varepsilon u = 0), \\ 0 & \text{otherwise;} \end{cases}$$

$$\pi_1 \alpha x = \begin{cases} U & \text{if } \bigwedge u \leqslant x (j_2 \varepsilon u = 0), \\ N_x & \text{otherwise.} \end{cases}$$

The projected sequences are denoted by $\alpha, \beta, \gamma, \ldots$. The following strong form of extensional continuity holds.

THEOREM 4.1. *Let X be an extensional predicate with a single non-lawlike variable, then*

$$\bigwedge \alpha \bigvee x X(\alpha, x) \to \bigvee e \in K \bigwedge \alpha X(\alpha, e(\pi_0 \alpha))$$

holds.

PROOF. X is extensional, i.e.

$$\pi_0 \alpha = \pi_0 \beta \to (X(\alpha, x) \to X(\beta, x)).$$

Suppose $\bigwedge\alpha\bigvee xX(\alpha, x)$, then $\bigwedge\varepsilon\bigvee xX(\text{Proj}\,\varepsilon, x)$. Using (2.10) for lawless sequences of natural numbers ([2], 2.4) we obtain an $e \in K$ such that $\bigwedge\varepsilon X(\text{Proj}\,\varepsilon, e(\varepsilon))$. Now take any α and define χ by $\chi \equiv_{\text{Def}} \lambda x\,.\,\{\pi_0\alpha x, 0\}$. Let z be such that $e\bar{\chi}z \neq 0$, and let $\pi_0\beta \in \overline{\pi_0\alpha z}$, $\beta = \text{Proj}\,\varepsilon$. Then either $\bar{\varepsilon}z = \bar{\chi}z$ and then $X(\beta, e(\chi))$ since $e(\chi) = e(\varepsilon)$ or

$$\bar{\varepsilon}z = \langle\{\pi_0\alpha 0, 0\}, \ldots, \{\pi_0\alpha u, 0\}, \{0, y_{u+1}\}, \ldots, \{0, y_{z-1}\}\rangle$$

with $y_{u+1} \neq 0$. Then if we take an η with $\bar{\eta}(z+1) = \bar{\chi}z * \langle\{0, 1\}\rangle$ we have $e(\eta) = e(\chi)$ and $\pi_0\,\text{Proj}\,\eta = \pi_0\,\text{Proj}\,\varepsilon$, so $X(\beta, e(\chi))$. Therefore $X(\beta, e(\chi))$ holds in all cases. Next one constructs an $f \in K$ such that

$$f(\overline{\pi_0\alpha z}) = e\langle\{\pi_0\alpha 0, 0\}, \ldots, \{\pi_0\alpha(z-1), 0\}\rangle.$$

Hence $\bigwedge\alpha X(\alpha, f(\pi_0\alpha))$.

To illustrate that finding a suitable projection operator is a rather delicate task we will change the operator defined above slightly and show that for the resulting notion we do not have extensional continuity.

Define the projection operator Proj by $\alpha = \text{Proj}\,\varepsilon$ if

$$\pi_0\alpha x = \begin{cases} j_1\varepsilon x & \text{if} \quad \bigwedge u \leqslant x(j_2\varepsilon u \neq 0), \\ 0 & \text{otherwise;} \end{cases}$$

$$\pi_1\alpha x = \begin{cases} U & \text{if} \quad \bigwedge u \leqslant x(j_2\varepsilon u \neq 0), \\ N_x & \text{otherwise.} \end{cases}$$

One can check that the proof of the above theorem does not go through, but we will do more and prove

THEOREM 4.2. *For suitable $X(\alpha, x)$ we have*

$$\neg(\bigwedge\alpha\bigvee xX(\alpha, x) \to \bigwedge\alpha\bigvee x\bigvee y\bigwedge\beta(\overline{\pi_0\alpha x} = \overline{\pi_0\beta x} \to X(\beta, y)).$$

PROOF. Take for $X(\alpha, x)$ the formula $\bigvee\varepsilon(\pi_0\alpha = \pi_0\,\text{Proj}\,\varepsilon \wedge j_2\varepsilon 0 = x)$. Clearly X is extensional and $\bigwedge\alpha\bigvee xX(\alpha, x)$ holds. Suppose

$$\bigwedge\alpha\bigvee x\bigvee y\bigwedge\beta(\overline{\pi_0\alpha x} = \overline{\pi_0\beta x} \to X(\beta, y)),$$

then

$$\bigwedge\varepsilon\bigvee x\bigvee y\bigwedge\eta(\overline{\pi_0\,\text{Proj}\,\varepsilon x} = \overline{\pi_0\,\text{Proj}\,\eta x} \to X(\text{Proj}\,\eta, y)).$$

Hence there is an $e \in K$ such that

$$\bigwedge\varepsilon\bigwedge\eta(\overline{\pi_0\,\text{Proj}\,\varepsilon}(j_1 e(\varepsilon)) = \overline{\pi_0\,\text{Proj}\,\eta}(j_1 e(\varepsilon)) \to X(\text{Proj}\,\eta, j_2 e(\varepsilon))).$$

Now take $\chi = \lambda x . \{0, 1\}$ and let $e\bar{\chi}u \neq 0$.

Put $j_1 e(\chi) = u_1$ and $j_2 e(\chi) = u_2$, then for any ε with $\bar{\varepsilon}u = \bar{\chi}u$

$$\bigwedge \eta(\overline{\pi_0 \text{ Proj } \varepsilon}\, u_1 = \overline{\pi_0 \text{ Proj } \eta}\, u_1 \to X(\text{Proj } \eta, u_2)).$$

Let $n = \langle 0, 0, \ldots, 0\rangle$ (u_1 times), then

$$\bigwedge \eta(\overline{\pi_0 \text{ Proj } \eta}\, u_1 = n \to X(\text{Proj } \eta, u_2)).$$

Hence for an η such that $\overline{\pi_0 \text{ Proj } \eta}\, u_1 = n$ we have

$$\bigvee \eta'(\pi_0 \text{ Proj } \eta = \pi_0 \text{ Proj } \eta' \wedge j_2\eta' 0 = u_2).$$

Let $Y(\eta, \eta')$ be the matrix of this formula, then

$$Y(\eta, \eta') \leftrightarrow j_2\eta 0 = u_2 \vee \bigvee m[\eta' \in m \wedge$$
$$\bigwedge \eta''((\eta'' \in m \wedge \eta'' \neq \eta) \to \pi_0 \text{ Proj } \eta = \pi_0 \text{ Proj } \eta'' \wedge j_2\eta'' 0 = u_2)]$$

(here we applied $\eta = \eta' \vee \eta \neq \eta'$).

Now choose an η such that $\overline{\pi_0 \text{ Proj } \eta}\, u_1 = n$ and $j_2\eta 0 \neq u_2$, then

$$\bigvee \eta' \bigvee m[\eta' \in m \wedge \bigwedge \eta''((\eta'' \in m \wedge \eta'' \neq \eta) \to$$
$$\pi_0 \text{ Proj } \eta = \pi_0 \text{ Proj } \eta'' \wedge j_2\eta'' 0 = u_2)].$$

Let $\eta \notin m * \langle z\rangle (= m')$ then

$$\bigwedge \eta'' \in m' \, (\pi_0 \text{ Proj } \eta'' = \pi_0 \text{ Proj } \eta),$$

so there exists an m'' such that

$$\eta \in m'' \wedge \bigwedge \eta''' \in m'' \bigwedge \eta'' \in m' \, (\pi_0 \text{ Proj } \eta'' = \pi_0 \text{ Proj } \eta''').$$

From this and the definition of Proj we easily conclude that η is lawlike. Thus

$$\bigwedge \eta(\overline{\pi_0 \text{ Proj } \eta}\, u_1 = n \wedge j_2\eta 0 \neq u_2 \to \bigvee x\, j_2\eta x = 0)$$

or

$$\bigwedge \eta \bigvee x(\overline{\pi_0 \text{ Proj } \eta}\, u_1 = n \wedge j_2\eta 0 \neq u_2 \to j_2\eta x = 0).$$

Again we can find an $f \in K$ such that

$$\bigwedge \eta(\overline{\pi_0 \text{ Proj } \eta}\, u_1 = n \wedge j_2\eta 0 \neq u_2 \to j_2\eta f(\eta) = 0) \qquad (*)$$

Define $\chi' = \lambda x . \{0, u_2 + 1\}$ and let v be such that $f\bar{\chi}'v \neq 0$, $v \geqslant f(\chi')$.

Choose $\eta \in \bar{\chi}'v$, then $j_2\eta f(\eta) = j_2\chi' f(\chi') \neq 0$, which contradicts(*). Therefore we have

$$\neg(\bigwedge\alpha\bigvee x\, X(\alpha, x) \rightarrow \bigwedge\alpha\bigvee x\bigvee y\bigwedge\beta(\overline{\pi_0\alpha}x = \overline{\pi_0\beta}x \rightarrow X(\beta, y)))$$

for the X chosen above.

Remark. We could have strengthened the result by using (2.7) and (2.8) instead of (2.10).

4.3. *Construction of projections.* Suppose a notion of choice sequence to be given which satisfies (A)–(F), and for which the classes $\boldsymbol{R}_x$ may be enumerated as $\{R[p, x]: p \in \boldsymbol{C}\}$. Further we assume $R[p^*, x] \equiv U$ for all x and for a certain fixed $p^* \in \boldsymbol{C}$.

We remark that condition (E) on choice sequences implies the existence of a function $s'' \in (\boldsymbol{C} \times \boldsymbol{N})\boldsymbol{C}$ (in virtue of a selection principle as indicated in 1.5) such that

$$\begin{aligned}\bigwedge a\bigwedge x\bigwedge p \in \boldsymbol{C}(\bigwedge y \leqslant (x+1)R^*[p, x](\bar{a}y) \rightarrow \\ R[s''(p, \bar{a}(x+1)), x+1] \sqsubset R[p, x] \wedge \\ \bigwedge y \leqslant (x+1)R^*[s''(p, \bar{a}(x+1)), x+1](\bar{a}y)).\end{aligned}$$

Now suppose $s' \in (\boldsymbol{C} \times \boldsymbol{N} \times \boldsymbol{C}')\boldsymbol{C}$ to be such that

$$\bigwedge p \in \boldsymbol{C}\bigvee r \in \boldsymbol{C}'(R[s'(p^*, 0, r), 0] \equiv R[p, 0]),$$

$$\begin{aligned}\bigwedge p \in \boldsymbol{C}\bigwedge q \in \boldsymbol{C}\bigwedge x(R[p, x+1] \sqsubset R[q, x] \leftrightarrow \\ \bigvee r \in \boldsymbol{C}'(R[s'(q, x+1, r), x+1] \equiv R[p, x+1])).\end{aligned}$$

We construct $s \in (\boldsymbol{C} \times \boldsymbol{N} \times \boldsymbol{C}')\boldsymbol{C}$ as follows. We put

$$s(p^*, 0, r) \equiv s'(p^*, 0, r).$$

Let $s'(q, x+1, r) \equiv p$; in case $\bigwedge y \leqslant (x+1)R^*[p, x+1](\bar{a}y)$, we take

$$s(q, \bar{a}(x+1), r) \equiv p,$$

and in case $\neg \bigwedge y \leqslant (x+1)R^*[p, x+1](\bar{a}y)$ we take

$$s(q, \bar{a}(x+1), r) \equiv s''(q, \bar{a}(x+1)).$$

Now we define a function $t \in (\boldsymbol{C} \times \boldsymbol{N}^2)\boldsymbol{N}$ such that

$$\{t(p, 0, u) : u \in \boldsymbol{N}\}$$

enumerates the v such that $R^*[p, 0](\hat{v})$, and in case $\bigwedge y \leqslant x R^*[p, x]\bar{a}y$

$$\{t(p, \bar{a}x, u) : u \in N\}$$

enumerates the v such that $R^*[p, x](\bar{a}x * \hat{v})$.

Now we define a projection operator Proj for lawless sequences of type $(N)N \times C'$ as follows. If $\bigwedge n(\varepsilon n \equiv \langle \pi_0 \varepsilon n, \pi_1 \varepsilon n\rangle)$, then

$$\text{Proj } \varepsilon = \langle\langle x_n, R[p(n), n]\rangle\rangle_n$$

is given by

$$p(0) \equiv s(p^*, 0, \pi_1 \varepsilon 0),$$

$$x_0 \;\; = t(p(0), 0, \pi_0 \varepsilon 0),$$

and for $v > 0$

$$p(v) \equiv s(p(v-1), \langle x_0, \ldots, x_{v-1}\rangle, \pi_1 \varepsilon v),$$

$$x_v \;\; = t(p(v), \langle x_0, \ldots, x_{v-1}\rangle, \pi_0 \varepsilon v).$$

4.4. A lawlike function of type $(N)N$ is said to be a *spreadlaw* if

$$a0 \neq 0 \wedge \bigwedge n \bigvee x(an \neq 0 \rightarrow a(n * \hat{x}) \neq 0) \wedge$$
$$\bigwedge n \bigwedge m(a(n * m) \neq 0 \rightarrow an \neq 0) \wedge \bigwedge n(an = 0 \vee an = 1).$$

We write $a \in \text{Spr}$ to indicate that a is a spreadlaw, and $\chi \in a$ is an abbreviation for $\bigwedge x(a\bar{\chi}x \neq 0)$. For spreadlaws a and b we define $a \subseteq b$ by $\bigwedge n(an \neq 0 \rightarrow bn \neq 0)$.

In Myhill's presentation in [3], which was inspired by Brouwer, sequences of pairs $\langle x_k, a_k\rangle$ with $x_k \in N$ and $a_k \in \text{Spr}$ are considered. These sequences must satisfy the conditions

(i) $$a_{k+1} \subseteq a_k \text{ for every } k,$$

and

(ii) $$a_k \langle x_0, \ldots, x_k\rangle \neq 0 \text{ for every } k.$$

As it stands, this notion of choice sequence is not 'basic', since the spreadlaws do not constitute a decidable subclass of the class of lawlike functions, and moreover, $\subseteq$ (which should play the role of $\sqsubset$) is not decidable relative to spreadlaws.

Therefore we describe a modified notion which is 'basic' (i.e. meets our general requirements in section 2), and which is closely related to Myhill's notion.

First we remark that we can codify a spreadlaw by an arbitrary lawlike function (cf. [**1**], p. 181). Let a be a lawlike function of type $(N)N$, then a spreadlaw c is defined by

$$c0 = 1,$$
$$c(n * \hat{x}) = \text{sg}\, cn \cdot \text{sg}(j_2 a\{n, x\} + (1 \dot{-} |x - j_1 an|)),$$

where $\text{sg}\, x = 0$ if $x = 0$, $\text{sg}\, x = 1$ otherwise. Note that the $j_2 a$-part enumerates choices permissible after n, and that the $j_1 a$-part makes certain the existence of at least one choice after n. Let Φ_0 be the (primitive recursive) operator which associates c with a as given above. Conversely, to each spreadlaw $c \in \text{Spr}$ we can find a lawlike a such that $c = \Phi_0 a$: let d be the choice function existing in virtue of $\bigwedge n \bigvee x(cn = 1 \to c(n * \hat{x}) = 1)$, define $a_1\{n, x\} = c(n * \hat{x})$, and $a_2 n = dn$, then if $a = \{a_1, a_2\} = \lambda x\{a_1 x, a_2 x\}$, $\Phi_0 a = c$ holds. (Thus we have constructed an operator Ψ such that $\Phi_0 \Psi c = c$ for $c \in \text{Spr}$.)

We also have a device for codifying subspreads of a given spread. Define d' from a spreadlaw c by

$$d'\{n, x\} = x \cdot c(n * \hat{x}) + (1 \dot{-} c(n * \hat{x})) \cdot c'n,$$

where $c'n = \min\{x : c(n * \hat{x}) = 1\}$. If $c = \Phi_0 a$, d' is primitive recursive in a. For every n, $\lambda x \,.\, d'\{n, x\}$ enumerates all possible 'next choices'. Now we define d primitive recursively from b, a by

$$d0 = 1,$$
$$d(n * \hat{x}) = \text{sg}\, dn \cdot \text{sg}[c(n * \hat{x}) \cdot \text{sg}\, j_2 b\{n, x\} + (1 \dot{-} |x - d'\{n, j_1 bn\}|)],$$

where $c \equiv \Phi_0 a$. Let Φ denote the operator which constructs d from c, b, then $d \equiv \Phi(\Phi_0 a, b)$. We put

$$\Phi_u(a_0, \ldots, a_u) \equiv \Phi(\Phi_{u-1}(a_0, \ldots, a_{u-1}), a_u).$$

Our notion of choice sequence is now described as follows. Let

$$\boldsymbol{R}_u \equiv_{\text{Def}} \{R\langle a_0, \ldots, a_u\rangle : a_0, \ldots, a_u \text{ lawlike}\} \cup \{U\},$$

where

$$R\langle a_0, \ldots, a_u\rangle \equiv_{\text{Def}} \lambda\chi \,.\, [\chi \in \Phi_u(a_0, \ldots, a_u)],\ R\langle\ \rangle \equiv U.$$

$\sqsubset$ is defined by

$$R\langle a_0, \ldots, a_u\rangle \sqsubset R\langle b_0, \ldots, b_v\rangle \quad \text{iff} \quad v+1 = u \quad \text{and} \quad \bigwedge w \leqslant v(a_w \equiv b_w),$$
$$R\langle a_0, \ldots, a_u\rangle \sqsubset U, \qquad U \sqsubset U.$$

$\sqsubset$ is clearly decidable. Take C' to be the class of all finite sequences of lawlike functions, and let C' be the class of all lawlike sequences together with 0. We index R_x in this case by stipulating:

$$R[\langle\ \rangle, x] \equiv U, \quad (p^* \equiv \langle\ \rangle);$$

$$R[\langle a_0, \ldots, a_u\rangle, x] \equiv \begin{cases} R\langle a_0, \ldots, a_u\rangle & \text{in case } u = x, \\ U & \text{otherwise.} \end{cases}$$

The function s'' we may take in this case to be defined by

$$\begin{cases} s''(\langle a_0, \ldots, a_x\rangle, \bar{a}(x+1)) \equiv \langle a_0, \ldots, a_x, \lambda x\,.\,\{1, 1\}\rangle, \\ s'' \equiv 0 \text{ in all other cases} \end{cases}$$

$(\Phi(a, \lambda x\,.\,\{1, 1\}) = a)$. For s' we stipulate

$$\begin{cases} s'(\langle\ \rangle, 0, 0) \equiv \langle\ \rangle, \\ s'(\langle\ \rangle, x, a) \equiv \langle a\rangle \quad \text{for all } x, \\ s'(\langle a_0, \ldots, a_x\rangle, x+1, a) = \langle a_0, \ldots, a_x, a\rangle, \\ s'(p, x, r) \equiv \langle\ \rangle \quad \text{in other cases.} \end{cases}$$

Now the projection-operator defined on lawless sequences of type $(N)N \times C'$ may be constructed as indicated in the previous subsection.

4.5. In the case of example (VI), we simply take all primitive recursive spreadlaws enumerated by a universal function; note that $\Phi_0 a$, $\Phi(\Phi_0 a, b)$ are primitive recursive in a, b.

For the enumerating class C' one may take N in this case, and one obtains an approximation by a suitable projection of lawless sequences of type $(N)N$. Details, which are similar to those in the case of example (V), are left to the reader.

§5. $\bigwedge \alpha \bigvee x$-continuity.

From theorem 4.2 we saw that $\bigwedge \alpha \bigvee x$-continuity is not always valid for projected sequences of the types considered. In fact, there are many more cases in which $\bigwedge \alpha \bigvee x$-continuity can be disproved; adapting the trick from theorem 4.2 to the choice sequences themselves we succeed for example in disproving $\bigwedge \alpha \bigvee x$-continuity for our example (II), taking for $X(\alpha, x)$:

$$\bigvee \beta(\pi_0 \alpha = \pi_0 \beta \wedge [(x = 0 \wedge \pi_1 \beta 0 \equiv U) \vee (x = 1 \wedge \pi_1 \beta 0 \equiv B_0) \vee (x = 2 \wedge \pi_1 \beta 0 \equiv N_0)]).$$

Similarly, $\bigwedge \alpha \bigvee a$-continuity may be disproved for example (V) by taking

$$X(\alpha, a) \equiv_{\mathrm{Def}} \bigvee \beta[\pi_0 \alpha = \pi_0 \beta \wedge (\pi_1 \beta 0 \equiv \lambda \chi . \chi \in \Phi_0(a) \vee (a \equiv \lambda x . 1 \wedge \pi_1 \beta 0 \equiv U))].$$

§6. Extensional continuity. In this section we will prove extensional continuity for an extensive class of notions of projected sequence. We shall employ (2.6)–(2.9) in the form

$$\bigwedge \varepsilon \bigvee x X(\varepsilon, x) \rightarrow \bigvee \Gamma \bigwedge \varepsilon X(\varepsilon, \Gamma \varepsilon),$$

where Γ is a continuous operator (ε lawless of type $(N)C'$).

In the following χ, ξ will be arbitrary sequences of type $(N)C'$ and $\varepsilon, \eta, \zeta, \vartheta$ are lawless sequences of type $(N)C'$. α, β, γ denote projected sequences. We now list some properties of Proj.

(1) $\bigwedge \chi[\bigwedge x(\pi_1 \operatorname{Proj} \chi x \equiv U) \rightarrow \bigwedge a \bigwedge y(a \in \overline{\pi_0 \operatorname{Proj} \chi y} \rightarrow \bigvee \varepsilon(\bar{\varepsilon} y \equiv \bar{\chi} y \wedge \pi_0 \operatorname{Proj} \varepsilon = a))]$,

(2) $\bigwedge x \bigwedge \varepsilon \bigvee a \bigvee \eta(\bar{\varepsilon} x \equiv \bar{\eta} x \wedge \pi_0 \operatorname{Proj} \eta = a)$,

(3) $\bigwedge \alpha \bigvee \chi \bigwedge x[\pi_0 \operatorname{Proj} \chi x = \pi_0 \alpha x \wedge \pi_1 \operatorname{Proj} \chi x \equiv U]$,

(4) $\bigwedge n \bigwedge \xi \bigwedge \chi(\bar{\xi} n \equiv \bar{\chi} n \rightarrow \overline{\operatorname{Proj} \xi} n \equiv \overline{\operatorname{Proj} \chi} n)$.

LEMMA 6.1. *Assume* (1)–(4) *and let* $X(\alpha, x)$ *be extensional, then*

$$\bigwedge \alpha \bigvee ! x X(\alpha, x) \rightarrow \bigwedge \alpha \bigvee ! x \bigvee y \bigwedge \beta(\overline{\pi_0 \alpha} y = \overline{\pi_0 \beta} y \rightarrow X(\beta, x)).$$

PROOF. Suppose $\bigwedge \alpha \bigvee ! x X(\alpha, x)$. Then we have $\bigwedge \varepsilon \bigvee ! x X(\operatorname{Proj} \varepsilon, x)$, hence there is a Γ such that

$$\bigwedge \varepsilon X(\operatorname{Proj} \varepsilon, \Gamma \varepsilon).$$

Moreover

$$\pi_0 \operatorname{Proj} \varepsilon = \pi_0 \operatorname{Proj} \eta \rightarrow \Gamma \varepsilon = \Gamma \eta. \tag{5}$$

Take any $\alpha \equiv \operatorname{Proj} \varepsilon$. Then we can find a χ such that

$$\bigwedge x[\pi_0 \operatorname{Proj} \chi x = \pi_0 \alpha x \wedge \pi_1 \operatorname{Proj} \chi x \equiv U]$$

(by (3)). We suppose Γ to be defined on all functions of $(N)C'$. There exists an n such that

$$\Gamma \chi = x \leftrightarrow \bigwedge \xi(\bar{\xi} n \equiv \bar{\chi} n \rightarrow \Gamma \xi = x). \tag{6}$$

Now suppose

$$\beta \equiv \operatorname{Proj} \zeta,$$

$$\overline{\pi_0 \beta n} = \overline{\pi_0 \alpha n} = \overline{\pi_0 \operatorname{Proj} \chi n}.$$

Then we can find x', n' such that

$$\Gamma\zeta = x' \leftrightarrow \bigwedge \xi(\bar{\xi}n' \equiv \bar{\zeta}n' \to \Gamma\xi = x'). \tag{7}$$

We may suppose $n' \geqslant n$. Furthermore there are m, z such that

$$\Gamma\varepsilon = z \leftrightarrow \bigwedge \xi(\bar{\xi}m = \bar{\varepsilon}m \to \Gamma\xi = z), \ m \geqslant n'.$$

Now there exist by (2) ε_1, a such that

$$\bar{\varepsilon}_1 m = \bar{\varepsilon}m \wedge \pi_0 \operatorname{Proj} \varepsilon_1 = a,$$

hence

$$\Gamma\chi = \Gamma\varepsilon = \Gamma\varepsilon_1. \tag{8}$$

By (1), we can find an η such that

$$\bar{\chi}m \equiv \bar{\eta}m \wedge \pi_0 \operatorname{Proj} \eta = a,$$

since $a \in \overline{\pi_0 \operatorname{Proj} \chi m}$. Also

$$\Gamma\chi = \Gamma\eta \tag{9}$$

(since $m \geqslant n$). Furthermore

$$\Gamma\varepsilon = \Gamma\chi = \Gamma\eta.$$

On account of (2), there are ϑ, b such that

$$\bar{\zeta}n' \equiv \bar{\vartheta}n' \wedge \pi_0 \operatorname{Proj} \vartheta = b \tag{10}$$

and because of (1) ϑ_1 exists such that

$$\bar{\vartheta}_1 n \equiv \bar{\chi}n \wedge \pi_0 \operatorname{Proj} \vartheta_1 = b \tag{11}$$

(since $b \in \overline{\pi_0 \operatorname{Proj} \chi n}$; this follows from

$$b \in \overline{\pi_0 \operatorname{Proj} \zeta n} = \overline{\pi_0 \beta n} = \overline{\pi_0 \alpha n} = \overline{\pi_0 \operatorname{Proj} \chi n}).$$

Therefore by (10), (7) and (11), (6)

$$\Gamma\zeta = \Gamma\vartheta \wedge \Gamma\chi = \Gamma\vartheta_1$$

hence using π_0 Proj $\vartheta = \pi_0$ Proj ϑ_1, (8)

$$\Gamma\zeta = \Gamma\chi = \Gamma\varepsilon.$$

Therefore with $\overline{\pi_0\beta n} = \overline{\pi_0\alpha n}$ etc.

$$\bigwedge\alpha\bigvee!xX(\alpha, x) \to \bigwedge\alpha\bigvee!x\bigvee y\bigwedge\beta(\bar{\alpha}y = \bar{\beta}y \to X(\beta, x)).$$

Remark I. A completely parallel argument may be given to prove:

$$\bigwedge\alpha\bigvee!aX(\alpha, a) \to \bigwedge\alpha\bigvee!a\bigvee y\bigwedge\beta(\overline{\pi_0\alpha}y = \overline{\pi_0\beta}y \to X(x, a))$$

under the same conditions.

Remark II. In the conditions (1), (2) of the lemma, the quantifiers $\bigwedge a$, $\bigvee a$ may be restricted to a species $\boldsymbol{Y}$ say $\bigwedge a \in \boldsymbol{Y}$, $\bigvee a \in \boldsymbol{Y}$. This does not alter the proof.

LEMMA 6.2. *Suppose the conditions* (1)–(4) *for our projection operator to be fulfilled, and let an operator* Γ' *of type* $((\boldsymbol{N})\boldsymbol{N})(\boldsymbol{N})\boldsymbol{C}'$ *be given which transforms* $\pi_0\alpha$ *into a sequence* $\chi \equiv_{\mathrm{Def}} \Gamma'\pi_0\alpha$ *which satisfies the requirements of condition* (3). *Then for projected sequences*

$$\bigwedge\alpha\bigvee!xX(\alpha, x) \to \bigvee e\bigwedge\alpha X(\alpha, e(\pi_0\alpha)).$$

PROOF. Let Γ be the operator of type $((\boldsymbol{N})\boldsymbol{C}')\boldsymbol{N}$ introduced in the proof of lemma 6.1. Since Γ is defined for any χ of type $(\boldsymbol{N})\boldsymbol{C}'$ (on account of the extension property), Γ is certainly defined for all $\Gamma'\varepsilon$, ε lawless of type $(\boldsymbol{N})\boldsymbol{N}$. Therefore (formula 2.10)

$$\bigvee e \in K\bigwedge\chi \in (\boldsymbol{N})\boldsymbol{N}(\Gamma\Gamma'\chi = e(\chi))$$

and hence

$$\bigwedge\alpha X(\alpha, e(\pi_0\alpha)).$$

THEOREM 6.3. *Let a notion of choice sequence be given for which* (A)–(H) *are satisfied, and let* Proj *be a projection operator corresponding to this notion which is constructed as indicated in subsection* 4.3. *Then for the projected sequences*:

$$\bigwedge\alpha\bigvee!xX(\alpha, x) \to \bigvee e\bigwedge\alpha X(\alpha, e(\pi_0\alpha)).$$

PROOF. Assume for simplicity the $\boldsymbol{C}$ in (G), (H) to be the collection of all lawlike sequences. We have to verify the validity of (1)–(4), in order to be able to apply the previous lemma. The validity of (4) is immediate. (1) is derived from (H) as follows. Let χ satisfy $\bigwedge x(\pi_1 \text{ Proj } \chi x \equiv U)$ and

$a \in \pi_0$ Proj χy. According to (H) there exists a choice sequence β such that

$$\bigwedge z < y(\pi_1 \beta z \equiv U) \wedge \pi_0 \beta = a.$$

Hence by 2.15 for some $\sigma \in \boldsymbol{A}_{\mathrm{adm}}$

$$\bigwedge \beta \in \sigma[\bigwedge z < y(\pi_1 \beta z \equiv U) \wedge \pi_0 \beta = a].$$

Suppose lth $\sigma > y$. Then for any $\xi \in \sigma$ such that $\bigwedge x(\bar{\xi} x \in \boldsymbol{A}_{\mathrm{adm}})$ we have

$$\bigwedge z < y(\pi_1 \xi z \equiv U) \wedge \pi_0 \xi = a.$$

For suppose $u \geqslant$ lth σ, then we can find a $\beta \in \sigma$ such that $\beta \in \bar{\xi}(u+1)$. Then $\pi_0 \beta = a$, so $\pi_0 \beta u = au = \pi_0 \xi u$; hence $\pi_0 \xi = a$. By our method of constructing Proj, $\bigvee \varepsilon(\text{Proj } \varepsilon \in \sigma)$ holds. Therefore

$$\bigwedge z < y(\pi_1 \text{ Proj } \varepsilon z \equiv U \wedge \pi_0 \text{ Proj } \varepsilon = a),$$

and thus

$$\bigvee \varepsilon(\bar{\varepsilon} y \equiv \bar{\chi} y \wedge \pi_0 \text{ Proj } \varepsilon = a).$$

(2) is derived from (G). We have to prove

$$\bigwedge x \bigwedge \varepsilon \bigvee a \bigvee \eta(\bar{\varepsilon} x \equiv \bar{\eta} x \wedge \pi_0 \text{ Proj } \eta = a).$$

Take any $\bar{\varepsilon} x$. (G) can be rewritten as

$$\bigwedge \sigma \in \boldsymbol{A}_{\mathrm{adm}} \bigvee \beta(\beta \in \sigma \wedge \pi_0 \beta = a).$$

Take $\sigma \equiv \overline{\text{Proj } \varepsilon} x \in \boldsymbol{A}_{\mathrm{adm}}$. Then

$$\bigvee \beta(\beta \in \sigma \wedge \pi_0 \beta = a),$$

and hence for some σ' (σ' an extension of σ)

$$\bigwedge \gamma \in \sigma'(\pi_0 \gamma = a).$$

By the preservation of 'local freedom of choice' for our projection operators we can find an η such that $\bar{\eta} x \equiv \bar{\varepsilon} x$ and Proj $\eta \in \sigma'$. Hence π_0 Proj $\eta = a$ (by a reasoning analogous to the argument given above).

(3) is satisfied automatically if we construct a Γ' as required in lemma 6.2. Γ' is constructed by giving a simultaneous recursive definition of certain continuous operators $\Gamma'' \in ((N)N)(N)N$, $\Gamma''' \in ((N)N)(N)C'$, such that Γ' is then given by

$$\lambda \chi \,.\, [\lambda x \,.\, \langle \Gamma'' \chi x, \Gamma''' \chi x \rangle].$$

Let ξ denote a sequence of $(N)N$. We can find $r_0 \in C'$, and a lawlike function c such that

$$R[p^*, 0] \equiv R[s(p^*, 0, r_0), 0]$$
$$z = t(p^*, 0, cz)$$

Let P_x denote the class $\{p: R[p, x] \equiv U\}$.

Now we may define a lawlike function φ such that

$$R[p^*, w] \equiv R[s(p, \bar{a}w, \varphi(\bar{a}w, p)), w]$$

for $w > 0$, $p \in P_w$ (we have made use of a selection principle here). Also we suppose Ψ to be such that

$$x = t(p, \bar{a}w, \Psi(p, \bar{a}w, x))$$

for $w > 0$, $p \in P_w$.

Now let $\Gamma''\xi \equiv \mu$, $\Gamma'''\xi \equiv \nu$. Then Γ'', Γ''' are defined by:

$$p_0^* \equiv p^*, \qquad \nu 0 \equiv r_0, \qquad \mu 0 = c\xi 0;$$
$$p_1^* \equiv s(p_0^*, \bar{\mu}1, \nu 0), \qquad \nu 1 \equiv \varphi(\bar{\mu}1, p_0^*), \qquad \mu 1 = \Psi(p_1^*, \bar{\mu}1, \xi 1);$$
$$p_n^* \equiv s(p_{n-1}^*, \bar{\mu}n, \nu(n-1)), \qquad \nu n \equiv \varphi(\bar{\mu}n, p_{n-1}^*), \qquad \mu n = \Psi(p_n^*, \bar{\mu}n, \xi n).$$

The verification that Γ has the required properties is now straightforward.

§7. Approximation relative to a restricted language.

7.1. As we have seen, projections approximate the corresponding choice sequences to a certain extent, but not completely. However, we might ask if projections associated with a certain notion of choice sequence yield better approximations if we make suitable restrictions on our language.

Let us consider a simple example as an illustration. Let Δ denote the continuous operator on sequences defined by:

$$\Delta\chi = \lambda x \,.\, \chi(x+1).$$

If $\varepsilon, \eta, \ldots$ are lawless sequences of $(N)N$, we may consider the sequences $\Delta\varepsilon, \Delta\eta, \ldots$; in many respects, these sequences behave like lawless sequences, although not entirely so. For if we use $\alpha, \beta, \ldots$ as variables for Δ-transformed lawless sequences, we have

$$\bigwedge \alpha \bigvee \varepsilon(\alpha = \Delta\varepsilon),$$

whereas

$$\neg \bigwedge \eta \bigvee \varepsilon(\eta = \Delta\varepsilon)$$

(even more, $\bigwedge \eta \bigwedge \varepsilon \neg (\eta = \varDelta\varepsilon)$, as is readily proved). Therefore these $\varDelta$-transforms are certainly not lawless sequences. One verifies easily

$$\varepsilon = \eta \leftrightarrow \varDelta\varepsilon = \varDelta\eta.$$

Continuity does not hold. Take $X(\alpha, x)$ to be:

$$X(\alpha, x) \equiv_{\text{Def}} \bigvee \varepsilon(\alpha = \varDelta\varepsilon \wedge \varepsilon 0 = x),$$

then X is extensional, and also $\bigwedge \alpha \bigvee ! x X(\alpha, x)$, but not

$$\bigwedge \alpha \bigvee x \bigvee y \bigwedge \beta(\bar{\alpha}x = \bar{\beta}x \rightarrow X(\beta, y));$$

this is easily refuted. But this disproof of $\bigwedge \alpha \bigvee x$-continuity uses a property which refers explicitly to the lawless sequences from which the $\varDelta$-transforms were obtained.

We may suspect that $\bigwedge \alpha \bigvee x$-continuity would hold in cases where $X(\alpha, x)$ does not explicitly refer to the original lawless sequence. This turns out to be true, in a sense which will be explained below.

7.2. Let $\mathscr{L}$ denote a second order language with variables for lawless sequences of type $(N)N$: $\varepsilon, \eta, \zeta, \vartheta$; variables for numbers: x, y, z, u, v, w, n, m; variables for lawlike functions: a, b, c, d; function constants for certain primitive recursive functions, like 0, $^+$, $+$, $\cdot$ etc.; a constant predicate K for lawlike functions, and a binary predicate $=$ for numbers. The logical operators are those of three sorted intuitionistic predicate calculus: $\wedge$, $\vee$, $\neg$, $\rightarrow$, $\bigwedge x$, $\bigvee x$, $\bigwedge \varepsilon$, $\bigvee \varepsilon$, $\bigwedge a$, $\bigvee a$.

Terms, atomic formulae and formulae are defined as usual; let Tm denote the class of terms, Fm the class of formulae.

Let $\varGamma$ be a continuous operator of type $((N)N)(N)N$. Fm($\varGamma$) consists of formulae which are obtained by replacing in each $F \in$ Fm every occurrence of a lawless variable by its $\varGamma$-transform, i.e. ε by $\varGamma\varepsilon$.

Now the following two assertions may be proved* for $\varGamma = \varDelta$, $\varGamma = \varGamma_b$ (definition follows), under the condition $\varepsilon = \eta \leftrightarrow \varGamma_b\varepsilon = \varGamma_b\eta$:

(i) For any $X \in \text{Fm}(\varGamma)$

$$X(\varepsilon, \varepsilon_0, \ldots, \varepsilon_n) \rightarrow \{\varGamma\varepsilon = \varGamma\varepsilon_0 \vee \ldots \vee \varGamma\varepsilon = \varGamma\varepsilon_n \vee \bigvee n[\varGamma\varepsilon \in n \wedge \bigwedge \eta(\varGamma\eta \in n \wedge \varGamma\eta \neq \varGamma\varepsilon_0 \wedge \ldots \wedge \varGamma\eta \neq \varGamma\varepsilon_n \rightarrow X(\eta, \varepsilon_0, \ldots, \varepsilon_n))]\},$$

* We are indebted to professor G. Kreisel for a hint towards the proof.

and the principle of Γ-continuity:

(ii) for any $X \in \mathrm{Fm}(\Gamma)$,

$$\bigwedge \varepsilon \bigvee x X(\varepsilon, x) \rightarrow \bigvee e \in K \bigwedge \varepsilon X(\varepsilon, e(\Gamma\varepsilon)).$$

For any lawlike b, Γ_b is defined by first introducing a lawlike function g, defined from b by primitive recursion:

$$g0 = 0,$$

$$g(n * \hat{x}) = b\{gn, \{x, \mathrm{lth}(n)\}\}$$

and then putting

$$\Gamma_b \chi = \lambda x \,.\, g(\bar{\chi}(x+1)).$$

The condition

$$\varepsilon = \eta \leftrightarrow \Gamma_b \varepsilon = \Gamma_b \eta$$

is ensured when

$$\bigwedge n \bigvee m \bigvee x \bigvee y\; g(n * m * \hat{x}) \neq g(n * m * \hat{y}). \tag{1}$$

A simple case of an operation Γ_b is the Γ defined by an (arbitrary) c such that

$$\Gamma\chi = \lambda x \,.\, c\{x, \chi x\}.$$

In order to ensure (1), we may require

$$\bigwedge x \bigvee y \bigvee z \bigvee z'(c\{y, z\} \neq c\{y, z'\} \wedge y > x).$$

We expect that much more general results in this direction can be proved; we hope to return to this matter in a further installment. Therefore we omit proofs.

7.3. Let us make a simple application to our example (I). Let for any x, $k_1 x$ be defined as $[x/2]$ (the maximal n such that $2n \leqslant x$). We put $k_2 x = x - 2k_1 x$. Now we define Proj_1 by:

$$\pi_0 \,\mathrm{Proj}_1\, \varepsilon x = \begin{cases} k_1 \varepsilon x & \text{if } \bigwedge u \leqslant x(k_2 \varepsilon u = 1), \\ 0 & \text{otherwise;} \end{cases}$$

$$\pi_1 \,\mathrm{Proj}_1\, \varepsilon x = \begin{cases} U & \text{if } \bigwedge u \leqslant x(k_2 \varepsilon u = 1), \\ N_x & \text{otherwise.} \end{cases}$$

By a simple adaptation of the proof of theorem 4.1 we see that we can prove continuity in the form:

$$\bigwedge \alpha \bigvee ! x X(\alpha, x) \rightarrow \bigvee e \in K \bigwedge \alpha X(\alpha, e(\alpha)). \tag{2}$$

Moreover, we see that in case X is such that $X(\alpha, x) \leftrightarrow X'(\pi_0 \alpha, x)$, $X'(\varepsilon, x) \in \mathrm{Fm}$, (2) can be proved from

$$\bigwedge \varepsilon \bigvee x Y(\varepsilon, x) \rightarrow \bigvee e \in K \bigwedge \varepsilon Y(\varepsilon, e(\varepsilon))$$

for $Y \in \mathrm{Fm}$. Now, if we define Γ_1 by

$$\Gamma_1 \varepsilon x = 2 j_1 \varepsilon x + \mathrm{sg}(j_2 \varepsilon x),$$

then Γ_1-continuity is valid.

Remark that $\mathrm{Proj}_1\, \Gamma_1$ is exactly the representation as defined in § 4 (theorem 4.2). Because of Γ_1-continuity and the remark made above, it follows that $\pi_0\, \mathrm{Proj}_1\, \Gamma_1$-continuity holds, i.e.

$$\bigwedge \alpha \bigvee x X(\alpha, x) \rightarrow \bigvee e \in K \bigwedge \alpha X(\alpha, e(\pi_0 \alpha))$$

holds for $\mathrm{Proj}_1\, \Gamma_1$-projections if X is such that for some $X'(\varepsilon, x) \in \mathrm{Fm}$

$$X(\alpha, x) \leftrightarrow X'(\pi_0 \alpha, x).$$

Rijksuniversiteit te Utrecht
Universiteit van Amsterdam

REFERENCES

[1] G. Kreisel, Informal rigour and completeness proofs, in *Problems in the philosophy of mathematics*, Amsterdam (1967) 138–186.

[2] G. Kreisel, Lawless sequences of natural numbers, *Compos. Math.* **20** (1968) 222–248.

[3] J. Myhill, Notes towards a formalization of intuitionistic analysis, *Logique et Analyse* **35** (1967) 280–297.

[4] A. S. Troelstra, The theory of choice sequences, in *Logic, methodology and philosophy of science III*, North-Holland, Amsterdam (1968) 332–354. *Errata:* page 221, line 14, read '$\bigwedge \beta \in \alpha$' for '$\bigwedge \beta$'; lines −9, −10 read '$fn \dot{-} 1$' for '$en \dot{-} 1$'.

[5] A. S. Troelstra, Informal theory of choice sequences, to appear in *Studia Logica*.

ON SUBJECTIVE MATHEMATICAL ASSERTIONS*

B. VAN ROOTSELAAR

According to Brouwer, mathematics is an individual mental activity and for that reason we need not be surprised that Brouwer's intuitionism shows a certain subjective aspect. This aspect appears particularly explicitly in his papers **[1]**, **[2]**, where he defined choice sequences depending on the experiences of the mathematician defining them (the creative subject). These examples will be the starting point for our discussion.

Brouwer's prescription of the creative subject's choice activity is quite unambiguous and runs essentially as follows:

1. The creative subject should take in mind a non-tested mathematical assertion $\mathfrak{A}$, i.e. a mathematical assertion for which no proof is known of $\neg\mathfrak{A} \vee \neg\neg\mathfrak{A}$.

2. Then he creates a choice sequence $\alpha = \{\alpha(n)\}$ according to the following prescription: as long as he has experienced neither the truth of $\neg\mathfrak{A}$ nor that of $\neg\neg\mathfrak{A}$ he chooses $\alpha(n) = 0$: but as soon as he has experienced the truth of $\mathfrak{A}$ after the choice of $\alpha(r-1)$, but before that of $\alpha(r)$ he chooses $\alpha(r+n) = 2^{-r}$ for all n; and as soon as the truth of $\neg\mathfrak{A}$ has been experienced between the choices of $\alpha(s-1)$ and $\alpha(s)$ he chooses $\alpha(s+n) = -2^{-s}$ for all n.

Then the sequence α converges and determines a real number a. At the moment we are not interested in the use Brouwer made of this construction, but concentrate on its subjective aspects.

As early as 1949, D. van Dantzig emphasized the ambiguity in Brouwer's terminology and tried to give subjectivistic as well as objectivistic interpretations of his terminology. In particular he proposed the subjectivistic interpretation of the term *mathematical assertion* as one of which the creative subject never will be in doubt as to whether it has or has not been proved by him.

This interpretation essentially has reappeared in Kreisel's more formal

* Revised Nov. 1, 1968.

treatment in his **[6]** as one of the axioms for the creative subject (formula (1) below).

In that paper G. Kreisel took the step of using Brouwer's notion of creative subject in a formal way in order to derive purely mathematical results. He deviated from Brouwer, who essentially recognized only one creative subject, by taking into consideration the existence of many (more than one) creative subjects.

His fundamental notion is

$$\Sigma \vdash_m \mathfrak{A}$$

to be read as: the creative subject Σ has evidence for asserting A at stage m.

Instead of Kreisel's $\Sigma \vdash_m \mathfrak{A}$ we shall use in the following

$$\mathrm{P}(\sigma, m, \mathfrak{A})$$

where σ is a variable for creative subjects.

In **[6]** Kreisel accepted the following axioms:

(1). $$\mathrm{P}(\sigma, m, \mathfrak{A}) \vee \neg \mathrm{P}(\sigma, m, \mathfrak{A})$$

(2). $$\mathfrak{A} \rightarrow (\sigma) \neg \neg (Em)\mathrm{P}(\sigma, m, \mathfrak{A})$$
$$(\sigma)[(Em)\mathrm{P}(\sigma, m, \mathfrak{A}) \rightarrow \mathfrak{A}]$$

In **[9]** the present author proposed

(3′). $$\mathfrak{A} \leftrightarrow (E\sigma)\mathrm{T}(\sigma, \mathfrak{A})$$

meaning: $\mathfrak{A}$ is true if and only if there is a creative subject σ, who has experienced the truth of A. The reference to stages was left out ($\mathrm{T}(\sigma, \mathfrak{A}) = (Em)\mathrm{P}(\sigma, m, \mathfrak{A})$), and in comparison to (2) there is equivalence instead of implication. Subsequently in **[10]** A. S. Troelstra rendered Kreisel's axioms as follows:

$$\mathrm{P}(\sigma, m, \mathfrak{A}) \vee \neg \mathrm{P}(\sigma, m, \mathfrak{A}),$$
$$\mathfrak{A} \rightarrow (\sigma) \neg \neg (Em)\mathrm{P}(\sigma, m, \mathfrak{A}),$$

(3). $$(E\sigma)(Em)\mathrm{P}(\sigma, m, \mathfrak{A}) \leftrightarrow \mathfrak{A}.$$

So the second part of (2) has been reinforced to (3) (similarly to (3′)). The first axiom of (2) is equivalent to

(2a). $$\neg (En)\mathrm{P}(\sigma, n, \mathfrak{A}) \rightarrow \neg \mathfrak{A},$$

Kreisel's axiom of christian charity, as reported by J. Myhill in [7], which seems to formalize a well-known argument of Brouwer's:

(4). *if the creative subject has evidence that he will never assert* $\mathfrak{A}$, *then he has evidence to assert* $\neg\,\mathfrak{A}$.

We shall return to this below for the motivation of axiom (6). First some observations are made in connection with the representation of subjectivity.

If the creative subject enters explicitly into the formalization of Brouwer's example and if at the same time we do not restrict ourselves to one creative subject, the resulting sequence in the example may be denoted by

$$\{\alpha(\sigma, \mathfrak{A})n\},$$

and its limit by $a(\sigma, \mathfrak{A})$. If this concept is to be really subjective, we should not have

$$a(\sigma, \mathfrak{A}) = a(\tau, \mathfrak{A})$$

for all σ and τ. However we are not able to derive a mathematical assertion to this effect, without making a further assumption. Note that in general one objects against Brouwer's definition on account of the fact that there is no proof for

$$(\sigma)(\tau)(n)(\alpha(\sigma, \mathfrak{A})(n) = \alpha(\tau, \mathfrak{A})(n)).$$

If we recall that

$$\alpha(\sigma, \mathfrak{A})(n) = 0 \leftrightarrow \neg\, \mathrm{P}(\sigma, n, \neg\mathfrak{A} \vee \neg\,\neg\mathfrak{A}),$$

$$(n)\alpha(\sigma, \mathfrak{A})(r+n) = 2^{-r} \leftrightarrow \mathrm{P}(\sigma, r, \mathfrak{A}),$$

$$(n)\alpha(\sigma, \mathfrak{A})(s+n) = -2^{-s} \leftrightarrow \mathrm{P}(\sigma, s, \neg\, \mathfrak{A}),$$

we see that $(En)(\alpha(\sigma, A)(n) \neq \alpha(\tau, \mathfrak{A})(n))$ implies $a(\sigma, A) \neq a(\tau, \mathfrak{A})$, hence if we assume $a(\sigma, \mathfrak{A}) = a(\tau, \mathfrak{A})$, it follows that

$$(n)(\alpha(\sigma, \mathfrak{A})(n) = \alpha(\tau, \mathfrak{A})(n));$$

consequently

$$(n)(\mathrm{P}(\sigma, n, \mathfrak{A}) \leftrightarrow \mathrm{P}(\tau, n, \mathfrak{A})),$$

an assertion we should like to deny, e.g. by

(5). $$\neg\,(\sigma)(\tau)(n)(\mathrm{P}(\sigma, n, \mathfrak{A}) \leftrightarrow \mathrm{P}(\tau, n, \mathfrak{A})),$$

for non-tested $\mathfrak{A}$. This formula expresses a minimal amount of freedom of deduction for creative subjects.

A formulation of non-testedness of $\mathfrak{A}$, implicit already in van Dantzig [**4**], is

$$\text{nontest}(\sigma, n, \mathfrak{A}) \leftrightarrow \neg\, \mathrm{P}(\sigma, n, (Em)\mathrm{P}(\sigma, m, \neg\mathfrak{A} \vee \neg\neg\mathfrak{A})).$$

On the basis of this definition it is clear how we are to ensure the intended minimal freedom of deduction for creative subjects and so obtain provable subjectivity (in various degrees).

Just as it seems to be reasonable to require a minimal amount of freedom of deduction, it seems reasonable also to put an upper bound on this freedom. In other words the creative subject should accept evidence on account of his having accepted other evidence, which leads one e.g. to assume

$$\mathrm{P}(\sigma, n, \mathfrak{A} \wedge \mathfrak{B}) \leftrightarrow \mathrm{P}(\sigma, n, \mathfrak{A}) \wedge \mathrm{P}(\sigma, n, \mathfrak{B}),$$

further:

$$\text{if } \mathrm{P}(\sigma, n, \mathfrak{A}) \text{ and } \mathrm{P}(\sigma, n, \mathfrak{A} \to \mathfrak{B}) \text{ then } \mathrm{P}(\sigma, n, \mathfrak{B}) \text{ for all } \mathfrak{A} \text{ and } \mathfrak{B},$$

and

$$\mathrm{P}(\sigma, n, \mathfrak{A} \to \mathfrak{B}) \to \mathrm{P}(\sigma, n, \mathfrak{A}) \to \mathrm{P}(\sigma, n, \mathfrak{B}).$$

Also

$$\text{if } \mathrm{P}(\sigma, m, (n)(\mathfrak{A}(n) \to \mathfrak{B}(n))) \text{ then } \mathrm{P}(\sigma, m, (n)\mathfrak{A}(n) \to (n)\mathfrak{B}(n)),$$

and

$$\text{if } \mathrm{P}(\sigma, m, (n)(\mathfrak{A}(n) \to \mathfrak{B}(n))) \text{ then } \mathrm{P}(\sigma, m, (En)\mathfrak{A}(n) \to (En)\mathfrak{B}(n)).^*$$

Remark. The assumption of

$$\text{if } \mathfrak{A} \to \mathfrak{B} \text{ then } \mathrm{P}(\sigma, n, \mathfrak{A}) \to \mathrm{P}(\sigma, n, \mathfrak{B})$$

or the assumption of

$$\text{if } \mathrm{P}(\sigma, n, \mathfrak{A}) \text{ and } \mathfrak{A} \to \mathfrak{B} \text{ then } \mathrm{P}(\sigma, n, \mathfrak{B})$$

for arbitrary $\mathfrak{A}$ and $\mathfrak{B}$ is not advisable on account of (3). However it seems to be useful to assume one of these rules for certain subclasses of formulas, e.g. for the theorems of intuitionistic predicate calculus (not involving P or σ).

* These five formulas will be referred to as 'the deduction rules for P-formulas' and employed tacitly in what follows. We shall also assume that if $\mathfrak{A}$ and $\mathfrak{B}$ are definitionally equivalent, then $\mathrm{P}(\sigma, m, \mathfrak{A} \leftrightarrow \mathfrak{B})$.

Another possibility is to assume $P(\sigma, k, \mathfrak{A})$ for all σ and k for these formulas. For the present we shall not make such a general assumption, but confine ourselves to some *ad hoc* assumptions in each case. The assumptions preceding this remark may be considered as such.

To find a basis for our system we look for a substitute of Kreisel's (2a), and indeed the proper relativization of (4) seems to be

(6). $$P(\sigma, m, (n)\neg P(\sigma, n, \mathfrak{A})) \rightarrow P(\sigma, m, \neg\mathfrak{A}).$$

In fact, in the following we consider as a basis the axioms

(1). $$P(\sigma, m, \mathfrak{A}) \vee \neg P(\sigma, m, \mathfrak{A})$$

(3). $$(E\sigma)(Em)P(\sigma, m, \mathfrak{A}) \leftrightarrow \mathfrak{A} \quad (\sigma \text{ and } m \text{ not free in } \mathfrak{A})$$

(6). $$P(\sigma, m, (n)\neg P(\sigma, n, \mathfrak{A})) \rightarrow P(\sigma, m, \neg\mathfrak{A}).$$

We shall not elaborate the system in detail, but mention additional axioms in case they are necessary for our discussion.

The resulting system is considerably weaker than Kreisel's, but seems to obviate some objections made by S. C. Kleene to Brouwer's relevant statements (cf. Kleene and Vesley [**5**], 174–176).

One of the features of Kreisel's system is the derivability of Kripke's schema. Whether this is considered attractive is a matter of taste; one might also prefer to drop the system altogether and merely adopt Kripke's schema instead. We shall not carry out a comparison between these possibilities, but see what remains of the derivation on our basis.

Kripke's schema is usually formulated as follows, where α stands for a free choice sequence:

$$(E\alpha)(((n)\alpha(n) = 0 \leftrightarrow \neg\mathfrak{A}) \wedge ((En)\alpha(n) \neq 0 \rightarrow \mathfrak{A}))$$

On Kreisel's basis, this is simply derived as follows:

Put

$$\alpha(n) = 0 \leftrightarrow \neg P(\sigma, n, \mathfrak{A}),$$

$$\alpha(n) = 1 \leftrightarrow \quad P(\sigma, n, \mathfrak{A}).$$

Then

$$(En)\alpha(n) = 1 \leftrightarrow (En)P(\sigma, n, \mathfrak{A}),$$

so

$$(En)\alpha(n) = 1 \rightarrow \mathfrak{A}.$$

Also

$$\neg (En)\alpha(n) = 1 \leftrightarrow \neg (En)\mathrm{P}(\sigma, n, \mathfrak{A}),$$

so

$$(n)\alpha(n) = 0 \leftrightarrow \neg \mathfrak{A}.$$

On our basis we have to proceed a little differently, already from the beginning.
First of all we should not start with

$$\alpha(\sigma, \mathfrak{A})(n) = 0 \leftrightarrow \neg \mathrm{P}(\sigma, n, \mathfrak{A})$$

$$\alpha(\sigma, \mathfrak{A})(n) = 1 \leftrightarrow \quad \mathrm{P}(\sigma, n, \mathfrak{A}),$$

for since this is to be looked upon as a definition valid for all σ, at least σ has every evidence to assert the above equivalences for every m. So we should start with

$$\mathrm{P}(\sigma, m, (n)(\alpha(\sigma, \mathfrak{A})(n) = 0 \leftrightarrow \neg \mathrm{P}(\sigma, n, \mathfrak{A}))),$$

and

$$\mathrm{P}(\sigma, m, (n)(\alpha(\sigma, \mathfrak{A})(n) = 1 \leftrightarrow \quad \mathrm{P}(\sigma, n, \mathfrak{A}))),$$

for every m and every σ. Then on account of the deduction rules for P-formulas

$$\mathrm{P}(\sigma, m, (n)\alpha(\sigma, \mathfrak{A})(n) = 0) \leftrightarrow \mathrm{P}(\sigma, m, (n)\neg\mathrm{P}(\sigma, n, \mathfrak{A}))$$

so on account of (6)

$$\mathrm{P}(\sigma, m, (n)\alpha(\sigma, \mathfrak{A})(n) = 0) \rightarrow \mathrm{P}(\sigma, m, \neg\mathfrak{A}).$$

and by (3)

$$\mathrm{P}(\sigma, m, (n)\alpha(\sigma, \mathfrak{A})(n) = 0) \rightarrow \neg\mathfrak{A},$$

or

$$(E\sigma)(Em)\mathrm{P}(\sigma, m, (n)\alpha(\sigma, \mathfrak{A})(n) = 0) \rightarrow \neg\mathfrak{A}.$$

Also

$$\mathrm{P}(\sigma, m, (En)\alpha(\sigma, \mathfrak{A})(n) = 1) \leftrightarrow \mathrm{P}(\sigma, m, (En)\mathrm{P}(\sigma, n, \mathfrak{A})),$$

so

$$(E\sigma)(Em)\mathrm{P}(\sigma, m, (En)\alpha(\sigma, \mathfrak{A})(n) = 1 \leftrightarrow (E\sigma)(Em)\mathrm{P}(\sigma, m, (En)\mathrm{P}(\sigma, n, \mathfrak{A})).$$

A further reduction of these formulas depends on the logic that is assumed. We have in mind intuitionistic logic, which seems to be a quite natural, although by no means the only possible, choice.

Then on account of (3) from $P(\sigma, m, (En)P(\sigma, n, \mathfrak{A}))$ follows $(En)P(\sigma, n, \mathfrak{A})$, hence $\mathfrak{A}$*, so we arrive at

$$(E\sigma)(Em)P(\sigma, m, (En)\alpha(\sigma, \mathfrak{A})(n) = 1) \rightarrow \mathfrak{A}.$$

So much is clear, that Kripke's schema is not self-evident on the present basis.

If we adopt the converse of (6)

$$\text{(6a).} \qquad P(\sigma, m, \neg\mathfrak{A}) \rightarrow P(\sigma, m, (n)\neg P(\sigma, n, \mathfrak{A})),$$

then we have

$$P(\sigma, m, (n)\alpha(\sigma, \mathfrak{A})(n) = 0) \leftrightarrow P(\sigma, m, \neg\mathfrak{A}),$$

and consequently

$$(E\sigma)(Em)P(\sigma, m, (n)\alpha(\sigma, \mathfrak{A})(n) = 0) \leftrightarrow \neg\mathfrak{A},$$

and our result has more resemblance to Kripke's schema.

Let us next apply the idea to some of Brouwer's examples. Suppose $\mathfrak{A}$ is non-tested by σ at stage k (fixed), i.e.

$$\neg P(\sigma, k, (En)P(\sigma, n, \neg\mathfrak{A} \vee \neg\neg\mathfrak{A})),$$

then define $\alpha(\sigma, \mathfrak{A})$ by

$$(n)(\alpha(\sigma, \mathfrak{A})(n) = 0 \leftrightarrow \neg P(\sigma, n, \neg\mathfrak{A} \vee \neg\neg\mathfrak{A}))$$

and

$$(n)(\alpha(\sigma, \mathfrak{A})(n) = 1 \leftrightarrow \quad P(\sigma, n, \neg\mathfrak{A} \vee \neg\neg\mathfrak{A}))$$

i.e. put

$$P(\sigma, p, (n)(\alpha(\sigma, \mathfrak{A})(n) = 0 \leftrightarrow \neg P(\sigma, n, \neg\mathfrak{A} \vee \neg\neg\mathfrak{A}))),$$
$$P(\sigma, p, (n)(\alpha(\sigma, \mathfrak{A})(n) = 1 \leftrightarrow \quad P(\sigma, n, \neg\mathfrak{A} \vee \neg\neg\mathfrak{A}))).$$

Then if

$$P(\sigma, k, (n)\alpha(\sigma, \mathfrak{A})(n) = 0),$$

also

$$P(\sigma, k, (n) \neg P(\sigma, n, \neg\mathfrak{A} \vee \neg\neg\mathfrak{A}));$$

so by (6)

$$P(\sigma, k, \neg(\neg\mathfrak{A} \vee \overline{\neg}\neg\mathfrak{A}))$$

Since by (3)

$$\neg(E\sigma)(Em)P(\sigma, m, \neg(\neg\mathfrak{A} \vee \neg\neg\mathfrak{A})),$$

* D. Scott pointed out a redundancy in the first version.

it follows that

$$\neg (E\sigma)(Em)\mathrm{P}(\sigma, m, (n)\alpha(\sigma, \mathfrak{A})(n) = 0),$$

i.e. no σ can ever prove $(n)\alpha(\sigma, \mathfrak{A})(n) = 0$ for his choice sequence $\alpha(\sigma, \mathfrak{A})$.

Next if

$$\mathrm{P}(\sigma, k, (En)\alpha(\sigma, \mathfrak{A})(n) = 1)$$

then

$$\mathrm{P}(\sigma, k, (En)\mathrm{P}(\sigma, n, \neg\mathfrak{A} \vee \neg\neg\mathfrak{A}),$$

contrary to the hypothesis, so

$$\neg \mathrm{P}(\sigma, k, (En)\alpha(\sigma, \mathfrak{A})(n) = 1),$$

i.e. σ has no proof of $(En)\alpha(\sigma, \mathfrak{A})(n) = 1$ at stage k. If $\mathfrak{A}$ is non-tested for all σ at stage k, then no σ has such a proof at stage k. It is not reasonable to expect more, because the non-testability of $\mathfrak{A}$ at stage k does not preclude the possibility of $\mathfrak{A}$ being tested at some later stage. Actually from (8) follows that it is impossible that $\mathfrak{A}$ is non-testable for all σ at all stages.

In another example Brouwer uses an $\mathfrak{A}$ which depends on a choice sequence parameter f. Let $\mathfrak{A}(f)$ be such that

$$(Ef)\mathfrak{A}(f) \;\&\; (Ef) \neg\mathfrak{A}(f);$$

of course this should make sense to σ, so the hypothesis should read

$$\mathrm{P}(\sigma, k, (Ef)\mathfrak{A}(f) \;\&\; (Ef) \neg\mathfrak{A}(f)).$$

Then if we put again

$$\mathrm{P}(\sigma, k, \alpha(\sigma, f)(n) = 0 \leftrightarrow \neg \mathrm{P}(\sigma, n, \neg\mathfrak{A}(f) \vee \neg\neg\mathfrak{A}(f))),$$

and

$$\mathrm{P}(\sigma, k, \alpha(\sigma, f)(n) = 1 \leftrightarrow \quad \mathrm{P}(\sigma, n, \neg\mathfrak{A}(f) \vee \neg\neg\mathfrak{A}(f))),$$

we find similarly

$$\neg (E\sigma)(Em)\mathrm{P}(\sigma, m, (n)\alpha(\sigma . f)(n) = 0)$$

Next suppose

$$\mathrm{P}(\sigma, k, (f)(En)\alpha(\sigma, f)(n) = 1),$$

then

$$\mathrm{P}(\sigma, k, (f)(En)\mathrm{P}(\sigma, n, \neg\mathfrak{A}(f) \vee \neg\neg\mathfrak{A}(f))),$$

hence if σ is convinced of the fan-theorem and f is understood to range over a finitary spread, we have

$$P(\sigma, k, (En)(f)P(\sigma, n, \neg\mathfrak{A}(f) \vee \neg\neg\mathfrak{A}(f))).$$

This is contradictory if σ also accepts Brouwer's corollary that the continuum cannot be split, so we obtain

$$\neg (E\sigma)(Em)P(\sigma, m, (f)(En)\alpha(\sigma, f)(n) = 1)$$

(Note that Myhill in his **[8]** criticizes the use of the fan theorem, because it is used in an intensional context. Our context is a little different from the one criticized by Myhill).

The above results do not seem to justify Brouwer's claims that he has proved classical mathematics to be contradictory. As far as I know, no one besides Brouwer has ever seriously believed so.

In this connection I wish to point out some consequences of another axiom (which in a more systematic representation might be dependent), viz.

(8). $$P(\tau, k, (\sigma)\mathfrak{A}(\sigma)) \rightarrow P(\tau, k, \mathfrak{A}(\rho)).$$

If we consider the result of the first example

$$\neg (E\sigma)(Em)P(\sigma, m, (n)\alpha(\sigma, \mathfrak{A})(n) = 0),$$

or

$$(\sigma)(m) \neg P(\sigma, m, (n)\alpha(\sigma, \mathfrak{A})(n) = 0),$$

then we have

$$(E\tau)(Ek)P(\tau, k, (\sigma)(m) \neg P(\sigma, m, (n)\alpha(\sigma, \mathfrak{A})(n) = 0)).$$

So by (8)

$$(E\tau)(Ek)P(\tau, k, (m) \neg P(\tau, m, (n)\alpha(\tau, \mathfrak{A})(n) = 0)).$$

so

$$(E\tau)(Ek)P(\tau, k, \neg (n)\alpha(\tau, \mathfrak{A})(n) = 0),$$

from which follows

$$(E\sigma) \neg (n)\alpha(\sigma, \mathfrak{A})(n) = 0.$$

A similar reduction is possible for both resulting formulas of the second example.

Another application of the axioms for creative subjects consists in the possibility of describing quite naturally different notions of choice sequences in terms of the knowledge about them possessed by the creative subject.

A variety of conditions may be imposed, some of which we mention, without pursuing the study of sequences which satisfy such conditions.

1. $\mathbf{AF}(\alpha, \sigma) \leftrightarrow (n)(m) \neg \mathrm{P}(\sigma, n, \alpha(n+1) = m)$.

Note that from $\mathbf{AF}(\alpha, \sigma)$ follows $\neg(En)\mathrm{P}(\alpha, n, (m)\sigma(m)=0)$ (cf. Myhill [7]).

2. $\mathbf{AF}(\alpha) \leftrightarrow (\sigma)\mathbf{AF}(\alpha, \sigma)$.

3a. $\boldsymbol{L}_0(\alpha, \sigma) \leftrightarrow (n)(Em)\mathrm{P}(\sigma, n, \alpha(n+1) = m)$.

3b. $\boldsymbol{L}(\alpha, \sigma) \leftrightarrow (k)\mathrm{P}(\sigma, k, \boldsymbol{L}_0(\alpha, \sigma))$.

4. $\boldsymbol{L}_0(\alpha) \leftrightarrow (\sigma)\boldsymbol{L}_0(\alpha, \sigma) \,\&\, (m)(n)(\sigma)(\tau)(\mathrm{P}(\sigma, n, \alpha(n+1) = m)$
$\leftrightarrow \mathrm{P}(\tau, n, \alpha(n+1) = m))$.

5. $\boldsymbol{L}_1(\alpha) \leftrightarrow (n)(Em)(\sigma)\mathrm{P}(\sigma, n, \alpha(n+1) = m)$.

Such notions (formulations) seem to be useful for the problems mentioned in e.g. Myhill [**8**] and Troelstra [**10**]. Observe that in the approach outlined above one does not encounter difficulties which might call for an assumption like the arrangement of proofs in a sequence, as mentioned in e.g. van Dantzig [**4**], Myhill [7] and Troelstra [**11**]. Questions as to what every creative subject σ should be able to deduce (as encountered by Troelstra [**11**]) may be handled on the basis of our remark.

REFERENCES

[1] L. E. J. Brouwer, Essentieel-negatieve eigenschappen, *Indag. Math.* **10** (1948) 322–323.

[2] L. E. J. Brouwer, De non-aequivalentie van de constructieve en de negatieve orderelatie in het continuum, *Indag. Math.* **11** (1949) 37–39.

[3] L. E. J. Brouwer, Points and spaces, *Canad. J. Math.* **6** (1953) 1–17.

[4] D. van Dantzig, Comments on Brouwer's theorem on essentially-negative predicates, *Indag. Math.* **11** (1949) 347–355.

[5] S. C. Kleene and R. E. Vesley, *The foundations of intuitionistic mathematics*, Amsterdam (1965).

[6] G. Kreisel, Informal rigour and completeness proofs, in *Problems in the Philosophy of Mathematics*, ed. I. Lakatos, Amsterdam (1967) 138–186.

[7] J. Myhill, Notes towards an axiomatization of intuitionistic analysis, *Logique et Analyse* **35** (1967) 280–297.

[8] J. Myhill, Formal systems of intuitionistic analysis I, in *Logic, methodology and philosophy of science III*, eds. B. van Rootselaar and J. F. Staal, Amsterdam (1968).

[9] B. van Rootselaar, Review of Myhill [7] in *Math. Rev.* **36** (1968) 9.

[10] A. S. Troelstra, The theory of choice sequences, in *Logic, methodology and philosophy of science III*, eds. B. van Rootselaar and J. F. Staal, Amsterdam (1968).

[11] A. S. Troelstra, Principles of intuitionism, *Lecture Notes in Mathematics* **95**, Springer (1969).

A PALATABLE SUBSTITUTE FOR KRIPKE'S SCHEMA

R. E. VESLEY

1. Introduction. We are concerned with certain intuitionistic refutations of theorems of classical analysis. Some of such refutations rely only on the intuitionistic but non-classical continuity condition attached to a $\forall\alpha\exists x$-prefix ('Brouwer's principle for numbers', [**5**] 7); since Kleene's investigation and formalization these seem well understood. But others, such as the refutation of $(\alpha)(\overline{\alpha \stackrel{\circ}{=} 0 \rightarrow \alpha \# 0})$ for α ranging over real number generators ([**2**] 8.1, [**5**] 17–18), rely on Brouwer's method employing sequences developed by a 'creating subject' who looks for the solution to some unsolved problem. These have been slower to yield to formalization. One way to deal with them has been proposed by Kripke. We shall describe another and much less bold way.

We shall not repeat here the details of Brouwer's method, for which one should read not only the references and discussions in [**2**] and [**5**] cited above but also Kreisel [**6**] and Myhill [**7**], [**8**].

Nor shall we discuss in any detail Kripke's proposed axiom schema (cf. [**6**], [**7**], [**8**]):

KS $\qquad \exists\beta\{[\forall x\beta(x) = 0 \sim \neg A]\} \;\&\; [\exists x\beta(x) \neq 0 \supset A]\},$

notation as in Kleene's system I of [**5**], with A an arbitrary formula possibly containing free function variables.

Let I* be I with *27.2 (Brouwer's principle for numbers) replacing $^{\times}27.1$ (Brouwer's principle for functions, or $\forall\alpha\exists\beta$-continuity) as axiom schema. The addition of KS to I* seems to make possible the derivation of all the refutations under discussion here. This has been verified by Hull [**3**] for those results written out in [**2**].

Why should one be interested in an alternative approach to the refutations? These are some reasons:

(a). One may wish a system retaining Brouwer's principle for functions ($^{\times}27.1$). As emphasized by Myhill [**7**], this form of continuity is inconsistent with KS. It seems to be true that Brouwer never explicitly asserted this principle, but under one interpretation of intuitionistic intention one would expect every assertion $(\alpha)(E\beta)A$ to be short for some assertion $(\alpha)(E!\beta)A'$, where $A' \to A$. And continuity for the latter follows from Brouwer's principle for numbers ([5], p. 89). So Kleene was led to $^{\times}27.1$ as a way to make this interpretation as explicit as possible in the notation of I.

(b). In an intuitionistic theory of species of higher order, one can be even more explicit. Here, as Myhill has observed, it seems natural to postulate

$$(S)\{(\alpha)(E\beta)S(\alpha, \beta) \to (ES')[(S' \subseteq S \;\&\; (\alpha)(E!\beta)S'(\alpha, \beta)]\},$$

which contradicts KS.

(c). Even if KS is weakened in that A is permitted no function variables, it still allows the derivation of formal theorems $\exists\alpha E$, E containing α as only function variable, for the intended interpretation of which the α cannot be recursive. So under even this weak KS one misses a property which on Church's thesis one might expect for an intuitionistic system (and which I possesses, by theorem 9.3 of [5]).

On the other hand, for those who accept KS our formal work below may have some interest in verifying explicitly that Brouwer's refutations do not use the full power of KS but can be obtained from a weaker principle.

2. A new schema

2.1. Suppose we want a system for intuitionistic analysis embracing the Brouwer refutations and the axioms of I (and hence not including KS). One possibility of course is simply to put in separately each refutation as an axiom or axiom schema. E.g. we would postulate $\neg\forall\alpha\{\neg\forall x\alpha(x) = 0 \supset \exists x\alpha(x) \neq 0\}$. Kleene's investigations in [5] 17–18 of several of these results have shown them to be independent and his arguments using realizability and special realizability also show that these at least can be added consistently to I. (Note that intuitionistically if independence of A means: not $\vdash_S A$ and not $\vdash_S \neg A$, then independence of A does not imply that $\neg A$ is consistent with S; one needs also not $\vdash_S \neg\neg A$.)

A more attractive possibility is to find a single axiom schema from which all the desired results would follow and which itself would be consistent with I. Since KS holds in some versions of intuitionistic analysis, it might provide intuitionistic support for the new schema if it could be deducible in I* from KS. Other support for it in the intuitionistic literature would be desirable also.

We now describe such a schema. It is related to the familiar principle of classical analysis: every continuous function f defined on a dense subset S of the continuum can be extended to a continuous function f^* defined on the entire continuum. We restrict the dense subset to be negative, i.e. there must be a predicate $A(\alpha)$ such that $\alpha \in S \equiv \bar{A}(\alpha)$. We omit the continuity conditions on f, f^* (f^* is continuous anyway if completely defined). And we should prefer not to use the words above either, but rather to avoid any suggestion of a notion of a function defined not on the entire continuum but only on a (possibly undecidable) subset, or subspecies, since this notion of a partially defined function presents difficulties.

Towards writing our new schema in I, we first express the density of the species $\bar{A}(\alpha)$ in an arbitrary spread σ ([5] p. 56) by means of the following formula:

$$\boldsymbol{Dense}(\neg A(\alpha), \sigma)\colon \forall\alpha_{\alpha\in\sigma}\forall x\exists\beta_{\beta\in\sigma}(\bar{\beta}(x) = \bar{\alpha}(x) \;\&\; \neg A(\beta)).$$

For the case σ is the universal spread υ, we have then

$$\vdash \boldsymbol{Dense}(\neg A(\alpha), \upsilon) \sim \forall z_{\mathrm{Seq}\,(z)}\exists\beta(\bar{\beta}(lh(z)) = z \;\&\; \neg A(\beta)).$$

We now state our axiom schema (1) as a postulate for υ rather than for the continuum of real numbers. (In (1) and (3) β is not free in A, and in (2) and (4) b is not free in A.)

$$(1).\quad \boldsymbol{Dense}(\neg A(\alpha), \upsilon) \;\&\; \forall\alpha(\neg A(\alpha) \supset \exists\beta B(\alpha, \beta)) \supset \forall\alpha\exists\beta(\neg A(\alpha) \supset B(\alpha, \beta)).$$

Actually, to obtain the Brouwer refutations we need postulate only the consequence for number-valued functions:

$$(2).\quad \boldsymbol{Dense}(\neg A(\alpha), \upsilon) \;\&\; \forall\alpha(\neg A(\alpha) \supset \exists b B(\alpha, b)) \supset \forall\alpha\exists b(\neg A(\alpha) \supset B(\alpha, b)).$$

Derivation of (2) from (1) in I is straightforward.

As consequences in I of (1) and (2) respectively, we can now obtain the corresponding statements for arbitrary spreads.

$$(3).\quad \mathrm{Spr}(\sigma) \;\&\; \boldsymbol{Dense}(\neg A(\alpha), \sigma) \;\&\; \forall\alpha_{\alpha\in\sigma}(\neg A(\alpha) \supset \exists\beta B(\alpha, \beta)) \supset \forall\alpha_{\alpha\in\sigma}\exists\beta(\neg A(\alpha) \supset B(\alpha, \beta)).$$

$$(4).\quad \mathrm{Spr}(\sigma) \;\&\; \boldsymbol{Dense}(\neg A(\alpha), \sigma) \;\&\; \forall\alpha_{\alpha\in\sigma}(\neg A(\alpha) \supset \exists b B(\alpha, b)) \supset \forall\alpha_{\alpha\in\sigma}\exists b(\neg A(\alpha) \supset B(\alpha, b)).$$

2.2. Let I° be I with (1) as added axiom schema. We shall show I° is consistent by showing its theorems are ${}_s$realizable ([**5**] 10–11).

THEOREM 1. *Let A, $B(\beta)$ be formulas of* I *of orders a and b respectively* ([**5**] 10.5), *A not containing β free. Then the following formula is ${}_s$realizable.*

$$(5).\ ({}^c\neg\, A\ {}^e\supset\ {}^d\exists\beta B(\beta))\ {}^h\supset\ {}^g\exists\beta[{}^c\neg\, A\ {}^f\supset B(\beta)]$$

where c is $a * 1$, etc.

PROOF. Let Ψ be a list of variables including all those except β free in A, $B(\beta)$. For any Ψ the formula (5) is ${}_s$realized-Ψ by ${}^h_g\Lambda\ {}^e\in\ \varphi[{}^e\in]$ where

$$\varphi[{}^e\in] = \langle({}^d\{{}^e\in\}[{}^c0])_0,\ {}^f_b\Lambda\,{}^c\alpha({}^d\{{}^e\in\}[{}^c0])_1\rangle.$$

For, suppose (i) ${}^e\in$ ${}_s$realizes-Ψ the hypothesis. We must infer that $\varphi[{}^e\in]$ ${}_s$realizes-Ψ the conclusion. We need that ${}^f_b\Lambda\,{}^c\alpha({}^d\{{}^e\in\}[{}^c0])_1$ ${}_s$realizes-Ψ $\{({}^d\{{}^e\in\}[{}^c0])_0\}\ {}^c\neg\, A\ {}^f\supset B(\beta)$. Suppose ${}^c\alpha$ ${}_s$realizes-Ψ ${}^c\neg\, A$. Then (ii) ${}^c0$ ${}_s$realizes-Ψ ${}^c\neg\, A$. We need that $({}^d\{{}^e\in\}[{}^c0])_1$ ${}_s$realizes-Ψ $\{({}^d\{{}^e\in\}[{}^c0])_0\}\ B(\beta)$. This follows from (i) and (ii).

COROLLARY 1. *If $\Gamma \vdash E$ in I° and the formulas Γ are ${}_s$realizable, then E is ${}_s$realizable.*

COROLLARY 2. *In* I° *not* $\vdash$ KS.

2.3.

THEOREM 2. *Let* S *be the formal system obtained by adding* KS *as axiom schema to Kleene's basic system* B ([**5**] p. 8), *or even to* B *less the bar theorem* $^\times$26.3. *Then in* S $\vdash$ (1).

PROOF. Assume the hypotheses (i) and (ii) of (1). By $^\times$2.1 applied to (i), assume

$$(\text{iii}).\ \forall z_{\mathrm{Seq}(z)}(\bar{\beta}_z(lh(z)) = z\ \&\ \neg\, A(\beta_z)),$$

where $\beta_z = \lambda x\beta(\langle z, x\rangle)$. By KS

$$\exists\gamma\{[\forall x\gamma(x) = 0 \sim \neg\, A(\alpha)]\ \&\ [\exists x\gamma(x) \neq 0 \supset A(\alpha)]\}.$$

Assume

$$(\text{iv}).\ [\forall x\gamma(x) = 0 \sim \neg\, A(\alpha)]\ \&\ [\exists x\gamma(x) \neq 0 \supset A(\alpha)].$$

Now define ζ

$$(\text{v}).\ \forall x\zeta(x) = \begin{cases}\alpha(x) & \text{if } \forall z_{z\leqslant x}\gamma(z) = 0,\\ \beta_{\bar{\alpha}(y)}(x) & \text{if } \exists z_{z\leqslant x}\gamma(z) \neq 0 \text{ and } y = \mu z_{z\leqslant x}\gamma(z) \neq 0.\end{cases}$$

Then (vi) $\neg A(\zeta)$, for assume for reductio ad absurdum (a) $A(\zeta)$. We shall deduce $\neg\neg\exists x\gamma(x) \neq 0$ and $\neg\exists x\gamma(x) \neq 0$. For the first, assume $\neg\exists x\gamma(x) \neq 0$. Then $\forall x\gamma(x) = 0$. So $\neg A(\alpha)$ by (iv) and also $\zeta = \alpha$ by (v). So $\neg A(\zeta)$, contradicting (a). For the second, assume $\exists x\gamma(x) \neq 0$. Assume $y = \mu z_{z \leqslant x}\gamma(z) \neq 0$. Then $\zeta = \beta_{\bar{\alpha}(y)}$ by (v) and by (iii) $\neg A(\zeta)$, again contradicting (a). Hence, (vi). So by (ii) and (vi) assume $B(\zeta, \sigma)$. Now toward deducing $\neg A(\alpha) \supset B(\alpha, \sigma)$, assume $\neg A(\alpha)$. Then $\forall x\gamma(x) = 0$ [(iv)]; so $\zeta = \alpha$. So $B(\alpha, \sigma)$. By $\supset$, $\forall$-introd. $\forall\alpha\exists\sigma(\neg A(\alpha) \supset B(\alpha, \sigma))$.

2.4. We shall not derive in I° (or I plus (2)) each of Brouwer's refutations, but only some representative ones. Though we have not written out every detail of the other derivations that would be required, we believe, on the basis of extensive checking not reproduced here, that in I plus (2) we can obtain all the counterexamples given or cited in [**2**] 8.1.

In theorem 3 the formula in (a) is the negation of 'Markov's principle' (extended to functions, cf. Kleene's remark 18.6 in [**5**] p. 185); (b) and (c) correspond to Brouwer's most often given counterexamples ([**2**] pp. 117–118); (d) is a lemma used to establish (e) (a description of our proof of (d) has already been given by Hull [**3**]); (e) establishes that the virtual ordering $\dot{<}$ of the continuum is not a pseudo-ordering ([**2**] p. 117 lines 7–8, [**3**]); (f) corresponds to Heyting's theorem 2 ([**2**] p. 118) with 1 replacing 0. This last is the only refutation treated here which appears not to be derivable from (a) as axiom replacing (1) (or (2)). Another in the same class is our formal version of the negation of the Bolzano-Weierstrass theorem ([**2**] p. 119).

THEOREM 3. *In* I° (*or in* I *plus* (2)):

(a). $\vdash \neg\forall\alpha(\neg\forall x\alpha(x) = 0 \supset \exists x\alpha(x) \neq 0)$.

(b). $\vdash \neg\forall\alpha_{\alpha\in R}(\neg\alpha \doteq 0 \supset \alpha \# 0)$.

(c). $\vdash \neg\forall\alpha_{\alpha\in R}(\alpha \dot{>} 0 \supset \alpha \gg 0)$.

(d). $\vdash \forall\gamma_{\gamma\in R}(0 \dot{<} \gamma \vee \gamma \dot{<} \alpha) \supset \alpha \gg 0$.

(e). $\vdash \neg\forall\alpha_{\alpha\in R}(\alpha \dot{>} 0 \supset \forall\gamma_{\gamma\in R}(\alpha \dot{>} \gamma \vee \gamma \dot{>} 0))$.

(f). $\vdash \neg\forall\alpha_{\alpha\in R}(\neg\alpha \doteq 1 \supset \alpha \dot{<} 1 \vee \alpha \dot{>} 1)$.

PROOF. (a). We easily deduce ***Dense***$(\neg\forall x\alpha(x) = 0, \upsilon)$. Next assume $\forall\alpha(\neg\forall x\alpha(x) = 0 \supset \exists x\alpha(x) \neq 0)$. By (2), $\forall\alpha\exists x(\neg\forall x\alpha(x) = 0 \supset \alpha(x) \neq 0)$. Using *27.2, assume

$$\text{(i).}\ \forall\alpha\exists y\{\tau(\bar{\alpha}(y)) > 0\ \&\ \forall x(\tau(\bar{\alpha}(x)) > 0 \supset x = y)\ \&\ (\neg\forall x\alpha(x) = 0 \supset \alpha(\tau(\bar{\alpha}(y)) \dot{-} 1) \neq 0)\}.$$

Letting $\alpha = \lambda x0$, we can assume

(ii). $\tau(\overline{\lambda x0}(y_1)) > 0$.

Define α_1:

(iii). $\forall x \alpha_1(x) = \begin{cases} 0 & \text{if } x \leqslant \tau(\overline{\lambda x0}(y_1)) \vee x < y_1, \\ 1 & \text{otherwise.} \end{cases}$

Then (iv) $\overline{\alpha_1}(y_1) = \overline{\lambda x0}(y_1)$. Putting α_1 in (i), we can assume

(v). $\tau(\overline{\alpha_1}(y_2)) > 0$,

(vi). $\forall x(\tau(\overline{\alpha_1}(x)) > 0 \supset x = y_2)$,

(vii). $\neg\forall x \alpha_1(x) = 0 \supset \alpha_1(\tau(\overline{\alpha_1}(y_2)) \dot{-} 1) \neq 0$.

From (ii), (iv), (vi) $y_1 = y_2$. Now $0 \neq \alpha_1(\tau(\overline{\alpha_1}(y_2)) \dot{-} 1)$ (by (vii), (iii)) $= \alpha_1(\tau(\overline{\alpha_1}(y_1)) \dot{-} 1) = \alpha_1(\tau(\overline{\lambda x0}(y_1)) \dot{-} 1)$ (by (iv)) $= 0$ [(iii)].

(b), (c). Cf. Kleene's remark 18.6 [**5**] p. 185.

(d). Assume (i) $\alpha \in R$ and (ii) $\forall \gamma_{\gamma \in R}(0 \lessdot \gamma \vee \gamma \lessdot \alpha)$. By (i) and *R1.11 ([**5**] p. 138), assume (iii) $\alpha' \in R'$ & $\alpha' \doteq \alpha$. Using (ii) and *R0.7 with (iii) and *R7.3, we deduce $\forall \gamma_{\gamma \in R'}(0 \lessdot \gamma \vee \gamma \lessdot \alpha')$. Thence from *R0.8 and *27.6, assume

(iv). $\forall \gamma_{\gamma \in R'} \exists y \{\forall x[\tau(\bar{\gamma}(x)) > 0 \supset y = x]$ &
$\{(0 \lessdot \gamma \;\&\; \tau(\bar{\gamma}(y)) = 1) \vee (\gamma \lessdot \alpha' \;\&\; \tau(\bar{\gamma}(y)) = 2)\}\}$.

Putting $\gamma \doteq \alpha'$, assume

(v). $\forall x[\tau(\overline{\alpha'}(x)) > 0 \supset y = x]$ &
$\{(0 \lessdot \alpha' \;\&\; \tau(\overline{\alpha'}(y)) = 1) \vee (\alpha' \lessdot \alpha' \;\&\; \tau(\overline{\alpha'}(y)) = 2)\}$.

Using *R7.6, (vi) $\tau(\overline{\alpha'}(y)) = 1$. Now (vii) $\alpha'(y \dot{-} 1) \dot{-} 1 > 0$, as follows. Assume (1) $\alpha'(y \dot{-} 1) \dot{-} 1 = 0$. Using *R9.20 assume (2) $\beta \in R'$ & $\bar{\beta}(y) = \overline{\alpha'}(y)$ and (3) $\beta \doteq (\alpha'(y \dot{-} 1) \dot{-} 1) \cdot 2^{-(y \dot{-} 1)}$. By (3) and (1), (4) $\beta \doteq 0 \cdot 2^{-(y \dot{-} 1)} \doteq 0$ [using *R9.4]. From (iv) with β for γ, (vi) and (2), $0 \lessdot \beta$, contradicting (4).

Now $\alpha' \not\lessdot (\alpha'(y \dot{-} 1) \dot{-} 1) \cdot 2^{-(y \dot{-} 1)}$ [*R9.16] $\gtrdot 0 \cdot 2^{-(y \dot{-} 1)} \doteq 0$. Then by (iii), *R7.3, $\alpha \gtrdot 0$.

(f). We shall show contradictory: (i) $\forall \alpha_{\alpha \in R'}(\neg\, \alpha \doteq 1 \supset \alpha \lessdot 1 \vee \alpha \gtrdot 1)$, whence (f) [using *R0.7]. From *R0.8 assume (ii) $\mathrm{Spr}(\sigma)$ & $\forall \alpha(\alpha \in R' \sim \alpha \in \sigma)$. We deduce (iii) ***Dense***$(\neg\, \alpha \doteq 1, \sigma)$, as follows. Assuming $\alpha \in \sigma$, define β

$$\text{(iv). } \forall x \beta(x) = \begin{cases} \alpha(x) & \text{if } x < y, \\ 2^x+1 & \text{if } x = y \;\&\; \alpha(y) = 2^y, \\ \alpha(x) & \text{if } x = y \;\&\; \alpha(y) \neq 2^y, \\ 2\beta(x \dot{-} 1) & \text{if } x > y. \end{cases}$$

Then (v) $\bar{\beta}(y) = \bar{\alpha}(y)$, and by cases ($x+1 < y$, $x+1 = y$, $x+1 > y$; with subcases ($\alpha(x+1) = 2^{x+1}$, $\alpha(x+1) \neq 2^{x+1}$) in the second case): $|2\beta(x) - \beta(x+1)| \leqslant 1$. Thence (vi) $\beta \in R'$. By induction on p, using (iv) $|\beta(y+p) - 2^{y+p}| \geqslant 2^p$, whence $2^y|\beta(y+p) - 2^{y+p}| \geqslant 2^{y+p}$ and

$$\neg \exists x \forall p \; 2^y |\beta(x+p) - 2^{x+p}| < 2^{x+p};$$

so (vii) $\neg \beta \triangleq \lambda x 2^x \triangleq 1$. Combining (v)-(vii): (iii). From (i) and (ii): (viii) $\forall \alpha_{\alpha \varepsilon \sigma}(\neg \alpha \triangleq 1 \supset \exists x[(x = 0 \;\&\; \alpha \dot{<} 1) \vee (x = 1 \;\&\; \alpha \dot{>} 1)])$. Using (iii) and (viii) in (2)

$$\forall \alpha_{\alpha \varepsilon \sigma} \exists x(\neg \alpha \triangleq 1 \supset (x = 0 \;\&\; \alpha \dot{<} 1) \vee (x = 1 \;\&\; \alpha \dot{>} 1)).$$

Using *27.5, assume

$$\text{(ix). } \forall \alpha_{\alpha \varepsilon \sigma} \exists y \{\tau(\bar{\alpha}(y)) > 0 \;\&\; \forall x(\tau(\bar{\alpha}(x)) > 0 \supset x = y) \;\& \\ [\neg \alpha \triangleq 1 \supset (\tau(\bar{\alpha}(y)) = 1 \;\&\; \alpha \dot{<} 1) \vee (\tau(\bar{\alpha}(y)) = 2 \;\&\; \alpha \dot{>} 1)]\}.$$

Putting $\alpha = \lambda x 2^x (\triangleq 1)$, let $w_1 = \tau(\overline{\lambda x 2^x}(y_1)) > 0$. By cases ($w_1 = 1$, $w_1 > 1$) with (ix) we can easily deduce a contradiction.

In the proof in **[1]** of the result (c) Brouwer seems to assert the continuity of a number-valued function defined on a particular negative dense proper subspecies of a certain spread, namely on the real number generators α with $\alpha \dot{>} 0$. See particularly p. 123 lines 8-10 from below. This is the closest we can come to direct evidence for (1) in Brouwer's texts, and it is very weak. For his use of what might be taken as a consequence of (1) appears unnecessary for his argument, which he bases instead on use of the creating subject.

3. Systems contradicting (5) or (1)

3.1. To derive the Brouwer refutations we could start not from (2) but from the stronger schema

$$\text{(6). } (\neg A \supset \exists x B(x)) \supset \exists x(\neg A \supset B(x)),$$

which is itself a consequence of (5). We do not do so, not only because we can find no derivation of (6) from KS and no evidence for the intuitionistic truth of (6), but also because we have evidence against (6), namely its inconsistency with the 'strong Kripke schema' [7]

$$\mathrm{KS}^s \qquad \exists\beta(\exists x\beta(x) \neq 0 \sim A).$$

Let S″ be the system obtained by adding KS^s to I*. We sketch the proof that (6) is contradictory in S″. By KS^s $\exists\beta(\exists x\beta(x) \neq 0 \sim \neg\,\forall x\alpha(x) = 0)$. Call this $\exists\beta K(\alpha, \beta)$. Assume $K(\alpha, \beta)$. Now

$$K(\alpha, \beta) \,\&\, (\neg\,\forall x\alpha(x) = 0 \supset \exists x\beta(x) \neq 0).$$

Using (6) etc. $\exists\beta\exists x(K(\alpha, \beta) \,\&\, (\neg\,\forall x\alpha(x) = 0 \supset \beta(x) \neq 0))$, whence $\forall\alpha\exists x\exists\beta(K(\alpha, \beta) \,\&\, (\neg\,\forall x\alpha(x) = 0 \supset \beta(x) \neq 0))$. Using continuity (*27.2) and then putting $\alpha = \lambda x0$, we can deduce (formulas from which we may assume)

$$\forall\alpha_{\alpha\in\sigma}\exists\beta(K(\alpha, \beta) \,\&\, (\neg\,\forall x\alpha(x) = 0 \supset \beta(y_2) \neq 0))$$

for σ, y_1, τ satisfying $\mathrm{Spr}(\sigma) \,\&\, \forall\alpha(\alpha \in \sigma \sim \forall x_{x<y_1}\alpha(x) = 0)$ and $y_2 = \tau(\overline{\lambda x0}(y_1)) \dot{-} 1$. Thence

$$\forall\alpha_{\alpha\in\sigma}\exists u\exists\beta(\beta(y_2) = u \,\&\, K(\alpha, \beta) \,\&\, (\neg\,\forall x\alpha(x) = 0 \supset \beta(y_2) \neq 0))$$

write $\forall\alpha_{\alpha\in\sigma}\exists u\exists\beta B(\alpha, \beta, u, y_2)$. Then assume by continuity

$$\forall\alpha_{\alpha\in\sigma}\{\exists! y\tau'(\bar{\alpha}(y)) > 0 \,\&\, \forall y(\tau'(\bar{\alpha}(y)) > 0 \supset \exists\beta B(\alpha, \beta, \tau'(\bar{\alpha}(y)) \dot{-} 1, y_2))\}.$$

Putting $\alpha = \lambda x0$, assume $\tau'(\bar{\alpha}(y_3)) > 0 \,\&\, \forall x(\tau'(\bar{\alpha}(x)) > 0 \supset x = y_3)$ and $B(\lambda x0, \beta, \tau'(\overline{\lambda x0}(y_3)) \dot{-} 1, y_2)$. If $\beta(y_2) \neq 0$ then by $K(\lambda x0, \beta)$ we have $\neg\,\forall x\lambda x0(x) = 0$; so $\tau'(\overline{\lambda x0}(y_3)) \dot{-} 1 = \beta(y_2) = 0$. Hence

$$\forall\alpha_{\alpha\in\sigma}[\forall x_{x<y_3}\alpha(x) = 0 \supset \exists\beta B(\alpha, \beta, 0, y_2)],$$

whence we can deduce

$$\forall\alpha_{\alpha\in\sigma}[\forall x_{x<y_3}\alpha(x) = 0 \supset \neg\,\neg\,\forall x\alpha(x) = 0],$$

which is easily shown contradictory.

3.2. A way of phrasing (1) is to say that in the assertion that α is in the negative dense species $\lambda\alpha\bar{A}(\alpha)$ there is conveyed no information necessary to determine a choice sequence β corresponding (via the relation B) to α. All such information is already given in α. On one view even this weakening of (5) is implausible; doesn't the assertion $\bar{A}(\alpha)$ tell us at least of the existence of a certain derivation from $A(\alpha)$ of a contradiction? One may prefer a formal theory in which (1) fails. We shall show that in Troelstra's theory

CS of **[9]** we can derive a contradiction from the conjunction of (1) and the following modification of (1) in which the β of (1) is replaced by a variable e ranging over K.

(7). $\boldsymbol{Dense}(\neg A(\alpha), \upsilon)$ & $\forall\alpha(\neg A(\alpha) \supset \exists e B(\alpha, e)) \supset \forall\alpha\exists e(\neg A(\alpha) \supset B(\alpha, e))$.

Using axiom schema F2 of CS

$$\forall\alpha(\neg\, \forall x\alpha(x) = 0 \supset \exists e(\exists\beta\; \alpha = e|\beta \;\&\; \forall\beta \neg\, \forall x e|\beta(x) = 0)).$$

Using (7)

$$\forall\alpha\exists e(\neg\, \forall x\alpha(x) = 0 \supset \exists\beta(\alpha = e|\beta \;\&\; \forall\beta \neg\, \forall x e|\beta(x) = 0)).$$

Applying the CS continuity schema F3, putting $\alpha = \lambda t0$, and then using (3), we may assume

$$\forall\alpha_{\alpha\in\sigma}\exists\beta(\neg\, \forall x\alpha(x) = 0 \supset \alpha = f|\beta \;\&\; \forall\beta \neg\, \forall x f|\beta(x) = 0)$$

for σ satisfying $\mathrm{Spr}(\sigma)$ & $\forall\alpha(\alpha \in \sigma \sim \forall x_{x<y_1}\alpha(x) = 0)$ for a certain y_1. Then by the $\forall\alpha\exists\beta$-continuity schema F4 assume

(i). $\forall\alpha_{\alpha\in\sigma}(\neg\, \forall x\alpha(x) = 0 \supset \alpha = f|(g|\alpha) \;\&\; \forall\beta \neg\, \forall x f|\beta(x) = 0)$.

Thence $\neg\, \forall x f|(g|\lambda t0)(x) = 0$. But also we can deduce $\forall x f|(g|\lambda t0)(x) = 0$ as follows. Assume $f|(g|\lambda t0)(x) \neq 0$. Thence assume $f(\hat{x} * \overline{(g|\lambda t0)}(y)) > 1$. We can deduce formulas from which we may assume

(ii). $\forall\alpha(\forall x_{x<y_2}\alpha(x) = 0 \supset f(\hat{x} * \overline{(g|\alpha)}(y)) > 1$.

Then define α_1

(iii). $\forall u\alpha_1(u) = \begin{cases} 0 & \text{if } u \leqslant \max(x, y_1, y_2), \\ 1 & \text{otherwise.} \end{cases}$

From (i) $\alpha_1 = f|(g|\alpha_1)$. But $\alpha_1(x) = 0$ [(iii)] $\neq f|(g|\alpha_1)(x)$ [(iii), (ii)].

We do not know if (1) alone is contradictory in CS, nor do we know the status of the Brouwer refutations with respect to CS.

(We should like to thank Joan R. Moschovakis for calling to our attention an error in our original discussion and for pointing out that our argument does not contradict (1) but only the conjunction of (1) and (7).)

4. A metatheoretical application of (2). Suppose one accepts the principles of I together with (2) as defining one kind of intuitionistic theory. Using this theory informally as metatheory what results concerning I or I° follow? We give in theorem 4 one result: there is a model for I in which the function variables range over the free choice sequences which are not not general recursive. Classically the theorem fails (by Kleene's corollary 9.9 **[5]** p. 113); its 'intuitionistic proof' here (i.e. proof in the informal version of I°)

requires not only (2) but (the classically invalid) Brouwer's principle for numbers.

Presumably there is a parallel to this theorem in which I° replaces I and $C/_{s}$realizable replaces C/realizable. I have not checked details of this.

For the theorem let C be the intuitionistic species of all choice sequences α satisfying $\overline{\overline{GR}}(\alpha)$ where $GR(\alpha) \equiv \alpha$ is general recursive. The theorem is proved under the hypothesis that the proof of Kleene's theorem 9.7 of **[5]** p.111 can be carried out in the informal version of I°. This hypothesis (or even that the proof could be carried out in B) seems extremely plausible but we make no attempt to justify or further elucidate it. Its verification may emerge from Kleene's recent work **[4]**.

THEOREM 4. *Using informally the principles of* I° (*and specifically* *27.2 *and* (2)): *If* $\vdash E$ *in* I *then* E *is* C/*realizable.*

PROOF. We apply Kleene's theorem 9.7 cited above. Additionally we need to consider the case of axiom schema $^{\times}26.3^{c}$ (the bar theorem). We adapt Kleene's treatment of that case in his proof of theorem 9.3 **[5]** p. 107, now using Brouwer's principle and (2) to show the well-foundedness of the tree for the informal bar induction. Specifically, we take over as (1′)–(4′) the statements (1)–(4) of p. 107, with the modification that Ψ, π, α, ρ_0, ρ_1, σ must be in C. Next, since we have by hypothesis only that $\{(\pi)_{0,0}\}[\alpha](\sigma)$ is defined for each α in C, and not for arbitrary α, we need to modify the argument at the top of p. 108. Let

$$R'(\pi, a) \equiv (\mathrm{E}\alpha)[\overline{\overline{GR}}(\alpha) \;\&\; a = \bar{\alpha}(x) \quad \text{for} \quad x = (\{(\pi)_{0,0}\}[\alpha](0))_0].$$

We shall show (5′) $(\beta)(\mathrm{E}x)R'(\pi, \bar{\beta}(x))$. By hypothesis, $(\pi)_{0,0}$ C/realizes-Ψ $\forall\beta\exists x R(\bar{\beta}(x))$; thence $(\beta)[\overline{\overline{GR}}(\beta) \rightarrow \{(\pi)_{0,0}\}[\beta](0)$ is defined]. So $(\beta)[\overline{\overline{GR}}(\beta) \rightarrow (\mathrm{E}!u)(\pi)_{0,0}(2 * \bar{\beta}(u)) > 0]$. By (2), and the density in our sense of the not not-general recursive choice sequences in the species of all choice sequences

$$(\beta)(\mathrm{E}u)[\overline{\overline{GR}}(\beta) \rightarrow (\pi)_{0,0}(2 * \bar{\beta}(u)) > 0 \;\&\; (v)[(\pi)_{0,0}(2 * \bar{\beta}(v)) > 0 \rightarrow u = v]].$$

Abbreviate this $(\beta)(\mathrm{E}u)[\overline{\overline{GR}}(\beta) \rightarrow B(\pi, \beta, u)]$. By Brouwer's principle assume

$$\text{(i).}\quad (\beta)(\mathrm{E}y)\{\tau(\bar{\beta}(y)) > 0 \;\&\; (z)(\tau(\bar{\beta}(z)) > 0 \rightarrow z = y) \\ \&\; [\overline{\overline{GR}}(\beta) \rightarrow B(\pi, \beta, \tau(\bar{\beta}(y)) \dot{-} 1)]\}.$$

Assume

$$\text{(ii).}\quad \tau(\bar{\beta}(y)) > 0 \;\&\; (z)(\tau(\bar{\beta}(z)) > 0 \rightarrow z = y). \\ \&\; [\overline{\overline{GR}}(\beta) \rightarrow B(\pi, \beta, \tau(\bar{\beta}(y)) \dot{-} 1)].$$

Let $x = ((\pi)_{0,0}(2 * \bar{\beta}(\tau(\bar{\beta}(y)) \dot{-} 1)) \dot{-} 1)_0$. Define α_1

$$\text{(iii).}\quad \alpha_1(t) = \begin{cases} \beta(t) & \text{if } t < \max\,[x, \tau(\bar{\beta}(y)) \dot{-} 1, y], \\ 0 & \text{otherwise.} \end{cases}$$

By (i) there is y_1 such that

$$\text{(iv).}\quad \tau(\overline{\alpha_1}(y_1)) > 0 \,\&\, (z)(\tau(\overline{\alpha_1}(z)) > 0 \rightarrow z = y_1) \\ \&\, [\overline{\overline{GR}}(\alpha_1) \rightarrow B(\pi, \alpha_1, \tau(\overline{\alpha_1}(y_1)) \dot{-} 1)].$$

Now $\overline{\overline{GR}}(\alpha_1)$; so (v) $B(\pi, \alpha_1, \tau(\overline{\alpha_1}(y_1)) \dot{-} 1)$. Then

$$\text{(vi).}\quad \{(\pi)_{0,0}\}[\alpha_1](0) = (\pi)_{0,0}(2^* \overline{\alpha_1}(\tau(\overline{\alpha_1}(y_1)) \dot{-} 1)) \dot{-} 1.$$

Also $\tau(\overline{\alpha_1}(y)) = \tau(\bar{\beta}(y))$ [(iii)] > 0 [(ii)]. By (iv) $y = y_1$. So $\tau(\overline{\alpha_1}(y_1)) = \tau(\bar{\beta}(y))$, and (vii) $\overline{\alpha_1}(\tau(\overline{\alpha_1}(y_1)) \dot{-} 1) = \bar{\beta}(\tau(\bar{\beta}(y)) \dot{-} 1)$ [(iii)]. So from (vi), (vii) $(\{(\pi)_{0,0}\}[\alpha_1](0)))_0 = ((\pi)_{0,0}(2^* \bar{\beta}(\tau(\bar{\beta}(y)) \dot{-} 1)) \dot{-} 1)_0 = x$. From (ii) $\bar{\beta}(x) = \overline{\alpha_1}(x)$. So $\overline{\overline{GR}}(\alpha_1) \,\&\, \bar{\beta}(x) = \overline{\alpha_1}(x) \,\&\, x = (\{(\pi)_{0,0}\}[\alpha_1](0))_0$, whence (5′).

Now the definition of R_1, the derivation of (6′) (with R' replacing R) and the remainder of the proof can proceed as before.

REFERENCES

[1] L. E. J. Brouwer, De non-aequivalentie van de constructieve en de negatieve orderelatie in het continuum, *Indag. Math.* **11** (1949) 37–39.

[2] A. Heyting, *Intuitionism*, North-Holland, Amsterdam (1956) (2nd ed. 1966).

[3] R. Hull, Counterexamples in intuitionistic analysis using Kripke's schema, *Z. f. Math. Logik* **15** (1969) 241–246.

[4] S. C. Kleene, *Formalized recursive functionals and formalized realizability*, Am. Math. Soc., Providence, R.I. (1969).

[5] S. C. Kleene and R. E. Vesley, *The foundations of intuitionistic mathematics*, North-Holland, Amsterdam (1965).

[6] G. Kreisel, Informal rigour and completeness proofs, in *Problems in the philosophy of mathematics*, ed. I. Lakatos, North-Holland, Amsterdam (1967).

[7] J. Myhill, Notes towards an axiomatization of intuitionistic analysis, *Logique et Analyse* **35** (1967) 280–297.

[8] J. Myhill, Formal systems of intuitionistic analysis I, in *Logic, methodology and philosophy of science III*, eds. B. van Rootselaar and J. F. Staal, North-Holland, Amsterdam (1968) 161–178.

[9] A. S. Troelstra, The theory of choice sequences, in *Logic, methodology and philosophy of science III*, eds. B. van Rootselaar and J. F. Staal, North-Holland, Amsterdam (1968) 201–223.

SECTION C

CLASSICAL INTERPRETATIONS OF INTUITIONISM

A CHARACTERIZATION OF THE INTUITIONISTIC PROPOSITIONAL CALCULUS*

D. H. J. DE JONGH

We will present here a characterization of the intuitionistic propositional calculus **Pp** from above, i.e. we will describe a property of **Pp** that no consistent propositional calculus stronger than **Pp** possesses. By a propositional calculus stronger than **Pp** (at least as strong as **Pp**) we understand one in which all formulas in **Pp** are provable and some others as well (and possibly some others as well), and which is closed under substitution and modus ponens. (Closure under substitution is, of course, guaranteed if no particular axioms are postulated, but only axiom schemata.) By a formula we understand a formula built up from $\mathscr{P}_1, \ldots, \mathscr{P}_n$ (the atomic formulas) with the connectives &, $\vee$, $\supset$ and $\neg$. We will follow the notation of Kleene [7].

Lukasiewicz [**11**] proposed the conjecture that **Pp** can be characterized from above by the property:

for any formulas $\mathfrak{A}, \mathfrak{B}$, if $\vdash_{\mathbf{Pp}} \mathfrak{A} \vee \mathfrak{B}$, then $\vdash_{\mathbf{Pp}} \mathfrak{A}$ or $\vdash_{\mathbf{Pp}} \mathfrak{B}$.

This conjecture was disproved by Kreisel and Putnam [**9**], who showed that **Pp**+ the axiom schema $(\neg \mathfrak{A} \supset \mathfrak{B} \vee \mathfrak{C}) \supset (\neg \mathfrak{A} \supset \mathfrak{B}) \vee (\neg \mathfrak{A} \supset \mathfrak{C})$ has the same property.

In [**8**] Kleene proved a stronger property of **Pp** and he subsequently proposed to the author the conjecture that this property characterizes **Pp** from above. First, one defines a notion $\Gamma|_{\mathbf{T}}\mathfrak{A}$ for any sequence Γ of formulas, any formula $\mathfrak{A}$ and any propositional calculus **T**, from the notion $\vdash_{\mathbf{T}}$ of provability in **T**. Kleene states the definition in [**8**] in particular for the case that **T** is **Pp** (cf. [**8**] § 4), and he proves (among other things) that, for each $\mathfrak{A}, \mathfrak{B}, \mathfrak{C}$, if $\mathfrak{A}|_{\mathbf{Pp}}\mathfrak{A}$ and $\vdash_{\mathbf{Pp}} \mathfrak{A} \supset \mathfrak{B} \vee \mathfrak{C}$, then $\vdash_{\mathbf{Pp}} \mathfrak{A} \supset \mathfrak{B}$ or $\vdash_{\mathbf{Pp}} \mathfrak{A} \supset \mathfrak{C}$. Kleene's conjecture, which we will confirm in this presentation is: if **T** is a

* Part of the author's typewritten doctoral dissertation.

propositional calculus at least as strong as **Pp**, possessing the property

$$\text{if } \mathfrak{A}|_{\mathbf{T}}\,\mathfrak{A} \text{ and } \vdash_{\mathbf{T}} \mathfrak{A} \supset \mathfrak{B} \vee \mathfrak{C}, \text{ then } \vdash_{\mathbf{T}} \mathfrak{A} \supset \mathfrak{B} \text{ or } \vdash_{\mathbf{T}} \mathfrak{A} \supset \mathfrak{C}, \qquad (*)$$

then **T** is **Pp**. Also we will give another characterization of **Pp** from above by replacing (*) by

$$\text{if } \mathfrak{A}|_{\mathbf{T}}\,\mathfrak{A} \text{ and } \vdash_{\mathbf{T}} (\mathfrak{A} \supset \mathfrak{B})\ \&\ (\mathfrak{B} \supset \mathfrak{A}), \text{ then } \mathfrak{B}|_{\mathbf{T}}\,\mathfrak{B}. \qquad (**)$$

For this purpose we discuss some connections between pseudo-Boolean algebras and *I*-valuations (see for the definition of *I*-valuations Beth [**1**], Kripke [**10**], de Jongh [**4**]). If $\mathfrak{A}(\mathscr{P}_1, \ldots, \mathscr{P}_n)$ is a formula we will write $\mathfrak{A}^*(\alpha_1, \ldots, \alpha_n)$ for the pseudo-Boolean algebraic term formed from $\alpha_1, \ldots, \alpha_n$ with $\cap$, $\cup$, $\Rightarrow$ and $\_$ in the same way as $\mathfrak{A}$ from $\mathscr{P}_1, \ldots, \mathscr{P}_n$ with &, $\vee$, $\supset$ and $\neg$. A formula $\mathfrak{A}$ is said to be *valid* in a pseudo-Boolean algebra $\boldsymbol{A}$, iff $\mathfrak{A}^*(\alpha_1, \ldots, \alpha_n) = \mathbf{1}$ for all $\alpha_1, \ldots, \alpha_n \in \boldsymbol{A}$.

THEOREM 1 (McKinsey and Tarski [**12**]).
(a). $\vdash_{\mathbf{Pp}} \mathfrak{A}$ *iff* $\mathfrak{A}$ *is valid in every pseudo-Boolean algebra.*
(b). $\vdash_{\mathbf{Pp}} \mathfrak{A}$ *iff* $\mathfrak{A}$ *is valid in every finite pseudo-Boolean algebra.*

DEFINITION 1. For any propositional calculus **T** at least as strong as **Pp** we say that a pseudo-Boolean algebra $\boldsymbol{A}$ is a **T**-*pseudo-Boolean algebra* iff for each formula $\mathfrak{A}$ such that $\vdash_{\mathbf{T}} \mathfrak{A}$, $\mathfrak{A}$ is valid in $\boldsymbol{A}$.

THEOREM 2. *For every propositional calculus* **T** *at least as strong as* **Pp**, $\vdash_{\mathbf{T}} \mathfrak{A}$ *iff* $\mathfrak{A}$ *is valid in every* **T**-*pseudo-Boolean algebra.*

PROOF. Immediate from results of Birkhoff [**3**] on equationally defined classes of algebras and the fact that **T**-pseudo-Boolean algebras can be defined by a system of equations, since pseudo-Boolean algebras can (cf. e.g. [**14**]).

Another special case of a theorem of Birkhoff [**3**] is

THEOREM 3. *The class of all* **T**-*pseudo-Boolean algebras is closed under the formation of sub-algebras, homomorphisms and direct products.*

The following definitions are from [**6**] (mostly originally from [**13**]).

DEFINITION 2. If a partially ordered set $\langle V, \leqslant \rangle$ is a complete lattice, then $\alpha \in V$ is called *join-irreducible* iff $\alpha > \bigcup \{\beta \colon \beta < \alpha\}$. The set of all join-irreducible elements of V will be denoted by V^0.

DEFINITION 3. A lattice V is called *join-representable* iff V is complete and completely distributive, and every $\alpha \in V$ can be written as $\alpha = \bigcup \{\beta : \beta \prec \alpha$ and $\beta \in V^0\}$.
DEFINITION 4. A subset F of $\langle V, \leqslant \rangle$ is called *M-closed* iff for all $p, q \in V$, $p \in F$ and $q \leqslant p$ imply $q \in F$.
The set of all M-closed subsets of a partially ordered set V will be denoted by $\overline{V}$. $\overline{V}$ is then complete and completely distributive.

THEOREM 4. ([**13**], [**6**]). *Every join-representable lattice V is isomorphic to* $\overline{V^0}$.

THEOREM 5. (e.g. [**2**]). *A complete and completely distributive lattice is a pseudo-Boolean algebra if we define* $\alpha \Rightarrow \beta = \bigcup \{\gamma : \alpha \cap \gamma \leqslant \beta\}$.

Every finite distributive lattice is complete, completely distributive, and join-representable (e.g. [**2**]). So theorem 5 implies that every finite distributive lattice is a pseudo-Boolean algebra $\overline{V}$ for some partially ordered set V. Since for every partially ordered set V, $\overline{V}$ is a distributive lattice, there is a 1–1 correspondence between finite pseudo-Boolean algebras and finite partially ordered sets.

DEFINITION 5. If V is a partially ordered set, then V is **T**-*admissible* iff $\overline{V}$ is a **T**-pseudo-Boolean algebra.
DEFINITION 6. A *P.O.G.-set* is a partially ordered set with a greatest element.

THEOREM 6. (essentially in [**6**]). *If V is a P.O.G.-set, then there is the following correspondence between any I-valuation* $\langle V, w \rangle$ *and the pseudo-Boolean algebra* $\overline{V}$:
for all formulas $\mathfrak{A}$, $\mathfrak{B}$, *if* $F = \{p \in V : w(p, \mathfrak{A}) = 1\}$ *and* $G = \{p : w(p, \mathfrak{B}) = 1\}$, *then*
(i). $F \cap G = \{p : w(p, \mathfrak{A} \,\&\, \mathfrak{B}) = 1\}$,
(ii). $F \cup G = \{p : w(p, \mathfrak{A} \vee \mathfrak{B}) = 1\}$,
(iii). $F \Rightarrow G = \{p : w(p, \mathfrak{A} \supset \mathfrak{B}) = 1\}$,
(iv). $\_F = \{p : w(p, \neg \mathfrak{A}) = 1\}$.

THEOREM 7. *If V is a P.O.G.-set with greatest element m, then V is* **T**-*admissible iff for all I-valuations* $\langle V, w \rangle$ *and all formulas* $\mathfrak{A}$ *such that* $\vdash_{\mathbf{T}} \mathfrak{A}$, $w(m, \mathfrak{A}) = 1$.

We will need a short resume of some results of [**5**].

DEFINITION 7.(a). An *I-function* is a function with domain a finite P.O.G.-set V and range the set $\{0, 1\}$ with the property that, if $q \leqslant p$ in V and $f(p) = 1$, then $f(q) = 1$.

(b). An *I^n-function* f is a function with domain a P.O.G.-set V and range the set $\{0, 1\}^n$ such that for all m $(1 \leqslant m \leqslant n)$ the function f^m defined on V by $f^m(p) = (f(p))(m)$ is an I-function.

We write F^n for the set of all I^n-functions and F for the set of all I-functions, m_f for the greatest element of D_f, the domain of f, and $\leqslant_f$ for the partial ordering of the domain of f.

DEFINITION 8.(a). $f, g \in F^n$ are *congruent by* φ iff φ is an isomorphism from D_f onto D_g such that $f(p) = g(\varphi(p))$ for all $p \in D_f$.

(b). f is *congruent* to g (in symbols $f \equiv g$) iff f is congruent to g by φ for some φ.

DEFINITION 9. An n-ary *I-operator* a is a function from F^n into F with the properties:

(i). $D_{a(f)} = D_f$ for all $f \in F^n$.

(ii). if $f \equiv g$ by φ, then $a(f) \equiv a(g)$ by φ.

If V is a partially ordered set and $p \in V$, then we write $V(p)$ for the set $\{p' \in V : p' \leqslant p\}$. If $f \in F^n$ and $p \in D_f$, we write f_p for the restriction of f to $D_f(p)$, $g \leqslant f$ iff $(\exists p)(g \equiv f)$.

DEFINITION 10. A function φ fiom the partially ordered set $\langle V, \leqslant \rangle$ onto the partially ordered set $\langle W, \leqslant_1 \rangle$ is *strongly isotone* iff

(i). for all $p', p \in V$, if $p' \leqslant p$, then $\varphi(p') \leqslant_1 \varphi(p)$

and

(ii). for all $p', p \in V$, if $\varphi(p') \leqslant_1 \varphi(p)$, then for some $p'' \leqslant p$, $\varphi(p'') = \varphi(p')$.

DEFINITION 11.(a). If $f, g \in F^n$, then g is a *reduced form* of f iff there is a strongly isotone function φ from D_f onto D_g such that, for all $p \in D_f$, $g(\varphi(p)) = f(p)$.

(b). f is *irreducible* iff all reduced forms of f are congruent to f.

(c). If g is a reduced form of f and g is irreducible, then we call g a *normal form* of f.

In [5] we proved that the normal form of an I^n-function is unique up to congruence (theorem 2.3). Also we proved that, if f is irreducible and $g \leqslant f$, then g is irreducible (lemma 2.2 Cor.).

DEFINITION 12. A *normal I*-operator a is an I-operator such that

(i). for all $f \in F^n$ and $p \in D_f$, $(a(f_p))(p) = (a(f))(p)$

and

(ii). if $f, g \in F^n$ and g is a reduced form of f, then $(a(g))(m_g) = (a(f))(m_f)$.

DEFINITION 13. The *normalized characteristic set* C_a^* of a normal n-ary

I-operator a is the set of all irreducible I^n-functions f such that $(a(f))(m_f) = 1$.

In [5] it was proved that a normal I-operator is uniquely characterized by its normalized characteristic set.

DEFINITION 14. A normal I-operator is *finite* iff its normalized characteristic set contains only a finite number of congruence classes.

In [5] we defined then I-operators corresponding to the usual connectives in a natural way. These I-operators were proved to be normal (and in the cases of & and $\neg$ finite) and we proved that, if we introduce definability in a natural way, then all finite normal I-operators are definable from the I-operators corresponding to the usual connectives (theorem 3.7). More in particular:

THEOREM 8. *Let $g \in F^n$, g irreducible, m_g has k immediate predecessors $q_1, \ldots, q_k$ with respect to $\leqslant_g$, for each i $(1 \leqslant i \leqslant k)$ q_i has k_i immediate predecessors with respect to $\leqslant_g$, and for all i and j $(1 \leqslant i \leqslant k,\ 1 \leqslant j \leqslant k_i)$ a_i and a_{i_j} are respectively the normal I-operators with normalized characteristic sets $C^*_{a_i} = \{f \in F^n : f \leqslant g_{q_i}\}$ and $C^*_{a_{ij}} = \{f \in F^n :\ f \leqslant g_{q_{ij}}\}$. Then, in the case that for all m $(1 \leqslant m \leqslant n)$ $f^m(p) = 0$ for some $p < m_g$, the normal I-operator a with normalized characteristic set $C^*_a = \{f \in F^n : f \leqslant g\}$ can be expressed as follows:*

$$a = \bigcup_{i=1}^{k} (a_i \supset \bigcup_{j=1}^{k_i} a_{i_j}) \supset \bigcup_{i=1}^{k} a_i$$

(with $\bigcup_{j=1}^{k_i} a_{i_j}$ standing for a_i if $k_i = 0$).

The main theorem is a little bit stronger than we need to establish the results predicted earlier. We have not checked the intuitionistic validity of it. Probably the double negation will hold intuitionistically.

THEOREM 9. *If* $\mathbf{T}$ *is a consistent propositional calculus stronger than* $\mathbf{Pp}$, *then for each integer $r \geqslant 2$ there is a formula $\mathfrak{A} \supset \mathfrak{B}_1 \vee \ldots \vee \mathfrak{B}_s$ $(s \geqslant r)$ such that $\mathfrak{A}|_{\mathbf{T}}\mathfrak{A}$ and $\vdash_{\mathbf{T}} \mathfrak{A} \supset \mathfrak{B}_1 \vee \ldots \vee \mathfrak{B}_s$, but not $\vdash_{\mathbf{T}} \mathfrak{A} \supset \mathfrak{B}_{i_1} \vee \ldots \vee \mathfrak{B}_{i_k}$ for any proper subsequence $(i_1, \ldots, i_k)$ $(k \geqslant 1)$* of $(1, \ldots, s)$.

OUTLINE OF PROOF. First we construct a finite P.O.G.-set $\langle W, \leqslant_0, q_0\rangle$ having $q_1, \ldots, q_k$ as the immediate predecessors of q_0 $(k \geqslant 1)$, such that W is not $\mathbf{T}$-admissible, but, for all i $(1 \leqslant i \leqslant k)$, $W(q_i)$ is $\mathbf{T}$-admissible.

Then from this P.O.G.-set W we construct a P.O.G.-set $\langle V, \leqslant, p_0 \rangle$ with $p_1, \ldots, p_s$ $(s \geqslant r)$ as immediate predecessors of p_0 such that V is not **T**-admissible, but for all j $(1 \leqslant j \leqslant s)$, $V(p_j)$ is. Then we construct an irreducible I^n-function g on V for some n such that, for all m $(1 \leqslant m \leqslant n)$, $g^m(p_i) = 0$ for some i $(1 \leqslant i \leqslant s)$.

Now assume $a, a_1, \ldots, a_s$ are the definable I-operators with normalized characteristic sets $C_a^* = \{f \in F^n : f \leqslant g\}$ and $C_{a_i}^* = \{f \in F^n : f \leqslant g_{p_i}\}$ $(1 \leqslant i \leqslant s)$, and assume that $\mathfrak{A}, \mathfrak{B}_1, \ldots, \mathfrak{B}_s$ are the formulas corresponding to these definable I-operators. We will show

(a). $\vdash_{\mathbf{T}} \mathfrak{A} \supset \mathfrak{B}_1 \vee \ldots \vee \mathfrak{B}_s$,

(b). not $\vdash_{\mathbf{T}} \mathfrak{A} \supset \mathfrak{B}_{i_1} \vee \ldots \vee \mathfrak{B}_{i_k}$ for any proper subsequence $(i_1, \ldots, i_k)$ of $(1, \ldots, s)$,

(c). $\mathfrak{A} |_{\mathbf{T}} \mathfrak{A}$.

(a). The crucial point of the proof is that the class of **T**-pseudo-Boolean algebras does not contain a pseudo-Boolean algebra on which $\mathfrak{A} \supset \mathfrak{B}_1 \vee \ldots \vee B_s$ is not valid (a 'counter-example' to this formula). More precisely, for any pseudo-Boolean algebra $\boldsymbol{A}$ on which $\mathfrak{A} \supset \mathfrak{B}_1 \vee \ldots \vee \mathfrak{B}_s$ is not valid, the pseudo-Boolean algebra $\overline{V}$ is isomorphic to a sub-algebra of a homomorphism of $\boldsymbol{A}$, and so theorem 3 implies that, since $\overline{V}$ is not a **T**-pseudo-Boolean algebra, $\boldsymbol{A}$ cannot be one, and therefore $\vdash_{\mathbf{T}} \mathfrak{A} \supset \mathfrak{B}_1 \vee \ldots \vee \mathfrak{B}_s$. In effect, if $\alpha_1, \ldots, \alpha_n \in \boldsymbol{A}$ are such that

$$\mathfrak{A}^* \Rightarrow \mathfrak{B}_1^* \cup \ldots \cup \mathfrak{B}_s^*(\alpha_1, \ldots, \alpha_n) \neq \mathbf{1},$$

then $\overline{V}$ can be proved to be isomorphic to the sub-algebra of the relativization of $\boldsymbol{A}$ with respect to $\mathfrak{A}^*(\alpha_1, \ldots, \alpha_n)$ generated by the images of $\alpha_1, \ldots, \alpha_n$ under the natural homomorphism on that relativization.

(b). If $t \notin (i_1, \ldots, i_k)$ $(0 \leqslant t \leqslant s)$, then we can prove that $\mathfrak{A} \supset \mathfrak{B}_{i_1} \vee \ldots \vee \mathfrak{B}_{i_k}$ is not valid on $\overline{V(p_t)}$; then, since $\overline{V(p_t)}$ is a **T**-pseudo-Boolean algebra, not $\vdash_{\mathbf{T}} \mathfrak{A} \supset \mathfrak{B}_{i_1} \vee \ldots \vee \mathfrak{B}_{i_k}$.

(c). This is easy to prove with the help of theorem 9 and the definition of $|_{\mathbf{T}}$.

For our second characterization we give first an equivalent expression for $\mathfrak{A} |_{\mathbf{T}} \mathfrak{A}$.

DEFINITION 15. a is a *connected* I-operator iff a is normal and for all $f, g \in C_a^*$ there exists an h such that $f \leqslant h$ and $g \leqslant h$.

Of the next theorem we again did not check the intuitionistic validity.

THEOREM 10. *For any formula $\mathfrak{A}$, $\mathfrak{A}|_{\mathbf{Pp}}\,\mathfrak{A}$ iff the I-operator corresponding to $\mathfrak{A}$ is connected.*

From this theorem and the proof of theorem 9 theorem 11 follows almost immediately.

THEOREM 11. *If* **T** *is a consistent propositional calculus at least as strong as* **Pp**, *and*

$$\textit{for each } \mathfrak{A}, \mathfrak{B} \textit{ if } \mathfrak{A}|_{\mathbf{T}}\,\mathfrak{A} \textit{ and } \vdash_{\mathbf{T}} (\mathfrak{A} \supset \mathfrak{B}) \;\&\; (\mathfrak{B} \supset \mathfrak{A}), \textit{ then } \mathfrak{B}|_{\mathbf{T}}\,\mathfrak{B}, \qquad (**)$$

then all theorems of **T** *are provable in* **Pp**.

REFERENCES

[1] E. W. BETH, Semantische Begründung der derivativen Implikationslogik, *Archiv. f. Math. Logik u. Grundl. Forsch.* **7** no. 1, 2 (1961) 23–28.

[2] G. BIRKHOFF, *Lattice theory*, New York (1948).

[3] G. BIRKHOFF, On the structure of abstract algebras, *Proc. Cambridge Phil. Soc.* **29** (1935) 433–454.

[4] D. H. J. DE JONGH, Recherches sur les *I*-valuations, rapp. no **17** Contr. Euratom 010-60-12, CETN (1962).

[5] D. H. J. DE JONGH, Investigations on the intuitionistic propositional calculus, dissertation (typewritten), University of Wisconsin (1968).

[6] D. H. J. DE JONGH and A. S. TROELSTRA, On the connection of partially ordered sets with some pseudo-Boolean algebras, *Indag. Math.* **28** no. 3 (1966).

[7] S. C. KLEENE, *Introduction to metamathematics*, Amsterdam (1952).

[8] S. C. KLEENE, Disjunction and existence under implication in elementary intuitionistic formalisms, *J. Symb. Logic.* **27** (1962) 11–18.

[9] G. KREISEL and H. PUTNAM, Eine Unableitbarkeitbeweismethode für den intuitionistischen Aussagenkalkül, *Archiv f. Math. Logik u. Grundl. Forsch.* **3** no. 3, 4 (1957) 74–78.

[10] S. A. KRIPKE, Semantical analysis of intuitionistic logic I, in *Formal systems and recursive functions*, eds. J. N. Crossley and M.A.E. Dummett, Amsterdam (1965) 92–130.

[11] J. LUKASIEWICZ, On the intuitionistic theory of deduction, *Indag. math.* **14** (1952) 202–212.

[12] J. C. MCKINSEY and A. TARSKI. Some theorems about the sentential calculi of Lewis and Heyting, *J. Symb. Logic* **13** (1948) 1–5.

[13] G. N. RANEY, Completely distributive complete lattices, *Proc. Am. Math. Soc.* **3** (1952) 667–680.

[14] H. RASIOWA and R. SIKORSKI, *The mathematics of metamathematics*, Warszawa (1963).

INTUITIONISTIC MODEL THEORY AND THE COHEN INDEPENDENCE PROOFS

MELVIN FITTING

Gödel proved the continuum hypothesis consistent with the other axioms of set theory [**2**] by constructing a transfinite sequence of (domains of) classical logic models $\{M_\alpha\}$, taking a limit L, over all ordinals, and showing it was a model for set theory and the continuum hypothesis (among other things). We will indicate how this procedure can be generalized to transfinite sequences of Saul Kripke's intuitionistic logic models [**7**] in such a way as to establish the independence results of Cohen [**1**].

This sort of thing has been done by Vopěnka and others (see refs. [**3**]–[**5**] and [**10**]–[**14**]) using topological intuitionistic models. Kripke's model structure is closer in form to Cohen's forcing technique, and the methods used are more 'logical'. Neither Vopěnka's nor this method requires countable models for set theory.

First I will briefly sketch Kripke's notion of an intuitionistic logic model, since the notation I use is different from his.

Notation. If P is a function ranging over sets of parameters, by $\hat{P}(\Gamma)$ we mean the collection of all first order formulas with constants from $P(\Gamma)$. $\mathfrak{A}$ is any atomic formula, $\mathfrak{X}$ and $\mathfrak{Y}$ are any formulas.

DEFINITION 1. By an *intuitionistic model* we mean an ordered quadruple $\langle G, \mathrm{R}, \models, P\rangle$, where G is a non-empty set, R is a transitive, reflexive relation on G, $\models$ is a relation between elements of G and formulas, and P is a map from G to non-empty sets of parameters, satisfying for any $\Gamma, \Delta \in G$

(1). $\Gamma \mathrm{R} \Delta \Rightarrow P(\Gamma) \subseteq P(\Delta)$;

(2). $\Gamma \models \mathfrak{A} \Rightarrow \mathfrak{A} \in \hat{P}(\Gamma)$;

(3). $\Gamma \models \mathfrak{A}, \Gamma \mathrm{R} \Delta \Rightarrow \Delta \models \mathfrak{A}$;

(4). $\Gamma \models (\mathfrak{X} \wedge \mathfrak{Y}) \Leftrightarrow \Gamma \models \mathfrak{X}$ and $\Gamma \models \mathfrak{Y}$;

(5). $\Gamma \models (\mathfrak{X} \vee \mathfrak{Y}) \Leftrightarrow (\mathfrak{X} \vee \mathfrak{Y}) \in \hat{P}(\Gamma)$ and $\Gamma \models \mathfrak{X}$ or $\Gamma \models \mathfrak{Y}$,

(6). $\Gamma \models \sim \mathfrak{X} \Leftrightarrow \sim \mathfrak{X} \in \hat{P}(\Gamma)$ and for every $\Delta \in G$ such that $\Gamma \mathrm{R} \Delta$, $\Delta \not\models \mathfrak{X}$;

(7). $\Gamma \models (\mathfrak{X} \supset \mathfrak{Y}) \Leftrightarrow (\mathfrak{X} \supset \mathfrak{Y}) \in \hat{P}(\Gamma)$ and for every $\Delta \in G$ such that $\Gamma \mathrm{R} \Delta$, if $\Delta \models \mathfrak{X}$, $\Delta \models \mathfrak{Y}$;

(8). $\Gamma \models (\exists x)\mathfrak{X}(x) \Leftrightarrow$ for some $a \in P(\Gamma)$, $\Gamma \models \mathfrak{X}(a)$;

(9). $\Gamma \models (\forall x)\mathfrak{X}(x) \Leftrightarrow$ for every $\Delta \in G$ such that $\Gamma \mathrm{R} \Delta$, and for every $a \in P(\Delta)$, $\Delta \models \mathfrak{X}(a)$.

DEFINITION 2. $\mathfrak{X}$ is *valid in the model* $\langle G, \mathrm{R}, \models, P \rangle$ if for every $\Gamma \in G$ such that $\mathfrak{X} \in \hat{P}(\Gamma)$, $\Gamma \models \mathfrak{X}$.

$\mathfrak{X}$ is *valid* if $\mathfrak{X}$ is valid in every model.

THEOREM 1. (Kripke [7]). *$\mathfrak{X}$ is a theorem of intuitionistic logic if and only if $\mathfrak{X}$ is valid.*

The above modeling may be briefly motivated as follows:

G is a collection of possible states of knowledge; any $\Gamma \in G$ may be considered to be a collection of physical facts. $\Gamma \mathrm{R} \Delta$ means if now we know Γ, later we might know Δ. $P(\Gamma)$ is the set of constants constructed by the stage Γ, or the set of parameters introduced in reaching Γ. Finally $\Gamma \models \mathfrak{X}$ means that from the facts Γ we may deduce $\mathfrak{X}$.

If a model $\langle G, \mathrm{R}, \models, P \rangle$ has a countable domain, i.e. $\bigcup \{P(\Gamma) | \Gamma \in G\}$, we may apply Cohen's complete sequence method [**1**]. Call $H \subseteq G$ an R-*chain* if any two elements are R-comparable. Call H a *complete* R-chain if for any formula $\mathfrak{X}$, only using parameters 'available' in H, for some $\Gamma \in H$, $\Gamma \models \mathfrak{X} \vee \sim \mathfrak{X}$. Then, as in [**1**], any $\Gamma \in G$ can be included in a complete R-chain. If H is a complete R-chain, $\{\mathfrak{X} |$ for some $\Gamma \in H$, $\Gamma \models \mathfrak{X}\}$ is, if we ignore the universal quantifier, a classical truth set. Now suppose $\mathfrak{X}$ has no universal quantifiers and $\sim\sim\mathfrak{X}$ is not an intuitionistic theorem. The analog of the Skolem-Löwenheim theorem holds for Kripke's models, so for some model with a countable domain $\langle G, \mathrm{R}, \models, P \rangle$ for some $\Gamma \in G$, $\Gamma \not\models \sim\sim\mathfrak{X}$. For some $\Delta \in G$, $\Gamma \mathrm{R} \Delta$ and $\Delta \models \sim\mathfrak{X}$. By the above remarks $\sim\mathfrak{X}$ must belong to some classical truth set, so $\mathfrak{X}$ is not classically valid. (This can be extended to a full proof of Kleene [**6**] theorem 59).

Suppose we could find some intuitionistic model $\langle G, \mathrm{R}, \models, P \rangle$ in which for some $\Gamma \in G$, $\Gamma \models$ ZF and $\Gamma \not\models \sim\sim$AC, where ZF is the set of Zermelo-Fraenkel axioms, and AC is the axiom of choice, all expressed in (classically equivalent) forms not using the universal quantifier. Then by the above we would have the *classical* independence of the axiom of choice. (Note that $\vdash_{\mathrm{I}} (\mathfrak{X} \supset \sim\sim\mathfrak{Y}) \equiv \sim\sim(\mathfrak{X} \supset \mathfrak{Y})$.) Before showing how this may be done, we present the Gödel construction in order to bring out the analogy.

Let V be a classical Zermelo-Fraenkel model. In [2] Gödel defined over V the sequence $\{M_\alpha\}$ of sets as follows:

$M_0 = \emptyset$,

$M_{\alpha+1}$ is the collection of all definable subsets of M_α,

$M_\lambda = \bigcup_{\alpha<\lambda} M_\alpha$ for limit ordinals λ.

Let L be the class $\bigcup_{\alpha\in V} M_\alpha$. Gödel showed that L was a classical ZF model.

As an introduction to the intuitionistic generalization, we restate the Gödel construction using characteristic functions instead of sets. Now of course '$\in$' is to be considered as a formal symbol, not as set membership.

Let M be some collection and let $\mathfrak{v}$ be a truth function on the set of formulas with constants from M. We say a (characteristic) function f is *definable over* $\langle M, \mathfrak{v}\rangle$ if domain$(f) = M$, range$(f) \subseteq \{\mathrm{T}, \mathrm{F}\}$, and for some formula $\mathfrak{X}(x)$ with one free variable and all constants from M, for all $a \in M$

$$f(a) = \mathfrak{v}(\mathfrak{X}(a)).$$

Let M' be the elements of M together with all functions definable over $\langle M, \mathfrak{v}\rangle$.

We define a truth function $\mathfrak{v}'$ on the set of formulas with constants from M' by defining it for atomic formulas. If $f, g \in M'$ we have three cases:

(1). $f, g \in M$. Let $\mathfrak{v}'(f \in g) = \mathfrak{v}(f \in g)$;

(2). $f \in M$, $g \in M' - M$. Let $v'(f \in g) = g(f)$;

(3). $f \in M' - M$. Let $\mathfrak{X}(x)$ be the formula which defines f over $\langle M, \mathfrak{v}\rangle$. If there is an $h \in M$ such that $\mathfrak{v}((\forall x)(x \in h \equiv \mathfrak{X}(x))) = \mathrm{T}$ and $\mathfrak{v}'(h \in g) = \mathrm{T}$ let $\mathfrak{v}'(f \in g) = \mathrm{T}$, otherwise let $\mathfrak{v}'(f \in g) = \mathrm{F}$. (Case 3 reduces the situation to case 1 or 2.)

We call the pair $\langle M', \mathfrak{v}'\rangle$ the *derived model of* $\langle M, \mathfrak{v}\rangle$.

Now, let $M_0 = \emptyset$ and let $\mathfrak{v}_0$ be the obvious truth function. Thus we have $\langle M_0, \mathfrak{v}_0\rangle$.

Let $\langle M_{\alpha+1}, \mathfrak{v}_{\alpha+1}\rangle$ be the derived model of $\langle M_\alpha, \mathfrak{v}_\alpha\rangle$.

If λ is a limit ordinal, let $M_\lambda = \bigcup_{\alpha<\lambda} M_\alpha$. Let $\mathfrak{v}_\lambda(f \in g) = \mathrm{T}$ if for some $\alpha < \lambda$, $\mathfrak{v}_\alpha(f \in g) = \mathrm{T}$, otherwise let $\mathfrak{v}_\lambda(f \in g) = \mathrm{F}$. Thus we have $\langle M_\lambda, \mathfrak{v}_\lambda\rangle$.

Let $L = \bigcup_{\alpha\in V} M_\alpha$ and let $\mathfrak{v}(f \in g) = \mathrm{T}$ if for some $\alpha \in V$ $\mathfrak{v}_\alpha(f \in g) = \mathrm{T}$, otherwise let $\mathfrak{v}(f \in g) = \mathrm{F}$. Thus we have the 'class' model $\langle L, \mathfrak{v}\rangle$. All the axioms of ZF will be valid in this model.

Before proceeding to the intuitionistic generalization, we note that it can be shown that for formulas without universal quantifiers it suffices to consider only intuitionistic models with the P-map constant. From now on we will assume this, and we will write the range of the map instead of the map itself. Thus our models now are quadruples $\langle G, \mathrm{R}, \vDash, S\rangle$, where S is a collection of parameters, etc. Also, for convenience, let B be the collection of all R-closed subsets of G.

Let $\langle G, \mathrm{R}, \vDash, S\rangle$ be some model. We say a function f is definable over $\langle G, \mathrm{R}, \vDash, S\rangle$ if domain$(f) = S$, range$(f) \subseteq B$, and for some formula $\mathfrak{X}(x)$ with one free variable, all constants from S and no universal quantifiers, for any $a \in S$

$$f(a) = \{\Gamma | \Gamma \vDash \mathfrak{X}(a)\}.$$

Let S' be the elements of S together with all functions definable over $\langle G, \mathrm{R}, \vDash, S\rangle$.

We define a $\vDash'$ relation by giving it for atomic formulas over S'. If $f, g \in S'$ we have three cases:

(1). $f, g \in S$. Let $\Gamma \vDash' (f \in g)$ if $\Gamma \vDash (f \in g)$.

(2). $f \in S$, $g \in S' - S$. Let $\Gamma \vDash' (f \in g)$ if $\Gamma \in g(f)$.

(3). $f \in S' - S$. Let $\mathfrak{X}(x)$ be the formula which defines f over $\langle G, \mathrm{R}, \vDash, S\rangle$. Let $\Gamma \vDash' (f \in g)$ if there is an $h \in S$ such that $\Gamma \vDash \sim(\exists x) \sim (x \in h \equiv \mathfrak{X}(x))$ and $\Gamma \vDash' (h \in g)$. (This reduces the situation to case 1 or 2).

We call the model $\langle G, \mathrm{R}, \vDash', S'\rangle$ the *derived model of* $\langle G, R, \vDash, S\rangle$.

Now, as above, let V be a classical model for ZF. We define a sequence of intuitionistic models as follows:

Let $\langle G, \mathrm{R}, \vDash_0, S_0\rangle$ be any intuitionistic model satisfying the following five conditions:

(1). $\langle G, \mathrm{R}, \vDash_0, S_0\rangle \in V$;

(2). S_0 is a collection of functions such that if $f \in S_0$, domain$(f) \subseteq S_0$ and range $(f) \subseteq B$;

(3). for $f, g \in S_0$, $\Gamma \vDash_0 (f \in g)$ if and only if $\Gamma \in g(f)$;

(4). (extensionality) for $f, g, h \in S_0$, if $\Gamma \vDash_0 \sim(\exists x) \sim (x \in f \equiv x \in g)$ and $\Gamma \vDash_0 \sim\sim(f \in h)$ then $\Gamma \vDash_0 \sim\sim(g \in h)$;

(5). (regularity) S_0 is well-founded with respect to the relation $x \in$ domain(y).

Remark 1. If we consider the symbols $\vee, \wedge, \sim, \supset, \forall, \exists, (,), \in, x_1, x_2, x_3, \ldots$ to be suitably coded as sets, formulas are sequences of sets, and hence sets. It is in this sense that (1) is meant.

Next, let $\langle G, \mathrm{R}, \vDash_{\alpha+1}, S_{\alpha+1}\rangle$ be the derived model of $\langle G, \mathrm{R}, \vDash_\alpha, S_\alpha\rangle$. If λ is a limit ordinal, let $S_\lambda = \bigcup_{\alpha<\lambda} S_\alpha$. Let $\Gamma \vDash_\lambda (f \in g)$ if for some $\alpha < \lambda$, $\Gamma \vDash_\alpha (f \in g)$. Thus we have $\langle G, \mathrm{R}, \vDash_\lambda, S_\lambda\rangle$.

Finally, let $S = \bigcup_{\alpha \in V} S_\alpha$ and $\Gamma \vDash (f \in g)$ if for some $\alpha \in V$, $\Gamma \vDash_\alpha (f \in g)$.

Thus we have the 'class' model $\langle G, \mathrm{R}, \models, S\rangle$.

At this point, let me remark without giving the proofs that the techniques which are used in handling the $\{M_\alpha\}$ sequence have their analogues for the above sequences. As in the classical case we may show:

THEOREM 2. *All the axioms of Zermelo–Fraenkel (stated without universal quantifiers) are valid in any such* $\langle G, \mathrm{R}, \models, S\rangle$.

Remark 2. As a special case, let $S_0 = \emptyset$ and let G have one element (then B has two elements, G and $\emptyset$). If we define functions $\mathfrak{v}_\alpha(X) = \{\Gamma \in G | \Gamma \models_\alpha \mathfrak{X}\}$ and we identify G with T and $\emptyset$ with F, the resulting sequence $\langle S_\alpha, \mathfrak{v}_\alpha\rangle$ is identical with the sequence $\langle M_\alpha, v_\alpha\rangle$ above. Thus, as a special case of the above theorem, L is a (classical) ZF model.

At this point it is possible to produce a particular $\langle G, \mathrm{R}, \models_0, S_0\rangle$ with so much symmetry built in that in the resulting class model $\langle G, \mathrm{R}, \models, S\rangle \sim \mathrm{AC}$ is valid. From this, as shown above, the classical independence of the axiom of choice follows. Since this model requires a fair amount of detail, rather than give it here I refer you to **[15]** and go on to show how ordinals may be represented in these models.

By putting one more requirement on $\langle G, \mathrm{R}, \models_0, S_0\rangle$ it becomes possible to find quite satisfactory representatives of all the ordinals of V in the class models. Essentially, as in the classical case, each 'ordinal' will be the 'set' of all smaller 'ordinals'. Let us make this more precise.

We use a formula *ordinal*(x) with no universal quantifiers which classically defines the ordinals.

Let us define ordinal representatives as follows: Suppose for each $\beta < \alpha$ we have already defined representatives in S. We call $f \in S$ a *general representative* of α if

(1) if $g \in S$ represents any ordinal $<\alpha$, $(g \in f)$ is valid in $\langle G, \mathrm{R}, \models, S\rangle$.

(2) if for some $\Gamma \in G$, $\Gamma \models (g \in f)$, then for some R-successor Δ of Γ, some $\beta < \alpha$ and some $h \in S$ representing β, $\Delta \models (g = h)$, that is, $\Delta \models \sim(\exists x) \sim(x \in g \equiv x \in h)$.

General representatives would be quite satisfactory to work with, if they existed, even if they were not unique. However, it is convenient to single out canonical representatives.

If f is a general representative of α, we call f a *canonical representative* of α if

(1) for no $g \in \mathrm{domain}(f)$ and for no $\Gamma \in G$ does $\Gamma \models (f = g)$;

(2) if $\Gamma \models \sim\sim(g \in f)$, then $\Gamma \models (g \in f)$ for all $g \in \mathrm{domain}(f)$.

For reasons to be given in a moment, canonical representatives, if they existed would be delightful to work with. To ensure their existence, we place two requirements on the 0-th models which say essentially that canonical representatives in S_0 (if any) are unique and that there are sufficiently many canonical representatives in S_0 that any element of S_0 which at some point is an ordinal may later be a canonical one.

Formally, call $\langle G, \mathrm{R}, \models_0, S_0 \rangle$ *ordinalized* if

(1) no ordinal has more than one canonical representative in S_0;

(2) if $f \in S_0$ and $\Gamma \models_0$ ordinal(f) for some $\Gamma \in G$, then for some R-successor Δ of Γ and some $h \in S_0$ which is a canonical ordinal representative of some ordinal, $\Delta \models_0 (f = h)$.

Now it is not difficult to show the following results:

If $\langle G, \mathrm{R}, \models_0, S_0 \rangle$ is ordinalized,

(1) every ordinal of V is uniquely canonically representable by an element of S (denote the representative of α by $\hat{\alpha}$);

(2) $\alpha = \beta$ iff $(\hat{\alpha} = \hat{\beta})$ is valid in $\langle G, \mathrm{R}, \models, S \rangle$,
$\alpha \in \beta$ iff $(\hat{\alpha} \in \hat{\beta})$ is valid in $\langle G, \mathrm{R}, \models, S \rangle$;

(3) ordinal$(\hat{\alpha})$ is valid in $\langle G, \mathrm{R}, \models, S \rangle$;

(4) if for some $\Gamma \in G$, $\Gamma \models$ordinal(f), then for some R-successor Δ of Γ and some ordinal α, $\Delta \models (f = \hat{\alpha})$;

(5) if the canonical representative $\hat{\alpha}$ is in $S_{\beta+1} - S_\beta$, $\hat{\alpha}$ is the function defined over the model $\langle G, \mathrm{R}, \models_\beta, S_\beta \rangle$ by the formula ordinal(x).

Again we do not present proofs, but they can be found in **[15]**. Let me remark that making 0th models ordinalized is a natural requirement; models which are not are rather contrived things.

There is an analogue to the classical notion of absoluteness: Call a formula $\mathfrak{X}(x_1, \ldots, x_n)$ *dominant* if for any $f_1, \ldots, f_n$ in S_α and any $\Gamma \in G$, $\Gamma \models \mathfrak{X}(f_1, \ldots, f_n)$ iff $\Gamma \models_\alpha \mathfrak{X}(f_1, \ldots, f_n)$. Formulas like $(x \in y)$, $(x = y)$ and *ordinal*(x) are dominant, so whether a 0th model is ordinalized or not can be determined by considering it alone.

Let *cardinal*(x) be a formula with no universal quantifiers, which classically defines the cardinals. Then the following may be shown:

THEOREM 3. *Suppose* $\langle G, \mathrm{R}, \models_0, S_0 \rangle$ *is ordinalized and for some* $\Gamma \in G$ *and some ordinal* α, $\Gamma \models$ *cardinal*$(\hat{\alpha})$. *Then* α *is a cardinal in the model L of constructable sets.*

It is the opposite of this situation that is needed to show the independence of the continuum hypothesis. A proof in Cohen may be adapted to these models to show the following:

$\Gamma, \Delta \in G$ are called *incompatible* if they have no common R-successor. G is called *countably incompatible* if any subset of G of mutually incompatible elements is at most countable in V.

THEOREM 4. *If* $\langle G, R, \models_0, S_0 \rangle$ *is ordinalized,* G *is countably incompatible, and* α *is a cardinal of* V, *then cardinal*$(\hat{\alpha})$ *is valid in* $\langle G, \mathrm{R}, \models, S \rangle$.

Now a specific 0th model can be given which produces a class model in which $\sim$(continuum hypothesis) and AC are valid. The model is essentially the same as the one in Cohen and the methods he uses can be adapted.

We remark that constructible set representatives can also be defined and the proof of the independence of the axiom of constructibility of Cohen can be adapted to these models.

I am afraid the foregoing has been only a collection of definitions and results, without proofs. To give the proofs in detail would take pages. To give them in outline is to say they are the analogues of classical proofs or of proofs in Cohen. But now I am going to give even less details than before, only indicating the types of theorems that exist without stating them precisely.

To the best of my knowledge there are three versions of the independence proofs (not counting those above): Cohen's forcing technique, Vopěnka's topological method and Scott and Solovay's Boolean-valued logic approach **[9]**.

The connection between the above intuitionistic methods and those of Cohen should be clear to anyone familiar with Cohen's work.

Since there is a topological model theory for intuitionistic logic, there is of course a topological version of the above. In fact there is a direct translation between Kripke's models and topological models, without going through the respective completeness theorems. I do not know how close translations of the above mentioned proofs would be to those of Vopěnka.

There are also pseudo-Boolean algebra models for intuitionistic logic **[8]**, and again there is a direct translation between Kripke's models and algebraic ones. There are also some connections between pseudo-Boolean and Boolean algebras which apply in this case. Thus the above may be put into the language of Boolean-valued logics. The result is *not* the Scott and Solovay proof. We generalized the $\{M_\alpha\}$ sequence, they generalized the $\{R_\alpha\}$ sequence (sets with rank). Thus two more methods of showing independence become available, a Boolean-valued $\{M_\alpha\}$ sequence and an intuitionistic (or forcing) $\{R_\alpha\}$ sequence. Some details of both may be found in **[15]**.

REFERENCES

[1] P. Cohen, *Set theory and the continuum hypothesis*, W. A. Benjamin, New York (1966).

[2] K. Gödel, Consistency proof for the generalized continum hypothesis, *Proc. Nat. Acad. Sci. U.S.A.* **25** (1939) 220–224.

[3] P. Hajek and P. Vopěnka, Some permutation submodels of the model ∇, *Bull. Acad. Polonaise Sci.* **14** (1966) 1–7.

[4] T. Jech and A. Sochor, On Θ model of the set theory, *Bull. Acad. Polonaise Sci.* **14** (1966) 297–303.

[5] T. Jech and A. Sochor, Applications of the Θ model, *Bull. Acad. Polonaise Sci.* **14** (1966) 351–355.

[6] S. C. Kleene, *Introduction to metamathematics*, Van Nostrand, New York (1952).

[7] S. Kripke, Semantical analysis of intuitionistic logic I, in *Formal systems and recursive functions*, North-Holland, Amsterdam (1965) 92–130.

[8] H. Rasiowa and R. Sikorski, *The mathematics of metamathematics*, Panstwowe Wydawnictwo Naukowe, Warszawa (1963).

[9] D. Scott and R. Solovay, Boolean-valued models for set theory, *Summer institute on axiomatic set theory*, Univ. of Cal., Los Angeles, 1967.

[10] P. Vopěnka, The limits of sheaves and applications on constructions of models, *Bull. Acad. Polonaise Sci.* **13** (1965) 189–192.

[11] P. Vopěnka, On ∇ model of set theory, *Bull. Acad. Polonaise Sci.* **13** (1965) 267–272.

[12] P. Vopěnka, Properties of ∇ model, *Bull Acad. Polonaise Sci.* **13** (1965) 441–444.

[13] P. Vopěnka, ∇ models in which the generalized continuum hypothesis does not hold, *Bull. Acad. Polonaise Sci.* **14** (1966) 95–99.

[14] P. Vopěnka, The limits of sheaves over extremally disconnected compact Hausdorff spaces, *Bull. Acad. Polonaisc Sci.* **15** (1967) 1–4.

[15] M. Fitting, *Intuitionistic logic model theory and forcing*, thesis, Yeshiva Univ., New York (1968); North-Holland, Amsterdam (1969).

AN ABSTRACT NOTION OF REALIZABILITY FOR WHICH INTUITIONISTIC PREDICATE CALCULUS IS COMPLETE

H. LÄUCHLI

To each formula A of predicate logic and each assignment p of 'proofs' to the atomic parts of A we shall associate a set $p[A]$, the set of 'proofs of A'. The proofs of $A \to B$ are just the functions from $p[A]$ into $p[B]$; the proofs of $\exists vA$ are the pairs $\langle c, x\rangle$ such that x is a proof of A^v_c (substitution of c for v).

Instead of 'proofs of A' we could as well say 'realizing functionals for A'. In contrast to Kleene's (second version of the) notion of realizability [**3**], we consider arbitrary, not necessarily countable functionals.

We shall show that A is derivable in Heyting's predicate calculus if and only if there is an explicitly definable functional Θ such that $\Theta \in p[A]$ for all p, i.e. if and only if there is a well defined 'proof' of A which does not make use of the internal structure of proofs of the atomic parts of A.

The 'only if' part will be clear from the known results about realizability. For the proof of the 'if' part we make use of the following analogy between Kripke's semantics for intuitionistic logic [**4**] and the theory of permutation groups. In the former, we can assert the implication $A \to B$ in a situation H iff in any later situation H' where we can assert A, we also can assert B. In the latter, the following is true: Given sets A, B and a group H of permutations of the elements of $A \cup B$ leaving A and B invariant. Then there is an H-invariant function from A into B iff any subgroup H' with a fixed element in A also has a fixed element in B.

The theorem will be established classically. The corresponding result for propositional logic was announced in an abstract [**5**].

Similar interpretations have been considered by Dana Scott (derived from Gödel's Dialectica interpretation) and by Goodman, Kreisel, Troelstra, Scott (derived from the intuitionistic notion of 'construction'; see [**1**]). To my knowledge, completeness of intuitionistic predicate calculus has not been established for any of these interpretations.

1. We consider formulas containing n-place predicate letters, a propositional constant f ('false'), individual constants, variables $u, v, w, \ldots$, connectives $\wedge, \vee, \rightarrow, \exists, \forall$. We write $\neg A$ for $A \rightarrow f$. $F(\Gamma)$ denotes the set of all *closed* formulas with individual constants from a set Γ.

In the following Γ and Π are countably infinite sets, $c_0 \in \Gamma$ is a designated element of Γ, $X \times Y$ denotes the Cartesian product of the sets X and Y, $X \dot{\cup} Y$ is the disjoint union $(\{0\} \times X) \cup (\{1\} \times Y)$, Y^X is the set of all functions from X into Y.

To each formula A, not necessarily closed, we associate a set $S(A)$, the set of 'possible proofs of A':

$$
\begin{aligned}
S(A) &= \Pi \text{ if } A \text{ is atomic,}\\
S(A \wedge B) &= S(A) \times S(B),\\
S(A \vee B) &= S(A) \dot{\cup} S(B),\\
S(A \rightarrow B) &= S(B)^{S(A)},\\
S(\forall v A) &= S(A)^{\Gamma},\\
S(\exists v A) &= \Gamma \times S(A).
\end{aligned}
$$

Note that $S(A^v_c) = S(A)$ for all individual constants c. Thus $S(\forall v A)$ can be interpreted as the set of all choice functions which assign to each $c \in \Gamma$ an element of $S(A^v_c)$.

A *proof assignment* is any function p which assigns to every (closed) formula $A \in F(\Gamma)$ a set $p[A]$ such that

$$
\begin{aligned}
p[f] \subseteq p[A] &\subseteq \Pi \text{ if } A \text{ is atomic,}\\
p[A \wedge B] &= p[A] \times p[B],\\
p[A \vee B] &= p[A] \dot{\cup} p[B],\\
p[A \rightarrow B] &= \{x \in S(A \rightarrow B)\colon xy \in p[B] \text{ for all } y \in p[A]\},\\
p[\forall v A] &= \{x \in S(\forall v A)\colon xc \in p[A^v_c] \text{ for all } c \in \Gamma\},\\
p[\exists v A] &= \{\langle c, x\rangle\colon c \in \Gamma \text{ and } x \in p[A^v_c]\}.
\end{aligned}
$$

Note that $p[A] \subseteq S(A)$ for all p and A. The elements of $p[A \rightarrow B]$ are functions with domain $S(A)$. Thus the identity function on $S(A)$ belongs to $p[A \rightarrow A]$ for each p.

2. Let $\mathscr{D}$ be the least class containing the sets $\{0, 1\}$, Γ, Π, such that whenever $D_1, D_2 \in \mathscr{D}$, then $D_1 \times D_2$, $D_1 \cup D_2$, $D_1^{D_2} \in \mathscr{D}$. The elements of $D_1 \times D_2$ are viewed as functions with domain $\{0, 1\}$. Let $\mathscr{F} = \bigcup \mathscr{D}$. The elements of $\mathscr{F}$ will be called *functionals*. *Simple* functionals are those which can be defined explicitly. The following kind of explicit definition will do: We consider terms built from constants 0, 1, c_0 and variables, using the following formation rules: If t, s are terms and x is a variable and $D \in \mathscr{D}$, then $t(s)$, $\langle t, s\rangle$, $\lambda^D x(t)$ are terms. Terms are interpreted as follows:

Let V be an assignment of functionals to variables. Then $V[t]$ is the following functional:

$V[0] = 0$;

$V[1] = 1$;

$V[c_0] = c_0$;

$V[x]$ is the functional assigned to x;

$V[t(s)]$ is the value of $V[t]$ at $V[s]$ if $V[t]$ is a function and $V[s]$ belongs to its domain, $V[t(s)] = 0$ otherwise;

$V[\langle t, s\rangle]$ is the function with domain $\{0, 1\}$ and values $V[t]$ and $V[s]$ at 0 and 1 respectively;

$V[\lambda^D x(t)]$ is the function with domain D, taking the value $V_a^x[t]$ for $a \in D$; V_a^x assigns a to x and agrees with V otherwise.

If t is closed (all variables bound by λ), then the functional $V[t]$ does not depend on V. Simple functionals are by definition those given by closed terms.

Example 1. Let A, B, C be closed formulas. Let

$$D = S((A \to C) \wedge (B \to C)),$$
$$E = S(A \vee B).$$

Then the term

$$\lambda^D x(\lambda^E y(\langle x0(y1), x1(y1)\rangle(y0)))$$

defines a simple functional which belongs to

$$p[(A \to C) \wedge (B \to C) \to (A \vee B \to C)]$$

for all proof assignments p.

Example 2. Let

$$D = S(\neg\forall v(R(v) \vee \neg R(v))).$$

Then

$$\lambda^D x(x(\lambda^\Gamma x(\langle 1, \lambda^\Pi x(x)\rangle)))$$

defines a simple functional which belongs to

$$S(\neg\neg\forall v(R(v) \vee \neg R(v))).$$

3. Let σ be a permutation on $\Gamma \cup \Pi$ (i.e. a one–one function from $\Gamma \cup \Pi$ onto itself), which leaves invariant the sets Γ, Π and the designated element c_0. σ extends in a natural way to a permutation on $\mathscr{F}$: $\sigma 0 = 0$, $\sigma 1 = 1$; if

g is a function then $(\sigma g)x = \sigma(g(\sigma^{-1}x))$. In particular $\sigma\langle a, b\rangle = \langle \sigma a, \sigma b\rangle$.

A functional $\Theta \in \mathscr{F}$ is said to be *invariant*, if $\sigma\Theta = \Theta$ for all such σ. Simple functionals are invariant since c_0, 0, 1 and all sets $D \in \mathscr{D}$ are invariant. On the other hand, there are uncountably many invariant functionals in $\mathscr{F}$ that are not simple.

4. In the following A denotes a closed formula containing no individual constants other than c_0. The symbol $\vdash$ denotes derivability in the intuitionistic predicate calculus.

THEOREM. (1). *If* $\vdash A$, *then there is a simple functional* Θ *such that* $\Theta \in p[A]$ *for all proof assignments* p.

(2). *If not* $\vdash A$, *then there is* p *such that* $p[A]$ *contains no invariant functional.*

COROLLARY. *The following are equivalent* (*classically*):

(a). $\vdash A$;

(b) $\exists$ *simple* Θ, $\forall p$, $\Theta \in p[A]$;

(c). $\forall p \, \exists$ *simple* Θ, $\Theta \in p[A]$;

(d) $\exists$ *invariant* Θ, $\forall p$, $\Theta \in p[A]$;

(e). $\forall p \, \exists$ *invariant* Θ, $\Theta \in p[A]$.

The corollary indicates a certain stability of the property '$\vdash A$'. For conditions (b), (c), (d) and (e), which are quite different intensionally, turn out to coincide with '$\vdash A$' extensionally.

If we drop the restrictions put on Θ, then we get classical logic in one case and an intermediate thing in the other: $\forall p \, \exists$(*arbitrary*) Θ *with* $\Theta \in p[A]$ *iff* A *is derivable in classical predicate calculus.* On the other hand, the condition $\exists\Theta\forall p$ holds for some intuitionistically invalid formulas, e.g. for

$$\forall v(R(v) \vee Q) \rightarrow (\forall v R(v) \vee Q),$$

but not for all classically valid ones, e.g. not for $Q \vee \neg Q$.

Part (2) of the theorem is not true if only those p are considered with $p[f] = \Lambda$ (empty). The formula $\neg\neg \forall v(R(v) \vee \neg R(v))$, call it $\neg\neg B$, gives a counterexample. For if $p[f] = \Lambda$ then $p[\neg B] = \Lambda$ since $p[B] \neq \Lambda$, B being classically valid. Hence $p[\neg\neg B] = S(\neg\neg B)$. But $S(\neg\neg B)$ contains invariant functionals, as was shown in example 2.

The proof of part (1) of the theorem is a routine variation on the proof of theorem 62, **[2]** p. 504. The remainder of this paper is devoted to the proof of part (2).

5. Let N be the set of the natural numbers (including 0). Let Σ be the set of all finite sequences of natural numbers (including the empty sequence Λ) together with an 'ideal element' U. Let R be the binary relation on Σ such that $s\mathrm{R}s'$ iff either s' is U or s is a (not necessarily proper) initial segment of s'. Let Ψ be a function with domain Σ and countable sets as values, such that whenever $s\mathrm{R}s'$ and $s \neq s'$, then $\Psi(s) \subseteq \Psi(s')$ and the complement $\Psi(s') - \Psi(s)$ is infinite. We also assume $\Psi(\Lambda)$ infinite. $F(\Psi(s))$ denotes the class of all closed formulas with individual constants from $\Psi(s)$.

Everything introduced so far will remain fixed. In particular, we shall not vary the function Ψ.

A *model* is a binary function $\Phi(A, s)$, where A ranges over $F(\Psi(U))$ and s over Σ, whose range is the set $\{T, F\}$, and which satisfies the following conditions:

(1). if $\Phi(A, s) = T$, then $A \in F(\Psi(s))$;

(2). if $\Phi(A, s) = T$ and $s\mathrm{R}s'$, then $\Phi(A, s') = T$;

(3). if $\Phi(f, s) = T$, then $\Phi(A, s) = T$ for all $A \in F(\Psi(s))$;

(4). $\Phi(A \wedge B, s) = T$ iff $A \wedge B \in F(\Psi(s))$, and $\Phi(A, s) = T$ and $\Phi(B, s) = T$;

(5). $\Phi(A \vee B, s) = T$ iff $A \vee B \in F(\Psi(s))$, and $\Phi(A, s) = T$ or $\Phi(B, s) = T$;

(6). $\Phi(A \rightarrow B) = T$ iff $A \rightarrow B \in F(\Psi(s))$ and for all s' with $s\mathrm{R}s'$, if $\Phi(A, s') = T$ then $\Phi(B, s') = T$;

(7). $\Phi(\forall v A, s) = T$ iff $\Phi(A^v_c, s') = T$ for all s' with $s\mathrm{R}s'$ and all $c \in \Psi(s')$

(8). $\Phi(\exists v A, s) = T$ iff $\Phi(A^v_c, s) = T$ for some $c \in \Psi(s)$.

LEMMA 1. *Let $A \in F(\Psi(\Lambda))$ with not $\vdash A$. Then (and only then) there is a model Φ such that $\Phi(A, \Lambda) = F$.*

The proof is clear from Kripke's work **[4]**.

The element U is no bother: Any Φ which is defined on $\Sigma - \{U\}$ can be extended to Σ by setting $\Phi(A, U) = T$ for all $A \in F(\Psi(U))$.

6. In this section we establish a relationship between models Φ and proof assignments p.

Let q be a one-one function from Σ into the set of positive prime numbers. The function φ from Σ into N is defined by $\varphi(\Lambda) = 1$, $\varphi(s{*}n) = \varphi(s) \cdot q(s{*}n)$, $\varphi(U) = 0$ ($s{*}n$ denotes adjunction of the last term n to the sequence s). Let $|$ denote the relation of divisibility. Each non-empty subset of Σ has a greatest lower bound (glb) with respect to R. For $n \in N$ let

$s_n = \text{glb}\{s: n|\varphi(s)\}$ (the set is non-empty since $n|\varphi(U)$). For instance $s_1 = \Lambda$ and $s_0 = s_4 = U$.

The following are simple consequences of the definitions:

(1). $\varphi(s)|\varphi(s')$ iff $s\text{R}s'$,

(2). $n|\varphi(s_n)$,

(3). $n|\varphi(s)$ iff $s_n\text{R}s$,

(4). $n|m$ implies $s_n\text{R}s_m$,

(5). $s_{\varphi(s)} = s$,

Let I denote the set of all integers, including the negative ones. Let n' denote the set of residue classes of I modulo n: $1'$ is a one element set, $0'$ is I. We have $n' \cap m' = \Lambda$ for $n, m \in N$, $n \neq m$.

We now define $\Gamma = \Pi = \bigcup \{\Psi(s_n) \times n' : n \in N\}$. (More precisely: We impose a certain structure on the given countable sets Γ and Π. The structure on Γ is isomorphic to that on Π. Thus, as a notational convenience, we identify Γ with Π.)

The designated element c_0 of Γ is to belong to $\Psi(s_1) \times 1'$. Let $\Gamma_n = \bigcup \{\Psi(s_k) \times k' : k|n\}$. Thus $\Gamma = \Gamma_0$ and $c_0 \in \Gamma_1$ and

(6). $n|m$ implies $\Gamma_n \subseteq \Gamma_m$.

The elements of Γ are ordered pairs. If $c \in \Gamma$, let c^- denote its first component: $c^- \in \Psi(s_n)$ for some n. In virtue of (4), if $k|n$ then $\Psi(s_k) \subseteq \Psi(s_n)$. Hence

(7). $c \in \Gamma_n$ implies $c^- \in \Psi(s_n)$.

The converse is not true for all $c \in \Gamma$, but we have

(8). if $d \in \Psi(s_n)$ then there is $c \in \Gamma_n$ with $c^- = d$.

If $A \in F(\Gamma)$, let A^- denote the formula obtained by replacing each individual constant c by c^-.

(9). $A \in F(\Gamma_n)$ implies $A^- \in F(\Psi(s_n))$.

Let σ be the following permutation on Γ: If $c = \langle d, i/n \rangle \in \Psi(s_n) \times n'$, then $\sigma c = \langle d, (i+1)/n \rangle$. Then, for all $c \in \Gamma$ and $n \in N$ we have

(10). $\sigma^n c = c$ iff $c \in \Gamma_n$.

In particular $\sigma c_0 = c_0$ since $c_0 \in \Gamma_1$.

To each model Φ we associate a proof assignment p as follows. Let $A \in F(\Gamma)$ be atomic. We define

$$p[A] = \bigcup \{\Psi(s_k) \times k' : \Phi(A^-, s_k) = T \text{ or } \Phi(f, s_k) = T\}.$$

The requirement $p[f] \subseteq p[A] \subseteq \Pi$ for atomic A is satisfied. $p[A]$ only depends on A^-. This carries over to compound formulas. Hence for all $A, B \in F(\Gamma)$

(11). $A^- = B^-$ implies $p[A] = p[B]$.

Furthermore it is easy to see that

(12). $\sigma(p[A]) = p[A]$, for all A in $F(\Gamma)$.

LEMMA 2. *For all $n \in N$ and $A \in F(\Gamma_n)$, σ^n has fixed elements in $p[A]$ if and only if $\Phi(A^-, s_n) = T$.*

(Thus we have a world constant σ such that for all Φ there is a p such that lemma 2 is true.)

PROOF. The proof is by induction on the complexity of A:

1. Let A be atomic. By (10), σ^n has fixed elements in $p[A]$ iff $\Gamma_n \cap p[A] \neq \Lambda$, i.e. iff there is a k, $k|n$, such that $\Phi(A^-, s_k) = T$ or $\Phi(f, s_k) = T$. By (4), the latter holds iff $\Phi(A^-, s_n) = T$ or $\Phi(f, s_n) = T$. Since $A \in F(\Gamma_n)$ (9) gives $A^- \in F(\Psi(s_n))$. Thus $\Phi(f, s_n) = T$ implies $\Phi(A^-, s_n) = T$. Hence σ^n has fixed elements in $p[A]$ iff $\Phi(A^-, s_n) = T$.

2. Let A be $B \wedge C$ or $B \vee C$. The induction step is clear.

3. Let A be $B \rightarrow C$. '*only if*': let $x \in p[A]$ with $\sigma^n x = x$. Consider s with $s_n \mathrm{R} s$ and $\Phi(B^-, s) = T$. Let $m = \varphi(s)$. Then $n|m$ by (3), and hence $B \in F(\Gamma_m)$ by (6). By (5) s is s_m. The induction hypothesis gives an element $y \in p[B]$ with $\sigma^m y = y$. Now $xy \in p[C]$ and $\sigma^m(xy) = (\sigma^m x)(\sigma^m y) = xy$ and $C \in F(\Gamma_m)$. The induction hypothesis gives $\Phi(C^-, s) = T$. Hence $\Phi(A^-, s_n) = T$.

'*if*': Let $\Phi(A^-, s_n) = T$. If $n|m$ then $s_n \mathrm{R} s_m$ (by (4)) and hence $\Phi(B^-, s_m) = T$ implies $\Phi(C^-, s_m) = T$. By the induction hypothesis for each m with $n|m$, if σ^m has fixed elements in $p[B]$, then it also has fixed elements in $p[C]$. Let H be the permutation group generated by σ^n, and let $H(y)$ denote the largest subgroup of H leaving y fixed. Since any subgroup of H is generated by σ^m for some m with $n|m$ (at worst $m = 0$), we have that for each $y \in p[B]$ $H(y)$ has fixed elements in $p[C]$.

We say y_1 is equivalent to y_2, if $hy_1 = y_2$ for some $h \in H$. Let S be a maximal set of pairwise non-equivalent elements of $p[B]$. Let g be a function from S into $p[C]$ such that gy is fixed under $H(y)$ for all $y \in S$. Let $x_1 = \{\langle hy, h(gy)\rangle : y \in S \text{ and } h \in H\}$. x_1 represents a function: If $hy = h'y$, then $h^{-1}h' \in H(y) \subseteq H(gy)$, whence $h(gy) = h'(gy)$; $\mathrm{dom}(x_1) = p[B]$ because of the maximality of S and the invariance of $p[B]$ (see (12)). Also $\mathrm{rg}(x_1) \subseteq p[C]$. Thus x_1 is an H-invariant function from $p[B]$ into $p[C]$.

Recall that the elements of $p[B \rightarrow C]$ are functions with domain $S(B)$, the set of 'possible proofs of B'. Let x_2 be any invariant function from $S(B) - p[B]$ into $S(C)$, for instance the constant function with an invariant element of $S(C)$ as value (which is easily seen to exist, since both Γ and Π

contain the σ-invariant element c_0). Then $x = x_1 \cup x_2$ belongs to $p[B \to C]$ and is invariant under σ^n.

4. Let A be $\forall vB$. *'only if'*: Let $x \in p[\forall vB]$, $\sigma^n x = x$. Let $s_n R s$, $d \in \Psi(s)$. As before, we have $n|m$ and $s = s_m$ for $m = \varphi(s)$. By (8) there is $c \in \Gamma_m$ such that $c^- = d$. By (10) $\sigma^m c = c$. Therefore $\sigma^m(xc) = xc$. Also $xc \in p[B_c^v]$ and $B_c^v \in F(\Gamma_m)$. Induction hypothesis gives $\Phi((B_c^v)^-, s) = T$. $(B_c^v)^-$ is $(B^-)_d^v$. Hence $\Phi(\forall vB^-, s_n) = T$.

'if': Let $\Phi(\forall vB^-, s_n) = T$. Let $c \in \Gamma$. If H is the group generated by σ^n, then $H(c)$ is generated by σ^m for some m with $n|m$. By (10) $c \in \Gamma_m$. By (7) $c^- \in \Psi(s_m)$. By (4) $s_n R s_m$. Therefore $\Phi((B_c^v)^-, s_m) = T$. Also $B_c^v \in F(\Gamma_m)$. By induction hypothesis $H(c)$ has fixed elements in $p[B_c^v]$. As before we get an invariant function. There is no trouble with the range, since for all $h \in H$, $h(p[B_c^v]) = p[B_c^v] = p[B_{hc}^v]$ in virtue of (12) and (11). Therefore σ^n has fixed elements in $p[\forall vB]$.

5. Let A be $\exists vB$. The proof is straightforward, using (7), (8) and (10).

This concludes the proof of the lemma.

Proof of part (2) of the theorem:

Let A be a closed formula containing no individual constants other than c_0. Then $A \in F(\Gamma_1)$ and $A^- \in F(\Psi(s_1)) = F(\Psi(A))$. Assume not $\vdash A$. Lemma 1 gives a model Φ such that $\Phi(A^-, A) = F$. Let p be the proof assignment associated to Φ. Then by lemma 2, σ has no fixed element in $p[A]$. Therefore $p[A]$ contains no invariant functional.

REFERENCES

[1] N. GOODMAN, A theory of constructions equivalent to arithmetic, these proceedings, 101–120.

[2] S. C. KLEENE, *Introduction to metamathematics*, Amsterdam (1952).

[3] S. C. KLEENE, Realizability, *Summer Inst. Symb. Logic Cornell Univ., Princeton* 1957, vol. 1, 100–104.

[4] S. A. KRIPKE, Semantical analysis of intuitionistic logic I, in *Formal systems and recursive functions, Proc. 8th Logic colloquium Oxford* 1963, North-Holland, Amsterdam (1965).

[5] H. LÄUCHLI, Intuitionistic propositional calculus and definably non-empty terms (abstract), *J. Symb. Logic* **30** no. 2 (1965).

EXTENDING THE TOPOLOGICAL INTERPRETATION TO INTUITIONISTIC ANALYSIS, II

DANA SCOTT*

This paper is a sequel to the paper [12] written for Professor Heyting under the same title. Nearly all of the questions left open in [12] have been answered. In particular the results of section 3 in [12] having to do with universal formulae of the theory of $<$ in *three* variables have been extended to *arbitrary* universal formulae in section 5. (Our numbering of sections continues that of [12].) We then discuss in section 6 the general metamathematical implications of the method of section 5 for the theory of the topological model of intuitionistic analysis. In section 7 the important step is taken of enlarging the model to encompass arbitrary (extensional) real functions. The main result is the verification in the model of Brouwer's theorem on continuity: *all functions are uniformly continuous on closed intervals*. The proof is given in detail along with several related results. (The reader will have to refer to [12] for notation and the definition of the model.)

The author was thus able to conclude this paper feeling that he had a rather good grasp of the basic properties of the real numbers of the model. Several further projects remain to be carried out, however. The next important step is to discuss the corresponding topological interpretation of *second-order arithmetic* and the theory of free-choice sequences of integers. This will make possible an exact comparison of the theory of the model and the usual axiomatic theories of intuitionistic analysis (which will no doubt be one of the main topics of part III of this series of papers.) Following such work it is obvious that attention must be given to obtaining a constructive version of the model. Kreisel has suggested that the theory of constructive and lawless sequences (the system of [8]) may provide the proper framework

* Research on this paper has been supported by a grant from the National Science Foundation. Special thanks are due to Professor G. Kreisel for the many hours of discussion on intuitionism in general and the helpful criticisms of earlier drafts of this paper in particular.

for this discussion in view of the connection between the topological interpretation and lawless sequences **[5]** (part IV?) In this connection it is appropriate to take this opportunity to retract a remark of **[12]**, p. 194. Contrary to what was said, Kreisel has all along felt that the topological interpretation has relevance. Indeed in **[6]** he mentions it along with realizability and his own elimination of free choice sequences. Moreover in **[5]**, p. 370, paragraph 2, he had already presented the clearest possible statement of his view of the interpretation.

In another direction the theory of species and higher-order functions will require consideration. That study will of course bring in connections with the Boolean models for set theory (**[11]** and **[13]**.) To date no particular technical results about the Boolean models have played a role in the discussion of these topological models. In fact, the main effort was given to the consideration of those properties of the models and topological spaces most appropriate to foundations of intuitionism. However, it was the success of the Boolean models in making clear certain aspects of Cohen's remarkable independence results (such as the type of construction of generic and random reals) that encouraged the author to take up again the study of the topological interpretation which he had put down some ten years before. And he is most happy to see now just how well things fit together. It does not seem altogether impossible that work in the intuitionistic theories may throw additional light on the properties of the Boolean models (cf. **[2]** and other references given there).

5. Further independence results. In section 3 we discussed universally quantified three-variable consequences of the axioms of order (1.1)–(1.2) and noted that such questions could be thrown back to propositional calculus as well as being determined by the model. At the time of writing the earlier section the results were rather special, and the author suggested that they should generalize. They do. Kreisel has pointed out the relevance of the following well-known fact about HPC (Heyting's predicate calculus):

A universal sentence is a consequence in HPC *of a given universal axiom if and only if its matrix is a propositional consequence of a finite number of substitution instances of the axiom using the variables mentioned in the conclusion.*

Note that our language has only relation symbols, in fact only $<$, which makes the result so simple; in particular, we have a decision method for universal consequences of a universal axiom. The proof of this general result requires no special knowledge of models.

Let us consider the theory of $<$. We can schematically indicate the general universal sentence as

$$\forall x_0, \ldots, x_{n-1} A(x_i < x_j: i, j < n),$$

where we mean to suggest that the expression involves the various atomic formulae $x_i < x_j$. Let P_{ij} be propositional letters and let

$$A(P_{ij}: i, j < n)$$

indicate the result of replacing $x_i < x_j$ by P_{ij} in the matrix of our universal sentence. Further let

$$B(P_{ij}: i, j < n)$$

be the conjunction of all formulae of the two forms

$$\neg [P_{ij} \wedge P_{ji}]$$

and

$$[P_{ij} \rightarrow P_{ik} \vee P_{kj}]$$

for $i, j, k < n$. In our case the general result mentioned above shows that the given universal sentence is a consequence of (1.1)–(1.2) if and only if

$$[B(P_{ij}: i, j < n) \rightarrow A(P_{ij}: i, j < n)]$$

is a *propositional* theorem in HPC; hence the decision method. This approach is definitely only suited to universal prenex formulae, however. The author is rather inclined to believe that the full first-order intuitionistic theory based on (1.1)–(1.2) is *undecidable*.

Having noted the above purely formal result, we may now ask: *Are the axioms* (1.1)–(1.2) *complete for the universal sentences valid in our model*? We shall prove that, under suitable conditions on the topological space T, if the universal sentence is *not* provable in the theory of $<$, then it *fails* in the model. Indeed we shall find that the contradictory sentence

$$\forall x_0 \neg \forall x_1, \ldots, x_{n-1} A(x_i < x_j: i, j < n)$$

is actually *valid* in the model. For this purpose in view of **[10]**, pp. 130–131 we find it convenient to assume that T is a non-empty, dense-in-itself, totally disconnected, metric space; the two best known examples being the Cantor space 2^N and the Baire space N^N. We prefer the latter because of its naturalness in interpreting second-order number theory. Thus for the remainder of the paper we may as well fix $T = N^N$. In the future there may be reason for greater generality, but this choice of T gives a complicated enough model with sufficiently many interesting properties.

Suppose, then, that the universal sentence is *not* provable from (1.1)–(1.2). Thus the corresponding propositional formula is not provable either. By what we know about $T = N^N$, we can assign open sets $[\![P_{ij}]\!]$ to the P_{ij} in such a way that

$$[\![B(P_{ij}\colon i, j < n)]\!] = T;$$

while

$$[\![A(P_{ij}\colon i, j < n)]\!] \neq T.$$

We wish to find continuous functions $\xi_i \in \mathscr{R}$ such that

$$[\![\xi_i < \xi_j]\!] = [\![P_{ij}]\!],$$

and this will give us the counterexample in the model.

It seems convenient to construct certain auxiliary functions before obtaining the ξ_i. In the first place, given open sets $[\![P_{ij}]\!]$ and given a subset $I \subseteq \{0, 1, \ldots, n\}$, we can define continuous functions $\sigma_I \in \mathscr{R}$ that are *non-negative* and such that

$$[\![\sigma_I > 0]\!] = \bigcap_{k \in I} \bigcap_{l \notin I} [\![P_{kl}]\!].$$

Next, for given $i, j < n$, we define $\pi_{ij} \in \mathscr{R}$ such that

$$\pi_{ij} = \sum_{\substack{i \in I \\ j \notin I}} \sigma_I - \sum_{\substack{j \in J \\ i \notin J}} \sigma_J,$$

where the summations run over all the subsets satisfying the indicated restrictions. Finally we set for $i < n$

$$\xi_i = \pi_{0i},$$

but it takes several steps to see that these functions so defined have the desired properties. (These formulae, by the way, do indeed generalize those of section 3.)

We note first that, for $i, j < n$,

$$\pi_{ii} = 0$$

and

$$\pi_{ji} = -\pi_{ij}$$

hold by definition. The π_{ij} are by no means non-negative, but we shall see that

$$[\![\pi_{ij} > 0]\!] = [\![P_{ij}]\!].$$

Assume that $\pi_{ij}(t) > 0$, then by the definition of the π_{ij} and the non-negative character of the σ_I, we find $\sigma_I(t) > 0$ for at least one subset I such that $i \in I, j \notin I$. But then by the construction of σ_I, we have $t \in [\![P_{ij}]\!]$. Now for the converse, assume that $t \in [\![P_{ij}]\!]$. We must obtain a particular $I \subseteq \{0, 1, \ldots, n-1\}$ such that $i \in I$, $j \notin I$, and

$$t \in \bigcap_{k \in I} \bigcap_{l \notin I} [\![P_{kl}]\!],$$

where of course k, l range over all indices less than n satisfying the restrictions. To construct I we proceed by induction. Let $I_0 = \{i\}$ and $I_0' = \{j\}$. Since

$$[\![P_{ij}]\!] \cap [\![P_{ji}]\!] = \emptyset$$

we know that $i \neq j$, because $t \in [\![P_{ij}]\!]$ but $t \notin [\![P_{ji}]\!]$. Hence $I_0 \cap I_0' = \emptyset$ and

$$t \in \bigcap_{k \in I_0} \bigcap_{l \in I_0'} [\![P_{kl}]\!].$$

Suppose now $q < n$, and $I_q \cap I_q' = \emptyset$, and

$$t \in \bigcap_{k \in I_q} \bigcap_{l \in I_q'} [\![P_{kl}]\!].$$

Let m be the least integer where $m < n$, $m \notin I_q \cap I_q'$. We will show how to adjoin m to I_q or to I_q' preserving the above properties. Because, from the assumptions about the P_{ij}, we have

$$[\![P_{kl}]\!] \subseteq [\![P_{km}]\!] \cup [\![P_{ml}]\!],$$

so that

$$\bigcap_{k \in I_q} \bigcap_{l \in I_q'} [\![P_{kl}]\!] \subseteq \Big(\bigcap_{k \in I_q} [\![P_{km}]\!] \cup \bigcap_{l \in I_q'} [\![P_{ml}]\!]\Big).$$

Now if $t \in \bigcap_{k \in I_q} [\![P_{km}]\!]$, set $I_{q+1} = I_q$ and $I_{q+1}' = I_q' \cup \{m\}$. While if $t \in \bigcap_{l \in I_q'} [\![P_{ml}]\!]$, set $I_{q+1} = I_q \cup \{m\}$ and $I_{q+1}' = I_q'$. The required properties are obvious in either case. Proceeding in this way to $q = n$ (or is it $n-2$ since we started with i, j as given?) we obtain I and its complement as desired. Having found this I we see $\sigma_I(t) > 0$. Now if J is any subset with $j \in J$ and $i \notin J$, then since $t \notin [\![P_{ji}]\!]$, we have $\sigma_J(t) = 0$. We have thus proved that $\pi_{ij}(t) > 0$.

To complete the proof we must prove in addition

$$\pi_{ij}+\pi_{jk}+\pi_{ki} = 0.$$

Note that in view of our above remarks about the π_{ij}, it is sufficient to assume the $i, j, k < n$ are all *distinct*. We must, unfortunately, write out the sum on the left-hand side of the above equation, namely:

$$\sum_{\substack{i\in I\\ j\notin I}} \sigma_I - \sum_{\substack{j\in J\\ i\notin J}} \sigma_J + \sum_{\substack{j\in I\\ k\notin I}} \sigma_I - \sum_{\substack{k\in J\\ j\notin J}} \sigma_J + \sum_{\substack{k\in I\\ i\notin I}} \sigma_I - \sum_{\substack{i\in J\\ k\notin J}} \sigma_J .$$

There are two kind of terms: positive and negative, and there are *equal* numbers of each. Thus if we can show that each positive term can be cancelled by a *unique* negative term that is formally equal to it, then the whole expression cancels to zero. In view of the symmetry of the situation, consider a typical term σ_I with $i \in I$ and $j \notin I$. By inspection, of the *six* kinds of restrictions on the capital letter subscripts in the expression only *two* could contain an occurrence of the *same* subscript I. And actually only *one* can arise: the cases $k \in I$ and $k \notin I$ are disjoint. Thus indeed a positive occurrence of σ_I cancels with a unique negative occurrence with the same subscript. Our argument is complete.

From the equation just proved we see that

$$\xi_j - \xi_i = \pi_{ij}$$

which implies that

$$[\![\xi_i < \xi_j]\!] = [\![P_{ij}]\!].$$

It follows that

$$[\![A(\xi_i < \xi_j : i, j < n)]\!] \neq T.$$

Since the only interesting situation is where $n \geqslant 2$, we can derive exactly as in section 3 the validity in the model of

$$\forall x_0 \neg \forall x_1, \ldots, x_{n-1} A(x_i < x_j : i, j < n), \tag{5.1}$$

which gives us a large number of independence results. What we would like to discuss next is whether there are reasonable *axioms* for intuitionistic analysis from which these formulae (5.1) become *provable*.

6. Maximality of propositional calculus. In classical logic we have a very easy time of it: an unprovable propositional schema leads at once to contradiction after a suitable substitution of quite trivial formulae for the propositional letters. Thus we know in a most direct way that in our formalization no valid principles have been overlooked. The predicate calculus is not that simple, otherwise it would be decidable. Nevertheless, if we consider a theory such as that of all (classically) true sentences of first-order arithmetic, we conclude from Gödel's theorem that each unprovable predicate calculus schema has an instance in the language of arithmetic that is indeed false. Let us formulate this idea as a general metamathematical notion.

On the one hand we have a *logical calculus* (classical or intuitionistic propositional or predicate calculus, to be definite) which consists of various schemata and some rules (maybe, only modus ponens and generalization.) On the other hand we have a *theory* which consists of a set (species) of valid formulae in a certain (applied) language. We assume that we know what it means to form an *instance* of a logical schema in the applied language. Obviously we want to assume that the logic is *sound* for the theory; that is, all instances of schemata are valid and all instances of rules lead from valid formulae to valid formulae. What is more interesting is the question of whether the logic is *maximal* for the theory. This means that if we take a schema *not* provable in the logical calculus, then the adjunction of all instances of this new schema render the given theory *inconsistent* in the sense of the original logical calculus. (We can take the inconsistency to be the resultant provability of arbitrary formulae.) We use the word 'maximal' here as being more descriptive than the overworked 'complete'. As pointed out, classical propositional calculus is maximal for *any* (classical) theory. Classical predicate calculus is maximal for certain theories, though not for any recursively enumerable theory. What about the intuitionistic logical calculi?

An analysis of the argument of section 5 shows that atomic formulae of the form $y > 0$ have instances which, in the model, take on any value (any open set). Thus with our choice of $T = N^N$ we can easily argue that if $C(P_i\colon i < m)$ is a propositional formula not provable in HPC, then

$$\neg \forall y_0, \ldots, y_{m-n} C(y_i > 0\colon i < m) \tag{6.1}$$

is valid in the model. Note that the negation falls outside the scope of the universal quantifiers. Thus no instance of the unprovable $C(P_i\colon i < m)$ is likely to lead to a *propositional* contradiction (unless it is classically invalid.) However, an obvious instance combined with *universal generalization* does lead to a contradiction. Therefore we can say that the propositional part of HPC is maximal for the theory of valid sentences of the model in the context of *all* the rules of HPC. Whether the full HPC is maximal for this theory the author cannot see at the moment; though this may in fact follow from the known topological completeness proofs for HPC.

A question that should be answered concerns those axiomatic theories of analysis for which we have the same HPC maximality. Kreisel has verified in [**5**], p. 378, propositional maximality for a theory of lawless sequences. The theories of Kleene–Vesley [**4**] and Kreisel–Troelstra [**14**] need investigation on this point. The many fragmentary results of [**4**] point in this direction; and one should consider in this connection whether the full $\forall\alpha\exists\beta$-continuity is really needed or just $\forall\alpha\exists!\beta$. Another question: could there be any intuitionistically acceptable extension of Heyting's arithmetic (HA) for which we would have propositional maximality? It seems unlikely.

From the axiomatic point of view, propositional maximality has certain useful consequences. We shall now show that (6.1) together with some very elementary *algebra* allow us to formally derive the results of section 5. Hence, if in [**4**] it would have been possible to obtain (6.1), many of the results of [**4**], ch. IV would have followed directly.

Let us recall the notation from the previous section: $B(P_{ij}\colon i,j < n)$ stood for a certain conjunction related to the axioms of order; $A(P_{ij}\colon i,j < n)$ was an arbitrary formula such that

$$[B(P_{ij}\colon i,j < n) \to A(P_{ij}\colon i,j < n)]$$

was *unprovable* in HPC. Let p_{ij} be distinct real variables for $i,j < n$. Our construction of the ξ_i in section 5 could be turned into a formal proof of

$$B(p_{ij} > 0\colon i,j < n) \leftrightarrow \exists x_0, \ldots, x_{n-1} \bigwedge_{i,j<n} [x_i < x_j \leftrightarrow p_{ij} > 0], \tag{6.2}$$

where $\bigwedge$ is the sign of conjunction of several formulae. The proof would be rather long: Assuming the left-hand side, we would have to first introduce

$$p_{ij}^{+} = \max(p_{ij}, 0),$$

to get non-negative variables, and then invoke the elementary theorems to have

$$p_{ij}^{+} > 0 \leftrightarrow p_{ij} > 0.$$

But that is easy. Next we would have to introduce for $I \subseteq \{0, 1, \ldots, n-1\}$

$$s_I = \prod_{k\in I} \prod_{l\notin I} p_{kl}^{+},$$

where $\prod$ is the sign of arithmetic product. Elementary algebra tells us that a product of non-negative terms is strictly positive if and only if *all* the terms are strictly positive. Thus the formal s_I correspond to our use of σ_I in the informal proof of section 5. Then we could introduce $\tilde{p}_{ij}$ corresponding to the π_{ij} and then the x_i corresponding to the ξ_i. Again by elementary algebra we could transcribe our proof to finally establish (6.2).

Now we invoke (6.1) and the unprovability of the implication combined with (6.2) to prove

$$\neg \forall x_0, \ldots, x_{n-1} A(x_i < x_j : i, j < n), \tag{6.3}$$

which is not quite as strong as what we validated in section 5. But note that $[x_i < x_j \leftrightarrow x_i + y < x_j + y]$ by elementary algebra. This translation invariance makes it easy to prove, as in section 3, the following

$$\forall x_0, \ldots, x_{n-1} A(x_i < x_j : i, j < n) \leftrightarrow \forall x_1, \ldots, x_{n-1} A(x_i < x_j : i, j < n), \tag{6.4}$$

where on the right-hand side we have left x_0 *free*. Obviously the implication goes from left to right; for the converse one just translates the *fixed* x_0 to an *arbitrary* x_0. The reader can surely do this for himself. That is how we get the formal proof of (5.1).

The deduction just outlined illustrates a familiar phenomenon: a result purely in the theory of one predicate (in this case it was $<$) was obtained only with the aid of several auxiliary notions (viz. $+$, $\cdot$, $-$, max, min) together with their elementary properties. In classical theories we have examples in various fragments of integer arithmetic but not in the theory of order in the continuum. This is another indication that the intuitionistic theory of $<$ is more complicated than the classical theory.

To further illustrate the usefulness of the auxiliary notions for understanding the basic theory of $<$ we may mention the definitions of $z \in [x, y]$ and $z \in (x, y)$ given in (4.2)–(4.3). These are equivalent to the definitions in [3] (3.3.2.1, p. 40), and we find in [3], p. 41 a proof that

$$z \in [x, y] \leftrightarrow \min(x, y) \leqslant z \leqslant \max(x, y). \tag{6.5}$$

That obviously makes very good sense and clears up the doubts the author had when he wrote section 4. However, in the case of the open interval the best we can do is

$$z \in (x, y) \leftrightarrow \neg\neg [\min(x, y) < z < \max(x, y)]. \tag{6.6}$$

The author is only very slowly beginning to understand the role of $\neg\neg$ in intuitionistic mathematics, and hopes to discuss it again at another time.

A different kind of consequence of the method used to verify (6.1) shows us that for arbitrary formulae A

$$\exists y[y > 0 \leftrightarrow A] \tag{6.7}$$

is valid in the model. This is a strong version of *Kripke's schema* first mentioned in print by Myhill [7], p. 174. Myhill's weaker statement of the principle would read in our notation:

$$\exists y[[y \leqslant 0 \rightarrow \neg A] \wedge [y > 0 \rightarrow A]].$$

Clearly this statement follows from (6.7) but one would guess not conversely. Assuming that the system of analysis supplied by our model is at all reasonable intuitionistically, we thus obtain a consistency proof for this form of Kripke's schema. As Myhill has already pointed out, (6.7) is incompatible with $\forall\alpha\exists\beta$-continuity ([7], pp. 173–174). Thus to justify the reasonableness of our model, we must now turn to a discussion of what continuity properties actually are valid since such principles are desirable intuitionistically.

7. Functions and continuity. We are now going to enrich our language of analysis by the adjunction of *function variables*. We reserve f, g, h (with or without subscripts) for such variables and employ the usual function-value notation $f(x)$ in the formal language. We are assuming our functions to be everywhere defined, real-valued functions of *one* argument. The extension of the language and the results to functions of several arguments seems to present no difficulties and is left to the reader.

The interpretation of these functions in the model will be given in a very straightforward way and will lead to several obviously basic principles being valid. In the first place our functions will be extensional:

$$\forall f \forall x, y[x = y \rightarrow f(x) = f(y)], \tag{7.1}$$

and *apartness* and *equality* of functions will be given by the following definitions:

$$\forall f, g[f \neq g \leftrightarrow \exists x\ f(x) \neq g(x)], \tag{7.2}$$

$$\forall f, g[f = g \leftrightarrow \neg f \neq g]. \tag{7.3}$$

Next we will have the principle of *function existence*:

$$\forall x \exists ! y\ A(x, y) \rightarrow \exists ! f \forall x\ A(x, f(x)), \tag{7.4}$$

where $A(x, y)$ is an arbitrary formula which is assumed to be *extensional* (as are all of our formulae for the time being) in the sense that

$$\forall x, x', y, y' \; [A(x, y) \wedge x = x' \wedge y = y' \rightarrow A(x', y')]$$

must be valid.

There are no surprises here, since (7.1)–(7.4) are clearly rather fundamental for any reasonable theory of functions. What is surprising is that, without seeming to have built the fact into our interpretation, we do validate the principle of *continuity*:

$$\forall f \forall z, w \forall e > 0 \, \exists d > 0 \, \forall x, y \in [z, w][|x-y| < d \rightarrow |f(x)-f(y)| < e], \quad (7.5)$$

where we have used e and d as rational variables in place of the conventional ε and δ. Note that (7.5) is not just *point-wise* continuity of every function but *uniform* continuity on every closed interval.

A simple consequence of uniform continuity is: *every rational-valued function is constant.* A moment's reflection shows it is enough to prove that every *integer-valued* function is constant; and, even simpler, it is sufficient to prove that every *two-valued* function is constant. This last principle has a simple schematic statement:

$$\forall x[A(x) \vee \neg A(x)] \rightarrow [\forall x A(x) \vee \forall x \neg A(x)], \quad (7.6)$$

a principle which states, in Brouwer's terminology, that the continuum is 'unzerlegbar' (cf. [**4**], *R10.4, p. 155). The proof of (7.6) begins with the introduction of a function f such that

$$\forall x[[A(x) \wedge f(x) = 0] \vee [\neg A(x) \wedge f(x) = 1]],$$

which is justified by (7.4). Then one applies (7.5) with $e = 1$ for an arbitrary pair of numbers z, w. The interval $[z, w]$ can easily be covered by intervals of length d, where d is supplied by (7.5), and the inequalities together with an inductive argument imply that f is constant on $[z, w]$.

It is tempting on rather formal grounds to assume a version of the *axiom of choice*:

$$\forall x \exists y A(x, y) \rightarrow \exists f \forall x A(x, f(x)), \quad \text{(AC-RR)}$$

where we have followed Kreisel [**8**], pp. 233f, in style of terminology with RR meaning that the choices are from *reals* to *reals*. Without thought, (AC–RR) would seem to be a reasonable strengthening of (7.4); however, in view of the remarks in connection with (7.6) we see that it is actually *invalid* for the *extensional* notion of function intended here. Indeed the formula $[x < y \wedge y \in Q]$ gives the obvious counter-example.

It is quite pleasant that to be able to achieve all the above results the interpretation in the model can be as simple as possible: we take as functions those mappings $\varphi : \mathscr{R} \to \mathscr{R}$ such that for $\xi, \eta \in \mathscr{R}$ we have

$$[\![\xi = \eta]\!] \subseteq [\![\varphi(\xi) = \varphi(\eta)]\!].$$

This is the extensionality principle: we make (7.1) valid *by definition*. We let $\mathscr{R}^{\mathscr{R}}$ denote the class of all these extensional functions $\varphi : \mathscr{R} \to \mathscr{R}$. Further we define for $\varphi, \psi \in \mathscr{R}^{\mathscr{R}}$

$$[\![\varphi \neq \psi]\!] = \bigcup_{\xi \in \mathscr{R}} [\![\varphi(\xi) \neq \psi(\xi)]\!].$$

This convention makes (7.2) valid also *by definition*; similarly for (7.3). But this is all that is trivial by definition; the remaining facts require proof.

To prove the validity of (7.4) it is clearly enough to prove *existence* of f, because the uniqueness will follow in view of the hypothesis and (7.2–7.3). Thus we must show that

$$[\![\forall x \exists ! y A(x, y)]\!] \subseteq [\![\exists f \forall x A(x, f(x))]\!].$$

We will take advantage here of the fact that $T = N^N$ is *totally disconnected* (though no doubt all we really need to know is that T is metric.) In such a space every open set is the union of its *clopen* subsets. Hence it is sufficient to prove for every clopen set $K \subseteq T$ that if

$$K \subseteq [\![\forall x \exists ! y A(x, y)]\!],$$

then

$$K \subseteq [\![\exists f \forall x A(x, f(x))]\!].$$

Indeed, to prove this last inclusion, we need only find a function $\varphi_K \in \mathscr{R}^{\mathscr{R}}$ corresponding to K such that

$$K \subseteq [\![\forall x A(x, \varphi_K(x))]\!].$$

The advantage of working with *clopen* K is that for $t \in K$ and $\xi \in \mathscr{R}$ we will have a special way of defining $\varphi_K(\xi)(t)$, but for $t \notin K$ we can simply set $\varphi_K(\xi)(t) = 0$. The clopenness of K will assure that $\varphi_K(\xi) \in \mathscr{R}$ so defined is *continuous*.

Thus let $\xi \in \mathscr{R}$ be fixed. Our assumption implies that

$$K \subseteq [\![\exists ! y A(\xi, y)]\!],$$

To define $\varphi_K(\xi)$ we use the same method as in section 2 and set

$$\varphi_K(\xi)(t) = \inf\{r \in Q : t \in [\![\exists y[A(\xi, y) \wedge y < r]]\!]\}$$

for $t \in K$; otherwise the value is 0, as mentioned above. As in the proof of (2.7) it is elementary to check that

$$K \cap \varphi_K(\xi)^{-1}(q, q') = K \cap [\![\exists y[A(\xi, y) \wedge q < y < q']]\!],$$

which shows that $\varphi_K(\xi)$ is continuous on K. Therefore $\varphi_K(\xi)$ is continuous everywhere in T. This does not yet prove that $\varphi_K \in \mathscr{R}$. We must still verify

$$K \cap [\![\xi = \eta]\!] \subseteq [\![\varphi_K(\xi) = \varphi_K(\eta)]\!];$$

but this easily follows from the extensionality of A. Since $\varphi_K(\xi)$ is 0 outside of K, we see that indeed $\varphi_K \in \mathscr{R}^{\mathscr{R}}$. Finally it is clear by construction that

$$K \subseteq [\![A(\xi, \varphi_K(\xi))]\!],$$

and the desired conclusion follows.

The proof that (7.5) is valid is by no means as straightforward. Note first that (7.5) implies

$$\forall f \forall x, y[f(x) \neq f(y) \rightarrow x \neq y], \tag{7.7}$$

which is a stronger version of (7.1). As it turned out, it is very useful to validate (7.7) first as a lemma, and then establish (7.5). (This point was a stumbling block for the author, who formulated the problem in a lecture at the University of Texas at Austin. Shortly thereafter the idea of the following proof was communicated to the author by Professor Jack Hardy, whose assistance it is a pleasure to acknowledge.)

To prove (7.6) we note first that what we have to establish is this inclusion for $\xi, \eta \in \mathscr{R}$ and $\varphi \in \mathscr{R}^{\mathscr{R}}$:

$$[\![\varphi(\xi) \neq \varphi(\eta)]\!] \subseteq [\![\xi \neq \eta]\!].$$

Now after translation back to subsets of T, we can complement both sides of the inclusion to obtain:

$$\{t \in T : \xi(t) = \eta(t)\} \subseteq \{t \in T : \varphi(\xi)(t) = \varphi(\eta)(t)\}. \tag{*}$$

That is what we must prove; what we are assuming (because $\varphi \in \mathscr{R}^{\mathscr{R}}$) is equivalent to:

$$\text{In}\,\{t \in T : \xi(t) = \eta(t)\} \subseteq \{t \in T : \varphi(\xi)(t) = \varphi(\eta)(t)\}. \tag{**}$$

We can state the problem in words: (*) means that φ is an operator on continuous functions (to continuous functions) such that if two arguments ξ, η are equal at a point, then their images $\varphi(\xi)$, $\varphi(\eta)$ are equal at the *same* point. Thus $\varphi(\xi)(t)$ only depends on t and $\xi(t)$, not on the whole of ξ. It would seem that (**) is much weaker: $\varphi(\xi)(t)$ depends on knowing t and knowing ξ *in some neighborhood of* t, that is, on the local behaviorof ξ around t. (The author imagined at first that one could have a function φ satisfying (**) without its satisfying (*). It seems odd that a problem like this has not been considered before, but inquiry failed to uncover any relevant information. It would fair to say that most of the operators considered in mathematics usually depend on the *whole* of ξ (like integration) or do *not* give continuous functions $\varphi(\xi)$ as values (like right-hand derivatives).)

The first main step in deducing (*) (for *all* $\xi, \eta \in \mathscr{R}$) from (**) (for *all* $\xi, \eta \in \mathscr{R}$) is to remark that the set on the right-hand side of (**) is *closed* because $\varphi(\xi)$ and $\varphi(\eta)$ are each *continuous*. This means that we can strenghten (**) to read:

$$\mathrm{Cl}\,\mathrm{In}\,\{t \in T : \xi(t) = \eta(t)\} \subseteq \{t \in T : \varphi(\xi)(t) = \varphi(\eta)(t)\}, \qquad (***)$$

which we are assuming for *all* $\xi, \eta \in \mathscr{R}$. Now we must prove (*) for a particular pair $\xi_0, \eta_0 \in \mathscr{R}$. Suppose $t_0 \in T$ is a point such that $\xi_0(t_0) = \eta_0(t_0)$. We will show below that we can find *open* subsets U, V of T such that

$$\mathrm{Cl}\,(U) \cap \mathrm{Cl}\,(V) = \{t_0\},$$

and such that ξ_0 is *bounded* on U and η_0 is *bounded* on V. Now the function

$$\zeta_0 = \xi_0 \restriction \mathrm{Cl}\,(U) \cup \eta_0 \restriction \mathrm{Cl}\,(V)$$

is obviously *continuous* on $\mathrm{Cl}\,(U) \cup \mathrm{Cl}\,(V)$ because $\xi_0(t_0) = \eta_0(t_0)$, and it is *bounded*. Thus by the well-known Tietze extension theorem (T is a metric space) we can extend the function to the whole of T. We call the extension ζ_0 also. (This construction of ζ_0, which is due to Prof. Hardy, is the main idea of the proof.) Now we make use of (***) for ξ_0, ζ_0 and for ζ_0, η_0. In the first instance we see by the construction of ζ_0 that:

$$t_0 \in \mathrm{Cl}\,\mathrm{In}\,\{t \in T : \xi_0(t) = \zeta_0(t)\},$$

and so by (***), $\varphi(\xi_0)(t_0) = \varphi(\zeta_0)(t_0)$. In the second instance we have

$$t_0 \in \mathrm{Cl}\,\mathrm{In}\,\{t \in T : \zeta_0(t) = \eta_0(t)\},$$

and so again by (***), $\varphi(\zeta_0)(t_0) = \varphi(\eta_0)(t_0)$. Now it follows at once that $\varphi(\xi_0)(t_0) = \varphi(\eta_0)(t_0)$, which is what we needed to establish (*).

Filling in the part of the argument about U and V that we had postponed, we note first that if t_0 is *isolated* we can take $U = V = \{t_0\}$. Assume then that t_0 is not isolated and let $t_1, t_2, t_3, \ldots, t_n, \ldots$ be an infinite sequence of *distinct* points converging to t_0. Inasmuch as ξ_0 and η_0 are continuous, they both must be *bounded* on $\{t_1, t_2, \ldots, t_n, \ldots\}$. Around each of these points we can put small *open* spheres with $t_n \in S_n$ such that the *closures* of the spheres are pairwise disjoint (T is a metric space!) and on which ξ_0 and η_0 are uniformly bounded. It follows that

$$U = \bigcup_{n=1}^{\infty} S_{2n}$$

and

$$V = \bigcup_{n=1}^{\infty} S_{2n-1}$$

are the required open sets.

We shall now investigate the nature of the functions $\varphi \in \mathscr{R}^{\mathscr{R}}$ more closely. The reader will appreciate that it is necessary to keep his wits about him in thinking about the model. We already use *functions* $\xi : T \to R$ to play the role of *real* numbers in the model, so that when we come to *functions* in the model we have to use *operators* $\varphi : \mathscr{R} \to \mathscr{R}$. Thus $\varphi(\xi)$ is a function for each $\xi \in \mathscr{R}$, as we had to consider in the above proof of (7.7). Looking from the outside, the type of the objects used in the model is always *higher* than the formal type of the variable which ranges over them. This process of going up in type for the definition of the model is very convenient for making the construction simple, but we shall now show that a reduction in type is possible helping in the analysis of the model.

Since $\varphi \in \mathscr{R}^{\mathscr{R}}$ satisfies (*) we define $\Phi : T \times R \to R$ by the condition:

$$\Phi(t, a) = b \textit{ iff for some } \xi \in \mathscr{R},\ \xi(t) = a \text{ and } \varphi(\xi)(t) = b.$$

We thus have Φ well-dertermined and such that for $\xi \in \mathscr{R}$, $t \in T$:

$$\varphi(\xi)(t) = \Phi(t, \xi(t)).$$

The point of bringing in Φ is that, as we shall now show, the function Φ is *continuous* on the *product space* $T \times R$. We argue by contradiction: suppose that Φ is *not* continuous at some point (t, a). Then there must exist an $\varepsilon > 0$ and a sequence of neighborhoods U_n of t and a sequence of reals δ_n, such that the U_n monotonically decrease to $\{t\}$ and the δ_n to 0. Further we can find a sequence of points (t_n, a_n) where $t_n \in U_n$, and $|a_n - a| < \delta_n$, and

$$|\Phi(t_n, a_n) - \Phi(t, a)| > \varepsilon$$

for all n. Since for fixed a_n, a the two expressions $\Phi(t, a_n)$ and $\Phi(t, a)$ represet *continuous* functions of t, we can clearly assume that all $t_n \neq$ t. (Otherwise we could 'adjust' $t_n \in U_n$ and still preserve the above strict inequality). Furthermore, because the diameters of the U_n are converging to 0, we can assume that the t_n are all distinct. (If not, we can choose a suitable subsequence.) After that fuss, we can now remark that we are able to construct a *continuous* function $\xi \in \mathscr{R}$ such that $\xi(t_n) = a_n$ and $\xi(t) = a$, because the a_n *do* converge to a. But then since $\varphi(\xi)$ is continuous, $\varphi(\xi)(t_n)$ would have to converge to $\varphi(\xi)(t)$, which contradicts the above inequality.

Now that we see why Φ is continuous, we can quickly establish the validity of (7.5) for φ. Note first that it is sufficient to consider $z = q$ and $w = r$, where $q, r \in Q$ and $q < r$. Let $\varepsilon > 0$, $\varepsilon \in Q$. We must show:

$$T = \bigcup_{\delta < 0} \mathrm{In} \bigcap_{\xi, \eta \in \mathscr{R}} \mathrm{In}\, \{t \in T: [\xi(t), \eta(t) \in [q, r] \wedge |\xi(t) - \eta(t)| < \delta \rightarrow$$
$$|\Phi(t, \xi(t)) - \Phi(t, \eta(t))| < \varepsilon]\}.$$

Introduce an auxiliary function $\varepsilon: T \times (0, \infty) \rightarrow R$ by:

$$\varepsilon(t, \delta) = \sup\, \{|\Phi(t, a) - \Phi(t, b)|: a, b \in [q, r],\ |a - b| \leqslant \delta\}.$$

The function inside the sup is a continuous function of three variables t, a, b, and the sup is being taken over a *compact* subset of $R \times R$. It follows for a fixed δ that $\varepsilon(t, \delta)$ is a continuous (and well-defined!) function of t. Since for fixed t the real function $\Phi(t, a)$ is *uniformily continuous* for $a \in [q, r]$, we conclude that $\varepsilon(t, \delta)$ decreases to 0 as δ decreases to 0. Let, then, $t_0 \in T$ and choose δ so that $\varepsilon(t_0, \delta) < \varepsilon$. Let $U \subseteq T$ be a neighborhood of t_0 such that $\varepsilon(t, \delta) < \varepsilon$ for all $t \in U$. We must verify that U is included in the right-hand side of the above topological equation. It is immediate.

The method of proof just employed for (7.5) is also very helpful in other problems: for example we shall now validate in the model a principle which states that every positive function on a closed interval is bounded away from zero:

$$\forall f \forall z, w[\forall x \in [z, w][f(x) > 0] \rightarrow \exists y > 0 \forall x \in [z, w][f(x) \geqslant y]]. \quad (7.8)$$

In view of continuity, and the denseness of the rationals, it is sufficient to treat only the case where $z = q$, $w = r$, $q < r$. For simplicity we shall in addition assume for our $\varphi \in \mathscr{R}^{\mathscr{R}}$ that

$$T = [\![\forall x \in [q, r][\varphi(x) > 0]]\!].$$

The more general case can be treated as in the proof of (7.4). In terms of Φ we are thus assuming that

$$\Phi(t, a) > 0$$

for all $t \in T$ and all $a \in [q, r]$. Define $\eta \in \mathscr{R}$ by $\eta(t) = \inf\{\Phi(t, a) : a \in [q, r]\}$ for $t \in T$. Again by virtue of the compactness of $[q, r]$, we can check that η is continuous. But for fixed t we have $\Phi(t, a)$ as a positive continuous function of $a \in [q, r]$, therefore $\eta(t) > 0$ for all $t \in T$. We can thus easily verify that

$$T = [\![\forall x \in [q, r][\varphi(x) \geqslant \eta]]\!],$$

and (7.8) is established. We may remark that this construction of η shows also that every function has a greatest lower bound on every closed interval – a fact that can fairly easily be deduced from continuity (cf **[1]**, p. 35 for example.)

Our reduction of the $\varphi : \mathscr{R} \to \mathscr{R}$ to the $\Phi: T \times \mathrm{R} \to R$ is very useful in discussing other questions about the model. For example, every ordinary continuous function $F : R \to R$ can be extended to $\mathscr{R}$, as we have often remarked, by the formula

$$\varphi(\xi)(t) = F(\xi(t)).$$

The question is whether *every* $\varphi \in \mathscr{R}^{\mathscr{R}}$ is *ordinary* in this sense. Well, obviously not: let $\alpha \in \mathscr{R}$ be fixed and define

$$\varphi(\xi)(t) = \xi(t) + \alpha(t).$$

Could there be an $F : R \to R$ such that

$$F(\xi(t)) = \xi(t) + \alpha(t)$$

holds in general? If so, we could take ξ to be constant, say 0, and deduce

$$F(0) = \alpha(t),$$

thus making α constant. Since α need not be constant, the desired counterexample is produced.

The foregoing simple argument leads naturally to a modification of our question: given $\varphi \in \mathscr{R}^{\mathscr{R}}$ could we find a continuous function $G : R \times R \to R$ and a particular $\alpha \in \mathscr{R}$ such that

$$\varphi(\xi)(t) = G(\alpha(t), \xi(t))$$

for all $\xi \in \mathscr{R}$ and $t \in T$? The answer is again *no*, but the argument is more difficult. (The author is indebted to Kenneth Kunen for the suggestion of the counter-example.) In terms of the correspondng Φ the problem is to find G and α such that

$$\Phi(t, \xi(t)) = G(\alpha(t), \xi(t))$$

for all $\xi \in \mathscr{R}$ and $t \in T$. This simplifies to

$$\Phi(t, a) = G(\alpha(t), a)$$

for all $a \in R$ and $t \in T$. We have only to choose a very bad Φ to get into trouble. In view of the universal properties of N^N, we can choose Φ so that the functions $\psi_t : R \to R$ where

$$\psi_t(a) = \Phi(t, a)$$

give us *all* continuous functions from reals into reals. That is, Φ would be a *universal* function for all real continuous functions with the parameter in $T = N^N$. That is possible; but, by the equation for G above, *it* would also be universal with parameter in R. That is *not* possible.

We have just shown that in the model not every function need be ordinary or even quasi-ordinary (i.e. ordinary in a parameter α.) There is a common special case where we can, however, conclude that the function is indeed ordinary. Suppose φ has been introduced to validate

$$\forall x\, A(x, \varphi(x))$$

where $\forall x \exists ! y\, A(x, y)$ is valid *and* $A(x, y)$ has *no* additional parameters. (The formula can involve $<$, $+$, $\cdot$, other ordinary functions and predicates, the predicates Q and D, and so on.) We note first that φ must be somehow invariantly determined.

Now we ask: in what sense is φ invariant? Well, let $\tau : T \to T$ be any autohomeomorphism of T. This extends to the model. For $\xi \in \mathscr{R}$ we define $\tau(\xi)$ so that

$$\tau(\xi)(\tau(t)) = \xi(t)$$

for all $t \in T$. (Thus $\tau(\xi) = \xi \circ \tau^{-1}$) This makes it possible to regard $\tau : \mathscr{R} \to$

$\to \mathscr{R}$. However, it is *not* the case in general that $\tau \in \mathscr{R}^{\mathscr{R}}$; for we have

$$[\![\tau(\xi) = \tau(\eta)]\!] = \tau([\![\xi = \eta]\!]).$$

(Recall that τ is naturally defined on open subsets of T also!) We can regard τ as acting on $\mathscr{R}^{\mathscr{R}}$, nevertheless. For any $\psi \in \mathscr{R}^{\mathscr{R}}$ we define $\tau(\psi)$ so that

$$\tau(\psi)(\tau(\xi)) = \tau(\psi(\xi))$$

for all $\xi \in \mathscr{R}$. It is easy to check that $\tau(\psi) \in \mathscr{R}$. Having done this, we remark that by the usual kind or argument, if B is any formula involving ordinary functions and predicates bound real and function variables, *and* parameters from $\mathscr{R}$ and $\mathscr{R}^{\mathscr{R}}$, then

$$\tau([\![B(\xi, \ldots, \psi, \ldots)]\!]) = [\![B(\tau(\xi), \ldots, \tau(\psi), \ldots)]\!].$$

Applying this automorphism principle to A we have

$$\tau([\![A(\xi, \eta)]\!]) = [\![A(\tau(\xi), \tau(\eta))]\!]$$

because there are no other parameters. But

$$[\![A(\xi, \eta)]\!] = [\![\varphi(\xi) = \eta]\!],$$

hence

$$[\![\tau(\varphi)(\tau(\xi)) = \tau(\eta)]\!] = [\![\varphi(\tau(\xi)) = \tau(\eta)]\!].$$

It follows at once that $\tau(\varphi) = \varphi$.

We have thus proved that if $\varphi \in \mathscr{R}^{\mathscr{R}}$ is defined by a parameterless formula, then it is invariant under all automorphisms of the model determined by autohomeomorphisms of T. Let us see what this means about the corresponding continuous function $\Phi : T \times R \to R$. Now

$$\varphi(\xi)(t) = \Phi(t, \xi(t)),$$

so by substitution

$$\begin{aligned}\varphi(\tau(\xi))(\tau(t)) &= \Phi(\tau(t), \tau(\xi)(\tau(t))) \\ &= \Phi(\tau(t), \xi(t)).\end{aligned}$$

But $\tau(\varphi) = \varphi$, so we derive

$$\begin{aligned}\varphi(\tau(\xi))(\tau(t)) &= \tau(\varphi)(\tau(\xi))(\tau(t)) \\ &= \tau(\varphi(\xi))(\tau(t)) \\ &= \varphi(\xi)(t).\end{aligned}$$

Putting two and two together we find:

$$\Phi(t, \xi(t)) = \Phi(\tau(t), \xi(t)).$$

Since ξ is arbitrary we can say

$$\Phi(t, a) = \Phi(\tau(t), a)$$

for all $t \in T$ and all $a \in R$. But hold, the autohomeomorphism τ is arbitrary, and $T = N^N$ has a transitive autohomeomorphism group; thus

$$\Phi(t, a) = \Phi(t', a)$$

for all $t, t' \in T$. This means that Φ does not depend on t at all and we can write

$$\Phi(t, a) = F(a)$$

where $F : R \to R$ so obtained is continuous. Thus

$$\varphi(\xi)(t) = F(\xi(t)),$$

and we have finally proved that φ is just an ordinary function.

In words we could say that the above argument suggests that in intuitionistic analysis it is impossible to give an outright *extensional* definition of any function not already known from classical analysis. (Of course, the simple-minded identification of intuitionistic analysis with the theory of this model is not justified because the model is defined classically.)

We close this section with a problem about continuity. In (7.6) the hypothesis means that the property $A(x)$ decomposes the continuum into two disjoint parts. Let us weaken this by having *two* properties $A(x)$ and $B(x)$ where $\forall x[A(x) \vee B(x)]$, but where we do not make any disjointness assumption. (For example $\forall x[x < 1 \vee x > 0]$ is valid.) We can obviously not hope to have any such strong conclusion as $[\forall x A(x) \vee \forall x B(x)]$ (by the example!), but what about this principle:

$$\forall x[A(x) \vee B(x)] \to \exists q, r[q < r \wedge [\forall x \in [q, r]\, A(x) \vee \forall x \in [q, r]\, B(x)]]?$$

The author has not yet been able to see an answer to the question of the validity of this formula. The situation may become clearer after a study of second-order arithmetic in the model.

REFERENCES

[1] E. Bishop, *Foundations of constructive analysis,* New York (1967).

[2] M. Fitting, Intuitionistic model theory and the Cohen independence proofs, these proceedings 219–226.

[3] A. Heyting, *Intuitionism, an introduction,* Amsterdam (1956).

[4] S. C. Kleene and R. E. Vesley, *Foundations of intuitionistic mathematics,* Amsterdam (1965).

[5] G. Kreisel, A remark on free choice sequences and the topological completeness proofs, *J. Symb. Logic* **23** (1958) 369–388.

[6] G. Kreisel, Mathematical logic, in *Lectures on modern mathematics,* vol. III, ed. T. L. Saaty, New York (1965) 95–195.

[7] G. Kreisel, Informal rigour and completeness proofs, in *Problems in the philosophy of mathematics,* ed. I. Lakatos, Amsterdam (1967) 138–171, with following discussion.

[8] G. Kreisel, Lawless sequences of natural number, *Compositio Math.* **20** (1968) 222–248.

[9] J. Myhill, Notes towards an axiomatization of intuitionistic analysis, *Logique et Analyse* **35** (1967) 280–297.

[10] H. Rasiowa and R. Sikorski, *The mathematics of metamathematics,* Warsaw (1963).

[11] D. Scott, A proof of the independence of the continuum Hypothesis, *Math. Systems Theory* **1** (1967) 89–111.

[12] D. Scott, Extending the topological interpretation to intuitionistic analysis, *Compositio Math.* **20** (1968) 194–210.

[13] D. Scott and R. Solovay, Boolean-valued models for set theory, to appear.

[14] A. S. Troelstra, The theory of choice sequences, in *Logic, methodology and philosophy of science III,* eds. B. van Rootselaar and J. F. Staal, North-Holland, Amsterdam (1968) 201–223.

SECTION D

PROOF THEORY OF INTUITIONISM

SOME RESULTS FOR INTUITIONISTIC LOGIC WITH SECOND ORDER QUANTIFICATION RULES

DAG PRAWITZ

Consider the second order logical system obtained by adding ordinary quantification rules for predicate variables (including an abstraction principle) to first order intuitionistic logic. For this system, I shall prove a Gentzen Hauptsatz (i.e. a cut elimination theorem), which will give the following corollaries:

(1). If $A \vee B$ is provable, then either A or B is provable.

(2). If $\exists x A(x)$ is provable, then $A(t)$ is provable for some individual term t.

(3). If $\exists X^n A(X^n)$ is provable, then $A(T^n)$ is provable for some predicate term T^n (T^n is here an abstraction term defining an n-ary relation).

These results, which certainly are consonant with intuitionistic principles, may have some bearing on the debated question whether a second order system of the described kind is intuitionistic acceptable.*

A Gentzen Hauptsatz for classical second order logic was obtained by Tait [7] and later by Takahashi [**8**] and Prawitz [**5**] and [**6**]. Unlike the situation in first order logic, where a syntactical proof of Gentzen's Hauptsatz for classical logic can be carried over almost without change to intuitionistic logic, these results have no immediate impact on the system that we are considering here. All the proofs of Gentzen's Hauptsatz for classical second order logic are semantical, and to give an analogous proof for our present second order system, we have to supply the system with some suitable interpretation. This can be done by extending either Beth's [**1**] (as modified by Dyson and Kreisel [**2**]) or Kripke's [**3**] interpretation of first order intuitionistic logic. It turns out that second order Beth models may be construed as special cases of second order Kripke models. We thus obtain

* The intuitionistic significance of the described system has been advocated by Professor Georg Kreisel especially. I am grateful to him for encouraging me to carry out these investigations.

a stronger result by proving the completeness of our system with respect to Beth models. I shall now carry out this task following the pattern of Prawitz [**5**] and [**6**].

1. The languages. We consider languages containing at least individual parameters and variables (denoted '*a*' and '*x*' respectively), *n*-ary predicate parameters and variables for each $n = 0, 1, 2, \ldots$ (denoted 'P^n' and 'X^n' respectively, sometimes leaving out the superscript), the implication sign ($\supset$), the universal quantifier ($\forall$), the abstraction operator (λ), and parenthesis. In addition, the languages may contain *n*-ary function symbols for functions from the individuals to the individuals. Each category of parameters and variables is supposed to be denumerably infinite unless otherwise stated. We assume that the parameters of each category are given in a certain alphabetic order.

The individual terms (denoted '*t*'), *n*-ary predicate terms (abstractions) (denoted 'T^n') and formulas (denoted '*A*', '*B*', ...) are defined as usual (see e.g. Prawitz [**4**], p. 63–64); it is to be noted that terms and formulas never contain free variables. We shall assume that the terms of each catagory have been ordered in some way.

Negation, conjunction, disjunction, and existential quantification are defined as in Prawitz [**4**], p. 67. We shall also use some other ordinary syntactical abbreviations and notations, which can all be found in Prawitz [**4**].

2. The calculus $\mathcal{T}$. By a sequent in a language *L* we understand an expression of the form $\Gamma \rightarrow \Delta$, where Γ and Δ are (possibly empty) finite strings of formulas in *L* separated by commas.

If Π and Σ are sets of formulas, $\Pi \Rightarrow \Sigma$ is to denote any sequence whose formulas occuring in the antecedent (succedent) are exactly those of Π (Σ). Usual abbreviations are used, e.g. $A, \Pi \Rightarrow B$ is an abbreviation for $\{A\} \cup \Pi \Rightarrow \{B\}$.

We now set up the following calculus of sequents called $\mathcal{T}$:
Axioms. All sequents of the form $A, \Pi \Rightarrow A$.
Inference rules.

$\rightarrow\supset)$ $$\frac{A, \Pi \Rightarrow B}{\Pi \Rightarrow A \supset B}$$

$\supset\rightarrow)$ $$\frac{\Pi \Rightarrow A \quad B, \Pi \Rightarrow C}{A \supset B, \Pi \Rightarrow C}$$

$\rightarrow\forall_1)$ $$\frac{\Pi \Rightarrow A}{\Pi \Rightarrow \forall x A^a_x}$$

$\forall_1\rightarrow)$ $$\frac{A^x_t, \Pi \Rightarrow B}{\forall x A, \Pi \Rightarrow B}$$

$\to\forall_2)\quad \dfrac{\Pi\Rightarrow A}{\Pi\Rightarrow\forall X^n A^{P^n}_{X^n}}\qquad \forall_2\to)\quad \dfrac{A^{X^n}_{T^n},\ \Pi\Rightarrow B}{\forall X^n A,\ \Pi\Rightarrow B}$

$\to\lambda)\quad \dfrac{\Pi\Rightarrow(S^{x_1x_2\ldots x_n}_{t_1t_2\ldots t_n}A)}{\Pi\Rightarrow\lambda x_1x_2\ldots x_nAt_1t_2\ldots t_n}\qquad \lambda\to)\quad \dfrac{(S^{x_1x_2\ldots x_n}_{t_1t_2\ldots t_n}A),\ \Pi\Rightarrow B}{\lambda x_1x_2\ldots x_nAt_1t_2\ldots t_n,\ \Pi\Rightarrow B}$

$\text{cut})\quad \dfrac{\Gamma\Rightarrow A\quad A,\Gamma\Rightarrow B}{\Gamma\Rightarrow B}$

The rules $\to\forall_1$ and $\to\forall_2$ are with the restriction that a and P^n, respectively, do not occur in the sequent below the line.

Proofs (in tree form) and provability are defined as usual.

Remark. It is easily seen that structural rules that have not been stated above (e.g. thinning) hold as derived rules. It is also to be noted that the ordinary inference rules for negation, conjunction, disjunction, and existential quantification hold as derived rules by the way we have defined these concepts.

A sequent containing at most one formula in the succendent will be called an *intuitionistic sequent.* All sequents provable in the calculus $\mathcal{T}$ above are of course intuitionistic. However, to prove that the cut rule is derivable from the other rules of $\mathcal{T}$, it will be convenient to consider another calculus $\mathcal{T}'$ where also other sequents may be provable.

3. The calculus $\mathcal{T}'$. The calculus $\mathcal{T}'$ is set up as follows:

Axioms. All sequents of the form $A, \Pi \Rightarrow \Sigma, A$, where A is atomic.

Inference rules.

$\to\supset)\quad \dfrac{A,\ \Pi\Rightarrow B}{\Pi\Rightarrow\Sigma,\ A\supset B}\qquad \supset\to)\quad \dfrac{\Pi\Rightarrow\Sigma,\ A\quad B,\ \Pi\Rightarrow\Sigma}{A\supset B,\ \Pi\Rightarrow\Sigma}$

$\to\forall_1)\quad \dfrac{\Pi\Rightarrow A}{\Pi\Rightarrow\Sigma,\ \forall xA^a_x}\qquad \forall_1\to)\quad \dfrac{A^x_t,\ \Pi\Rightarrow\Sigma}{\forall xA,\ \Pi\Rightarrow\Sigma}$

$\to\forall_2)\quad \dfrac{\Pi\Rightarrow A}{\Pi\Rightarrow\Sigma,\ \forall X^nA^{P^n}_{X^n}}\qquad \forall_2\to)\quad \dfrac{A^{X^n}_{T^n},\ \Pi\Rightarrow\Sigma}{\forall X^nA,\ \Pi\Rightarrow\Sigma}$

$\to\lambda)\quad \dfrac{\Pi\Rightarrow\Sigma,\ (S^{x_1x_2\ldots x_n}_{t_1t_2\ldots t_n}A)}{\Pi\Rightarrow\Sigma,\ \lambda x_1x_2\ldots x_nAt_1t_2\ldots t_n}\qquad \lambda\to)\quad \dfrac{(S^{x_1x_2\ldots x_n}_{t_1t_2\ldots t_n}A),\ \Pi\Rightarrow\Sigma}{\lambda x_1x_2\ldots x_nAt_1t_2\ldots t_n,\ \Pi\Rightarrow\Sigma}$

$\text{cut})\quad \dfrac{\Pi\Rightarrow\Sigma,\ A\quad A,\ \Pi\Rightarrow\Sigma}{\Pi\Rightarrow\Sigma}$

The rules $\to\forall_1$ and $\to\forall_2$ are with the same restrictions as in $\mathcal{T}$.

One easily shows (by induction on the length of the given proof) that a sequent $\Gamma \to \Delta$ is provable in $\mathcal{T}'$ only if there is a formula A in Δ such that $\Gamma \to A$ is provable in $\mathcal{T}'$. From this, one easily obtains:

LEMMA 1. *An intuitionistic sequent, i.e. of the form* $\Gamma \to A$, *is provable in* $\mathcal{T}$ *(without cut) if and only if it is provable in* $\mathcal{T}'$ *(without cut).*

To prove that the cut rule is derivable from the other rules of the calculus $\mathcal{T}$, it is thus sufficient to prove the corresponding thing for the calculus $\mathcal{T}'$.

4. Beth models. The (second order) Beth models will be certain trees of formulas paired with a language. By an (undecorated) *tree* we understand a pair (K, R) where K is a non-empty set of points or nodes and such that there is a relation S in K and a point $k \in K$ (called the *origin*) with the properties: (i) R is the ancestral of S, (ii) there is no k' in K such that $k'Sk$, (iii) to each k' in K except k, there is a unique k'' such that $k''Sk$, (iv) for each k' in K, kRk'. The relation S just described may be read '*stands immediately below*'. By a *path* in a tree (K, R), we understand a sequence k_1, $k_2, \ldots$ of points in K such that k_1 is the origin, k_i stands immediately below k_{i+1} (for each k_i and k_{i+1} in the sequence), and k_n is the last point of the sequence only if it is a top node (i.e., there is no k' in K different from k_n such that k_nRk'). A path is said to go *through* k if k belongs to the path. A point that belongs to a path is said to be *on* the path.

A *Beth model* is now defined as a quadruple (L, K, R, φ) where L is a language, (K, R) is a tree, and φ is a function that assigns a set φ_k of atomic formulas in L to each k in K, satisfying the following condition: for each point k in K, if A does not belong to φ_k, then there is a path in (K, R) through k such that A does not belong to $\varphi_{k'}$, for any k' on the path.

Let $\mathcal{M}$ be a given Beth model (L, K, R, φ), let A be a formula in L, and let k be a point in K. By definition, A is *true* (*in* $\mathcal{M}$) *at* the point k, abbreviated $\mathrm{S}(A, k)$ (or $\mathrm{S}_{\mathcal{M}}(A, k)$), if and only if either

(1). A is atomic and A belongs to φ_k, or

(2). A is $B \supset C$, and for each k' such that kRk', if $\mathrm{S}(B, k')$, then $\mathrm{S}(C, k')$, or

(3). A is $\forall xB$ and for each t in L, $\mathrm{S}(B^x_t, k)$, or

(4). A is $\forall X^nB$ and for each P^n in L, $\mathrm{S}(B^{X^n}_{P^n}, k)$, or

(5). A is $\lambda x_1 x_2 \ldots x_n B t_1 t_2 \ldots t_n$ and $\mathrm{S}((S^{x_1 x_2 \ldots x_n}_{t_1 t_2 \ldots t_n} B), k)$.

A sequent $\Pi \Rightarrow \Sigma$ in L is *true* (in $\mathcal{M} = (L, K, R, \varphi)$) at k, if for each k'

in K such that kRk', if all formulas of Π are true at k', then some formula of Σ is true at k'.

One easily proves by induction over the length of the formulas:

LEMMA 2. *If A is not true in $\mathcal{M} = (L, K, R, \varphi)$ at k, then there is some path in (K, R) through k such that A is not true in $\mathcal{M}$ at any point on the path.*

By the *denotation* (*in* a Beth model $\mathcal{M} = (L, K, R, \varphi)$) of a predicate term T^n in L *at* a point k in K, abbreviated $\mathrm{d}(T^n, k)$ (or $\mathrm{d}_{\mathcal{M}}(T^n, k)$), we understand (i) the set of n-tuples $(t_1, t_2, \ldots, t_n)$ such that $T^n t_1 t_2 \ldots t_n$ is true (in $\mathcal{M}$) at k, when $n > 0$, and (ii) when $n = 0$, the truth value 1 or 0 if T^n is true or not true, respectively, (in $\mathcal{M}$) at k.

One easily verifies:

Substitutivity of equivalence. Let $\mathcal{M} = (L, K, R, \varphi)$ be a Beth model, let A be a formula in L, let T and T' be n-ary terms in L such that $\mathrm{d}_{\mathcal{M}}(T, k) = \mathrm{d}_{\mathcal{M}}(T', k)$ for each k in K, and let A' be obtained from A by replacing some occurences of T with T'. Then, for each k in K, A is true in $\mathcal{M}$ at k if and only if A' is.

A Beth model $\mathcal{M} = (L, K, R, \varphi)$ is said to be *normal* if for each T^n in L there is a parameter P^n in L such that $\mathrm{d}_{\mathcal{M}}(T^n, k) = \mathrm{d}_{\mathcal{M}}(P^n, k)$ for each k in K.

A formula or sequent in L is said to be *valid* if it is true in each normal Beth model (L, K, R, φ) at each point k in K.

By the definition of truth and the substitutivity of equivalence we obtain:

LEMMA 3. *If $\mathcal{M} = (L, K, R, \varphi)$ is a normal Beth model, then $\forall X^n A$ is true in $\mathcal{M}$ at k, if and only if $A^X_{T^n}$ is true in $\mathcal{M}$ at k for each T^n in L.*

Using lemma 3, one proves by induction over the length of proofs:

THEOREM 1. *Every sequent provable in $\mathcal{T}$ or $\mathcal{T}'$ is valid.*

Remark 1. A somewhat more natural procedure would be to replace the language L in a Beth model with a sequent of domains $D^0, D^1, D^2, \ldots,$ where D^0 is a set of individuals and D^n is a set of n-ary relations in D^0, and then to define satisfaction in the usual way. However, the definition given above (which of course amounts to the same thing) will be convenient in the subsequent completeness proof.

Remark 2. A (second order) Kripke model would be defined as a quadruple (K, R, φ, ψ), where K, R, and φ are as before, and ψ is a function that assigns a language (or a sequence of domains as in remark 1) to each point in K, and where the following two conditions are satisfied: for each k and k' in K

if kRk', then $\varphi(k) \subseteq \varphi(k')$ and $\psi(k) \subseteq \psi(k')$. Unlike the situation in the first order case, the second order Beth models are thus a special kind of the second order Kripke models.

5. Refutations. The points in a tree may be divided into levels in an obvious way, and the levels may then be numbered in such a way that the origin is the point on level 1. By a refutation of a sequent S, we understand a language L paired with an infinite tree of sequents (i.e. a quadruple (L, K, R, ψ) where (K, R) is a tree and ψ assigns a sequent to each point in K), where L is a language which contains infinitely many parameters of each kind besides the symbols of S, and where the following conditions are satisfied:

(1) S is the bottom-sequent (i.e. assigned to the origin).

(2). No sequent (assigned to a point) in the tree is an axiom.

(3). If the sequent $S_1 = \Gamma \rightarrow A, \Delta$ is a sequent on an odd level (i.e. assigned to a point on an odd level), then there is one sequent S_2 or two sequents S_2 and S_3 immediately above S_1 (i.e. assigned to point(s) k_2 (and k_3) such that k_1 stands immediately below k_2 (and k_3)) as follows:

(a). If A is atomic, then S_2 is $\Gamma \rightarrow \Delta, A$ and there is no S_3.

(b). If A is $B \supset C$, then S_2 is $\Gamma \rightarrow \Delta$ and S_3 is $\Gamma, B \rightarrow \Delta, C$.

(c). If A is $\forall xB$, then S_2 is $\Gamma \rightarrow \Delta$ and S_3 is $\Gamma \rightarrow B^x_a$ where a is the first individual parameter in L not in S_1.

(d). If A is $\forall X^n B$, then S_2 is $\Gamma \rightarrow \Delta$ and S_3 is $\Gamma \rightarrow B^{X^n}_{P^n}$ where P^n is the first n-ary predicate parameter in L not in S_1.

(e). If A is $\lambda x_1 x_2 \ldots x_n B t_1 t_2 \ldots t_n$, then S_2 is $\Gamma \rightarrow \Delta, (S^{x_1 x_2 \ldots x_n}_{t_1 t_2 \ldots t_n} B)$ and there is no S_3.

(4). If the sequent $S_1 = A, \Gamma \rightarrow \Delta$ is a sequent on an even level, then there is one sequent S_2 immediately above S_1 as follows:

(a). If A is atomic, then S_2 is $\Gamma, A \rightarrow \Delta$.

(b). If A is $B \supset C$, then S_2 is $\Gamma, B \supset C \rightarrow \Delta, B$ or $\Gamma, C \rightarrow \Delta$.

(c). If A is $\forall xB$, then S_2 is $\Gamma, B^x_t, \forall xB \rightarrow \Delta$ where t is the first individual parameter in L such that B^x_t does not occur in the antecedent of a sequent below S_2.

(d). If A is $\forall X^n B$, then S_2 is $\Gamma, B^{X^n}_{T^n}, \forall X^n B \rightarrow \Delta$ where T^n is the first n-ary predicate term in L such that $B^{X^n}_{T^n}$ does not occur in the antecedent of a sequent below S_2.

(e). If A is $\lambda x_1 x_2 \ldots x_n B t_1 t_2 \ldots t_n$, then S_2 is $\Gamma, (S^{x_1 x_2 \ldots x_n}_{t_1 t_2 \ldots t_n} B) \rightarrow \Delta$.

A refutation of a sequent S is uniquely determined except for L and the choice to be made in (4b). By comparing the inference rules in $\mathscr{T}'$

with the clauses (3) and (4), it is easily seen that if the sequent(s) S_2 (and S_3) stands (stand) immediately above S_1 and is not determined by clause (4b), then if S_1 is unprovable in $\mathscr{T}'$ without the cut rule so is (are) S_2 (and S_3). Furthermore, if $B \supset C, \Gamma \to \Delta$ is unprovable in $\mathscr{T}'$ (without cut), then $\Gamma, B \supset C \to \Delta, B$ and $\Gamma, C \to \Delta$ cannot both be provable in $\mathscr{T}'$ (without cut). Hence, if S is unprovable in $\mathscr{T}'$ without the cut rule, we can construct a refutation of S by choosing an unprovable S_2 in clause (4b). We have thus proved

LEMMA 4. *There is a refutation of each sequent which is unprovable in* $\mathscr{T}'$ *without the cut rule.*

Note that the choice to be made at applications of clause (4b) is not effective in general; lemma 4 is thus proved only classically.

Given a refutation (L, K, R, ψ) and a point k in K, we define:

A is *positive at* k if and only if on each path in (K, R) through k, there is a point k' such that A occurs in the antecendent of the sequent $\psi_{k'}$.

A is *negative at* k if and only if there is some point k' such that kRk' and A occurs in the succedent of $\psi_{k'}$.

From the definition of a refutation (L, K, R, ψ), we verify the following facts:

LEMMA 5. (a). *If A is atomic and negative at k, then there is a path through k such that A is negative at each point on the path.*

(b) *If A is atomic and positive at k, then A is not negative at k.*

(c)(1). *If $A \supset B$ is positive at k, then for each point k' such that kRk', either A is negative at k' or B is positive at k'.*

(2). *If $\forall xA$ is positive at k, then A^x_t is positive at k for each t.*

(3). *If $\forall X^n A$ is positive at k, than $A^{X^n}_{T^n}$ is positive at k for each T^n.*

(4). *If $\lambda x_1 x_2 \ldots x_n A t_1 t_2 \ldots t_n$ is positive at k, then $(S^{x_1 x_2 \ldots x_n}_{t_1 t_2 \ldots t_n} A)$ is positive at k.*

(d)(1). *If $A \supset B$ is negative at k, then for some k' such that kRk', A is positive at k' and B is negative at k'.*

(2). *If $\forall xA$ is negative at k, then A^x_t is negative at k for some t.*

(3). *If $\forall X^n A$ is negative at k, then $A^{X^n}_{T^n}$ is negative at k for some T^n.*

(4). *If $\lambda x_1 x_2 \ldots x_n A t_1 t_2 \ldots t_n$ is negative at k, then $(S^{x_1 x_2 \ldots x_n}_{t_1 t_2 \ldots t_n} A)$ is negative at k.*

PROOFS. All the proofs are quite straightforward with the exception of case (c1), which is obtained as follows: Assume that $A \supset B$ is positive at k and that kRk'. We consider two cases:

Case (i): $A \supset B$ is positive at k' with respect to the subtree whose origin is k'. Then for each path through k' there is a point k'' such that $k'Rk''$ and such that the sequent assigned to k'' is obtained by applying case (4b) to the formula $A \supset B$. There are now two possible cases: either all of these applications of (4b) are obtained by writing B in the antecedent in which case B is positive at k', or some of these applications of (4b) are obtained by writing A in the succedent in which case A is negative at k'.

Case (ii): $A \supset B$ is not positive at k' with respect to the subtree whose origin is k'. Then there must be some point k'' such that $k''Rk'$ and such that the sequent assigned to k'' is obtained by applying the case (4b) to $A \supset B$ writing B in the antecedent. Hence, in this case, B is positive at k'.

6. Main results

THEOREM 2. *Every valid sequent is provable in* $\mathscr{T}'$ *without the cut rule.*

PROOF. Let $\Gamma \rightarrow \Delta$ be a sequent that is not provable in $\mathscr{T}'$ without the cut rule, and let $\mathscr{R} = (L, K, R, \psi)$ be a refutation of $\Gamma \rightarrow \Delta$ (lemma 4).

By a possible value of a term T^n, $n > 0$, (with respect to $\mathscr{R}$) we understand a function V on K such that for each k in K

(1). $V(k)$ is a set of n-tuples $(t_1, t_2, \ldots, t_n)$;
(2). if $Tt_1 t_2 \ldots t_n$ is positive at k, then $(t_1, t_2, \ldots, t_n) \in V(k)$;
(3). if $Tt_1 t_2 \ldots t_n$ is negative at k, then $(t_1, t_2, \ldots, t_n) \notin V(k)$;
(4). if $(t_1, t_2, \ldots, t_n) \notin V(k)$, then there is a path in (K, R) through k such that $(t_1, t_2, \ldots, t_n) \notin V(k')$ for each k' on the path.

By a possible value of a term T^0, (with respect to $\mathscr{R}$), we understand a function V on K such that for each k in K:

(1). $V(k)$ is one of the two truth values 1 (truth) and 0 (falsehood);
(2). if T^0 is positive at k, then $V(k) = 1$;
(3). if T^0 is negative at k, then $V(k) = 0$;
(4). if $V(k) = 0$, then there is a path in (K, R) through k such that $V(k') = 0$ for each k' on the path.

For each T^n and for each possible value V of T^n, we introduce a new constant P_V^n not in L in such a way that P_V^n is different from $P_{V'}^n$, if $V \neq V'$. The language obtained from L by adding all these new parameters is denoted by L'. If A is a formula in L', then A^* is to be a formula obtained from A by replacing every one of the new constants P_V^n with a term T in L that has V as a possible value.

Let $\mathcal{M}$ be the quadruple (L', K, R, φ) where L', K and R are as above and φ is the function from K such that φ_k (k in K) is the set containing (i) all atomic formulas positive in $\mathcal{R}$ at k, (ii) all formulas P_V^0 such that $V(k) = 1$, and (iii) all sentences $P_V^n t_1 t_2 \ldots t_n$ such that $(t_1, t_2, \ldots, t_n)$ belongs to $V(k)$. We want to prove:

(a). $\mathcal{M}$ is a Beth model.

(b). If A^* is positive in $\mathcal{R}$ at k, then A is true in $\mathcal{M}$ at k.

(c). If A^* is negative in $\mathcal{R}$ at k, then A is not true in $\mathcal{M}$ at k.

(d). $\mathcal{M}$ is a normal Beth model.

The theorem may then be inferred as follows: Since the formulas of Γ (Δ) are positive (negative) in $\mathcal{R}$ at the origin of the tree (K, R), they are thus true (not true) in $\mathcal{M}$ at this origin (note that $A^* = A$, if A is a formula in L). It follows that $\Gamma \rightarrow \Delta$ is not true in the normal Beth model $\mathcal{M}$. Hence, $\Gamma \rightarrow \Delta$ is not valid.

Proof of (a). Follows from lemma 5(a) and clause (4) in the definition of possible value.

Proof of (b) *and* (c). The proof is by induction over the length of the formula A. If A is atomic and is a formula in L, then (b) is obvious from the construction of φ, and (c) follows from this construction and lemma 5(b). If A is P_V^0 or $P_V^n t_1 t_2 \ldots t_n$, then (b) and (c) are obvious from the construction of φ and clauses (2) and (3) in the definition of possible value.

The induction step is obvious by comparing lemma 5(c) and 5(d) with the definition of truth. We take one example: Suppose $(\forall X^n B)^*$ is positive at k. Since $(\forall X^n B)^* = \forall X^n B^*$, it follows from lemma 5(c3) that $B^{*X^n}_{T^n}$ is positive at k for each T^n in L. For any P^n in L', $(B^{X^n}_{P^n})^* = B^{*X^n}_{T^n}$ for some term T^n in L. Hence, for each P^n in L', $(B^{X^n}_{P^n})^*$ is positive at k. By the induction assumption, $B^{X^n}_{P^n}$ is then true in $\mathcal{M}$ at k for each P^n in L', i.e. by clause (4) in the definition of truth, $\forall X^n B$ is true in $\mathcal{M}$ at k.

Proof of (d). We first verify that for each term T, $d_{\mathcal{M}}(T, k)$ (considered as a function on K) is a possible value of T^*. Condition (1) is obviously satisfied; conditions (2) and (3) are satisfied according to (b) and (c), respectively; and condition (4) is satisfied according to lemma 2. It follows that there is a parameter P_V in L' such that $d_{\mathcal{M}}(T, K) = d_{\mathcal{M}}(P_V, k)$ for each k in K.

THEOREM 3. *If a sequent is provable in $\mathcal{T}$ or $\mathcal{T}'$, it is provable without using the cut rule.*

PROOF. Assume that $\Gamma \rightarrow \Delta, A$ and $A, \Gamma \rightarrow \Delta$ are provable in $\mathcal{T}$ or $\mathcal{T}'$.

By theorem 1, $\Gamma \to \Delta, A$ and $A, \Gamma \to \Delta$ are then valid. It follows that $\Gamma \to \Delta$ is valid, and hence, by theorem 2 (and lemma 1), also provable in $\mathscr{T}'$ ($\mathscr{T}$) without using the cut rule.

THEOREM 4. (a). *If* $\to A \vee B$ *is provable, then either* $\to A$ *or* $\to B$ *is provable.* (b). *If* $\to \exists x A$ *is provable, then so is* $\to A^x_t$ *for some* t.
(c). *If* $\to \exists X^n A$ *is provable, then so is* $A^{X^n}_{T^n}$ *for some* T^n.

PROOF. We prove part (a) and (c) of the theorem for the calculus $\mathscr{T}$. The proof of part (b) is similar to that of part (c).

Proof of (a). Assume that $\to A \vee B$, i.e.

$$\to \forall X((A \supset X) \supset ((B \supset X) \supset X))$$

(where X is a 0-ary variable not occuring in A or in B) is provable. It follows (by the fact that the rules $\to\forall$ and $\to\supset$ are inversible) that

$$A \supset P, B \supset P \to P$$

is provable, where P may be choosen foreign to A and B. Hence, either

$$A \supset P, B \supset P \to A \quad \text{or} \quad A \supset P, B \supset P \to B$$

is provable. Since P does not occur in A or B, we obtain by substituting $A \vee B$ for P that, either

$$A \supset (A \vee B), B \supset (A \vee B) \to A \quad \text{or} \quad A \supset (A \vee B), B \supset (A \vee B) \to B$$

is provable. Since $\to A \supset (A \vee B)$ and $\to B \supset (A \vee B)$ are provable, it follows that either $\to A$ or $\to B$ is provable.

Proof of (c). Assume that $\to \exists X^n A$, i.e.

$$\to \forall Y(\forall X^n(A \supset Y) \supset Y)$$

(where Y is 0-ary variable not occuring in $\forall X^n A$) is provable. As in the proof of (a), we can infer that for some P not occuring in $\forall X^n A$ and for some n-ary terms $T_1, T_2, \ldots, T_m$,

$$\forall X^n(A \supset P), A^{X^n}_{T_1} \supset P, A^{X^n}_{T_2} \supset P, \ldots, A^{X^n}_{T_m} \supset P \to A^{X^n}_{T_i}$$

(where $1 \leqslant i \leqslant m$) is provable. Since sequents of the form

$$\to \forall X^n(A \supset \exists X^n A) \quad \text{and} \quad \to A^{X^n}_{T'} \supset \exists X^n A$$

are provable, we infer by substituting $\exists X^n A$ for P that $\to A^{X^n}_T$ is provable for some n-ary term T.

Remark. Theorem 4 also holds when the antecedent is not empty as long as there is no predicate variable in an atomic and strictly positive part of a formula in the antecedent. The strictly positive parts of a formula A are defined recursively as follows:

(1). A is a strictly positive part of A.

(2). If $C \supset B$, $\forall xB$, or $\forall X^n B$ is a strictly positive part of A, then so is B.

(3). If $\lambda x_1 x_2 \ldots x_n B t_1 t_2 \ldots t_n$ is a strictly positive part of A, then so is $(S^{x_1 x_2 \ldots x_n}_{t_1 t_2 \ldots t_n} B)$.

REFERENCES

[1] E. W. Beth, Semantic construction of intuitionistic logic, *Mededel. Koninkl. Ned. Akad. Wetenschap. Afdel. Letterkunde*, **19** no. 11 (1956).

[2] V. H. Dyson and G. Kreisel, Analysis of Beth's semantic construction of intuitionistic logic, *Appl. Math. Statist. Lab. Stanford University*, *Tech. Rept.* no. **3** (1961).

[3] S. Kripke, Semantic analysis of intuitionistic logic I, in *Formal systems and recursive functions*, ed. J. Crossley and M. Dummet, Amsterdam (1965) 92–130.

[4] D. Prawitz, *Natural deduction*, a proof-theoretical study, Stockholm (1965).

[5] D. Prawitz, Completeness and Hauptsatz for second order logic, *Theoria* **33** (1967) 246–253.

[6] D. Prawitz, Hauptsatz for higher order logic, *J. Symb. Logic* **33** (1968) 452–457.

[7] W. Tait, A nonconstructive proof of Gentzen's Hauptsatz for second order predicate logic, *Bull. Am. Math. Soc.* **72** (1966) 980–988.

[8] M. Takahashi, A proof of cut-elimination theorem in simple type theory, *J. Math. Soc. Japan* **19** (1967) 399–410.

ON CUT ELIMINATION IN INTUITIONISTIC SYSTEMS OF ANALYSIS

B. SCARPELLINI

In what follows we consider certain intuitionistic systems of analysis, formulated in terms of the sequential calculus. Our aim is to outline proofs of certain results, in part on cut elimination, about these systems.

1. We start by giving a quick review of Gentzen's second consistency proof. As language L we take one whose alphabet contains the following kinds of symbols:

(1). logical symbols $\wedge$, $\vee$, $\supset$, $\exists$, $\forall$,
(2). brackets (,),
(3). the individual constant 0,
(4). constants for certain primitive recursive (p.r.) functions such as $+$, $\times$, $'$, etc.,
(5). the equality sign $=$,
(6). individual variables $x_1, x_2, \ldots, x, y$, etc.,
(7). function variables for one place number theoretic functions α_1, $\alpha_2, \ldots, \beta, \gamma$ etc.,
(8). for every finite sequence $w = \langle u_0, \ldots, u_s \rangle$ of natural numbers a denumerable list of so called special function constants $\alpha_w^1, \alpha_w^2, \ldots$,
(9). the sequential arrow $\rightarrow$.

Terms, prime formulas and arbitrary formulas are defined as usual inductive ly. An expression $\mathfrak{A}_1, \ldots, \mathfrak{A}_s \rightarrow \mathfrak{B}_1, \ldots, \mathfrak{B}_t$ where $\mathfrak{A}_i, \mathfrak{B}_k$ are formulas is called a sequent. As sublanguage L* of L we take the one whose alphabet contains only the symbols listed under (1)–(6) and (9). Formulas and se quents are then defined with respect to this alphabet. The rest of section 1 refers only to L* as basic language. The terms $0, 0', 0'', \ldots$ are called numerals and correspond as usual to the natural numbers. A sequent is called a prime sequent if it contains only formulas of the form $\mathfrak{p} = \mathfrak{q}$, that is prime formulas. At this stage let us associate once and for all with every n-place constant $\mathfrak{c}$ for p.r. functions a fixed p.r. function $\varphi_{\mathfrak{c}}$ of n arguments; in particular we associate with $+$, $\times$, $'$, addition, multiplication and successor, in that order. This valuation induces in a natural way a mapping h which associates with every term $\mathfrak{t}$ containing precisely n variables a p.r. function $h_{\mathfrak{t}}$ of n arguments. In particular if $n = 0$ then $h_{\mathfrak{t}}$ is a number which will also be denoted by $|\mathfrak{t}|$. Now we can call a constant prime sequent *true* if it is true under the usual interpretation. A prime sequent is called *verifiable* if it is true whenever we replace the free variables by constant terms. Finally let us call two formulas $\mathfrak{A}$, $\mathfrak{A}'$ *isomorphic* (to each other) if there is a formula $\mathfrak{B}(x_1, \ldots, x_s)$ and two lists of constant terms $\mathfrak{t}_1, \ldots, \mathfrak{t}_s$ and $\mathfrak{q}_1, \ldots, \mathfrak{q}_s$ such that

(1). $\mathfrak{A}$ is $\mathfrak{B}(\mathfrak{t}_1, \ldots, \mathfrak{t}_s)$,
(2). $\mathfrak{A}'$ is $\mathfrak{B}(\mathfrak{q}_1, \ldots, \mathfrak{q}_s)$,
(3). $|\mathfrak{q}_i| = |\mathfrak{t}_i|$ for $i \leqslant s$.

Now we can introduce the sequential version ZT of classical number theory. The rules of ZT are given by the following list:

(1). the rules of the first order sequential predicate calculus,
(2). induction,
(3). a special rule called conversion, defined as follows:

$$\frac{\mathfrak{A}_1, \ldots, \mathfrak{A}_s \rightarrow \mathfrak{B}_1, \ldots, \mathfrak{B}_t}{\mathfrak{A}'_1, \ldots, \mathfrak{A}'_s \rightarrow \mathfrak{B}'_1, \ldots, \mathfrak{B}'_t}$$

where $\mathfrak{A}_i$, $\mathfrak{A}'_i$ and $\mathfrak{B}_k$, $\mathfrak{B}'_k$ are isomorphic.

The axioms of ZT are roughly speaking the following:

(1). all numerically true prime sequents with at most one formula in the succedent,
(2). a sufficiently large set of verifiable sequents containing among others all axioms of equality,
(3). all sequents of the form $\mathfrak{D} \rightarrow \mathfrak{D}'$ with $\mathfrak{D}$, $\mathfrak{D}'$ isomorphic.

Having the rules and the axioms we can define proofs in the usual way. Proofs will always be considered as trees whose nodes are sequents. A classical proof $\mathscr{P}$ is intuitionistic if it has the property: $\mathscr{P}$ contains only sequents having at most one formula in the succedent. If we admit only intuitionistic proofs then we obtain the intuitionistic version of ZT, to be denoted by ZTi.

Before looking at Gentzen's second consistency proof let us repeat the definition of the final part of a proof $\mathscr{P}$: a sequent S belongs to the final part of a proof if it is either the end-sequent, or if it is a premise of a conversion, or a structural rule whose conclusion belongs already to the final part. We also use the self-explaining notions of 'successor' and 'image' for formulas in the final part. Definititions of this or similar notions are given in [**1**], [**4**], [**6**]. In order to prove consistency Gentzen introduced in [**1**] certain syntactical transformations of proofs, called reduction steps. There are three kinds of these, namely

(1). elimination of logical axioms and of thinnings from the final part,

(2). elimination of logical inferences from the final part,

(3). elimination of induction inferences from the final part.

Reduction steps of type (1) will be referred to as preliminary reduction steps, while steps of type (2) and (3) are called essential reduction steps. The precise definition of these reduction steps (or simply reductions) is not needed. It is sufficient to know a few of their properties.

The proof of the following theorem is elementary and is given in [**1**].

THEOREM 1. (a). *Only finitely many successive preliminary reduction steps can be applied to a given proof* $\mathscr{P}$.

(b). *Let* $\mathscr{P}$ *be a proof whose final part contains no variables and which does not admit any reduction step. If* $\mathscr{P}$ *is different from its final part then there is at least one logical inference whose conclusion is in the final part and whose principal formula has an image in the end-sequent.*

If $\mathscr{P}'$ is obtained from $\mathscr{P}$ by means of a series of preliminary reductions and one essential reduction then we denote this fact symbolically by $\mathscr{P}'\mathrm{V}\mathscr{P}$. Then we define: $\mathscr{P}'\mathbf{V}^*\mathscr{P}$ iff there are proofs $\mathscr{P}_0, \ldots, \mathscr{P}_s$ such that $\mathscr{P}_0 = \mathscr{P}$, $\mathscr{P}_s = \mathscr{P}'$ and $\mathscr{P}_{i+1}\mathrm{V}\mathscr{P}_i$ for $i < s$. It is clear that $\mathbf{V}^*$ is transitive.

Gentzen's main result is

THEOREM 2. *The relation* $\mathbf{V}^*$ *is well founded.*

Gentzen proved theorem 2 by associating with every proof $\mathscr{P}$ an ordinal $g(\mathrm{P})$ and by showing that $\mathscr{P}'\mathbf{V}\mathscr{P}$ implies $g(\mathscr{P}') < g(\mathscr{P})$.

In order to state an immediate consequence of theorems 1 and 2 we recall the notion of a constructive, infinite cut free proof, introduced in [**1**]. By transfinite induction over $\mathbf{V}^*$, making thereby use of theorems 1–2 one proves easily

THEOREM 3. *If* $\mathscr{P}$ *is a proof in* ZT *of S then there exists a constructive infinite cut free proof* $\mathscr{P}'$ *of S. If* $\mathscr{P}$ *is intuitionistic then* $\mathscr{P}'$ *is intuitionistic.*

Gentzen proved his results for a subsystem of ZT which does not contain conversion or implication. However, it is easy to extend his procedure so as to include ZT; details concerning this are given in **[6]**. It is also not difficult to extend Gentzen's method so as to include the intuitionistic system ZTi; this is also treated in **[6]**.

Another immediate consequence of theorems 1–2 for ZTi, which is proved in **[6]** is

THEOREM 4. (a). *If $\mathscr{P}$ is an intuitionistic proof of* $\to \mathfrak{A} \vee \mathfrak{B}$, where $\mathfrak{A}, \mathfrak{B}$ *contain no free variables, then one can find effectively a proof $\mathscr{P}'$ of* $\to \mathfrak{A}$ *or* $\to \mathfrak{B}$.

(b). *If $\mathscr{P}$ is an intuitionistic proof of* $\to \exists x \mathfrak{A}(x)$ *where $\mathfrak{A}$ contains only x free, then one can find effectively a term* $\mathfrak{t}$ *and an intuitionistic proof $\mathscr{P}'$ of* $\to \mathfrak{A}(\mathfrak{t})$.

2. Next we look at weak extensions of ZT for which Gentzen's method still works. Let $D(x)$ be a p.r. predicate and $\prec$ a p.r. partial ordering of $\{x|D(x)\}$; assume that $\prec$ is well founded. Let $\mathfrak{g}$ and $\mathfrak{d}$ be two constants in ZT which express $\prec$ and D numeralwise. For easier reading we abbreviate $\mathfrak{g}(x, y) = 0$ by $x \prec y$ without danger of confusion and for $\mathfrak{d}(x) = 0$ we write just $d(x)$. Assume for simplicity that ZT contains already the following axioms:

(1). $\mathfrak{p} \prec \mathfrak{q}, \mathfrak{q} \prec \mathfrak{t} \to \mathfrak{p} \prec \mathfrak{t}$,

(2). $\mathfrak{p} \prec \mathfrak{q}, \mathfrak{q} \prec \mathfrak{p} \to$

(3). $\mathfrak{p} \prec \mathfrak{q}, \mathfrak{p} = \mathfrak{q} \to$,

(4). $\mathfrak{p} \prec \mathfrak{q} \to d(\mathfrak{p})$,

(5). $\mathfrak{p} \prec \mathfrak{q} \to d(\mathfrak{q})$,

where $\mathfrak{p}, \mathfrak{q}, \mathfrak{t}$ are terms. By ZT($\prec$) we denote that extension of ZT which has the following additional rules:

$$\mathrm{TI} \quad \frac{d(y), (x)(x \prec y \supset \mathfrak{A}(x)), \Gamma \to \Delta, \mathfrak{A}(y)}{d(t), \Gamma \to \Delta, \mathfrak{A}(\mathfrak{t})}$$

and for every $\mathfrak{t}$ with $D(|\mathfrak{t}|)$ true the following rule

$$\mathrm{TI}_{|\mathfrak{t}|} \quad \frac{y \prec \mathfrak{t}, (x)(x \prec y \supset \mathfrak{A}(x)), \Gamma \to \Delta, \mathfrak{A}(y)}{\mathfrak{p} \prec \mathfrak{t}, \Gamma \to \Delta, \mathfrak{A}(\mathfrak{p})}$$

where y does not occur in the conclusions and where $\mathfrak{t}$ in the first case and $\mathfrak{p}$ in the second are supposed to be free for y in $\mathfrak{A}(y)$. The two rules are denoted by TI and TI_n respectively (with $|\mathfrak{t}| = n$) and have already been introduced in this form in [**2**]; they express adequately transfinite induction with respect to $\prec$ and $\{\langle x, y\rangle \mid x \prec n \wedge y \prec n \wedge x \prec y\}$. The rules TI_n are superfluous but have been added for technical reasons as will be seen below.

To the reduction steps already used by Gentzen we add new ones, namely those for TI- and TI_n-inferences with conclusion in the final part. Let $\mathscr{P}$ be a proof containing no variables in the final part. Let there be a particular TI-inference having its conclusion in the final part.

Case 1. $D(|\mathfrak{t}|)$ is false. Then $d(\mathfrak{t}) \to$ is an axiom from which $d(\mathfrak{t}), \Gamma \to \Delta, \mathfrak{A}(\mathfrak{t})$ can be derived by thinning and interchange.

Case 2. $D(|\mathfrak{t}|)$ is true. Now $y \prec \mathfrak{t} \to d(y)$ is an axiom and so we can perform the new derivation presented below. Here we have suppressed Γ, Δ in order to save space, and abbreviated $(x)(x \prec y \supset \mathfrak{A}(x))$ by $(x)_{\prec y}\mathfrak{A}$.

$$y \prec \mathfrak{t} \to d(y) \qquad d(y), (x)_{\prec y}\mathfrak{A} \to \mathfrak{A}(y)$$

cut

$$y \prec \mathfrak{t}, (x)_{\prec y}\mathfrak{A} \to \mathfrak{A}(y)$$

$\mathrm{TI}_{|\mathfrak{t}|}$

$$\mathfrak{s} \prec \mathfrak{t} \to \mathfrak{A}(\mathfrak{s})$$

$\to \supset$

$$\to \mathfrak{s} \prec \mathfrak{t} \supset \mathfrak{A}(\mathfrak{s})$$

$\to \forall$

$$\to (s)_{\prec \mathfrak{t}}\mathfrak{A} \qquad (x)_{\prec \mathfrak{t}}\mathfrak{A}, d(\mathfrak{t}) \to \mathfrak{A}(\mathfrak{t})$$

cut

$$d(\mathfrak{t}) \to \mathfrak{A}(\mathfrak{t})$$

The reduction step for TI_n looks quite similar:

Case 1. $|\mathfrak{p}| \not\prec |\mathfrak{t}|$. Then $\mathfrak{p} \prec \mathfrak{t} \to$ is an axiom from which $\mathfrak{p} \prec \mathfrak{t}, \Gamma \to \Delta, \mathfrak{A}(\mathfrak{p})$ can be derived by thinning and interchange.

Case 2. $|\mathfrak{p}| \prec |\mathfrak{t}|$. Now $y \prec \mathfrak{p}, \mathfrak{p} \prec \mathfrak{t} \to y \prec \mathfrak{t}$ is an axiom and so we can perform the new derivation presented below. There we observe the same conventions as before.

$$y \prec \mathfrak{p}, \mathfrak{p} \prec \mathfrak{t} \to y \prec \mathfrak{t} \qquad y \prec \mathfrak{t}, (x)_{\prec y}\mathfrak{A} \to \mathfrak{A}(y)$$

cut

$$y \prec \mathfrak{p}, (x)_{\prec y}\mathfrak{A}, \mathfrak{p} \prec \mathfrak{t} \to \mathfrak{A}(y)$$

$\mathrm{TI}_{|\mathfrak{p}|}$

$$\mathfrak{s} \prec \mathfrak{p}, \mathfrak{p} \prec \mathfrak{t} \to \mathfrak{A}(\mathfrak{s})$$

$\to \supset$

$$\frac{\dfrac{\;}{\mathfrak{p} \prec \mathfrak{t} \to \mathfrak{s} \prec \mathfrak{p} \supset \mathfrak{A}(\mathfrak{s})}\;\to\supset}{\mathfrak{p} \prec \mathfrak{t} \to (x)_{\prec \mathfrak{p}} \mathfrak{A}}\;\to\forall \qquad (x)_{\prec \mathfrak{p}} \mathfrak{A}, \mathfrak{p} \prec \mathfrak{t} \to \mathfrak{A}(\mathfrak{p})$$

$$\text{cut}\quad \overline{\mathfrak{p} \prec \mathfrak{t} \to \mathfrak{A}(\mathfrak{p})}$$

With these reduction steps (called TI- and TI_n-reductions for short) added to the previous ones it is an easy task to prove the analogue of theorem 1 in an elementary way. Gentzen's program is completed if we can prove theorem 2 also for the present case. Let us indicate briefly how this is achieved. In this context we use the notions and notations used in [**1**] and [7]. First we associate with every premise S of a TI- or a TI_n-inference the number of logical symbols in $(x)_{\prec y}\mathfrak{A}$ and call it the order of S. If S is the premise of a cut or an induction then we take as the order of S the number of logical symbols in the cut formula or the induction formula respectively. Now we can, as in [**1**] and [7] associate with every sequent S in a proof $\mathscr{P}$ another number, called its height and to be denoted by $h(S)$. Finally let ξ be the ordinal associated with $\prec$ and ξ_n the ordinal associated with $\{\langle x, y\rangle | x \prec n \wedge y \prec n \wedge x \prec y\}$ where $D(n)$ is true. Let S be the premise of a TI-inference and S' its conclusion. If α is the ordinal of S then we take $\omega_d((\alpha \# \omega^\xi)\omega^\xi)$ as ordinal of S' where $d = h(S) - h(S')$. If S is the premise of a TI-inference then we take $\omega_d((\alpha \# \omega^\lambda)\omega^\lambda)$ as ordinal of S' where $\lambda = \xi_n$. The verification that a TI- or TI_n-reduction lowers the ordinal of (the end-sequent of) the proof $\mathscr{P}$ requires a routine calculation which is omitted. For the previous reduction steps everything remains the same as before and so we obtain in a straightforward way the analogue of theorem 2 for $\text{ZT}(\prec)$. With theorems 1–2 at our disposal we can prove theorem 3 by transfinite induction over $\mathbf{V}^*$ where $\mathbf{V}^*$ is defined as in section 1 but with respect to the reduction steps of $\text{ZT}(\prec)$. In the same way we can now also prove theorem 4 proceeding exactly as in [**6**].

3. Before coming to the main part of this paper we consider a conservative extension $\text{ZT}^*(\prec)$ of $\text{ZT}(\prec)$. Formulas and sequents of $\text{ZT}^*(\prec)$ are now defined with respect to L. While the valuation of constants for p.r. functions is retained, we can explain the role of the special function constants as follows: if $w = \langle u_0, \ldots, u_{s-1}\rangle$ then α_w^i represents a function whose first s values are determined by w but which is unspecified otherwise. This leads us to consider a term such as e.g. $\mathfrak{t}(\alpha, \alpha_w^i, x)$ (containing no other variables and special function constants) as representing a certain continuous functional $\tau(\alpha, \beta, x)$ where α may run over arbitrary functions while β is restricted to those functions for which $\beta(\mathrm{i}) = u_i$ for $0 \leqslant i \leqslant s-1$. Let us call a term *saturated* if (1) it contains no variables but possibly special function constants $\alpha^1_{w_1}, \ldots, \alpha^s_{w_s}$, (2) if the sequences $w_1, \ldots, w_s$ determine the numerical value of $\mathfrak{t}$ completely. For a saturated term we denote by $|\mathfrak{t}|$ its numerical value. The notion '$\mathfrak{A}$ is isomorphic with $\mathfrak{A}'$' is defined as in section 1 except that the terms $\mathfrak{t}$, $\mathfrak{q}$ are now only required to be saturated. A prime sequent is called saturated if it contains only prime formulas $\mathfrak{t} = \mathfrak{q}$ with $\mathfrak{t}, \mathfrak{q}$ saturated. A saturated prime sequent is called numerically true if it is true under the usual interpretation. Verifiable sequents are defined as before. We now take as axioms for ZT*($\prec$) all those of ZT($\prec$) (with 'isomorphic' and 'numerically true' in the new sense) plus for every special function constant α^i_w with $w = \langle u_0, \ldots. u_{s-1}\rangle$ the axioms $\rightarrow \alpha^i_w(k) = u_k$ for $k \leqslant s-1$. The rules of ZT*($\prec$) are essentially the same as those of ZT($\prec$) except that now also quantifier rules for function symbols are available and that the conversion rule is now defined with respect to the new notion of isomorphism. We can now prove in exactly the same way theorems 1, 2 as before. A minor complication related to the presence of function variables appears now in the proof of theorem 3; it is in this connection where the use of the α^i_w is very convenient. We will meet this complication again in the proof of theorem 3* in section 4. Theorem 4 remains true under the additional assumption that the formulas $(\exists x)\mathfrak{A}$ and $\mathfrak{A} \vee \mathfrak{B}$ contain neither function variables nor special function constants; its proof parallels the one in **[6]**.

4. Denote by ZT* the theory which we obtain from ZT*($\prec$) by omitting TI, TI_n (that is just classical number theory but with reference to the language L). Let $L(y, z, x)$ and $D(y, x)$ be two p.r. relations such that for every $x \in \{\langle y, z\rangle | L(y, z, x)\}$ is a partial ordering of $\{y | D(y, x)\}$. Let $\mathfrak{g}(x, y, z)$ and $\mathfrak{d}(y, x)$ be terms such that L and D are formally represented by $\mathfrak{g}(x, y, z) = 0$ and $\mathfrak{d}(y, x) = 0$. Let us abbreviate $\mathfrak{g}(x, y, z) = 0$ by $y \prec_x z$ or sometimes even more simply by $y \prec z$; let us abbreviate $\mathfrak{d}(y, x) = 0$ by $d(y)$ or by $d_x(y)$. For simplicity we assume that ZT* contains all the axioms

(1). $\mathfrak{p} \prec \mathfrak{q}, \mathfrak{q} \prec \mathfrak{t} \rightarrow \mathfrak{p} \prec \mathfrak{t}$,

(2). $\mathfrak{p} \prec \mathfrak{q}, \mathfrak{q} \prec \mathfrak{p} \rightarrow$,

(3). $\mathfrak{p} \prec \mathfrak{q}, \mathfrak{p} = \mathfrak{q} \rightarrow$,

(4). $\mathfrak{p} \prec \mathfrak{q} \rightarrow d(\mathfrak{p})$,

(5). $\mathfrak{p} \prec \mathfrak{q} \rightarrow d(\mathfrak{q})$.

The system ZB is obtained from ZT* by adding the following new rule:

$$\text{TRI} \quad \frac{d_t(y), (x)(x \prec_t y \supset \mathfrak{A}(x)), \Gamma \to \Delta, \mathfrak{A}(y)}{W(\prec_t), d_t(\mathfrak{q}), \Gamma \to \Delta, \mathfrak{A}(\mathfrak{q})}$$

where $\mathfrak{t}$ is an arbitrary term, $\mathfrak{q}$ a term free for y in $\mathfrak{A}(y)$ and y a variable which is not free in the conclusion. $W(\prec_t)$ is the formula $(\alpha)(\exists x)(\neg\alpha(x+1) \prec_t \alpha(x))$. By an appropriate choice of $\prec_x$ it is easy to show that ZB is equivalent to the classical version of the theory TI_{QF} in [**3**]. The intuitionistic version ZBi is again obtained by admitting only those proofs which contain only sequents having at most one formula in the succedent. If we enquire whether it is possible to prove theorems 1–4 also for ZB (with appropriate reduction steps) it turns out that this is impossible in view of a theorem of G. Kreisel whose proof is outlined in the appendix of section 1 of the Stanford report. For ZBi however we shall see that reduction steps can be introduced so as to obtain theorems 1, 2 and 4 and a restricted version of theorem 3. To this end we need a lemma which is almost trivial to prove but which is basic for all later considerations. We remind that a proof $\mathscr{P}$ in ZBi is a certain finite tree; the final part of $\mathscr{P}$ (which is defined in the same way as before) is a certain subtree of $\mathscr{P}$. Therefore we can arrange the uppermost sequents of the final part in a well-determined way from left to right: $S_0, \ldots, S_n$. One easily shows: for two uppermost sequents S', S'' of the final part, S' is left of S'' iff there is a cut in the final part with left premise S_1^* and right premise S_2^*, such that S_1^* is below or equal to S' and S_2^* is below or equal to S''.

(Basic) LEMMA 1. *Let $\mathscr{P}$ be an intuitionistic proof which contains no thinning on the right in the final part and whose end-sequent has the form $\to \mathfrak{A}$. Let $S_0, \ldots, S_n$ be the uppermost sequents of the final part listed from left to right, let S_i be $\Gamma_i \to \mathfrak{A}_i$.*

(1). *If $i < n$ we can effectively find a proof $\mathscr{P}'$ of $\to \mathfrak{A}_i$,*

(2). *if $\mathfrak{B}$ occurs in some $\Gamma_j, j \leqslant n$, then one can find effectively a proof of $\to \mathscr{B}$.*

REMARK. A stronger version of this lemma is given in [**6**], theorem 7 but only for ZT. The assumption that there is no thinning on the right in the final part of $\mathscr{P}$ could be dropped but helps to simplify the argument below.

PROOF. We proceed by simultaneous induction with respect to i. If $i = 0$ then (1) and (2) are satisfied by S_0 which necessarily has to be of the form

$\rightarrow \mathfrak{A}_0$. Let (1) and (2) be true up to i–1. If $\mathfrak{B}$ occurs in Γ_i, then there is a cut with left- and right-premises S' and S'' respectively whose cut formula $\mathfrak{B}^*$ in S'' is an image of this $\mathfrak{B}$. Since there is no right thinning present in the final part of $\mathscr{P}$ we necessarily find an S_α with $\alpha < i$ such that the cut formula $\mathfrak{B}^*$ in S' is an image of the $\mathfrak{A}_\alpha$ in $\Gamma_\alpha \rightarrow \mathfrak{A}_\alpha$. By induction there is a proof of $\rightarrow \mathfrak{A}_\alpha$. Since $\mathfrak{B}^*$ is isomorphic both with $\mathfrak{A}_\alpha$ and with $\mathfrak{B}$, there is also a proof of $\rightarrow \mathfrak{B}$. Since now $\rightarrow \mathfrak{B}$ is provable for every $\mathfrak{B}$ in Γ_i and since a proof of $\Gamma_i \rightarrow \mathfrak{A}_i$ is already at hand there is also a proof of $\rightarrow \mathfrak{A}_i$, thus verifying both (1) and (2) for S_i.

Next we say that a proof in ZB has degree n if every formula in $\mathscr{P}$ contains at most n logical symbols. Denote by ZBi_n the subsystem of ZBi obtained by admitting only proofs of degree n. Now we introduce a certain conservative extension of ZBi, namely ZBi′ which has all the rules and axioms of ZBi and in addition the following rules:

(1). If e is the Gödel number of a proof $\mathscr{P}$ in ZBi of $W(\prec_{\mathfrak{t}})$ where $\mathfrak{t}$ is a saturated term, the rule

$$\mathrm{TRI}_e \quad e \quad \frac{d_{\mathfrak{t}}(y),\ (x)(x \prec_{\mathfrak{t}} y \supset \mathfrak{A}(x)),\ \Gamma \rightarrow \mathfrak{A}(y)}{d_{\mathfrak{t}}(q),\ \Gamma \rightarrow \mathfrak{A}(\mathfrak{q})}$$

with $\mathfrak{q}$ free for y in $\mathfrak{A}(y)$ and y not free in the conclusion.

(2). With e, $\mathfrak{t}$, $\mathfrak{q}$ as before and for n such that $D(n, \mathfrak{t})$ is true, the rule

$$\mathrm{TRI}_e^n \quad e \quad \frac{y \prec_{\mathfrak{t}} n,\ (x)(x \prec_{\mathfrak{t}} y \supset \mathfrak{A}(x)),\ \Gamma \rightarrow \mathfrak{A}(y)}{\mathfrak{q} \prec_{\mathfrak{t}} n,\ \Gamma \rightarrow \mathfrak{A}(\mathfrak{q})}$$

A proof $\mathscr{P}'$ in ZBi′ has degree n if all formulas in $\mathscr{P}'$ contain at most $\frac{1}{2}n$ logical symbols and if every Gödel number e in an inference TRI_e or TRI_e^n, is the Gödel number of a proof of degree n. Restriction to proofs of degree n yields a subsystem ZBi'_n of ZBi′. It is easy to prove

LEMMA 2. *If* $\mathrm{ZBi}'_n \vdash \mathfrak{F}$ *then* $\mathrm{ZBi}_n \vdash \mathfrak{F}$.

For each n we make the following assumption A_n: if $\mathfrak{B}$ is a Π_1^1-formula such that $\mathrm{ZBi}_n \vdash \mathfrak{B}$ then $\mathfrak{B}$ is true.

REMARK. Lemma 1 holds of course invariably for ZBi′, ZBi'_n and ZBi_n, as follows from its proof and lemma 2. By lemma 2, A_n remains true if we replace there ZBi_n by ZBi'_n. Call a proof $\mathscr{P}$ in ZBi'_n *normal* if all its terms in the final part are saturated, if its end sequent has the form $\rightarrow \mathfrak{A}$, and if no thinning occurs in the final part. For normal proofs we define reduction steps; with the exception of one we have introduced all these reduction steps in sections 1 and 2 already. Specifically we have (1) elimination of logical axioms and thinnings from the final part, (2) elimination of logical inferences from the final part, (3) elimination of induction steps from the final part. We have TRI_e- and TRI_e^n-reduction steps which are exact copies of the corresponding TI- and TI_n-reduction steps introduced in section 2. Finally, if there is a TRI-inference

$$\text{TRI}\quad \frac{d_t(y), (x)_{\prec y}\mathfrak{A}, \Gamma \rightarrow \mathfrak{A}(y)}{W(\prec_t), d_t(\mathfrak{q}), \Gamma \rightarrow \mathfrak{A}(\mathfrak{q})}$$

with conclusion in the final part, then, in view of lemmas 1 and 2, the remark, and the definition of normal proof, we find a Gödel number e of a proof in ZBi of $W(\prec_t)$. Hence we can replace the TRI-inference by a TRI_e-inference:

$$\begin{array}{ll} \text{TRI}_e & \dfrac{d_t(y), (x)(x \prec_t y \supset \mathfrak{A}(x)), \Gamma \rightarrow \mathfrak{A}(y)}{\mathrm{d}_t(\mathfrak{q}), \Gamma \rightarrow \mathfrak{A}(\mathfrak{q})} \\ \text{thinning} & \dfrac{}{W(\prec_t), d_t(q), \Gamma \rightarrow \mathfrak{A}(\mathfrak{q})} \end{array}$$

Reduction steps of type (1) above are again called preliminary, all other reduction steps are called essential. For normal proofs $\mathscr{P}, \mathscr{P}'$ we define $\mathscr{P}\mathbf{V}\mathscr{P}$ iff $\mathscr{P}'$ follows from $\mathscr{P}$ by means of some preliminary and one essential reduction step. The relation $\mathbf{V}^*$ is then defined in the same way as the $\mathbf{V}^*$ in section 1. For normal proofs we can again prove theorem 1 in section 1 in an elementary way. In order to prove theorem 2 for our $\mathbf{V}^*$ we have to associate ordinals with proofs in such a way that an essential reduction step lowers the ordinal of the corresponding proof $\mathscr{P}$. Let us denote by λ_n the smallest ordinal larger than the ordinal of any $\prec_m$ for which $\text{ZBi}_n' \vdash W(\prec_m)$ holds. Next, a natural number, called order, is associated with every sequent S in a proof $\mathscr{P}$ which is premise of one of the following inferences: (1) cut, (2) induction, (3) TRI, TRI_e or TRI_e^n. In cases (1), (2) we take the number of logical symbols in the cut or induction formula, in case (3) we take the number of logical symbols in $(x)(x \prec_t y \supset \mathfrak{A}(x))$. Having defined the order we can associate a height $h(S)$ with every sequent S in $\mathscr{P}$ in the same way as in **[1]** and **[7]**. Now we associate an ordinal $o(S)$ with every sequent S in $\mathscr{P}$ and distinguish cases according to whether S is (1) an axiom or else the conclusion of (2) a conversion or a structural rule other than cut, (3) of a logical rule, an induction or a cut, (4) of a TRI-, TRI_e- or a TRI_e^n-inference. In the cases (1)–(3) we proceed as in [**1**], [7]. If S is the conclusion of an inference under (4) with premise S' and if $o(S') = \alpha$ has already been determined then we put $o(S) = \omega_d((\alpha \# \omega^\xi)\omega^\xi)$ where d and ξ are determined as follows:

(1). $d = h(S') - h(S)$,

(2). ξ is λ_n if the inference is a TRI,

(3). if the inference is a TRI_e then ξ is the ordinal of $\prec_t$ where e is the Gödel number of a proof of $\rightarrow W(\prec_t)$,

(4). if the inference is a TRI_e^m, then ξ is the ordinal of $\{\langle x, y\rangle | x \prec_t y \wedge x, y \prec_t m\}$ where e is as before.

The ordinal of $\mathscr{P}$ is the ordinal of its end-sequent. The verification that an essential reduction step lowers the ordinal of a normal proof is now only a matter of routine, which leads to the same calculations as in the case of $\mathrm{ZT}(\prec)$. As a corollary of this fact we reobtain now theorem 2 of section 1 for the present relation $\mathbf{V}^*$. From theorems 1,2 we obtain theorem 4 for ZBi_n' and hence also for ZBi_n but with the same additional assumption as in section 3.

We sketch the proof of theorem 4. Let $\mathscr{P}$ be a normal proof of $\rightarrow (\exists x)\mathfrak{A}(x)$. In view of theorem 2 we can transform $\mathscr{P}$ by means of finitely many reduction steps into a normal proof $\mathscr{P}'$ which does not admit any reduction step at all. Then there is an inference in $\mathscr{P}'$ which satisfies the requirements of theorem 1. It is now easy to see that this inference is the right-most one amongst all inferences having their conclusions in the final part and it must have the particular form

$$\frac{\Gamma \rightarrow \mathfrak{A}(\mathfrak{q})}{\Gamma \rightarrow (\exists x)\mathfrak{A}(x)}$$

for some constant term $\mathfrak{q}$. By omitting this inference we obtain the proof required by theorem 4.

In order to state that form of theorem 3 which holds in our case we define by induction the notion- of a positive formula:

(1). a prime formula is positive,

(2). if $\mathfrak{A}$, $\mathfrak{B}$ are positive then $\mathfrak{A} \wedge \mathfrak{B}$, $\mathfrak{A} \vee \mathfrak{B}$, $(\exists x)\mathfrak{A}$, $(\forall x)\mathfrak{A}$, $(\exists \alpha)\mathfrak{A}$, $(\forall \alpha)\mathfrak{A}$ are all positive.

THEOREM 3*, *If $\mathscr{P}$ is a proof in* ZBi'_n *of* $\rightarrow \mathfrak{A}$ *with* $\mathfrak{A}$ *positive then there is an infinite constructive proof of* $\rightarrow \mathfrak{A}$.

PROOF. We will give a brief sketch of the proof. We proceed by induction with respect to the number n of logical symbols in $\mathfrak{A}$ and for fixed n by transfinite induction with respect to $\mathbf{V}^*$. In order to fix the ideas we consider an $\mathfrak{A}$ of the form $\mathfrak{B} \vee \mathfrak{C}$. We assume for simplicity that $\mathfrak{A}$ contains no variables and exactly one constant α_w; we may therefore write $\mathfrak{A}(\alpha_w)$ in place of $\mathfrak{A}$. Without restriction we may assume that $\mathscr{P}$ does not admit any preliminary reduction step.

Case 1. $\mathscr{P}$ is normal and admits an essential reduction step which transforms $\mathscr{P}$ into $\mathscr{P}'$. After a possible application of some preliminary reduction steps to $\mathscr{P}'$ we obtain a $\mathscr{P}''$ which is normal, has the same endsequent as $\mathscr{P}$ and satisfies $\mathscr{P}'\mathbf{V}^*\mathscr{P}$. The statement then follows by transfinite induction.

Case 2. $\mathscr{P}$ is normal and does not admit any reduction step. Using theorem 4 we find a proof $\mathscr{P}'$ of $\rightarrow \mathfrak{B}$ or $\rightarrow \mathfrak{C}$. The statement then follows from the induction hypothesis.

Case 3. $\mathscr{P}$ is not normal. This means that not every term in the final part of $\mathscr{P}$ is saturated. Call a finite sequence v good if (1) v is an extension of w, (2) replacing α_w by α_v in $\mathscr{P}$ gives a normal proof $\mathscr{P}_v$, (3) if v is a proper extension of v' then v' does not satisfy (1) and (2). For each good v case (1) or (2) applies to $\mathscr{P}$ and so we obtain cut free proofs $\mathscr{P}_v$ of $\rightarrow \mathfrak{A}(\alpha_v)$. With the aid of the ω-rule we can piece the $\mathscr{P}'_v$ together so as to obtain a cut free proof of $\rightarrow \mathfrak{A}(\alpha_w)$.

Theorem 3* remains true if all quantifier-free formulas are admitted as positive. In the system ZBi only numerical parameters are allowed in $\prec$; however only routine additional work is needed in order to carry through the arguments of section 4 for a system in whicn $\prec$ may depend on function parameters.

5. We consider briefly a generalization of the above to stronger theories. To this end let $\subset$ be a p.r. relation such that $v \subset w$ iff v, w are finite sequences and v is a proper extension of w; denote for simplicity by $\subset$ also a fixed prime formula $\mathfrak{t}(x, y) = 0$ representing this relation. Denote by $x \prec y$ the formula $x \subset y \wedge \mathfrak{D}(x) \wedge \mathfrak{D}(y)$ where $\mathfrak{D}$ is arbitrary. By $\mathbf{W}^\circ(\prec)$ we denote the formula $(\xi)\neg(x)(\xi(x+1) \prec \xi(x))$. We note that the formulas $\mathfrak{p} \prec \mathfrak{q}$, $\mathfrak{q} \prec \mathfrak{r} \rightarrow \mathfrak{p} \prec \mathfrak{r}$, $\mathfrak{p} \prec \mathfrak{q} \rightarrow \mathfrak{D}(\mathfrak{p})$, $\mathfrak{p} \prec \mathfrak{q} \rightarrow \mathfrak{D}(\mathfrak{q})$ have cut free proofs containing only propositional inferences. The extension ZBC of ZT* contains the rules and axioms of ZT* and for every formula $\mathfrak{D}$ the following rule:

$$\text{TRI} \quad \frac{\mathfrak{D}(y), (x)_{\prec y}\mathfrak{A}, \Gamma \to \Delta, \mathfrak{A}(y)}{W^{\circ}(\prec), \mathfrak{D}(\mathfrak{q}), \Gamma \to \Delta, \mathfrak{A}(\mathfrak{q})}$$

with $\mathfrak{q}$ free for y in $\mathfrak{A}(y)$, y not free in the conclusion and $\prec$ related to $\mathfrak{D}$ as described above.

From ZBC we can pass to its intuitionistic version ZBCi and to subsystems ZBCi'_n in a similar way to before. Without proof we note that (1) ZBC is as strong as classical analysis, (2) ZBC can be interpreted by means of the mapping $\mathfrak{A} \Rightarrow \mathfrak{A}^{\circ}$ (see [5], p. 493) in ZBCi. Let ZBK be that subsystem of ZBC which is obtained by putting the following restrictions on the formulas $\mathfrak{D}$:

(1). $\mathfrak{D}$ contains no function variables and no α_w^i,

(2). the free variables of $\mathfrak{D}$ are x, z.

We write $x \prec_{\mathrm{t}} y$ for $x \subset y \wedge \mathfrak{D}(x, t) \wedge \mathfrak{D}(y, t)$. The intuitionistic version of ZBK exists again, namely ZBKi and if we admit only proofs of degree n we get the subsystems ZBKi_n. The passage from ZBKi to a conservative extension ZBKi′ is now performed in the same way as in section 4. The only difference is that the rules TRI_e^n are now replaced by the following slightly different ones:

$$\text{TRI}^m_{e, e_1} \qquad e, e_1 \quad \frac{y \prec_{\mathrm{t}} \boldsymbol{m}, (x)(x \prec_{\mathrm{t}} y \supset \mathfrak{A}(x)), \Gamma \to \mathfrak{A}(y)}{q \prec_{\mathrm{t}} \boldsymbol{m}, \Gamma \to \mathfrak{A}(q)}$$

where e, t, $\mathfrak{q}$ have the same meaning as for TRI_e^n while e_1 is the Gödel-number of a proof in ZBKi of $\to \mathfrak{D}(m, \mathrm{t})$.

For ZBKi'_n (defined as in section 4) we can introduce the following kinds of reduction steps: (1) preliminary steps, (2) logical reduction steps, (3) induction reductions, (4) TRI-, TRI_e- and TRI^m_{e, e_1}-reduction steps. Reduction steps of kinds (1)–(3) and TRI-reduction steps are defined in exactly the same way as in section 4. Reduction steps TRI_e and TRI^m_{e, e_1} are almost the same as their counterparts TI and TI_n in section 2 with the following exceptions:

(1). the cases (1) in the definitions of the TI- and TI_n-reduction steps in section 2 are omitted now,

(2). the axiom $y \prec \mathrm{t} \to d(y)$ which appears leftmost at the top in the first of the two figures in section 2 is now replaced by a propositional cut-free proof of $y \prec_{\mathrm{t}} \mathfrak{q} \to \mathfrak{D}(y, \mathrm{t})$ in case of a TRI_e-reduction,

(3). the axiom $y \prec \mathfrak{p}, \mathfrak{p} \prec \mathfrak{t} \rightarrow y \prec \mathfrak{t}$ which appears leftmost at the top in the second figure of section 2 is now replaced by a propositional cut free proof of $y \prec_{\mathfrak{t}} \mathfrak{q}, \mathfrak{q} \prec_{\mathfrak{t}} \boldsymbol{m} \rightarrow y \prec_{\mathfrak{t}} \boldsymbol{m}$ in case of a $\mathrm{TRI}^{m}_{e, e_1}$-reduction.

With these reduction steps we can apply the arguments outlined in section 4 with almost no change to ZBKi'_n. As a result we reobtain theorems 1, 2, 3* and 4 for ZBKi'_n. We have considered ZBKi′ instead of ZBCi′ only in order to illustrate how to pass from ZBi′ with number parameters to ZBKi′. The theory ZBCi′ however bears to ZBi′ with function parameters about the same relation as ZBKi′ to ZBi′ with number parameters. It is therefore not difficult to transform the proofs of theorems 1, 2, 3*, 4 for ZBi′ with function parameters into proofs of theorems 1, 2, 3* and 4 for ZBCi′. Lack of space prevents us from considering details. They will be presented elsewhere.

6. We conclude by mentioning some further results without proof.

THEOREM 5. (a). *For fixed n we can prove in* ZBi (*with number or function parameters*) *the following three statements*:

(1). *if* $\mathrm{ZBi}'_n \vdash \rightarrow \mathfrak{A}$ *with* $\mathfrak{A}$ *positive then there is an intuitionistic constructive infinite cut free proof of* $\rightarrow \mathfrak{A}$,

(2). *if* $\mathrm{ZBi}'_n \vdash \rightarrow \mathfrak{A} \vee \mathfrak{B}$ *where* $\mathfrak{A} \vee \mathfrak{B}$ *contains no variables and no special function constants then* $\mathrm{ZBi}'_n \vdash \rightarrow \mathfrak{A}$ *or* $\mathrm{ZBi}'_n \vdash \rightarrow \mathfrak{B}$,

(3). *if* $\mathrm{ZBi}'_n \rightarrow (\exists x)\mathfrak{A}(x)$ *where* $(\exists x)\mathfrak{A}(x)$ *contains no free variables and no special function constants then there is a term* $\mathfrak{t}$ *such that* $\mathrm{ZBi}'_n \vdash \rightarrow \mathfrak{A}(\mathfrak{t})$.

(b). *For fixed n we can prove in* ZBC *the three statements in* (a) *but with* ZBCi'_n *in place of* ZBi'_n.

A proof of theorem 5(a) amounts to reproducing for fixed n in ZBi the classical arguments of sections 2 and 4; and a similar remark applies to theorem 5(b). If we add to ZBCi the rule

$$\frac{(x) \neg \mathfrak{R}(x), \Gamma \rightarrow \mathfrak{A}}{\neg (\exists x)\mathfrak{R}(x), \Gamma \rightarrow \mathfrak{A}}$$

where $\mathfrak{R}$ is p.r. and may contain parameters of any kind then we obtain a theory ZBCi* for which the exact counterparts of theorem 5(a) holds. In order to state the last results, let ZbCi be the theory which differs from ZBCi in the following respects: (1) there is no induction rule in ZbCi, (2) the special function constants and their axioms are omitted. Then we have the following two theorems whose proofs are very similar to those in section 4.

THEOREM 6. *If* $\mathscr{P}$ *is a proof in* ZbCi *of* $\rightarrow \mathfrak{A}$ *with* $\mathfrak{A}$ *positive then one can find effectively a finite cut free proof* $\mathscr{P}'$ *in* ZbCi *of* $\rightarrow \mathfrak{A}$. *If* $\mathscr{P}$ *is a proof in* ZbCi *of* $\rightarrow (\exists x)\mathfrak{A}(x)$ *where* $\mathfrak{A}$ *may contain any kind of variables then one can find effectively a term* t *and a proof* $\mathscr{P}'$ *in* ZbCi *of* $\rightarrow \mathfrak{A}(\mathrm{t})$.

In this paper we have only presented the smaller part of the conclusions which can be drawn from our basic lemma 1. Detailed proofs together with other results will be presented elsewhere.

REFERENCES

[1] G. GENTZEN, Neue Fassung des Widerspruchfreiheitsbeweises für die reine Zahlentheorie, *Forsch. Logik* N.S. **4** (1938).

[2] G. GENTZEN, Beweisbarkeit und Unbeweisbarkeit von Anfangsfällen der transfiniten Induktion in der reinen Zahlentheorie, *Math. Ann.* **119** (1943).

[3] W. HOWARD and G. KREISEL, Transfinite induction and bar induction of type zero and the role of continuity in intuitionistic analysis, *J. Symb. Logic* **31** no. 3 (1966).

[4] S. C. KLEENE, Permutability of inferences in Gentzen's calculi LK and LJ, *Memoirs Am. Math. Soc.* **10** (1952).

[5] S. C. KLEENE, *Introduction to metamathematics*, North-Holland, Amsterdam (1962).

[6] B. SCARPELLINI, Applications of Gentzen's second consistency proof, *Math. Ann.* **181** (1969) 325–354.

[7] K. SCHÜTTE, *Beweistheorie*, Springer (1960).

SECTION E

PROOF-THEORETIC ORDINALS

HEREDITARILY REPLETE FUNCTIONALS OVER THE ORDINALS

SOLOMON FEFERMAN*

Introduction. Orderings used in proof theory may be thought of as orderings of terms built up from constants and function symbols corresponding to functions on the ordinals Ω, e.g. 0, $+$, $\exp_\omega$ for the ordering of type ε_0.† The ordering $\preccurlyeq$ of the terms t is induced by the (natural) order of their values Val (t) in Ω:

$$t_1 \preccurlyeq t_2 \Leftrightarrow \text{Val}(t_1) \leqslant \text{Val}(t_2).$$

The function symbols faithfully represent the given system of functions $\boldsymbol{F}$ on $\preccurlyeq$ if for each t the order type $|t|_{\preceq}$ of t in $\preccurlyeq$ is the same as Val (t). Equivalently, this holds if the system $\boldsymbol{F}$ is *complete*, i.e. it fills up an initial segment of Ω. Three things are needed to make the ordering useful for proof theory: it should be (i) faithful, (ii) recursive,‡ and (iii) provably well-founded by elementary methods.

This paper continues the general study of [3] of properties of systems $\boldsymbol{F}$ which ensure that the associated orderings $\preccurlyeq_{\boldsymbol{F}}$ satisfy (i) and (ii), and the study of operations on systems which preserve these properties. (iii) is not taken up here. The properties (i) and (ii) are not in general preserved under the well-known process of adjoining the *critical function* of $\boldsymbol{F}$ (to $\boldsymbol{F}$). However, it was shown in [3] that stronger properties of $\boldsymbol{F}$, called *repleteness* and *effective relative categoricity*, are preserved under this process, as

* Research supported by grant DA-ARO-D-31-124-G655.

† In proof theory one uses other orderings too, suggested by reductions in proof figures (Takeuti's ordinal diagrams [12]). These orderings are, to begin with, partial orderings of proof figures induced by a reducibility relation, which are then embedded, more or less arbitrarily, in a total ordering.

‡ The need for this is evident where proof theoretical reductions to quantifier-free systems are to be given (as is commonly possible). However, this is also required for reductions to constructive systems when the equivalence of the two notions of well-foundedness, *WF* and *TI*, is to be used. Kreisel [7] Technical Note IV has pointed out how Brouwer's argument for this equivalence depends on the assumption of decidability of the ordering.

well as under its *transfinite iteration.* These notions and results are reviewed briefly in § 1 below.

By means of a pairing function in $\Omega \times \Omega \to \Omega$, systems of functions **F** can be coded by functions $F: \Omega \to \Omega$, indicated here by $F \in \Omega^1$. Then the process of adjunction of the critical function is given by a functional $\Phi: \Omega^1 \to \Omega^1$, or $\Phi \in \Omega^2$. The process of transfinitely iterating such a Φ can be regarded as given by a functional from Ω^2 to Ω^2. Let Ω^{n+1} consist of functionals from Ω^n to Ω^n. When formulated in this type structure, the notion of repleteness for F in Ω^1 is readily generalized to a notion of *hereditary repleteness* for functionals of every finite type n. The main result obtained here (§ 2, theorem 3) is that the *iteration functionals* of type n ($n \geqslant 3$), when defined properly, are all hereditarily replete.

A suitable generalization of the notion of effective relative categoricity to functionals of higher type has not yet been developed. However, it is possible to show that orderings induced by iteration in all types of the critical process have isomorphic recursive ordinals (§ 2, theorem 5). This is accomplished here by the use of effective operations over the recursive ordinals.

The remainder of the paper consists of three brief sections. Some open problems suggested by the preceding notions and results are formulated in general terms in § 3. In § 4 we consider the relation between the functions induced by iteration of the critical process and the functions of Bachmann's hierarchy [**1**], and in § 5 the relation to other theories of functionals over the ordinals. These sections contain some further problems and conjectures.

1. Systems of type level 1. Let Ω be the 1st uncountable ordinal; $\alpha, \beta, \gamma, \xi, \eta, \zeta$ range over Ω. Ordinals are taken so that $\alpha = \{\xi | \xi < \alpha\}$. $F: \Omega \to \Omega$ is *normal* if it is continuous and strictly increasing; $A \subseteq \Omega$ is *normal* if it is closed and unbounded. Let $\mathscr{R}(F)$ = range of F.

Basic facts

(i). A is normal $\Leftrightarrow$ there exists (unique) normal F with $A = \mathscr{R}(F)$.

(ii). F normal $\Rightarrow \{\xi | F(\xi) = \xi\}$ is normal; in this case, F' denotes the normal function enumerating this set.

Special facts

(iii). If $\langle A_\xi \rangle_{\xi<\alpha}$ is a sequence of normal sets with $A_\xi \supseteq A_\eta$ for $\xi < \eta$ and if $\alpha < \Omega$ then $\bigcap_{\xi<\alpha} A_\xi$ is normal.

(iv). If $\langle F_\xi \rangle_{\xi<\Omega}$ is a sequence of normal functions with $0 < F_\xi(0)$ and

$\mathscr{R}(F_{\xi+1}) \subseteq \mathscr{R}(F'_\xi)$ for each ξ and $\mathscr{R}(F_\xi) = \bigcap_{\eta<\xi}\mathscr{R}(F_\eta)$ for limit ξ, then $\lambda\xi F_\xi(0)$ is normal.

The facts (i)–(iii) lead to the definition of a certain transfinite iteration of the critical process applied to any initial normal F_0 with $F_0(0) > 0$: let $F_{\alpha+1} = F'_\alpha$ for $\alpha < \Omega$, and let F_α enumerate $\bigcap_{\xi<\alpha}\mathscr{R}(F_\xi)$ for α a limit number. The sequence $\langle F_\xi\rangle_{\xi<\Omega}$ is called the *first hierarchy* beginning with F_0; further such hierarchies of normal functions are incorporated in the Bachmann hierarchy discussed in § 4 below. By (iv), $\lambda\xi F_\xi(0)$ is again a normal function. As an example, consider the trivial normal function $F_0 = \lambda\xi(1+\xi)$. Then $F_\alpha(\xi) = \omega^\alpha+\xi$ and $F_\xi(0) = \omega^\xi$. The first hierarchy beginning with $\lambda\xi(\omega^\xi)$ is a sequence of functions $\kappa^{(\alpha)}$, in the notation of [3]. Thus $\kappa^{(1)}(\xi) = \varepsilon_\xi$, $\kappa^{(2)}(\xi) = \xi$th fixed point of $\kappa^{(1)}$, etc. The normal function $\lambda\xi\kappa^{(\xi)}(0)$ has as its first fixed point the least impredicative ordinal Γ_0.

The theory of [3] §§ 1, 2, deals with sequences $\boldsymbol{F} = \langle F_1, \ldots, F_m\rangle$ of any functions of one or more arguments $F_i\colon \Omega\times\ldots\times\Omega \to \Omega$. Let $\mathrm{Cl}_{\boldsymbol{F}}(A)$ be the closure under $\boldsymbol{F}$ of the set $A \cup \{0\}$. The set of $\boldsymbol{F}$-*inaccessibles* $\mathrm{In}_{\boldsymbol{F}} = \{\alpha|\mathrm{Cl}_{\boldsymbol{F}}(\alpha) = \alpha\}$ is normal; let $\boldsymbol{F}'$ enumerate $\mathrm{In}_{\boldsymbol{F}}$. The members of $\mathrm{Cl}_{\boldsymbol{F}}(0)$ are represented by closed terms in a formal symbolism $Tm(\boldsymbol{f})$ containing symbols 0 and $f_1, \ldots, f_m$. Put $\mathrm{t}_1 \leqslant_{\boldsymbol{F}} \mathrm{t}_2$ if $\mathrm{Val}_{\boldsymbol{F}}(\mathrm{t}_1) \leqslant \mathrm{Val}_{\boldsymbol{F}}(\mathrm{t}_2)$. The basic properties wanted of a system $\boldsymbol{F}$ are

(a). $\boldsymbol{F}$ is complete, i.e. $\mathrm{Cl}_{\boldsymbol{F}}(0) \in \Omega$,

(b). $\leqslant_{\boldsymbol{F}}$ is effective (recursive).

Example. $\boldsymbol{F} = \langle\lambda\xi, \eta(\omega^\xi+\eta)\rangle$ has both these properties. For this case one has $\mathrm{Cl}_{\boldsymbol{F}}(0) = \varepsilon_0$ and in general $(\boldsymbol{F})'(\xi) = \varepsilon_\xi$. Adjunction of G to $\boldsymbol{F}$ is denoted by $\boldsymbol{F} * \langle G\rangle$. For the specific example, $\boldsymbol{F} * \langle\boldsymbol{F}'\rangle = \langle\lambda\xi, \eta(\omega^\xi+\eta), \lambda\xi(\varepsilon_\xi)\rangle$.

As mentioned in the introduction, the properties (a), (b) are not in general preserved in the passage from $\boldsymbol{F}$ to $\boldsymbol{F} * \langle\boldsymbol{F}'\rangle$. This leads to the definition of stronger properties: $\boldsymbol{F}$ is said to be *replete* if for each α, $\mathrm{Cl}_{\boldsymbol{F}}(\alpha) \in \Omega$. A suitable strengthening of (b) is more recondite: $\boldsymbol{F}$ is *effectively relatively categorical* (*e.r.c.*) if, roughly speaking, the order relation between any two terms $\mathrm{t}_1(x_1, \ldots, x_k)$, $\mathrm{t}_2(x_1, \ldots, x_k)$ can be effectively determined from the ordering among $x_1, \ldots, x_k$, provided that these all represent $\boldsymbol{F}$-inaccessibles.

The following illustrate the general theorems which can be obtained (l.c.):

I. *If* $\boldsymbol{F}$ *is replete* (*e.r.c.*) *then* $\boldsymbol{F} * \langle\boldsymbol{F}'\rangle$ *is replete* (*e.r.c.*).

II. *If* $\boldsymbol{F}$ *is replete* (*e.r.c.*) *and* G_α *is the* α*th function in the first hierarchy of* *normal functions starting with* $G_0 = \boldsymbol{F}'$ *then* $\boldsymbol{F} * \langle \lambda\xi, \eta G_\xi(\eta)\rangle$ *is replete (e.r.c.).*

Consider $\langle \lambda\xi(1+\xi)\rangle$, which is trivially replete and e.r.c. By II so is $\langle \lambda\xi(1+\xi), \lambda\xi, \eta(\omega^\xi+\eta)\rangle$, and then by I so is $\langle \lambda\xi(1+\xi), \lambda\xi, \eta(\omega^\xi+\eta), \lambda\xi\varepsilon_\xi\rangle$, and finally by II the same holds for $\langle \lambda\xi(1+\xi), \lambda\xi, \eta(\omega^\xi+\eta), \lambda\xi, \eta\kappa^{(\xi)}(\eta)\rangle$.

Both I, II have the form: if $\boldsymbol{F}$ is replete (e.r.c.) then so is $\Phi(\boldsymbol{F})$, where Φ is a functional from systems $\boldsymbol{F}$ to extended systems $\boldsymbol{F} * \langle G\rangle$. The functional in II can be considered to be a transfinite iteration of the functional in I. To generalize these results, one would want to deal with the iteration of arbitrary functionals Φ which preserve repleteness (e.r.c.). This is done in the following section in a way which doesn't depend on the special facts about normal functions given above. This gives generalizations at least for functionals which preserve repleteness.

2. Hereditarily replete functionals. The following part of the finite type structure over Ω is used: $\Omega^0 = \Omega$ and Ω^{n+1} consists of all F: $\Omega^n \to \Omega^n$. For simplicity, m-tuples of ordinals will now be (naturally) coded by ordinals, and sequences of functions will be coded by single functions.*

Take $\langle \xi, \eta\rangle = 2^\xi(2\eta+1)$; this is bi-unique from $\Omega\times\Omega$ to $\Omega-\{0\}$. For $\xi > 0$, let $\xi = \langle (\xi)_0, (\xi)_1\rangle$; take $(0)_0 = (0)_1 = 0$. Given $\alpha \leqslant \Omega$ and any sequence $\langle F_\xi\rangle_{\xi<\alpha}(F_\xi \in \Omega^1)$, let $\Lambda_{\xi<\alpha}F_\xi = G$, where $G(\xi) = F_{(\xi)_0}((\xi)_1)$ if $(\xi)_0 < \alpha$, and $G(\xi) = 0$ otherwise (*enumeration*). Let $(F_0, \ldots, F_m) = \Lambda_{\xi<m+1}F_\xi$. Now take $\mathrm{Cl}_F(A)$ to be the smallest set which includes $A \cup \{0\}$ and which contains $\langle \xi, \eta\rangle$ and $F(\xi)$ whenever it contains ξ, η. As before, $\mathrm{In}_F = \{\alpha | \mathrm{Cl}_F(\alpha) = \alpha\}$ and F' enumerates In_F. Now take $\mathrm{Cr}(F) = (F, F')$. Write $F \in \mathrm{Rp}^1$ if for each $\alpha(< \Omega)$, $\mathrm{Cl}_F(\alpha) \in \Omega$. Put $F \trianglelefteq_1 G$ if $\mathrm{Cl}_F(\alpha) \subseteq \mathrm{Cl}_G(\alpha)$ for each α. If a sequence of functions $\boldsymbol{F}$ is coded as a single function F for all α and $\mathrm{Cl}_{\boldsymbol{F}}(\alpha)$ is closed under $+$ and $\exp_2$ then $\mathrm{Cl}_{\boldsymbol{F}}(\alpha) = \mathrm{Cl}_F(\alpha)$, and $\boldsymbol{F}$ is replete iff $F \in \mathrm{Rp}^1$. The following is a reformulation of theorem 1 of § 1, with additional observations.

THEOREM 1. *Suppose* $F \in \mathrm{Rp}^1$. *Then*

(i). $\mathrm{Cr}(F) \in \mathrm{Rp}^1$,

(ii). $F \trianglelefteq_1 \mathrm{Cr}(F)$,

(iii). $G \in \mathrm{Rp}^1$ & $F \trianglelefteq_1 G \Rightarrow \mathrm{Cr}(F) \trianglelefteq_1 \mathrm{Cr}(G)$.

PROOF. The proof of (i) is like that of § 1, I; the proofs of (ii) and (iii) are easy.

* An alternative is to start with Ω^0 = set of all finite sequences of elements of Ω.

The functional $\mathrm{Cr} \in \Omega^2$. We shall analyze § 1, II as a result about iteration of this functional $\mathrm{It}(\mathrm{Cr})$, where now $\mathrm{It} \in \Omega^3$. This is obtained by extending the notion Rp, and the operation Λ to higher types.

For any sequence $\langle F_\xi \rangle_{\xi<\alpha}$, $\alpha \leqslant \Omega$, of members of Ω^{n+1}, let $\Lambda_{\xi<\alpha} F_\xi = G \in \Omega^{n+1}$ where for all $H \in \Omega^n$, $G(H) = \Lambda_{\xi<\alpha}(F_\xi(H))$. Again, take $(F_0, \ldots, F_m) = \Lambda_{\xi<m+1} F_\xi$. For each $F, G \in \Omega^n$, $n \geqslant 2$, let $(F \circ G) \in \Omega^n$ with $(F \circ G)(H) = F(G(H))$ for each $H \in \Omega^{n-1}$.

For each $n > 2$, an iteration functional $\mathrm{It}^{n+1} \in \Omega^{n+1}$ is defined as follows: for each $F \in \Omega^n$, $\mathrm{It}^{n+1}(F) = F^{(\Omega)}$ where $F^{(0)} = F$ and for each $\alpha > 0$, $\alpha \leqslant \Omega$, $F^{(\alpha)} = \Lambda_{\xi<\alpha}(F \circ F^{(\xi)})$.

Suppose Rp^n ($\subseteq \Omega^n$) and $\trianglelefteq_n$ have been defined ($n \geqslant 1$). A functional $F \in \Omega^{n+1}$ is said to be *hereditarily replete* and we write $F \in \mathrm{Rp}^{n+1}$ if $F\colon \mathrm{Rp}^n \to \mathrm{Rp}^n$. *Example.* $\mathrm{Cr} \in \mathrm{Rp}^2$ (theorem 1(i)).

For $F_0, F_1 \in \mathrm{Rp}^{n+1}$, define

$$F_0 \trianglelefteq_{n+1} F_1 \Leftrightarrow \text{for all } G \in \mathrm{Rp}^n,\ F_0(G) \trianglelefteq_n F_1(G).^*$$

The subscript 'n' is dropped from $\trianglelefteq_n$ in the following.
The following gives the basic closure conditions on the Rp^n.

THEOREM 2

(i). *Suppose $n \geqslant 2$ and $F, G \in \mathrm{Rp}^n$; then $F \circ G \in \mathrm{Rp}^n$.*

(ii). *Suppose $n \geqslant 1$, $0 < \alpha \leqslant \Omega$ and $F_\xi \in \mathrm{Rp}^n$ for each $\xi < \alpha$; then $(\Lambda_{\xi<\alpha} F_\xi) \in \mathrm{Rp}^n$.*

PROOF. (i). This is trivial by definition.

(ii). This is proved by induction on n. For $n = 1$, let $F = (\Lambda_{\xi<\alpha} F_\xi)$. First show for any β

$$\mathrm{Cl}_F(\beta) = \bigcup \mathrm{Cl}_{(F_{\xi_0}, \ldots, F_{\xi_m})}(\beta)[\xi_0, \ldots, \xi_m \in \mathrm{Cl}_F(\beta) \cap \alpha].$$

When each $F_\xi \in \mathrm{Rp}^1$, the right hand side is a union of ordinals, so $\mathrm{Cl}_F(\beta)$ is an ordinal. The induction step from n to $n+1$ is obvious by definition of Rp^{n+1} and the commutativity of Λ with application.

As a corollary, $F_0, \ldots, F_m \in \mathrm{Rp}^n \Rightarrow (F_0, \ldots, F_m) \in \mathrm{Rp}^n$. The proof of the following is now straightforward.

* The definition of Rp^{n+1} given in the talk imposed some additional conditions in terms of $\trianglelefteq$. These are satisfied by the particular functionals we are interested in, but can be dispensed with in general.

THEOREM 3. *Suppose* $n \geqslant 2$. Then

(i). $\mathrm{It}^{n+1} \in \mathrm{Rp}^{n+1}$.

(ii). $F \in \mathrm{Rp}^n \Rightarrow F \trianglelefteq \mathrm{It}^{n+1}(F)$.

(iii). $F, G \in \mathrm{Rp}^n \;\&\; F \trianglelefteq G \Rightarrow \mathrm{It}^{n+1}(F) \trianglelefteq \mathrm{It}^{n+1}(G)$.

As a corollary (new version of § 1, II): for any $F \in \mathrm{Rp}^1$, $(\mathrm{It}^3(\mathrm{Cr}^2))(F) \in \mathrm{Rp}^1$ and $F \trianglelefteq (\mathrm{It}^3(\mathrm{Cr}^2))(F)$.

Given $K \subseteq \bigcup_{0<n} \Omega^n$ and $A \subseteq \Omega$, define $\mathrm{Cl}_K(A)$ to be the smallest class $C \subseteq \bigcup_{n \geq 0} \Omega^n$ satisfying the following conditions:

(i). $A \cup \{0\} \subseteq C$,

(ii). $\xi, \eta \in C \Rightarrow \langle \xi, \eta \rangle \in C$,

(iii). $n \geqslant 1 \;\&\; F_0, F_1 \in C \cap \Omega^n \Rightarrow (F_0, F_1) \in C$,

(iv). $n \geqslant 1 \;\&\; F \in C \cap \Omega^n \;\&\; G \in C \cap \Omega^{n-1} \Rightarrow F(G) \in C$,

(v). $n \geqslant 2 \;\&\; F_0, F_1 \in C \cap \Omega^n \Rightarrow F_0 \circ F_1 \in C$.

If $K \subseteq \bigcup_{0<n} \mathrm{Rp}^n$ and K is countable, then K is *replete* in the sense that for each $\alpha < \Omega$, $\mathrm{Cl}_K(\alpha) \cap \Omega \in \Omega$.

Suppose given an enumeration of $K = \{H_0, H_1, \ldots, H_n, \ldots\}$ and an enumeration of $\alpha = \{\alpha_0, \ldots, \alpha_n, \ldots\}$. Corresponding to these enumerations is a symbolism with terms of finite type. It contains for each m constant symbols of the same type as H_m and symbols $\mathbf{0}$ and $\boldsymbol{\alpha}_m$ of type 0. If $\mathrm{t}_0, \mathrm{t}_1$ are terms of type 0 then $\langle \mathrm{t}_0, \mathrm{t}_1 \rangle$ is a term of type 0. If $\mathrm{t}_0, \mathrm{t}_1$ are of type $n \geqslant 1$ then $(\mathrm{t}_0, \mathrm{t}_1)$ is of type n and for $n \geqslant 2$ so is $(\mathrm{t}_0 \circ \mathrm{t}_1)$. If t_0 is of type $n \geqslant 1$ and t_1 is of type $n-1$, then $\mathrm{t}_0(\mathrm{t}_1)$ is of type $n-1$. Each term t of type n has a value Val (t) in $\mathrm{Cl}_K(\alpha) \cap \Omega^n$. Define

$$\mathrm{t}_0 \preccurlyeq \mathrm{t}_1 \Leftrightarrow \mathrm{t}_0, \mathrm{t}_1 \text{ are of type } 0 \;\&\; \mathrm{Val}(\mathrm{t}_0) \leqslant \mathrm{Val}(\mathrm{t}_1).$$

We call this the ordering between terms induced by (the given enumeration of) K and α. When K is replete, this ordering (after identifying $\mathrm{t}_0, \mathrm{t}_1$ such that $\mathrm{t}_0 \preccurlyeq \mathrm{t}_1$ and $\mathrm{t}_1 \preccurlyeq \mathrm{t}_0$) is isomorphic to the ordering of the ordinals $< \mathrm{Cl}_K(\alpha) \cap \Omega$.

Let $K_0 = \{\lambda\xi(1+\xi), \mathrm{Cr}, \mathrm{It}^3, \ldots, \mathrm{It}^{n+1}, \ldots\}$.

THEOREM 4. $K_0 \subseteq \mathrm{PR}_\Omega$, *where* PR_Ω *is the class of primitive recursive functionals over* Ω.

PR_Ω is the obvious extension to Ω of Gödel's primitive recursive functionals over ω; cf. **[4]** § 1. It is shown in **[4]** § 3 that $\mathrm{PR}_\Omega \cap \Omega$ is a recursive ordinal. The argument uses effective operations in metarecursion theory. The same argument establishes

THEOREM 5. *For each* $\alpha < \omega_1$ (*the least non-recursive ordinal*), $\mathrm{Cl}_{K_0}(\alpha) \cap \Omega < \omega_1$.

PROOF. Actually a simpler proof can be given in this case, using ordinary partial recursive functions over O. The subscript 'p' in the following is used to distinguish the notions here from those in **[4]**. Let

$$E_p^0 = 0$$

$$f \in E_p^{n+1} \Leftrightarrow (\forall g)[g \in E_p^n \Rightarrow \{f\}(g) \in E_p^n],$$

$$\mathrm{Nr}_p(a, \alpha, 0) \Leftrightarrow a \in O \;\&\; |a| = \alpha$$

and

$$\mathrm{Nr}_p(f, F, n+1)$$
$$\Leftrightarrow f \in E_p^{n+1} \;\&\; F \in \Omega^{n+1} \;\&\; (\forall G, g)\{\mathrm{Nr}_p(g, G, n) \Rightarrow \mathrm{Nr}_p(\{f\}(g), F(G), n)\}.$$

We say that f is a number of F if $\mathrm{Nr}_p(f, F, n)$ when $F \in \Omega^n$. Now it can be shown that each $F \in K_0$ has a number $\nu(F)$. Moreover whenever F_0, F_1 of the same type have numbers, so do $F_0 \circ F_1$ and (F_0, F_1). It follows that for each $a \in O$, each $F \in \mathrm{Cl}_{K_0}(|a|)$ has a number $\nu(F)$; moreover the set of these $\nu(F)$ is recursively enumerable. Hence $\{\nu(\beta) | \beta \in \mathrm{Cl}_{K_0}(|a|) \cap \Omega\}$ is recursively enumerable and is a subset of O_γ for some $\gamma < \omega_1$.

Note that this argument does not establish the recursiveness of the ordering of terms induced by K_0 and α, but only of an ordering isomorphic to it.

3. Open problems. The following problems are suggested by the general direction of this work. I do not have precise formulations, but the intent is clear enough to guide their study and to test the adequacy of proposed solutions.

The following is the main problem.

(i). *What is the general notion of (transfinite) iteration of the critical process?* It would not be surprising if the type structure had to be suppressed or abandoned in a solution of this. Moreover, it should include a solution to the following problem; this is stated here because it seems more tractable at the moment.

(ii). *What is a suitable generalization of iteration to transfinite types* (*in the present context*)? Part of the problem here is to find the right transfinite type structure; this should automatically provide for a generalization of the notion of repleteness. In a sense, the consideration of countable $K \subseteq \bigcup_{0<n} \mathrm{Rp}^n$ is an extension to type ω. Then we can consider the functional Φ of type $\omega+1$, $\Phi(K) = K \cup \{K'\}$, where K' enumerates $\{\xi | \mathrm{Cl}_K(\xi) \cap \Omega = \xi\}$, etc. The following economy can be achieved here. Given countable $K \subseteq \bigcup_{0<n} \mathrm{Rp}^n$, let $\mathrm{Cl}_K(0) \cap \Omega^1 = \{F_0, \ldots, F_n, \ldots\}$. Define $\overline{K} = \Lambda_{n<\omega} F_n$. Then $\overline{K} \in \mathrm{Rp}^1$ and for any α, $\mathrm{Cl}_K(\alpha) \cap \Omega = \mathrm{Cl}_{\overline{K}}(\alpha)$, independent of the enumeration $F_0, \ldots, F_n, \ldots$. Any such $\overline{K}$ is said to *represent* K. Then $\mathrm{Cr}(\overline{K})$ represents $\Phi(K)$. This gives us a new basic functional $\mathrm{Cr}_1 \in \mathrm{Rp}^2$, namely $\mathrm{Cr}_1(F) = \mathrm{Cr}(\overline{K_0 \cup \{F\}})$. From this is obtained in turn $\mathrm{Cr}_2 \in \mathrm{Rp}^2$ with $\mathrm{Cr}_2(F) = \mathrm{Cr}(K_1 \cup \{F\})$ where $K_1 = \{\lambda\xi(1+\xi), \mathrm{Cr}, \mathrm{Cr}_1, \mathrm{It}^3, \mathrm{It}^4, \ldots\}$. Obviously this process can be iterated, but it is not yet clear how to organize this in a coherent way.

Returning to the notation of § 1, when an F is e.r.c., we get much more information about it than that it is effective (e.g. theorem 2.10 of **[3]**). Thus, although one can obtain various recursiveness results such as theorem 5, it would be hoped to solve the following problem:

(iii). *What is a suitable generalization of the notion of effective relative categoricity to functionals?* If such can be found, it should be possible to show, for example, that the ordering of terms induced by K_0 is recursive (cf. the remark at the end of § 2).

4.1. Relations to (Bachmann) hierarchies of normal fuctions. As described in § 1, associated with any normal F_0 satisfying $F_0(0) > 0$ is a hierarchy of normal functions $\langle F_\alpha \rangle_{\alpha<\Omega}$ which are successively critical for the preceding functions. Then $G_0 = \lambda\xi F_\xi(0)$ is normal with $G_0(0) > 0$, so the hierarchy associated with G_0 gives a second hierarchy for F_0, etc. The Bachmann idea **[1]** is to keep track of the iteration of this process by going into an initial segment of the 3rd number class: let $F_\Omega = \lambda\xi F_\xi(0)$, then $F_{\Omega+\alpha}$ is the αth function in the first hierarchy starting with F_Ω, $F_{\Omega\cdot 2} = \lambda\xi F_{\Omega+\xi}(0)$, etc. This provides normal functions $F_\alpha \colon \Omega \to \Omega$ for α ranging over any initial segment of the ordinals $< \Omega_2$ for which one has associated fundamental sequences of order type $\leqslant \Omega$ with each limit number. (E.g. $F_{\Omega\cdot\omega}$ enumerates $\bigcap_{\xi<\omega} \mathscr{R}(F_{\Omega\cdot\xi})$, while $F_{\Omega^2} = \lambda\xi F_{\Omega\cdot\xi}(0)$). This is easily done for $\alpha \leqslant \varepsilon_{\Omega+1} =$ 1st fixed point of $\Omega^\nu = \nu$ for $\nu > \Omega$. (It is extended further by building hierarchies of normal functions over Ω_2; we return to this point below.) Using notation which has become fairly standard in this connection, let $\varphi_0 = \lambda\xi(1+\xi)$ and for $\alpha \leqslant \varepsilon_{\Omega+1}$ let φ_α be the αth function in the extended hierarchy starting with φ_0.*†

Note that fundamental sequences have to be considered in the definition of the φ_α in order to keep all functions normal and to apply the special facts (iii), (iv) of § 1 at limit numbers. This problem is avoided in the definition of the iteration processes It^n considered above by allowing non-normal functions and using the enumeration operator Λ to encode everything obtained at earlier stages. This suggests that it should be possible to cover the φ_α by functions in $\mathrm{Cl}_{K_0}(0) \cap \Omega^1$, or even extract them in some sense.

The following relations are conjectured. Superscripts n are dropped from the It^n where there is no ambiguity.

For any α,

$$\varphi_{\alpha+\Omega} \trianglelefteq (\mathrm{It}(\mathrm{Cr}))(\varphi_\alpha).$$

For $F_1 = \mathrm{It}(\mathrm{Cr})$

$$\varphi_{\alpha+\Omega\cdot 2} \trianglelefteq F_1^{(2)}(\varphi_\alpha), \ldots, \varphi_{\alpha+\Omega\cdot\xi} \trianglelefteq F_1^{(\xi)}(\varphi_\alpha) \quad \text{when } \xi < \Omega,$$

and

$$\varphi_{\alpha+\Omega^2} \trianglelefteq (\mathrm{It}(F_1))(\varphi_\alpha).$$

Let $F_2 = \mathrm{It}(F_1) = \mathrm{It}(\mathrm{It}(\mathrm{Cr}))$.

$$\varphi_{\alpha+\Omega^2\cdot 2} \trianglelefteq F_2^{(2)}(\varphi_2), \ldots, \varphi_{\alpha+\Omega^2\cdot\xi} \trianglelefteq F_2^{(\xi)}(\varphi_\alpha) \quad \text{for } \xi < \Omega,$$

and

$$\varphi_{\alpha+\Omega^3} \trianglelefteq F_3(\varphi_\alpha),$$

where $F_3 = \mathrm{It}(F_2) = \mathrm{It}(\mathrm{It}(\mathrm{It}(\mathrm{Cr})))$. In general

$$\varphi_{\alpha+\Omega^\xi} \trianglelefteq (\mathrm{It}^{(\xi)}(\mathrm{Cr}))(\varphi_\alpha) \quad \text{for } \xi < \Omega,$$

and

$$\varphi_{\alpha+\Omega^\Omega} \trianglelefteq ((\mathrm{It}(\mathrm{It}))(\mathrm{Cr}))(\varphi_\alpha).$$

In particular $\varphi_{\Omega^\Omega} \trianglelefteq \mathrm{It}^4\mathrm{It}^3\mathrm{Cr}\ \varphi_0$ (application associated to the left).If this holds one would guess that

* Bachmann starts with $\varphi_0(\xi) = \omega^\xi$ which is here $\varphi_\Omega(\xi)$. For $\alpha \geqq \Omega^2$ we have $\Omega+\alpha = \alpha$ and the function φ_α is the same with either starting point. A minor difference is that **[1]** begins enumerations with 1 rather than 0.

† An interesting comparison of the ordinals obtained by the Veblen-Schütte functions **[11]** and by these hierarchies has been made by Levitz **[8]**. He shows that Veblen's first E-number is just $\varphi_{\Omega^\Omega}(0)$.

$$\varphi_{\underbrace{\Omega^{\cdot^{\cdot^{\cdot^{\Omega}}}}}_{n}} \trianglelefteq \mathrm{It}^{n+2}\mathrm{It}^{n+1} \ldots \mathrm{It}^{3}\mathrm{Cr}\varphi_0.$$

$\varepsilon_{\Omega+1}$ is the limit of $\Omega, \Omega^{\Omega}, \Omega^{\Omega^{\Omega}}, \ldots$. Thus every ordinal $< \varphi_{\varepsilon_{\Omega+1}}(0)$ would be in $\mathrm{Cl}_{K_0}(0) \cap \Omega$.

By theorem 4, $\mathrm{Cl}_{K_0}(0) \cap \Omega \subseteq \mathrm{PR}_{\Omega} \cap \Omega$. Howard (unpublished) has shown that $\mathrm{PR}_{\Omega} \cap \Omega \leqslant \varphi_{\varepsilon_{\Omega+1}}(0)$. This leads me to the following

Conjecture. $\mathrm{Cl}_{K_0}(0) \cap \Omega = \varphi_{\varepsilon_{\Omega+1}}(0)$.

Let Ω_ν be the νth initial ordinal, with $\Omega = \Omega_1$. The hierarchy φ_α for $\alpha < \varepsilon_{\Omega+1}$ essentially uses the hierarchy of normal functions $\psi_\beta = \lambda\eta(\Omega^\beta + \eta)$ from Ω_2 to Ω_2. It can be extended further by building up hierarchies of normal functions over Ω_2. This in turn requires consideration of fundamental sequences in Ω_3, etc. Such use of the Ω_ν has been systematized to some extent in the (independent) work of Pfeiffer and Isles for finite ν and more generally by Isles [**6**] for certain transfinite ν. Assuming the conjecture above is correct, one is immediately led to the following question: *What corresponds in the present approach to the use of the initial ordinals Ω_ν for extending the hierarchies of normal functions?* Some obvious candidates are supplied by an extension of the theory to transfinite types as anticipated in § 3.

4.2. Remarks on the problems of associating fundamental sequences and well-orderings. An *association of fundamental sequences* in an initial segment of the 2nd number class is a relation $\mathfrak{F}(\alpha, \varphi)$ satisfying the following conditions:

(a)(i). $\mathfrak{F}(\alpha, \varphi) \Rightarrow \alpha$ is a limit number $< \Omega$ and $\varphi = \lambda n < \omega\varphi(n)$ is an increasing sequence of ordinals with $\alpha = \sup_{n<\omega}\varphi(n)$,

(ii). $\mathfrak{F}(\alpha, \varphi) \,\&\, \mathfrak{F}(\alpha, \psi) \Rightarrow \varphi = \psi$,

and

(iii). $\mathfrak{F}(\alpha, \varphi) \,\&\, \beta < \alpha \,\&\, \beta$ a limit number $\Rightarrow (\exists\psi)\mathfrak{F}(\beta, \psi)$.

An *association of well-orderings* in such an initial segment is a relation $\mathfrak{W}(\alpha, x)$ satisfying

(b)(i). $\mathfrak{W}(\alpha, x) \Rightarrow \alpha < \Omega$ and x is a well-ordering relation of order type α with field $\subseteq \omega$,

(ii). $\mathfrak{W}(\alpha, x) \,\&\, \mathfrak{W}(\alpha, y) \Rightarrow x = y$,

and

(iii). $\mathfrak{W}(\alpha, x) \,\&\, \beta < \alpha \Rightarrow (\exists y)\mathfrak{W}(\beta, y)$.

The domain $\alpha_{\mathfrak{W}}$ of $\mathfrak{W}$ is $\{\alpha | (\exists x)\mathfrak{W}(\alpha, x)\}$; the domain $\alpha_{\mathfrak{F}}$ of $\mathfrak{F}$ is defined to be $\{\gamma | (\exists \alpha \geqslant \gamma)(\exists \varphi)\mathfrak{F}(\alpha, \varphi)\}$. The existence of associations $\mathfrak{F}$, $\mathfrak{W}$ with $\alpha_{\mathfrak{F}} = \Omega$, $\alpha_{\mathfrak{W}} = \Omega$, is trivial assuming the axiom of choice.

The general aim of Bachmann's work is to produce associations $\mathfrak{F}$ with very large domains which are explicit, in some suitable sense. To see the matter in perspective, let us go over the simplest historical and logical relations.

The interest in fundamental sequences goes back to a result of Hardy (1903) (reproved in Church **[2]**): A well-ordering of type Ω of a subset of the continuum can be defined from any (association) $\mathfrak{F}$ with domain Ω. Hardy simply showed how to define a $\mathfrak{W}$ with domain Ω from such an $\mathfrak{F}$. Compare Lévy **[9]** who showed (1963): it is consistent with ZF+AC+GCH that no formula of the language $\mathfrak{L}_\in$ (of set theory) defines a well-ordering of type Ω of a subset of the continuum. So there is no $\mathfrak{F}$, definable in $\mathfrak{L}_\in$ for which (a)(i)–(iii) and $\alpha_{\mathfrak{F}} = \Omega$ can be proved in this system, let alone ZF.

The next logical question is whether for some countable α and possible $\mathfrak{F}$ and $\mathfrak{W}$ with domain α, one can be essentially 'simpler' than the other. An answer to this question, in terms of axiomatic set theory, follows from examination of the Hardy-Church arguments **[2]**. Given a definition of $\mathfrak{W}$, we can read off a definition of $\mathfrak{F}$ with the same domain; for the converse one uses a straightforward definition by transfinite induction. Put axiomatically, the two steps can be formalized in a set theory without the power-set axiom, with the Σ_1-axiom of choice as its only non-trivial existential axiom. (This system is quite weak, of the same strength as Σ_1^1–AC in Friedman **[5]**.) So, proof theoretically, the problems of finding $\mathfrak{F}$ and $\mathfrak{W}$ are, in an obvious sense, equivalent for systems containing this weak set theory.

What can be said about α which are provably domains of $\mathfrak{F}$ or $\mathfrak{W}$? Certainly, for Ω_1^L = the least constructibly uncountable α we have a $\mathfrak{W}_L$ with domain Ω_1^L, namely

$$\alpha < \Omega_1^L \;\&\; x \text{ is the first well-ordering of } \omega \text{ in } L \text{ of type } \alpha$$

('first' in the usual well-ordering of L). Since Ω_1^L must be considered too 'large' (at least for applications to proof theory), this implies that additional conditions should be imposed; for example (as suggested by Kreisel), add

(b)(iv). $\mathfrak{W}(\alpha, x) \;\&\; \mathfrak{W}(\beta, y) \;\&\; \beta < \alpha \Rightarrow y$ is an initial segment of x.

(It is less obvious what additional conditions on $\mathfrak{F}$ would be natural.)

Question. For any $\mathfrak{W}$ which can be proved (say in ZF) to satisfy (b)(i)–(iii) is there a $\mathfrak{W}'$ which can be proved to have the same domain as $\mathfrak{W}$ and to satisfy (b)(i)–(iv)?*

The general question of finding natural additional conditions on $\mathfrak{W}$ seems to have some independent set-theoretic interest.

To summarize: on the basis of the present evidence, there seem to be no logical advantages in associations $\mathfrak{F}$ as compared with associations $\mathfrak{W}$. It might be considered possible that the results are formally simpler to state for $\mathfrak{F}$ than for $\mathfrak{W}$. However, this possibility is slight if the conjectures above (concerning Bachmann's hierarchies of normal functions and the functions obtained by higher type iterations of the critical process) are true.

5. Relations to earlier work with functionals. Neumer has developed extensive classes of functionals over the ordinals, but without any general theoretical framework. The work has undergone a series of expansions and revisions in a number of papers; the most recent versions are to be found in the papers [**10**]. The 'operators' of [**10**] part I and 'selectors' of [**10**] part II, are both functionals of finite type, but the objects of type 1 are always normal functions. The operators $I, I', I'', \ldots$ of the former and $S, S', S'', \ldots$ of the latter correspond, respectively to the functionals Cr, $\mathrm{It}^3, \mathrm{It}^4, \ldots$ defined here. In addition, Neumer considers certain symbolic operators which he calls 'facients.' The facient $1_{\mathcal{U}}$ is really a functional making use of the iteration of the process of forming, for any normal $F \in \Omega^1$, the function enumerating the inaccessibles of $\{IF, I'IF, I''I'IF, \ldots\}$. In terms of § 3, it corresponds to $(\mathrm{It}(\mathrm{Cr}_1))'$. The facient $2_{\mathcal{U}}$ corresponds to $(\mathrm{It}(\mathrm{Cr}_2))'$, etc. I expect that a systematic development of the ideas concerning transfinite types indicated in § 4 would comprehend all the facients considered by Neumer.†‡

* It should be remarked that the domains of definable $\mathfrak{W}$ provably satisfying (b) (i)-(iv) are the same as the types of provably definable well-orderings R in ω, by $R = \bigcup [x| (\exists \alpha)\mathfrak{W}(\alpha, x)]$.

† I was not acquainted with Neumer's work at the time of my talk on §§ 1–4 at the conference. I wish to thank H. Levitz for bringing it to my attention.

‡ More recently, and independently, iterations of functionals of type 2 were used to analyze the ordinals of the Veblen–Schütte system [11] by Levitz [8] and Page (dissertation, Oxford). Using the footnote of p. 000 this jibes with the bounds involving $\varphi_{\alpha+\Omega^\xi}$ conjectured in § 3.

REFERENCES

[1] H. Bachmann, Die Normalfunktionen und das Problem der ausgezeichneten Folgen von Ordnungszahlen, *Vierteljahrschr. Naturf. Ges. Zurich* **95** (1950) 115–147.

[2] A. Church, Alternatives to Zermelo's assumption, *Trans. Am. Math. Soc.* **29** (1927) 178–208.

[3] S. Feferman, Systems of predicative analysis II: representations of ordinals, *J. Symb. Logic.* **33** (1968) 193–220.

[4] S. Feferman, Ordinals associated with theories for one inductively defined set, (mimeographed).

[5] H. Friedman, *Subsystems of set theory and analysis*, dissertation, M.I.T. (1967).

[6] D. Isles, Regular ordinals and normal forms, these proceedings 339–361.

[7] G. Kreisel, Church's thesis: a kind of reducibility axiom for constructive mathematics, these proceedings 121–149.

[8] H. Levitz, *On the ordinal notations of Schütte and the ordinal diagrams of Takeuti*, dissertation, Pennsylvania State University (1965).

[9] A. Lévy, Independence results in set theory by Cohen's method I, *Notices Am. Math. Soc.* **10** (1963) 592.

[10] W. Neumer, Algorithmen für Ordnungszahlen und Normalfunktionen, Part I, *Z. f. math. Logik u. Grundl. Math.* **3** (1957) 108–150; Part II, *ibid.* **6** (1960) 1–65.

[11] K. Schütte, Kennzeichnungen von Ordnungszahlen durch rekursiv erklärte Funktionen, *Math. Ann.* **127** (1954) 15–32.

[12] G. Takeuti, Ordinal diagrams, Part I, *J. Math. Soc. Japan* **9** (1957) 386–394, Part II, *ibid.* **12** (1960) 385–391.

FORMAL THEORIES FOR TRANSFINITE ITERATIONS OF GENERALIZED INDUCTIVE DEFINITIONS AND SOME SUBSYSTEMS OF ANALYSIS

SOLOMON FEFERMAN*

Summary. The first order systems ID_ν (for ordinals ν given by primitive recursive well-orderings $\prec$), described fully in § 1, express roughly speaking that a familiar principle for defining specific sets of natural numbers can be iterated ν times. Kleene's definition of O is a typical instance of ID_1. Such systems were first studied by Kreisel in **[6]**, where the principle was referred to as that of *generalized inductive definitions* (g.i.d.). More precise information on background is given in § 2.1 below, after the various systems considered have been described in detail. $\mathrm{ID}_{<\nu}$ is essentially $\bigcup_{\alpha<\nu} \mathrm{ID}_\alpha$.

The systems $(\Pi^1_1\text{-CA})_{<\nu}$ in the language of classical analysis (containing variables for sets of natural numbers) express roughly, that there are hierarchies obtained by iterating the hyperjump operation any number less than ν times. Such systems were first studied by Friedman **[4]**.

Let (BI) (in the language of analysis) denote the familiar principle of bar induction, that is the equivalence of two senses of well-foundedness of primitive recursive orderings.

The principal results of the present paper (§ 3) establish a strong form of 'proof-theoretical equivalence', called ω, *T-equivalence*, between the following systems:

(3.1.4) *For* $\nu = \omega^{\gamma+1}$, $\nu < \varepsilon_0$, $(\Pi^1_1-\mathrm{CA})_{<\nu}+(\mathrm{BI})$ *is* ω,*T-equivalent to* ID_ν.

(3.1.7) *For* $\nu = \omega^\gamma$, *with* γ *a limit number and* $\nu \leqslant \varepsilon_0$, $(\Pi^1_1\text{-CA})_{<\nu}+(\mathrm{BI})$, $(\Pi^1_1\text{-CA})_{<\nu}$ *and* $\mathrm{ID}_{<\nu}$ *are all* ω,*T-equivalent.*

* Research supported by grants DA-ARO(D)-31-124-G985 and NSF-GP-8764. A preliminary version of this paper was presented to this conference under the title 'Note I: GID_ω and the Π^1_1-comprehension axiom' of 'Two notes on theories GID_ν given by ν iterations of generalized inductive definitions.' (The version printed here does not include all the material presented at the conference. The rest is contained in [2]. *Eds.*)

ω,T-equivalence and a slightly weaker relation $\equiv$ are explained in § 1.5; when $S \equiv S'$, (there is a finitist proof that) S, S' have the same arithmetic theorems and, in a suitable sense, the same Π^1_1-theorems.

The following corollaries establish relations with more familiar subsystems of classical analysis:

(2.2.1) *For* $\nu = \omega$, $(\Pi^1_1\text{–CA})+(\text{BI})$ *is ω,T-equivalent to* ID_ν.

(3.2.2) *For* $\nu = \omega^\omega$, $(\Delta^1_2\text{–CR})$ *is ω,T-equivalent to* $\text{ID}_{<\nu}$.

(3.1.9) *For* $\nu = \varepsilon_0$, $(\Delta^1_2\text{–CA}) \equiv \text{ID}_{<\nu}$.

In fact, the argument for the first of these is the basis for the more general theorems above. In turn, it extends arguments in § 2.1 for related results concerning ID_1 and systems $(\Pi^1_1\text{-CA})^-$ and $(\text{BI})^-$ without set parameters. The theorems of § 3 were developed from these in collaboration with H. Friedman.

The significance of these results for constructive foundations of analysis is considered in § 4 and for the work of Tait **[12]** and Takeuti **[15]** in § 5.

§ 1. Preliminaries

1.1. Languages used. All the languages considered are sublanguages of a 2nd order language $\mathscr{L}_2(P_0, P_1, \ldots)$ where $P_0, P_1, \ldots$ are 2nd order (set) constants. The 1st order vocabulary has the (numerical) variables $x, y, z, \ldots$, the constant 0, and a symbol for each primitive recursive function; the $(n+1)$st numeral $0\overset{\prime\ldots\prime}{\underset{n}{}}$ is denoted by $\bar{n}$. $\mathrm{t}, \mathrm{t}_1, \ldots$ range over terms; the atomic formulas are $(\mathrm{t}_1 = \mathrm{t}_2)$ and $(\mathrm{t} \in P_i)$. The full language has in addition the 2nd order (set) variables $X, Y, Z, \ldots$ and atomic formulas of the form $(\mathrm{t} \in X)$. With any finite or infinite sequence $\langle k_i \rangle_{i<m}$ is associated the sublanguage $\mathscr{L}_2(P_{k_0}, P_{k_1}, \ldots)$ having only the P_{k_i} as set constants; this is written $\mathscr{L}_2$ when $m = 0$. $\mathscr{L}_1(P_{k_0}, P_{k_1}, \ldots)$ (or simply $\mathscr{L}_1$ when $m = 0$) is the sublanguage with no set variables.

Let $\mathscr{L}$ be any sublanguage of $\mathscr{L}_2(P_0, P_1, \ldots)$. All theories T in $\mathscr{L}$ will be assumed to contain the axioms and rules of classical two-sorted predicate calculus, with equality axioms in the 1st sort. When $\mathscr{L}$ is contained in $\mathscr{L}_1(P_0, P_1, \ldots)$, this is just the usual 1st order logic. In this case the P_i can be treated as predicate constants and we may write $P_i(\mathrm{t})$ instead of $(\mathrm{t} \in P_i)$. In addition, for any $\mathscr{L}$ it will be assumed that T contains all axioms of elementary number theory Z in $\mathscr{L}$, i.e. the usual axioms for

0, ′, and the defining equations for the primitive recursive functions, together with all instances of induction:

$$\mathfrak{F}(0) \wedge \bigwedge x[\mathfrak{F}(x) \to \mathfrak{F}(x')] \to \bigwedge x\mathfrak{F}(x),$$

where $\mathfrak{F}$ is any formula of $\mathscr{L}$.

By the (set) *parameters* of a formula we mean its free (set) variables. An *arithmetic formula* is one without set quantifiers or set constants; it may contain set parameters. $\mathfrak{A}$, $\mathfrak{B}$ range over arithmetic formulas. An arithmetical formula in which all quantifiers are bounded is said to be *elementary*. $\mathfrak{R}$ ranges over the elementary formulas; these include only formulas corresponding to relations primitive recursive in their parameters. The usual notations of recursion theory are used both formally and informally. $\langle x, y\rangle$ is written for $2^x \cdot 3^y$, and $x \in X_y$ for $\langle x, y\rangle \in X$.

For any formulas $\mathfrak{F}(X)$ and $\mathfrak{G}(x)$ (perhaps with other free variables), $\mathfrak{F}(\hat{x}\mathfrak{G}(x))$, or simply $\mathfrak{F}(\mathfrak{G})$, denotes the result of substituting $\mathfrak{G}(\mathrm{t})$ for each occurrence $(\mathrm{t} \in X)$ in $\mathfrak{F}$. Functions are identified with sets X such that $\bigwedge x \bigvee ! y\langle x, y\rangle \in X$; α, β range over functions. Thus $\alpha(\mathrm{t}_1)$ occurs in a formula only in contexts $\alpha(\mathrm{t}_1) = \mathrm{t}_2$, i.e. $\langle \mathrm{t}_1, \mathrm{t}_2\rangle \in \alpha$. Given $\mathfrak{F}(\alpha)$ and $\mathfrak{G}(x, y)$ where $\bigwedge x \bigvee ! y\mathfrak{G}(x, y)$ has been proved, $\mathfrak{F}(\lambda x\mathfrak{G}(x, -))$ denotes the result of substituting $\mathfrak{G}(\mathrm{t}_1, \mathrm{t}_2)$ for each occurrence $\alpha(\mathrm{t}_1) = \mathrm{t}_2$ in $\mathfrak{F}$. The notations $\mathfrak{F}(\bar{\alpha}(x))$ and $\mathfrak{F}(\overline{\mathfrak{G}}(x, -))$ are explained in terms of these.

The *well-foundedness* of a relation $Q(x, y)$ is expressed by the formula WF(Q): $\bigwedge \alpha \bigvee x \sim Q(\alpha(x+1), \alpha(x))$. The principle of transfinite induction w.r. to Q in $\mathscr{L}$ is the schema

$$\mathrm{TI}(Q, \mathfrak{F})\colon \bigwedge x\{\bigwedge y[Q(y, x) \to \mathfrak{F}(y)] \to \mathfrak{F}(x)\} \to \bigwedge x\mathfrak{F}(x)$$

where $\mathfrak{F}$ is any formula of $\mathscr{L}$. When $Q(x, y)$ is written $(x \prec y)$ these are written WF($\prec$) and TI($\prec$, $\mathfrak{F}$). Let $\prec_{\varepsilon_0}$ be the natural ordering of order-type ε_0 in ω. For each $\nu < \varepsilon_0$, let $\prec_\nu$ be the initial segment of $\prec_{\varepsilon_0}$ with $|\prec_\nu| = \nu$. All instances of TI($\prec_\nu$, $\mathfrak{F}$) in $\mathscr{L}$ are derivable from Z in $\mathscr{L}$ by **[11]** pp. 201–211.

1.2. ID$_1$. Let $\mathfrak{A}_0, \mathfrak{A}_1, \ldots$ be an enumeration of all arithmetic formulas $\mathfrak{A}(X, x)$ of $\mathscr{L}_2$ containing at most X, x free, and such that each occurrence $(\mathrm{t} \in X)$ in $\mathfrak{A}$ is positive. For each $\mathfrak{A} = \mathfrak{A}_i$ write $P_{\mathfrak{A}}$ for P_i. Let $\mathscr{L}$ be a sublanguage of $\mathscr{L}_1(P_0, P_1, \ldots)$ containing $P_{\mathfrak{A}}$. The axioms of ID$_1(\mathfrak{A})$ in $\mathscr{L}$ (in addition to those mentioned in 1.1) are

(1.2.1)(i). $\bigwedge x[\mathfrak{A}(P_{\mathfrak{A}}, x) \to P_{\mathfrak{A}}(x)]$,

and

(ii). $\bigwedge x[\mathfrak{A}(\mathfrak{B}, x) \to \mathfrak{B}(x)] \to \bigwedge x[P_{\mathfrak{A}}(x) \to \mathfrak{B}(x)]$,

for each formula $\mathfrak{B}$ of $\mathscr{L}$. ID_1 is the union of $\mathrm{ID}_1(\mathfrak{A}_i)$ in $\mathscr{L}_1(P_0, P_1, \ldots)$. Unless otherwise indicated, any one $\mathrm{ID}_1(\mathfrak{A})$ is always taken in $\mathscr{L}_1(P_{\mathfrak{A}})$.

Consider any $\mathfrak{A} = \mathfrak{A}_i$. A set X is called $\mathfrak{A}$-*closed* if $\bigwedge x[\mathfrak{A}(X, x) \to x \in X]$. The positivity condition on $\mathfrak{A}$ ensures the *monotonicity condition*

(1.2.2) $X \subseteq Y \to \bigwedge x[\mathfrak{A}(X, x) \to \mathfrak{A}(Y, x)]$.

(Here and below, $X \subseteq Y$ abbreviates $\bigwedge x[x \in X \to x \in Y]$ and $X = Y$ abbreviates $\bigwedge x[x \in X \leftrightarrow x \in Y]$.) Monotonicity in turn ensures in set theory that there is a least $\mathfrak{A}$-closed set. In other words a model for $\mathrm{ID}_1(\mathfrak{A})$ (in any $\mathscr{L}$) is obtained by defining

(1.2.3) $P_{\mathfrak{A}}(x) \leftrightarrow \bigwedge X\{\bigwedge y[\mathfrak{A}(X, y) \to y \in X] \to x \in X\}$,

where X ranges over arbitrary sets.

Thus (1.2.1i) expresses the existence of an $\mathfrak{A}$-closed set $P_{\mathfrak{A}}$ and (1.2.1ii) expresses that $P_{\mathfrak{A}}$ is least among the $\mathfrak{A}$-closed sets defined by formulas $\mathfrak{B}$ of $\mathscr{L}$. (i) is also often called the *inductive definition of* $P_{\mathfrak{A}}$ and (ii) the associated principle of *proof by induction on* $P_{\mathfrak{A}}$.

An important example of an $\mathrm{ID}_1(\mathfrak{A})$ is provided by the inductive definition of the *accessible part* of a relation $\prec$, taking $\mathfrak{A}(X, x)$ to be $\bigwedge y[y \prec x \to y \in X]$. Set theoretically, the least $\mathfrak{A}$-closed set is seen to be the same as $\{x\colon \prec \restriction x \text{ is well-founded}\}$. In this case (1.2.1)(ii) is just $\mathrm{TI}(\prec^*, \mathfrak{B})$ where $\prec^*$ is the restriction of $\prec$ to its accessible part. O can be defined to be the accessible part of a rec. enum. $\prec$. A closely related inductive definition of a set T of recursive trees (in 1.4) will be used extensively throughout the paper.

For each $\mathfrak{A} = \mathfrak{A}_i$, the monotonicity condition is logically derivable. Equivalently,

(1.2.4) $\bigwedge y[P(y) \to P'(y)] \to \bigwedge x[\mathfrak{A}(P, x) \to \mathfrak{A}(P', x)]$

is derivable in $\mathscr{L}_1(P, P')$. Kreisel has remarked ([7], p. 138) that conversely any $\mathfrak{A}$ for which this holds is equivalent to one of the $\mathfrak{A}_i$. This extends also to the case that (1.2.4) is derivable from axioms of the form $S(P) \cup S(P')$ where $S(P)$ consists of sentences $\mathfrak{B}(P)$ in $\mathscr{L}_1(P)$. For then there are $\mathfrak{B}_i(P)$ in $S(P)$, $i = 1, \ldots, m$ such that

$$\vdash \bigwedge y[P(y) \to P'(y)] \wedge \prod_{i=1}^{m} \mathfrak{B}_i(P) \wedge \mathfrak{A}(P, x) \to [\prod_{i=1}^{m} \mathfrak{B}_i(P') \to \mathfrak{A}(P', x)].$$

Hence by Lyndon's interpolation theorem **[10]**, we can find a formula $\mathfrak{A}_1(P', x)$ such that P' is positive at all occurrences in $\mathfrak{A}_1$ and such that

$$\vdash \bigwedge y[P(y) \to P'(y)] \wedge \prod_{i=1}^{m} \mathfrak{B}_i(P) \wedge \mathfrak{A}(P, x) \to \mathfrak{A}_1(P', x),$$

and

$$\vdash \mathfrak{A}_1(P', x) \to [\prod_{i=1}^{m} \mathfrak{B}_i(P') \to \mathfrak{A}(P', x)].$$

Hence $S(P) \vdash [\mathfrak{A}(P, x) \leftrightarrow \mathfrak{A}_1(P', x)]$.

1.3. $\mathrm{ID}_{\prec}$, ID_{ν} and $\mathrm{ID}_{<\nu}$. We now consider theories for iterations of inductive definitions relative to any given prim. rec. well-ordering $\prec$. In this section, let $\mathfrak{A}_0, \mathfrak{A}_1, \ldots$ be an enumeration of all arithmetic $\mathfrak{A}(X, Y, x, y)$ in $\mathscr{L}_2$ containing at most X, Y, x, y free, and such that each occurrence $(t \in X)$ in $\mathfrak{A}$ is positive. For each $\mathfrak{A} = \mathfrak{A}_i$ write $P^{\mathfrak{A}}$ for P_i. Now write $P^{\mathfrak{A}}_y(x)$ for $\langle x, y\rangle \in P^{\mathfrak{A}}$. Let $\mathscr{L}$ be a sublanguage of $\mathscr{L}_1(P_0, P_1, \ldots)$ containing $P^{\mathfrak{A}}$. The axioms of $\mathrm{ID}_{\prec}(\mathfrak{A})$ in $\mathscr{L}$ are

(1.3.1)(i). $\bigwedge x, y[\mathfrak{A}(P^{\mathfrak{A}}_y, \hat{z}((z)_1 \prec y \wedge P^{\mathfrak{A}}_{(z)_1}((z)_0), x, y) \to P^{\mathfrak{A}}_y(x)]$,

(ii). $\bigwedge y\{\bigwedge x[\mathfrak{A}(\mathfrak{B}, \hat{z}((z)_1 \prec y \wedge P^{\mathfrak{A}}_{(z)_1}((z)_0), x, y) \to \mathfrak{B}(x)] \to \bigwedge x[P^{\mathfrak{A}}_y(x) \to \mathfrak{B}(x)]\}$,

and

(iii). $\mathrm{TI}(\prec, \mathfrak{B})$,

for each $\mathfrak{B}$ in $\mathscr{L}$. $\mathrm{ID}_{\prec}$ is the union of $\mathrm{ID}_{\prec}(\mathfrak{A}_i)$ in $\mathscr{L}_1(P_0, P_1, \ldots)$. Unless otherwise noted, any one $\mathrm{ID}_{\prec}(\mathfrak{A})$ is taken to be in $\mathscr{L}_1(P_{\mathfrak{A}})$.

Given $\mathfrak{A} = \mathfrak{A}_i$, a model for $\mathrm{ID}_{\prec}(\mathfrak{A})$ in any $\mathscr{L}$ is set theoretically defined by the following transfinite recursion on $\prec$

(1.3.2) $P^{\mathfrak{A}}_y(x) \leftrightarrow \bigwedge X\{\bigwedge u[\mathfrak{A}(X, \hat{z}((z)_1 \prec y \wedge P^{\mathfrak{A}}_{(z)_1}((z)_0), u, y) \to u \in X] \to x \in X\}$.

Now the positivity of X in $\mathfrak{A}(X, Y, x, y)$ ensures that for each y, $P^{\mathfrak{A}}_y$ is the least set satisfying the closure condition $\bigwedge u[\ldots]$.

A variant of the preceding definition of $\mathrm{ID}_{\prec}$ applies to any prim. rec. relation $\prec$, giving theories for iterations of inductive definitions along its accessible part $\prec^*$. This is obtained by replacing $\prec$ by $\prec^*$ in (1.3.1i, ii) and by changing (1.3.1iii) to the axioms of ID_1 for the accessible part of $\prec$.

When $1 \leqslant \nu < \varepsilon_0$ and $\prec$ is $\prec_\nu$ we shall write $ID_\nu(\mathfrak{A})$, ID_ν for $ID_\prec(\mathfrak{A})$ and $ID_\prec$, resp. As noted in § 1.1, we can omit (1.3.1iii) in these cases. The results stated in this paper will concern various ID_ν; many of these can be generalized to arbitrary $ID_\prec$. The restricted formulations are taken for simplicity and because they suffice for the known applications of interest.

For $2 \leqslant \nu < \varepsilon_0$, $\mathfrak{A} = \mathfrak{A}_i$ and $\mathscr{L}$ containing $P^{\mathfrak{A}}$, we define $ID_{<\nu}(\mathfrak{A})$ in $\mathscr{L}$ to be the union of $ID_\mu(\mathfrak{A})$ in $\mathscr{L}$ for $1 \leqslant \mu < \nu$.* This is contained in $ID_\nu(\mathfrak{A})$ but may be weaker since we only have (1.3.1i, ii) for each section $\prec_\mu$ of $\prec_\nu$. We take $ID_{<\nu}$ to be the union of all $ID_{<\nu}(\mathfrak{A})$ in $\mathscr{L}_1(P_0, P_1, \ldots)$.

1.4. T_ν. The inductively defined sets T_ν to be discussed now play a central role in the reduction of certain subsystems of analysis to ID_ν. It also follows from these results that ID_ν can be reduced to $ID_\nu(\mathfrak{A})$, where $\mathfrak{A}$ determines the closure conditions for $\langle T_{1+\mu}\rangle_{\mu<\nu}$. T_1 is the set T of Gödel-numbers for the well-founded recursive trees. The set $O_1 = O$ and the higher constructive number classes O_ν could serve the same purposes; the T_ν have some technical advantages here.

Throughout the following, s, s_1 range over sequence numbers. $s_1 \subset s$ if s_1 represents a proper initial segment of s; $\langle\ \rangle$ is the number of the empty sequence. For any set Y, T^Y is defined to be the set of all e such that (i) $\{e\}^Y$ is total, (ii) $\bigwedge \alpha \bigvee y \{e\}^Y(\bar{\alpha}(y)) \neq 0$, and (iii) $\bigwedge s, s_1 [s_1 \subset s \wedge \{e\}^Y(s) = 0 \to \{e\}^Y(s_1) = 0]$. The branches of the tree determined by e are the (sequences represented by) sequence numbers s with $\{e\}^Y(s) = 0$. The tree may be empty. For $e \in T^Y$ take $|e|$ to be the ordinal of the associated tree.

The main result about T^Y is that it is complete for the predicates Π^1_1 in Y. This is by the standard unsecured-sequences argument: Given $R(s)$ with set parameter Y, associate a total $\{u_R\}^Y$ with

$$\{u_R\}^Y(s) = 0 \leftrightarrow \bigwedge s_1 [s_1 \subset s \to \sim R(s_1)].$$

Then $\bigwedge \alpha \bigvee y R(\bar{\alpha}(y)) \leftrightarrow u_R \in T^Y$. The set theoretical assumptions in this argument are examined formally in § 2.1 below.

Let S be a prim. rec. function such that for any Y, e, s_1 and s, $\{S(e, s_1)\}^Y(s) \simeq \{e\}^Y(s_1 * s)$. We write $e \restriction s_1$ for $S(e, s_1)$ and $e \restriction \langle n\rangle$ for $e \restriction 2^{n+1}$. When $e \in T^Y$, $e \restriction s_1$ is a number for the subtree below s_1. The

* One could consider more generally $ID_{<\nu}(\langle\mathfrak{A}_{i_\mu}\rangle_{1 \leqslant \mu < \nu})$; this would require assignment of distinct symbols $P^{\mathfrak{A}_{i_\mu}, \mu}$ to distinct μ.

following holds for any x, Y:

(1.4.1) T^Y *is the least set* X *satisfying* $\bigwedge x[\mathfrak{A}_T(X, Y, x) \to x \in X]$, *where* $\mathfrak{A}_T(X, Y, x)$ *is* $\bigwedge z \bigvee w(\{x\}^Y(z) \simeq w) \wedge [\bigwedge s(\{x\}^Y(s) \neq 0) \vee \bigwedge u(x \restriction \langle u \rangle \in X)]$.

The proof that T^Y satisfies the closure condition is direct by definition. For X satisfying the condition, $[e \in T^Y \to e \in X]$ is proved by induction on $|e|$.

Let $T_0 = \emptyset$ and $T_{n+1} = T^{T_n}$ for $n < \omega$. This is extended to a definition of T_ν for $\nu < \varepsilon_0$ by working with $\prec = \prec_{\varepsilon_0}$. We can assume that $\prec$ has field ω, 0 is the least element in this ordering, and that the successor $b \oplus 1$ of each element b is 2^b. Let Lim (b) hold if b is a limit element, i.e. $b \neq 0$, $b \neq (b)_0 \oplus 1$. T_b is defined by recursion on b as follows:

(1.4.2)(i). $T_b = \emptyset$ for $b = 0$,

(ii). $T_b = T^{T(b)_0}$ for $b = (b)_0 \oplus 1$, and

(iii). $x \in T_b \leftrightarrow (x)_1 \prec b \wedge (x)_0 \in T_{(x)_1}$, for Lim (b).

We also write T_ν for T_b when $|b| = \nu$ in the ordinary $\prec$; in this sense, T_n is the same as above.

Let $1 \leqslant \nu < \varepsilon_0$, $|a| = \nu$. Take $\mathfrak{A}_\nu(X, Y, x, y)$ to be the formula

$$y \prec \bar{a} \wedge \{[y = (y)_0 \oplus 1 \wedge \mathfrak{A}_T(X, Y_{(y)_0}x, y)] \vee [\mathrm{Lim}\,(y) \wedge (x)_1 \prec y \wedge (x)_0 \in Y_{(x)_1}]\}.$$

X is positive in $\mathfrak{A}_\nu$. By (1.4.1, 2), the model for $\mathrm{ID}_\nu(\mathfrak{A}_\nu)$ given by (1.3.2) has

$$P_y^{\mathfrak{A}_\nu}(x) \leftrightarrow y \prec a \wedge x \in T_y.$$

We shall write ID_{T_ν} for $\mathrm{ID}_{1+\nu}(\mathfrak{A}_{1+\nu})$ and $T_y(x)$ for $P_y^{\mathfrak{A}_{1+\nu}}(x)$ in the theory. Also, $\mathrm{ID}_{T,<\nu}$ is written for $\mathrm{ID}_{<(1+\nu)}(\mathfrak{A}_{1+\nu})$.

1.5. ***ω, T*-models.** We shall consider relationships between certain subsystems of analysis and systems ID_ν and ID_{T_ν}. The latter always contain ID_{T_1}. We can identify this with $\mathrm{ID}_1(\mathfrak{A}_T)$ where $\mathfrak{A}_T(X, x)$ is $\mathfrak{A}_T(X, \emptyset, x)$ of (1.4.1). In this case we write ID_T for ID_{T_1} and $T(x)$ for $P_{\mathfrak{A}_T}(x)$. The set theoretical definition (1.2.3) of a model of ID_T is expressed by a formula of $\mathscr{L}_2$, namely

(1.5.1) $\bigwedge X\{\bigwedge y[\mathfrak{A}_T(X, y) \to y \in X] \to x \in X\}$;

this formula is also denoted by $T(x)$.

Suppose S, S' are sets of axioms in $\mathscr{L}$, $\mathscr{L}'$ resp., where $\mathscr{L}$, $\mathscr{L}'$ are sublanguages of $\mathscr{L}_2(P_0, P_1, \ldots)$. A relative interpretation of S in S' ([**16**], pp. 20–21, 29) or uniform S'-model of S ([**8**], p. 364) assigns to each symbol of $\mathscr{L}$ a definition in $\mathscr{L}'$ and to each sort of variable in $\mathscr{L}$ a range of variation given by a formula of $\mathscr{L}'$, such that the translation $\mathfrak{F}'$ of each $\mathfrak{F}$ in S is provable in S'. By an *ω-model of S in S'* we mean a uniform S'-model of S which leaves the symbols and range of variables of $\mathscr{L}_1$ fixed.

Let S_1 be a set of axioms in $\mathscr{L} = \mathscr{L}_1(P_{k_0}, P_{k_1}, \ldots)$ and S_2 a set of axioms in $\mathscr{L}_2$. An *ω, T-model of S_1 in S_2* is an ω-model for which the translation $(T(x))'$ is provably equivalent to $T(x)$ in S_2. An ω, T-model of S_2 in S_1 is an ω-model for which the translation $(T(x))'$ of (1.5.1) is provably equivalent to $T(x)$ in S_1. In this case $(T(x))'$ has the form

$$\bigwedge z\{\mathfrak{M}(z) \wedge \bigwedge y[\mathfrak{A}'_T(z, y) \rightarrow y \in' z] \rightarrow x \in' z\},$$

where $(y \in' z)$ is the formula defining $(y \in z)$ in $\mathscr{L}$ and $\mathfrak{M}(z)$ is the formula of $\mathscr{L}$ giving the range of variation of the 2nd order variables.

A theory S is said to be *ω, T-reducible* to a theory S' if every finite subsystem of S has an ω, T-model in S'. S and S' are said to be *ω, T-equivalent* if each is ω, T-reducible to the other. In every case in the following where it is asserted that a theory S has an ω, T-model in a theory S', or is ω, T-reducible to S', we have a finitist proof of this fact. It follows that S is proof theoretically reducible to S' in the following strong sense: we have a finitist proof of the fact that every sentence provable in S, which is arithmetic in the formula $T(x)$, is provable in S'. We write $S \leqslant S'$ when this is established; trivially, $S \leqslant S'$ implies that S is consistent relative to S'. We write $S \equiv S'$ if $S \leqslant S'$ and $S' \leqslant S$.

1.6. Some subsystems of analysis. Let $\mathscr{F}$ be any collection of formulas $\mathfrak{F}(x)$ of $\mathscr{L}_2$ (parameters permitted). The *$\mathscr{F}$-comprehension axiom schema* ($\mathscr{F}$-CA) consists of (the universal closures of) all formulas

(1.6.1) $\bigvee X \bigwedge x[x \in X \leftrightarrow \mathfrak{F}(x)]$,

where $\mathfrak{F}(x)$ is in $\mathscr{F}$ and X is not free in $\mathfrak{F}(x)$. $(\mathfrak{F}\text{–CA})^-$ is $(\mathfrak{F}^-\text{–CA})$, where $\mathfrak{F}^-$ consists of the formulas in $\mathfrak{F}$ without set parameters. The *$\mathfrak{F}$-axiom of choice schema* ($\mathfrak{F}$–AC) and its restriction $(\mathfrak{F}\text{–AC})^-$ are obtained similarly from (AC_{01}) of [**8**], p. 326, when $\mathfrak{F}$ consists of formulas $\mathfrak{F}(x, \alpha)$.

Let $\Pi^0_0 = \Sigma^0_0$ be the collection of elementary formulas $\mathfrak{R}(x)$. All the systems in $\mathscr{L}_2$ considered here are assumed to contain (Π^0_0–CA). Each system is named by its corresponding additional axioms. $(\Pi^0_\infty\text{–CA}) = (\Sigma^0_\infty\text{–CA})$ is derivable (over $(\Pi^0_0\text{–CA})$) from the instance

$$\bigvee X \bigwedge x[x \in X \leftrightarrow \bigwedge y(\langle x, y\rangle \in Y)]$$

of $(\Pi^0_1\text{–CA})$. $(\Pi^1_1\text{–CA})^-$ has the additional axioms $\bigvee X \bigwedge x[x \in X \leftrightarrow \bigwedge \alpha \bigvee y \mathfrak{R}(x, \bar{\alpha}(y))]$, where $\mathfrak{R}$ contains no set parameters. $(\Pi^1_1\text{–CA})$ can be taken to consist of all sentences

$$\bigwedge \beta \bigvee X \bigwedge x[x \in X \leftrightarrow \bigwedge \alpha \bigvee y \mathfrak{R}(x, \bar{\alpha}(y), \bar{\beta}(y))].$$

$(\Pi^0_1\text{–CA})$ is derivable in $(\Pi^1_1\text{–CA})$. The systems $(\Pi^1_1\text{–CA})_{<\nu}$ mentioned in the introduction will be defined in § 3 below.

The (classical version of the) system (BI) of bar induction is given by the additional axioms

(1.6.2) $\mathrm{WF}(\mathfrak{R}) \to \mathrm{TI}(\mathfrak{R}, \mathfrak{F})$.

$(\mathrm{BI})^-$ denotes the restriction to the case that $\mathfrak{R}$ contains no set parameters, but where no restriction is made on $\mathfrak{F}$.

LEMMA 1.6.3. $[\bigwedge X \mathfrak{A}(X) \to \mathfrak{A}(\mathfrak{F})]$ *is provable in* $(\Pi^0_\infty\text{–CA})+(\mathrm{BI})$; *it is provable in* $(\Pi^0_\infty\text{–CA})+(\mathrm{BI})^-$ *when* $\bigwedge X \mathfrak{A}(X)$ *contains no set parameters.*

PROOF. The standard reduction of $\mathfrak{A}(X)$ to Π^1_1-normal form associates an $\mathfrak{R}(X, s)$ such that

$$(\Pi^0_\infty\text{–CA}) \vdash [\mathfrak{A}(X) \leftrightarrow \bigwedge \beta \bigvee x \mathfrak{R}(X, \bar{\beta}(x))]. \tag{1}$$

This is done in such a way that with each $\mathfrak{F}$ is associated a $\mathfrak{G}$ s.t.

$$\vdash \bigwedge x \bigvee ! y \mathfrak{G}(x, y) \wedge [\bigvee x \mathfrak{R}(\mathfrak{F}, \overline{\mathfrak{G}}(x, -)) \to \mathfrak{A}(\mathfrak{F})]. \tag{2}$$

For example, suppose $\mathfrak{A}(X)$ has the form $\bigvee x \bigwedge y \mathfrak{R}(X, x, y)$. This is equivalent to $\bigwedge \beta \bigvee x \mathfrak{R}(X, x, \beta(x))$; moreover, $[\bigvee x \mathfrak{R}(X, x, \beta_0(x)) \to \bigvee x \bigwedge y \mathfrak{R}(X, x, y)]$ for the function $\beta_0(x) = (\mu y) \sim \mathfrak{R}(X, x, y)$. In this case take $\mathfrak{G}(x, y)$ to be the formula

$$[\sim \mathfrak{R}(\mathfrak{F}, x, y) \wedge \bigwedge z < y \mathfrak{R}(\mathfrak{F}, x, z)] \vee [\bigwedge z \mathfrak{R}(\mathfrak{F}, x, z) \wedge y = 0].$$

$$(\mathrm{BI}) \vdash \bigwedge X \bigwedge \beta \bigvee x \mathfrak{R}(X, \bar{\beta}(x)) \to \bigvee x \mathfrak{R}(\mathfrak{F}, \overline{\mathfrak{G}}(x, -)). \tag{3}$$

More generally, for any $\mathfrak{R}(s)$ and $\mathfrak{G}$ such that $\bigwedge x \bigvee ! y \mathfrak{G}(x, y)$ has been proved we have

$$(\mathrm{BI}) \vdash \bigwedge \alpha \bigvee x \mathfrak{R}(\bar{\alpha}(x)) \to \bigvee x \mathfrak{R}(\overline{\mathfrak{G}}(x, -)). \tag{4}$$

This follows from $[\mathrm{WF}(\mathfrak{R}_1) \to \mathrm{TI}(\mathfrak{R}_1, \mathfrak{G}_1)]$ where $\mathfrak{R}_1(s, s')$ is

$$[\mathrm{Seq}(s) \wedge \mathrm{Seq}(s') \wedge \bigwedge z < Lh(s) \sim \mathfrak{R}(s \upharpoonright z) \wedge (s' \subset s)],$$

and $\mathfrak{G}_1(s)$ is

$$[\mathrm{Seq}(s) \wedge \bigwedge z < Lh(s) \mathfrak{G}(z, (s)_z - 1) \to \bigvee x \mathfrak{R}(\overline{\mathfrak{G}}(x, -))].$$

§ 2. Relationships between ID_1, ID_ω and subsystems of $(\Pi^1_1\text{-CA})+(\mathrm{BI})$

2.1. Relationships between ID_1, $(\Pi^1_1\text{-CA})^-$ and $(\mathrm{BI})^-$. The following are the known results on these systems; they are due to Kreisel (proved or sketched in [**6**], [**7**] p. 137, and [**8**] § **10**):

(2.1.1)(i). $\mathrm{ID}_1 \equiv \mathrm{ID}_O$.

(ii). $(\mathrm{BI}) \leqslant (\mathrm{BI})^- \leqslant \mathrm{ID}_O \leqslant (\mathrm{BI})$.

(iii). ID_1 *has an* ω-*model in* $(\Pi^0_\infty\text{-CA})+(\Pi^1_1\text{-CA})^-$.

Actually, these are special cases of Kreisel's results principally concerning intuitionistic systems, which will be considered in § 4. In particular, the proof of (ii) depends essentially on the use of such systems.

Though the results (i), (ii) are sharp for ID_1, ID_O (or equivalently ID_T), $(\mathrm{BI})^-$ and (BI), they leave open the exact relationship between ID_1 and $\Pi^1_1\text{-CA}^-$. This is established by the following theorem. More importantly, the model-theoretical formulation and proof are the basis for the results below relating various ID_ν with subsystems of analysis.

THEOREM 2.1.2.

(i). ID_1 *has an* ω,T-*model in* $(\Pi^0_\infty\text{-CA})+(\mathrm{BI})^-$, *as well as in* $(\Pi^0_\infty\text{-CA})+(\Pi^1_1\text{-CA})^-$.

(ii). $(\Pi^1_1\text{-CA})^- + (\mathrm{BI})^-$ *has an* ω,T-*model in* ID_T.

PROOF. (i). The definitions of the ω-models of ID_1 are the same in both cases, but the proofs differ in the treatment of the principles of proof by induction. For each $P_{\mathfrak{A}}$ of ID_1, translate $P_{\mathfrak{A}}(x)$ by

$$P'_{\mathfrak{A}}(x) = \bigwedge X\{\bigwedge y[\mathfrak{A}(X, y) \to y \in X] \to x \in X\}. \tag{1}$$

This determines a translation of $\mathscr{L}_1(P_{\mathfrak{A}_0}, P_{\mathfrak{A}_1}, \ldots)$ in $\mathscr{L}_2$ preserving $\mathscr{L}_1$. The translation

$$\bigwedge x[\mathfrak{A}(P'_{\mathfrak{A}}, x) \to P'_{\mathfrak{A}}(x)] \tag{2}$$

of (1.2.1i) is logically valid and so holds for both systems. For, given any two formulas $\mathfrak{F}(x)$ and $\mathfrak{G}(x)$, the proof of monotonicity applies equally well to show

$$\vdash \bigwedge z[\mathfrak{F}(z) \to \mathfrak{G}(z)] \to \bigwedge x[\mathfrak{A}(\mathfrak{F}, x) \to \mathfrak{A}(\mathfrak{G}, x)].$$

It follows that

$$\vdash \bigwedge y[\mathfrak{A}(X, y) \to y \in X] \to \bigwedge x[\mathfrak{A}(P'_{\mathfrak{A}}, x) \to \mathfrak{A}(X, x)],$$

so that (2) is derivable.

The translation of (1.2.1ii) is

$$\bigwedge x[\mathfrak{A}(\mathfrak{B}', x) \to \mathfrak{B}'(x)] \to \bigwedge x[P'_{\mathfrak{A}}(x) \to \mathfrak{B}'(x)], \tag{3}$$

where

$$\mathfrak{B}'(x) = \mathfrak{B}(P'_{\mathfrak{A}_0}, \ldots, P'_{\mathfrak{A}_m}, x)$$

is the translation of

$$\mathfrak{B}(x) = \mathfrak{B}(P_{\mathfrak{A}_0}, \ldots, P_{\mathfrak{A}_m}, x).$$

First consider (3) in $(\Pi^1_1\text{-CA})^-$. For each i,

$$(\Pi^0_\infty\text{-CA})+(\Pi^1_1\text{-CA})^- \vdash \bigvee Y \bigwedge x[x \in Y \leftrightarrow P'_{\mathfrak{A}_i}(x)] \tag{4}$$

by reduction of (1) to Π^1_1 normal form. Then also

$$(\Pi^0_\infty\text{-CA})+(\Pi^1_1\text{-CA})^- \vdash \bigvee X \bigwedge x[x \in X \leftrightarrow \mathfrak{B}(P'_{\mathfrak{A}_0}, \ldots, P'_{\mathfrak{A}_m}, x)], \tag{5}$$

giving derivability of (3) in this case.

To obtain (3) for the case of $(\mathrm{BI})^-$, apply lemma 1.6.3, taking $P'_{\mathfrak{A}}(x)$ for the formula $\bigwedge X\mathfrak{A}(X)$:

$$(\Pi^0_\infty\text{-CA})+(\mathrm{BI})^- \vdash P'_{\mathfrak{A}}(x) \to \{\bigwedge y[\mathfrak{A}(\mathfrak{B}', y) \to \mathfrak{B}'(y)] \to \mathfrak{B}'(x)\}. \tag{6}$$

Let us now turn to the proof of part (ii). We formalize the proof of the basis result for Π^1_1 predicates: $\bigwedge \alpha \bigvee x\mathfrak{R}(\bar{\alpha}(x)) \leftrightarrow \bigwedge \alpha_M \bigvee x\mathfrak{R}(\bar{\alpha}(x))$, where M is the collection of sets recursive in T. Thus M is trivially an ω-model for $(\Pi^1_1\text{-CA})^-$. But also if $\mathrm{WF}(\mathfrak{R})$ is true in M then $\mathfrak{R}$ must actually be well-founded; hence $\mathrm{TI}(\mathfrak{R}, \mathfrak{F})$ will hold in M for any formula $\mathfrak{F}$. Since M is definable in ID_T it need only be verified that the formal principles of ID_T are sufficient to derive these facts.

Let $\mathfrak{M}(x)$ be the formula $\bigwedge y \bigvee z(\{x\}^T(y) \simeq z)$ of $\mathscr{L}_1(T)$ and $(y \in' x)$ the formula $(\{x\}^T(y) \simeq 0)$. The range of variation of the 2nd order variables of $\mathscr{L}_2$ under the translation is given by relativization to $\mathfrak{M}$. This and the formula $(y \in' x)$ determine a translation of $\mathscr{L}_2$ into $\mathscr{L}_1(T)$ preserving the symbols and variables of $\mathscr{L}_1$.

Given $\mathfrak{M}(x)$, the 2nd order definition of being a function is translated as $\bigwedge y \bigvee ! z(\{x\}^T(\langle y, z\rangle) \simeq 0)$. With each such x is associated x_1 with $\{x_1\}^T(y) \simeq (\mu z)(\{x\}^T(\langle y, z\rangle) \simeq 0)$, so $\mathfrak{M}(x_1)$. Conversely, every x_1 in $\mathfrak{M}$ can be found in this way from its graph x in $\mathfrak{M}$. Hence the translation of a formula $\bigwedge \alpha \bigvee y \mathfrak{R}(\bar{\alpha}(y))$ is equivalent to $\bigwedge x[\mathfrak{M}(x) \to \bigvee y \mathfrak{R}(\overline{\{x\}^T}(y))]$. The latter will be written $\bigwedge \alpha_{\mathfrak{M}} \bigvee y \mathfrak{R}(\bar{\alpha}(y))$ in $\mathscr{L}_1(T)$.

The main step is to formalize the unsecured-sequences argument for the Π_1^1-completeness of T; cf. § 1.4. Given $\mathfrak{R}(s)$ (which may contain numerical parameters) the number $u_{\mathfrak{R}}$ is associated (uniformly in the parameters) with $\{u_{\mathfrak{R}}\}$ total and $\{u_{\mathfrak{R}}\}(s) \simeq 0 \leftrightarrow \bigwedge s_1[s_1 \subset s \to \sim \mathfrak{R}(s_1)]$. Let

$$\mathrm{Sec}_{\mathfrak{R}}(s) = T(u_{\mathfrak{R}} \restriction s); \tag{7}$$

this expresses $\mathfrak{R}$-securability of s. With this identification, the inductive definition of $\mathfrak{R}$-securability:

$$[\mathfrak{R}(s) \wedge \bigwedge s_1[s_1 \subset s \to \sim \mathfrak{R}(s_1)] \vee \bigwedge y\, \mathrm{Sec}_{\mathfrak{R}}(s * \langle y\rangle)] \to \mathrm{Sec}_{\mathfrak{R}}(s), \tag{8}$$

and also proof by induction:

$$\{\bigwedge s[\mathfrak{R}(s) \wedge \bigwedge s_1[s_1 \subset s \to \sim \mathfrak{R}(s_1)] \vee \bigwedge y \mathfrak{B}(s * \langle y\rangle)] \to \mathfrak{B}(s)\} \to \bigwedge s[\mathrm{Sec}_{\mathfrak{R}}(s) \to \mathfrak{B}(s)], \tag{9}$$

are both derivable in ID_T. Applying (9) we get

$$\mathrm{ID}_T \vdash \mathrm{Sec}_{\mathfrak{R}}(s) \to \bigwedge \alpha_{\mathfrak{M}}[\bar{\alpha}(Lh(s)) = s \to \bigvee y \mathfrak{R}(\bar{\alpha}(y))]. \tag{10}$$

On the other hand, $\sim \mathrm{Sec}_{\mathfrak{R}}(s) \to \bigvee y \sim \mathrm{Sec}_{\mathfrak{R}}(s * \langle y\rangle)$. Thus if $\sim \mathrm{Sec}_{\mathfrak{R}}(s_1)$ we get α in $\mathfrak{M}$ with $\bigwedge y \sim \mathfrak{R}(\bar{\alpha}(y)$ and $\bar{\alpha}(Lh(s_1)) = s_1$, by

$$\alpha(x) = (\mu y) \sim \mathrm{Sec}_{\mathfrak{R}}(\bar{\alpha}(x) * \langle y\rangle) = (\mu y) \sim T(u_{\mathfrak{R}} \restriction (\bar{\alpha}(x) * \langle y\rangle))$$

for $x \geqslant Lh(s_1)$. Formally,

$$\mathrm{ID}_T \vdash \bigwedge \alpha_{\mathfrak{M}}[\bar{\alpha}(Lh(s)) = s \to \bigvee y \mathfrak{R}(\bar{\alpha}(y))] \to \mathrm{Sec}_{\mathfrak{R}}(s). \tag{11}$$

In particular, $\bigwedge \alpha_{\mathfrak{M}} \bigvee y \mathfrak{R}(\bar{\alpha}(y)) \to \bigwedge s\, \mathrm{Sec}_{\mathfrak{R}}(s)$. Thus the translation of $(\mathrm{BI})^-$ is provable in ID_T from (9) and (11). To obtain $(\Pi_1^1\text{-CA})^-$, consider $\bigwedge \alpha_{\mathfrak{M}} \bigvee y \mathfrak{R}(x, \bar{\alpha}(y))$; here $u_{\mathfrak{R}}$ depends on x, $u_{\mathfrak{R}} = f(x)$ with prim. rec. f. (7), (10) and (11) yield

$$\mathrm{ID}_T \vdash \bigwedge \alpha_{\mathfrak{M}} \bigvee y \mathfrak{R}(x, \bar{\alpha}(y)) \leftrightarrow T(f(x)). \tag{12}$$

This proves $\bigvee z_{\mathfrak{M}} \bigwedge x[x \in' z \leftrightarrow \bigwedge \alpha_{\mathfrak{M}} \bigvee y \mathfrak{R}(x, \bar{\alpha}(y))]$. The fact that this is a T-model also follows from (12).

It does not follow from these results that ID_1 has an ω, T-model in ID_T. The obstacle is that the relative arithmetic CA does not hold in $\mathfrak{M}$. However, we can modify the proof of theorem 2.1.2 to obtain the following.

THEOREM 2.1.3. ID_1 *is* ω, *T-reducible to* ID_T.

PROOF (sketch). Let S be the subsystem of $(\Pi^0_\infty\text{–CA})+(\Pi^1_1\text{–CA})^-$ consisting of all instances of

$$\bigvee X \bigwedge x[x \in X \leftrightarrow \mathfrak{F}(x)]$$

where $\mathfrak{F}$ has no set parameters and no nested 2nd-order quantifiers; in other words $\mathfrak{F}$ is arithmetical in some formulas of the form $\bigwedge Y \mathfrak{A}(Y)$. The proof of theorem 2.1.2i (esp. (1), (5)) also shows that ID_1 has an ω, T-model in S. It thus suffices to show that any finite subsystem S_1 of S has an ω, T-model in ID_T. This is obtained by taking $\mathfrak{M}(x)$ to define the set of all numbers x of functions recursive in $T^{(n)}$ (nth jump of T) for sufficiently large n.

These model-theoretic arguments do not give the proof theoretical equivalence (2.1.1) of ID_1 with (BI).

2.2. Relationships between ID_ω and $(\Pi^1_1\text{–CA})+(\mathrm{BI})$. The main results here are simpler to state because $(\Pi^0_\infty\text{–CA})$ is derivable from $(\Pi^1_1\text{–CA})$.

THEOREM 2.2.1

(i). ID_ω *has an* ω, *T-model in* $(\Pi^1_1\text{–CA})+(\mathrm{BI})$.

(ii). $(\Pi^1_1\text{–CA})+(\mathrm{BI})$ *has an* ω, *T-model in* ID_{T_ω}.

PROOF. (i) By definition, $\mathrm{ID}_\omega = \mathrm{ID}_\prec$ for $\prec\; = \;\prec_\omega$; this has the same theorems as $\mathrm{ID}_<$ using the ordering $<$ of ω. Let $\mathrm{S} = (\Pi^1_1\text{–CA})+(\mathrm{BI})$. For each $P^{\mathfrak{A}}$ of ID_ω, the definition of $P^{\mathfrak{A}}_y(x)$ in $\mathscr{L}_2$ is obtained from (1.3.2) as follows. Let

$$\mathfrak{C}(X, y) = \bigwedge Y\{\bigwedge x[\mathfrak{A}(Y, \hat{z}((z)_1 < y \wedge (z)_0 \in X_{(z)_1}), x, y) \rightarrow x \in Y] \rightarrow X_y \subseteq Y\}, \quad (1)$$

which expresses that X_y is the smallest set satisfying the inductive definition from $\langle X_z \rangle_{z<y}$. Then let

$$P^{\mathfrak{A}}_y(x)' = \bigvee X[\bigwedge y_1 \leqslant y \mathfrak{C}(X, y_1) \wedge x \in X_y], \quad (2)$$

$$(\Pi_1^1\text{-CA}) \vdash \bigwedge y \bigvee Z \bigwedge x[x \in Z \leftrightarrow P_y^{\mathfrak{A}}(x)']. \tag{3}$$

This follows from

$$(\Pi_1^1\text{-CA}) \vdash \bigwedge y \bigvee X \bigwedge y_1 \leqslant y \mathfrak{C}(X, y_1), \tag{4}$$

which is proved by induction on y. We also have unicity of such X (up to y):

$$(\Pi_1^1\text{-CA}) \vdash \bigwedge y, X, X'[\bigwedge y_1 \leqslant y \mathfrak{C}(X, y_1) \wedge \mathfrak{C}(X', y_1) \rightarrow X_y = X'_y]. \tag{5}$$

It follows from these that the translation of axiom (1.3.1i) of ID_ω is provable in $(\Pi_1^1\text{-CA})$.

In contrast to the proof of (2.1.1), we cannot in general prove $\bigvee Z \bigwedge x, y[\langle x, y\rangle \in Z \leftrightarrow P_y^{\mathfrak{A}}(x)']$ in $(\Pi_1^1\text{-CA})$. Here we must use (BI) to get the translation of (1.3.1ii), which is (equivalent to the universal closure of)

$$\begin{aligned}&\bigwedge y_1 \leqslant y\, \mathfrak{C}(X, y_1) \wedge (x \in X_y) \rightarrow \\ &\qquad \{\bigwedge u[\mathfrak{A}(\mathfrak{B}', \hat{z}((z)_1 < y \wedge (z)_0 \in X_{(z)_1}), u, y) \rightarrow \mathfrak{B}'(u)] \rightarrow \mathfrak{B}'(x)\}.\end{aligned} \tag{6}$$

This is provable in (BI) by (1) and lemma 1.6.3. Thus the translation (2) determines an ω-model of ID_1 in $(\Pi_1^1\text{-CA})+(\mathrm{BI})$, which is easily checked to be an ω, T-model.

For (ii) we formalize the argument that $M = \bigcup_{n<\omega} Rc^{T_n}$ forms an ω-model of $(\Pi_1^1\text{-CA})+(\mathrm{BI})$, since $Rc^{T_{n+1}}$ is a basis for predicates $\bigwedge \alpha \bigvee y \mathfrak{R}(\bar{\alpha}(y), \bar{\beta}(y))$ where β is recursive in T_n. Formally, let $\mathfrak{M}(x)$ be the formula $\bigwedge y \bigvee z(\{(x)_0\}^{T(x)_1}(y) \simeq z)$ of $\mathscr{L}_1(T_\omega)$ and $(y \in' x)$ be $(\{(x)_0\}^{T(x)_1}(y) \simeq 0)$. This determines a translation of $\mathscr{L}_2$ preserving $\mathscr{L}_1$ and relativizing the 2nd order quantifiers to $\mathfrak{M}$. Given x such that $\mathfrak{M}(x)$ write β_x for $\lambda y\{(x)_0\}^{T(x)_1}(y)$.

The proof extends the argument for (2.1.2ii). Consider a formula $\bigwedge \alpha_{\mathfrak{M}} \bigvee y \mathfrak{R}(\bar{\alpha}(y), \bar{\beta}_x(y))$. A number $u_{\mathfrak{R}}^x$ of the tree of unsecured sequences of $\mathfrak{R}(s, \bar{\beta}_x(Lh(s)))$ is associated with $\mathfrak{R}$, uniformly in x. Let

$$\mathrm{Sec}_{\mathfrak{R}}^x(s) = T_{(x)_1+1}(u_{\mathfrak{R}}^x \upharpoonright s). \tag{7}$$

Proof by induction on $\mathrm{Sec}_{\mathfrak{R}}^x$ follows from the inductive description of $T_{(x)_1+1}$, and hence

$$\mathrm{ID}_{T_\omega} \vdash \mathfrak{M}(x) \wedge \mathrm{Sec}_{\mathfrak{R}}^x(s) \rightarrow \bigwedge \alpha_{\mathfrak{M}}[\bar{\alpha}(Lh(s)) = s \rightarrow \bigvee y \mathfrak{R}(\bar{\alpha}(y), \bar{\beta}_x(y))]. \tag{8}$$

By direct argument

$$\begin{aligned}\mathrm{ID}_{T_\omega} \vdash \mathfrak{M}(x) \wedge \sim \mathrm{Sec}_{\mathfrak{R}}^x(s) \rightarrow \bigvee \alpha\{&\mathfrak{R}c^{T(x)_1+1}(\alpha) \wedge \bar{\alpha}(Lh(s)) = s \\ &\wedge \bigwedge y \sim \mathfrak{R}(\bar{\alpha}(y), \bar{\beta}_x(y))],\end{aligned} \tag{9}$$

and thus

$$\mathrm{ID}_{T_\omega} \vdash \bigwedge \beta_{\mathfrak{M}} \bigvee v[\bigwedge \alpha_{\mathfrak{M}} \bigvee y \mathfrak{R}(\bar{\alpha}(y), \bar{\beta}(y)) \leftrightarrow T_{v+1}(u^v_{\mathfrak{R}})]. \tag{10}$$

The translations of $(\Pi^1_1\text{-CA})+(\mathrm{BI})$ follow as in (2.1.2ii).

§ 3. Relationships between ID_ν, $\mathrm{ID}_{<\nu}$ and subsystems of analysis

3.1. Relations between ID_ν, $\mathrm{ID}_{<\nu}$, $(\Pi^1_1\text{-CA})_{<\nu}$ and (BI). These relationships are stated for $\nu \leqslant \varepsilon_0$, using $\prec\, = \,\prec_{\varepsilon_0}$. All of the results can be generalized to any prim. rec. well-ordering $\prec$ by adding the appropriate instances of $\mathrm{TI}(\prec)$ to each system.

Let $|a| = \alpha$ in $\prec$, $a \neq 0$. *X is a hierarchy based on the hyperjump up to a (or α)* if

(3.1.1)(i). for each $b \oplus 1 \prec a$, $X_{b\oplus 1} = T^{X_b}$,

and

(ii). for each $b \prec a$ with $\mathrm{Lim}(b)$, $x \in X_b \leftrightarrow (x)_1 \prec b \wedge (x)_0 \in X_{(x)_1}$.

By (1.4.1), the equality in condition (i) is expressed in $\mathscr{L}_2$ by the formula $\bigwedge x[x \in X_{b\oplus 1} \leftrightarrow \bigwedge Y\{\bigwedge y[\mathfrak{A}_T(X, X_b, y) \rightarrow y \in Y] \rightarrow x \in Y\}]$. Let $\mathfrak{H}(a, X)$ be the formula of $\mathscr{L}_2$ expressing (3.1.1i, ii); for fixed a this is written $\mathfrak{H}_a(X)$ or $\mathfrak{H}_\alpha(X)$. Let $\mathfrak{H}_\alpha$ be the sentence

(3.1.2) $\bigwedge Z \bigvee X[\mathfrak{H}_\alpha(X) \wedge X_0 = Z]$.

$\mathfrak{H}_2$ expresses that for each Z, T^Z exists. For $\alpha, \beta \geqslant 1$, $(\mathfrak{H}_\alpha \wedge \mathfrak{H}_\beta \rightarrow \mathfrak{H}_{\alpha+\beta})$ is derivable in $(\Pi^0_0\text{-CA})$.

By $(\Pi^1_1\text{-CA})_{<\nu}$ for ν a limit number is meant the system with axioms $\mathfrak{H}_\alpha$ for each $\alpha < \nu$. $(\Pi^1_1\text{-CA})_{<\omega}$ is equivalent to $\mathfrak{H}_2$, which is provable in $(\Pi^1_1\text{-CA})$. Conversely, if $\mathfrak{H}_2$ is assumed we can prove the completeness of T^Z for predicates $\bigwedge \alpha \bigvee y \mathfrak{R}(\bar{\alpha}(y), Z)$. Hence the axioms of $(\Pi^1_1\text{-CA})$ follow from $\mathfrak{H}_2$. Thus

(3.1.3) *$(\Pi^1_1\text{-CA})_{<\omega}$ and $(\Pi^1_1\text{-CA})$ have the same theorems.*

The results of this section were obtained in collaboration with Friedman, who introduced the systems $(\Pi^1_1\text{-CA})_{<\nu}$ and established, in particular, that $(\Delta^1_2\text{-CA})$ is a conservative extension of $(\Pi^1_1\text{-CA})_{<\varepsilon_0}$ for Π^1_3 sentences (**[4]**). This subsection considers relationships involving $(\Pi^1_1\text{-CA})_{<\nu}$ and ID_ν, $\mathrm{ID}_{<\nu}$ for arbitrary ν satisfying certain closure conditions. In § 3.2 we consider the relation between these for $\nu = \omega^\omega$ and the comprehension rule $(\Delta^1_2\text{-CR})$.

The general pattern of the results is summarized in § 3.3.

The arguments are extensions of those of § 2; only the few essentially new points involved are indicated. The following generalizes theorem 2.2.1.

THEOREM 3.1.4

(i). *For each* $\nu < \varepsilon_0$ *of the form* $\gamma \cdot \omega$ *with* $\gamma > 0$, ID_ν *has an* ω, *T-model in* $(\Pi^1_1\text{-CA})_{<\nu}+(\mathrm{BI})$.

(ii). *For each* $\nu < \varepsilon_0$ *of the form* $\nu = \omega^\gamma$ *with* $\gamma > 0$, $(\Pi^1_1\text{-CA})_{<\nu}+(\mathrm{BI})$ *has an* ω, *T-model in* ID_{T_ν}.

PROOF. In (i), only $\{\mathfrak{H}_\gamma\}+(\mathrm{BI})$ is needed. For (ii) we use the fact that $\bigcup_{|b|<\nu} Rc^{T_b}$ is a model for $(\Pi^1_1\text{-CA})_{<\nu}+(\mathrm{BI})$. For suppose $Z \in Rc^{T_b}$ with $|b| = \beta < \nu$ and suppose $|a| = \alpha < \nu$. A hierarchy X up to α with $X_0 = Z$ can be found recursive in $T_{b\oplus a}$, where $|b \oplus a| = \beta+\alpha$; but $\alpha, \beta < \omega^\gamma$ implies $(\beta+\alpha) < \omega^\gamma$. This argument is formalized in ID_{T_ν}.

COROLLARY 3.1.5. *Suppose* $\nu \leqslant \varepsilon_0$ *is of the form* $\nu = \omega^\gamma$ *with limit* γ. *Then* $(\Pi^1_1\text{-CA})_{<\nu}+(\mathrm{BI})$ *is* ω, *T-reducible to* $\mathrm{ID}_{T,<\nu}$.

PROOF. Any finite subsystem S of $(\Pi^1_1\text{-CA})_{<\nu}+(\mathrm{BI})$ is contained in $(\Pi^1_1\text{-CA})_{<\nu_1}+(\mathrm{BI})$ for some $\nu_1 = \omega^{\gamma_1}$ with $0 < \gamma_1 < \gamma$.

THEOREM 3.1.6. *Suppose* $2 < \nu \leqslant \varepsilon_0$. *Then*

(i). *for* $\alpha < \nu$, ID_α *has an* ω, *T-model in* $(\Pi^1_1\text{-CA})_{<\nu}$;

(ii). $\mathrm{ID}_{<\nu}$ *is* ω, *T-reducible to* $(\Pi^1_1\text{-CA})_{<\nu}$.

PROOF. (i). The argument is similar to that for (3.1.4i) (extending that for (2.1.2i)) but is simpler. A model for ID_α can be defined from any X such that $\mathfrak{H}_\alpha(X)$ (with $X_0 = \emptyset$). (BI) is not needed here because the translation of any formula $\mathfrak{B}(x)$ is arithmetical in such an X; the work is taken over by $(\Pi^0_\infty\text{-CA})$.

(ii). This is a corollary of (i).

Summarizing, we have

THEOREM 3.1.7. *Suppose* $\nu \leqslant \varepsilon_0$ *is of the form* $\nu = \omega^\gamma$ *with limit* γ. *Then the theories* $(\Pi^1_1\text{-CA})_{<\nu}$, $(\Pi^1_1\text{-CA})_{<\nu}+(\mathrm{BI})$, $\mathrm{ID}_{<\nu}$ *and* $\mathrm{ID}_{T,<\nu}$ *are* ω, *T-equivalent.*

The condition that γ is a limit number cannot be omitted here since, by **[8]** § 8, the consistency of $(\Pi^1_1\text{-CA})$ (in fact the full reflection principle) can be proved in $(\Pi^1_1\text{-CA})+(\mathrm{BI})$.

By [4] we have

COROLLARY 3.1.8. $(\Delta_2^1\text{–CA}) \equiv \mathrm{ID}_{T, <\varepsilon_0}$.

3.2. $(\Delta_2^1$–CR) and $(\Pi_1^1$–CA$)_{<\omega^\omega}$. A formula of $\mathscr{L}_2$ is said to be *essentially* $\Pi_1^1(\Pi_2^1)$ if it can be brought to a prenex normal form in which every set quantifier is universal (every universal set quantifier precedes every existential set quantifier); it is said to be essentially $\Sigma_1^1(\Sigma_2^1)$ if its negation is essentially $\Pi_1^1(\Pi_2^1)$. The Δ_n^1-comprehension rule ($n = 1, 2$) is the rule of inference

$$(3.2.1) \qquad \frac{\bigwedge x[\mathfrak{F}(x) \leftrightarrow \mathfrak{G}(x)]}{\bigvee X \bigwedge x[x \in X \leftrightarrow \mathfrak{F}(x)]}$$

where $\mathfrak{F}$ is ess. Π_n^1 and $\mathfrak{G}$ is ess. Σ_n^1 (parameters permitted). $(\Delta_n^1$–CR) denotes the system obtained from $(\Pi_0^0$–CA) by adjoining (3.2.1) as a basic rule. The usual reduction of ess. Π_n^1 formulas to Π_n^1-normal form requires choice axioms which are not available in $(\Delta_n^1$–CR); this explains the use of the more general classes of formulas.

THEOREM 3.2.2

(i). $(\Delta_2^1$–CR) *is* ω, *T-reducible to* $(\Pi_1^1$–CA$)_{<\omega^\omega}$.

(ii). $(\Delta_2^1$–CR) *is a conservative extension of* $(\Pi_1^1$–CA$)_{<\omega^\omega}$ *for* Π_2^1 *sentences.*

PROOF. (i). The proof formalizes, in $(\Pi_1^1$–CA$)_{<\omega^\omega}$, the following model-theoretic argument. Let M_α be the collection of sets recursive in T_β for some $\beta < \alpha$. $M_\alpha = \bigcup_{\beta<\alpha} M_\beta$ for limit α. $\bigwedge X^\alpha(\ldots)$ abbreviates $\bigwedge X_{M_\alpha}(\cdots)$, and similarly for $\bigvee X^\alpha(\ldots)$. $\mathfrak{F}^\alpha$ denotes the result of relativizing every set-quantifier in $\mathfrak{F}$ to M_α. In this notation, the fact that Rc^{T_α} constitutes a basis for each predicate Σ_1^1 in some T_β, $\beta < \alpha$, is expressed by:

$$\bigwedge X^\alpha[\bigvee Y\mathfrak{A}(X, Y) \leftrightarrow \bigvee Y^{\alpha+1}\mathfrak{A}(X, Y)]. \tag{1}$$

We next claim that with any ess. Σ_1^1 formula $\mathfrak{G}(X)$ can be associated $\mathfrak{G}_1(X)$ of the form $\bigvee Y\mathfrak{A}(X, Y)$ such that for any α

$$\bigwedge X^\alpha[\mathfrak{G}^\alpha(X) \to \mathfrak{G}_1(X)] \wedge \bigwedge X^\alpha[\mathfrak{G}_1^\alpha(X) \to \mathfrak{G}^\alpha(X)]. \tag{2}$$

Suppose, for example $\mathfrak{G}(X) = \bigwedge k \bigvee Y \bigwedge m \bigvee Z \mathfrak{B}(k, m, X, Y, Z)$. Take $\mathfrak{G}_1(X) = \bigvee Y, Z \bigwedge k, m\mathfrak{B}(k, m, X, Y_k, Z_{k,m})$. The second implication is then trivial. For the first, given any α, enumerate $M_\alpha = \{W_0^\alpha, \ldots, W_n^\alpha, \ldots\}$ arithmetically in T_α. Then $\mathfrak{G}^\alpha(X) \leftrightarrow \bigwedge k \bigvee y \bigwedge m \bigvee z\mathfrak{B}(k, m, X, W_y^\alpha, W_z^\alpha)$; if this holds we can choose $y = f(k)$, $z = g(k, m)$ where f, g are arithmetical in T_α. The sets $Y = \{\langle x, k\rangle : x \in W^\alpha_{f(k)}\}$ and $Z = \{\langle x, \langle k, m\rangle\rangle : x \in W^\alpha_{g(k,m)}\}$ give the first implication in (2); in fact, since these are recursive in $T_{\alpha+1}$ we can take $\mathfrak{G}_1^{\alpha+2}(X)$ instead of $\mathfrak{G}_1(X)$ there.

It follows that if β is a limit number, $\beta < \alpha$, and $\mathfrak{F}(X)$ is ess. Π^1_2 then

$$\bigwedge X^\beta[\mathfrak{F}^\alpha(X) \rightarrow \mathfrak{F}^\beta(X)]. \tag{3}$$

Suppose, for example $\mathfrak{F}$ is of the form $\bigwedge Y\mathfrak{G}(X, Y)$ where $\mathfrak{G}$ is ess. Σ^1_1. Assume X is in M_β and that $\bigwedge Y^\alpha \mathfrak{G}^\alpha(X, Y)$. Given Y in M_β, it is to be shown that $\mathfrak{G}^\beta(X, Y)$ holds. By (2), $\mathfrak{G}_1(X, Y)$ holds with $\mathfrak{G}_1(X, Y) = \bigvee Z\mathfrak{A}(X, Y, Z)$. Let $\gamma < \beta$ with both X, Y in M_γ. By (1), $\bigvee Z^{\gamma+1}\mathfrak{A}(X, Y, Z)$ and hence $\mathfrak{G}_1^\beta(X, Y)$, giving $\mathfrak{G}^\beta(X, Y)$ by (2).

The main step is to show the following:

> Suppose $n > 0$ and that a sentence $\mathfrak{F}$ has been proved in (Δ^1_2–CR) using at most $(n-1)$ applications of the Δ^1_2-comprehension rule; (4)
> then $\mathfrak{F}^\alpha$ is true for every α of the form $\alpha = \omega^n \cdot \delta$ with $\delta > 0$.

This is proved by induction on n. It is sufficient to show that if $\mathfrak{F}(x, X)$, $\mathfrak{G}(x, X)$ are ess. Π^1_2, Σ^1_2 resp., without other parameters and

$$\bigwedge X^\beta \bigwedge x[\mathfrak{F}^\beta(x, X) \leftrightarrow \mathfrak{G}^\beta(x, X)] \tag{5}$$

holds for every $\beta = \omega^n \cdot \lambda$, $\lambda > 0$, then

$$\bigwedge X^\alpha \bigvee Y^\alpha \bigwedge x[x \in Y \leftrightarrow \mathfrak{F}^\alpha(x, X)] \tag{6}$$

holds for every $\alpha = \omega^{n+1} \cdot \delta$ with $\delta > 0$. Write $\alpha = \omega^n \cdot (\omega \cdot \delta)$; $\omega \cdot \delta$ is a limit number with $\omega \cdot \delta = \lim_k \lambda_k$ for some sequence of $\lambda_k > 0$. Each $\beta_k = \omega^n \cdot \lambda_k$ is also a limit number since $n > 0$. Then any X in M_α belongs to M_{β_k} for some k. By (3) and its dual, both

$$\bigwedge x[\mathfrak{F}^\alpha(x, X) \rightarrow \mathfrak{F}^{\beta_k}(x, X)] \quad \text{and} \quad \bigwedge x[\mathfrak{G}^{\beta_k}(x, X) \rightarrow \mathfrak{G}^\alpha(x, X)]$$

hold. Then by (5)

$$\bigwedge x[\mathfrak{F}^\alpha(x, X) \leftrightarrow \mathfrak{F}^{\beta_k}(x, X)].$$

(6) follows from this and

$$\bigwedge X^{\beta_k} \bigvee Y^\alpha \bigwedge x[x \in Y \leftrightarrow \mathfrak{F}^{\beta_k}(x, X)].$$

Let S be any derivation in (Δ^1_2–CR) containing, say, $(m-1)$ applications of the rule (3.2.1). (4) can be formalized to give an ω-model of S in $(\Pi^1_1\text{–CA})_{<\omega^{m+1}}$. As one proceeds by induction on $n \leqslant m$, it is only necessary to consider those $\alpha = \omega^n \cdot \delta$ with $\alpha \leqslant \omega^m$. This proves (i).

The entire argument can be relativized to any initial set Z. Write M^Z_α for the corresponding collections; Z is in M^Z_α for any α. If $(\Delta^1_2\text{–CR}) \vdash \bigwedge Z \bigvee Y \mathfrak{A}(Z, Y)$ then for some n, $(\Pi^1_1\text{–CA})_{<\omega^\omega}$ proves

$$(\bigwedge Z \bigwedge X_{M^Z{}_{\omega^n}} \bigvee Y_{M^Z{}_{\omega^n}} \mathfrak{A}(X, Y)$$

and hence $\bigwedge Z \bigvee Y \mathfrak{A}(Z, Y)$.

To complete the proof of (ii) it must also be shown that each axiom of $(\Pi^1_1\text{–CA})_{<\omega^\omega}$ is provable in $(\Delta^1_2\text{–CR})$. Note that for any $\alpha < \varepsilon_0$, $|a| = \alpha$,

$$\bigwedge y \preccurlyeq \bar{a}\{\mathfrak{H}(y, X) \wedge \mathfrak{H}(y, X') \to \bigwedge u \prec y(X_u = X'_u)\} \tag{7}$$

is provable by transfinite induction on $\prec_\alpha$. It is sufficient to show that for each $n < \omega$,

$$(\Delta^1_2\text{–CR}) \vdash \bigwedge Z \bigvee X[\mathfrak{H}_{\omega^n}(X) \wedge X_0 = Z]. \tag{8}$$

Let $|w_n| = \omega^n$, and let $\circ$ represent ordinal product on $\prec$. Suppose (8) holds for n; then also

$$\bigwedge y \bigwedge X\{\mathfrak{H}(y, X) \to \bigvee Y[Y_0 = X_0 \wedge \mathfrak{H}(y \oplus \bar{w}_n, Y)]\}$$

and

$$\bigwedge Z \bigwedge z \bigvee X[\mathfrak{H}(\bar{w}_n \circ z, X) \wedge X_0 = Z] \tag{9}$$

are provable in $(\Delta^1_2\text{–CR})$. Let $\mathfrak{F}(x, Z)$ be the formula

$$\bigvee y, z \bigvee X\{\mathfrak{H}(\bar{w}_n \circ z, X) \wedge X_0 = Z \wedge y \prec \bar{w}_n \circ z \wedge x \in X_y\}$$

and $\mathfrak{G}(x, Z)$ the formula

$$\bigvee y, z \bigwedge X\{\mathfrak{H}(\bar{w}_n \circ z, X) \wedge X_0 = Z \to y \prec \bar{w}_n \circ z \wedge x \in X_y\}.$$

$\mathfrak{H}(y, X)$ is arithmetical in an ess. Π^1_1 formula, so is both ess. Π^1_2 and ess. Σ^1_2. Thus $\mathfrak{F}(x, Z)$ is ess. Σ^1_2 and $\mathfrak{G}(x, Z)$ is ess. Π^1_2; moreover

$$\bigwedge Z \bigwedge x[\mathfrak{F}(x, Z) \leftrightarrow \mathfrak{G}(x, Z)] \tag{10}$$

is provable in $(\Delta^1_2\text{–CR})$ by (7) and (9). Then so also is $\bigwedge Z \bigvee X_1 \bigwedge x[x \in X_1 \leftrightarrow \mathfrak{F}(x, Z)]$, which immediately implies (8) for $n+1$.

COROLLARY 3.2.3. $(\Delta^1_2\text{–CR})$ *and* $\mathrm{ID}_{T, <\omega^\omega}$ *are* ω, *T-equivalent.*

It is worth noting that the proof of (3.2.2) also gives the following

THEOREM 3.2.4. $(\Delta^1_2\text{–CR})$ *is closed under the* Σ^1_2*-rule of choice.*

PROOF. Suppose, for example

$$(\Delta^1_2\text{–CR}) \vdash \bigwedge x \bigvee X \bigwedge Y \mathfrak{A}(x, X, Y).$$

By (4) above there is $\alpha = \omega^n$ such that

$$(\Pi_1^1\text{-CA})_{<\omega^\omega} \vdash \bigwedge x \bigvee X^\alpha \bigwedge Y^\alpha \mathfrak{A}(x, X, Y).$$

Using the enumeration of M_α arithmetical in T_α (hence recursive in $T_{\alpha+1}$) we derive

$$\bigvee X^{\alpha+2} \bigwedge x \bigvee Z^\alpha \{X_x = Z \wedge \bigwedge Y^\alpha \mathfrak{A}(x, Z, Y)\}.$$

Since α is a limit number, the basis result (1) gives

$$\bigwedge Y^\alpha \mathfrak{A}(x, Z, Y) \to \bigwedge Y \mathfrak{A}(x, Z, Y)$$

for Z in M_α. Hence $\bigvee X \bigwedge x \bigwedge Y \mathfrak{A}(x, X_x, Y)$ is derivable in $(\Pi_1^1\text{-CA})_{<\omega^\omega}$ and in $(\Delta_2^1\text{-CR})$.

3.3. General pattern. Consider the usual jump (not hyperjump) operation and write $\mathfrak{H}_\alpha^0(X)$ for

X is a hierarchy based on the ordinary jump up to α.

Let $(\Pi_1^0\text{-CA})_{<\nu}$ be the system with axioms $\bigwedge Z \bigvee X[\mathfrak{H}_\alpha^0(X) \wedge X_0 = Z]$ for each $\alpha < \nu$. It follows from Kleene **[5]** that $(\Pi_1^0\text{-CA})_{<\omega\cdot\gamma}$ is equivalent to ramified analysis with levels β for each $\beta < \gamma$. Write $(\Pi_0^1\text{-CA})$ for $(\Pi_1^0\text{-CA})$ or equivalently $(\Pi_\infty^0\text{-CA})$.

(3.3.1)(i). $(\Pi_1^0\text{-CA})_{<\omega} \equiv (\Pi_0^1\text{-CA})$

(ii). $(\Pi_1^0\text{-CA})_{<\omega^\omega} \equiv (\Delta_1^1\text{-CR})$

(iii). $(\Pi_1^0\text{-CA})_{<\varepsilon_0} \equiv (\Delta_1^1\text{-CA})$.

(i) is trivial; (ii) is from **[1]**, 6.14 (using the above remark on ramified analysis) and (iii) from **[3]** Ch. II.5. By the results of **[4]** and this section, the same pattern is followed when we increase the superscripts on the left and the subscripts on the right by 1:

(3.3.2)(i). $(\Pi_1^1\text{-CA})_{<\omega} \equiv (\Pi_1^1\text{-CA})$

(ii). $(\Pi_1^1\text{-CA})_{<\omega^\omega} \equiv (\Delta_2^1\text{-CR})$

(iii). $(\Pi_1^1\text{-CA})_{<\varepsilon_0} \equiv (\Delta_2^1\text{-CA})$

As a matter of fact, these results and their proofs were suggested by the previous ones. Though the proof of (ii) (i.e. (3.2.2)) simply generalizes my proof of 6.14 sketched in **[1]**, this possibility was noticed only recently by Friedman. It should be noted in addition that (3.2.4) corresponds to

[1] 6.27, according to which (Δ_1^1–CR) is closed under the Σ_1^1-rule of choice.*

There is an important difference between (Δ_1^1–CR) and (Δ_1^1–CA). While the jump hierarchy up to ω^ω actually is an ω-model for (Δ_1^1–CR), the hierarchy up to ε_0 is not an ω-model for (Δ_1^1–CA) since the least ω-model consists of all hyperarithmetic sets. A corresponding remark applies to (Δ_2^1–CR) and (Δ_2^1–CA).

§ 4. **Value of reductions to systems ID_ν.** The remarks below suggest definite technical advantages of these reductions and some limitations of their foundational significance; some additional technical advantages appear in the discussion in § 5.

4.1. The main results above yield conservative extension results for provably recursive well-orderings and ordinal functions as follows: In each case we have $S_2 \equiv S_1$, where S_2 is a subsystem of analysis and S_1 is one of the theories ID_{T_ν} or $\mathrm{ID}_{T,<\nu}$. If $S_2 \vdash \mathrm{WF}(\mathfrak{R})$ then we can find $e \in T$ with $\mathfrak{R}$ provably embedded in the tree of e and $S_2 \vdash T(\bar{e})$, so S_2 and S_1 have the same provably recursive well-orderings. But $S_2 \equiv S_1$ also implies that for f recursive, S_1, S_2 prove the same sentences of the form

$$\bigwedge x_1, \ldots, x_n[T(x_1) \wedge \ldots \wedge T(x_n) \rightarrow T(f(x_1, \ldots, x_n))].$$

This extends to any theory S_2' which is a conservative extension of S_2 for Π_2^1 sentences.

Since the ID_ν are very naturally associated with ordinals, it is not unreasonable to expect to be able to develop a theory of their provably recursive ordinals and ordinal functions. This is obviously so for ID_1 (cf. [2]). It is not obviously so for ID_ν for $\nu > 1$ since the natural orderings associated are non-recursive; however, some collapsing argument may perhaps be possible.

4.2. Evidently the familiar classical interpretation of g.i.d. is not relevant to the foundational significance of the reductions, because the existence of least sets (under suitable conditions on the defining formula $\mathfrak{A}$) is derived from the comprehension axiom or a theory of ordinals.

* (Δ_1^1—CA) $\equiv$ (Σ_1^1—AC) $\equiv$ (Σ_1^1—DC) by [3] Ch. 5, and (Δ_2^1—CA) $=$ (Σ_2^1—AC) $=$ (Σ_2^1—DC) by formalization of the Kondo–Addison theorem as verified by Mansfield; however, the arguments in this case are quite different.

Prima facie the reductions become candidates for constructive consistency proofs because of the following observation of Kreisel **[6]**.

Let $\mathrm{ID}_\nu^0(\mathfrak{A})$ be the system $\mathrm{ID}_\nu(\mathfrak{A})$ with the logic restricted to be intuitionistic, except that only derivability of the monotonicity condition (1.2.4) on $\mathfrak{A}$ is required,* and let ID_ν^0 be the union of $\mathrm{ID}_\nu^0(\mathfrak{A})$ for such $\mathfrak{A}$. Then $\mathrm{ID}_\nu \leqslant \mathrm{ID}_\nu^0$.

However, Kreisel points out (in **[8]**, esp. pp. 344 and 352, and in **[9]**, §§ 4, 5) that for $\nu > 1$, the principles used to justify ID_ν^0 with (the usual interpretation of) intuitionistic logical operations also justify the whole theory of species of natural numbers, where the reduction of full classical analysis is immediate. Therefore the special significance of these results for constructive foundations of analysis is open.

§ 5. **Connections with the literature.** We consider work by Tait and Takeuti. It so happens that in both cases the principles of ID_ν enter into their work and also variants, that is, formally quite different principles of inductive definitions, are considered.

5.1.1. Tait gives consistency proofs for (Δ_2^1–CR) and (Σ_2^1–AC) by cut-elimination arguments in infinitary propositional systems $\mathrm{PL}^{\omega^\omega}$ and $\mathrm{PL}^{\varepsilon_0}$, resp. (**[12]**, §§ 4, 5). The formulas and derivations of PL^ν are represented by trees indexed by members of T_α for $\alpha < \nu$. The same cut-elimination arguments apply even more simply and more intelligibly to the theories $\mathrm{ID}_{T,<\nu}$, by assigning to every sentence $\mathfrak{F}$ a sentence $\mathfrak{F}^*$ of PL^ν with $(T_\alpha(\bar{n}))^* = \bigvee\!\!\bigvee_{a \in T_\alpha}(\bar{n} = \bar{a})$.

5.1.2. The 2nd-order theory **Ind** of **[12]** § 1 has constants for set functionals $p_{\mathfrak{A}}$ and axioms of the form

$$\bigwedge x[\mathfrak{A}(p_{\mathfrak{A}}(X), x, X) \rightarrow x \in p_{\mathfrak{A}}(X)]$$

and

$$\bigwedge x[\mathfrak{A}(\mathfrak{B}, x, X) \rightarrow \mathfrak{B}(x)] \rightarrow \bigwedge x[x \in p_{\mathfrak{A}}(X) \rightarrow \mathfrak{B}(x)],$$

where Y is positive in $\mathfrak{A}(Y, x, X)$. It can be seen that **Ind** is ω, T-equivalent to ID_ω by the same arguments as in 2.2.

5.2.1. Takeuti **[15]** has given a consistency proof for (Π_1^1–CA) by transfinite induction on the ordinal diagrams $O(\omega+1, \omega^3)$ applied to a prim.

* The argument in § 1.2 reducing to $\mathfrak{A}_1(P, x)$ with positive P does not hold intuitionistically.

rec. predicate. The principles of g.i.d. enter this work implicitly, in the following sense. At the present time, the most elementary proof of the well-foundedness of $O(\omega+1, \omega^3)$ uses ID_ω; the method is by an extension of the proof by Kreisel (*review Zentr. f. Math.* **106** (1964) 237–238) and by making use of **[13]**.

It seems likely that the following converse holds; a proof of consistency of ID_ω, and hence of $(\Pi^1_1\text{-CA})$, should be given using induction on $O(\omega+1, -)$; moreover, this should be much simpler than **[15]**.

5.2.2. In **[14]** and **[15]** ch. 4, Takeuti considers 2nd order systems with additional symbols $P(x, y)$, $P(x, y, \mathscr{V})$ resp. and axioms of the form

(1) $P(x, y) \leftrightarrow \mathfrak{F}(\hat{z}((z)_1 \prec y \wedge P((z)_0, (z)_1)), x, y)$,

(2) $P(x, y, \mathscr{V}) \leftrightarrow \mathfrak{F}\,(\hat{z}((z)_1 \prec y \wedge P((z)_0, (z)_1, \mathscr{V})), x, y, \mathscr{V})$,

where $\prec$ is a given prim. rec. well-ordering, $\mathfrak{F}(X, x, y)$ resp. $\mathfrak{F}(X, x, y, Y)$ is arithmetical in Π^1_1-formulas, and, in (2), $\mathscr{V}$ ranges over arbitrary 'varieties', i.e. abstracts $\hat{x}\mathfrak{G}(x)$ (written $\{x\}\mathfrak{G}(x)$ in **[15]** for any formula $\mathfrak{G}$. Thus, in contrast to our systems $\mathrm{ID}_\prec$ these axioms contain also 2nd order *variables*.

We establish relations between the systems in the text and, for reasons to be explained in a moment, somewhat modified variations of Takeuti's systems.

Let $\alpha = |\prec|$, and suppose (for simplicity) that α is of the form ω^γ. Let $\mathrm{S}_\prec$ be obtained from schema (1) by adding $\mathrm{TI}(\prec)$ and $(\Pi^0_\infty\text{-CA})$; P is treated as a 2nd order constant symbol. Then

(3) (i). *$\mathrm{S}_\prec$ is ω,T-reducible to* ID_{T_α}.
(ii). ID_{T_α} *is ω,T-reducible to $\mathrm{S}_\prec$ for suitable choice of* $\mathfrak{F}$.

(It is understood as in § 1.3 that ID_{T_α} is described by reference to $\prec$ and contains $\mathrm{TI}(\prec)$.) The proof of (3i) is obtained by formalizing the construction of an ω-model of $\mathrm{S}_\prec$ with P recursive in T_α.

Let $\mathrm{S}^+_\prec$ be obtained from schema (2) by restricting $\mathscr{V}$ to be a set variable, and adding $\mathrm{WF}(\prec)$, (BI) and $(\Pi^1_1\text{-CA})$; P is now treated as a functional symbol for $\lambda Y\, \hat{z} P_n((z)_0, (z)_1, Y)$. Then

(4) (i). *$\mathrm{S}^+_\prec$ is ω,T-reducible to* $\mathrm{ID}_{T_{\alpha\cdot\omega}}$,
(ii). $\mathrm{ID}_{T_{\alpha\cdot\omega}}$ *is ω,T-reducible to $\mathrm{S}^+_\prec$ for suitable choice of* $\mathfrak{F}$.

The proof of (4i) goes via an ω,T-model of $\mathrm{S}^+_\prec$ in $(\Pi^1_1\text{-CA})_{<\alpha\cdot\omega}+(\mathrm{BI})$ (including $\mathrm{TI}(\prec)$) and the generalization of (3.1.4ii).

These results can be generalized to systems involving iterations of the schemata (1), (2) considered in **[14]**, **[15]**.

Concerning the modifications, it seems that TI($\prec$) must have been intended (though it was not explicitly included) since it is difficult to see how the schemas (1), (2) can be applied non-trivially without it. In any case, inasmuch as the concern in **[14]**, **[15]** is with consistency proofs, if one can get a reduction for an extended system by the same principles, so much the better. With regard to the restriction to set variables in (2), no explanation is given in **[15]** for the substitution of $\hat{x}\mathfrak{G}(x)$ for Y in the atomic formula $P(x, y, Y)$, and it is not clear exactly what was intended. A form of (2) is derivable in $S^+_\prec$ for those abstracts $\mathscr{V} = \hat{x}\mathfrak{G}(x)$ which can be proved to define a set, e.g. when $\mathfrak{G}(x) = \mathfrak{G}_1(x, P)$ with $\mathfrak{G}_1(x, X)$ arithmetical in Π^1_1-formulas.

REFERENCES

[1] S. FEFERMAN, Systems of predicative analysis, *J. Symb. Logic* **29** (1964) 1–30.

[2] S. FEFERMAN, Ordinals associated with theories for one inductively defined set (mimeographed).

[3] H. FRIEDMAN, *Subsystems of set theory and analysis*, dissertation, M.I.T. (1967).

[4] H. FRIEDMAN, Iterated inductive definitions and Σ^1_2–AC, these proceedings 435–442.

[5] S. C. KLEENE, Quantification of number-theoretic functions, *Comp. Math.* **14** (1959) 23–40.

[6] G. KREISEL, Generalized inductive definitions, *Reports for the seminar on foundations of analysis, Stanford*, vol. **1** § III (1963) (mimeographed).

[7] G. KREISEL, Mathematical logic, in *Lectures on modern mathematics III*, ed. Saaty, Wiley, New York (1965) 95–195.

[8] G. KREISEL, A survey of proof theory, *J. Symb. Logic* **33** (1968) 321–388.

[9] G. KREISEL, Functions, ordinals, species, in *Logic, methodology and philosophy of science III*, eds. B. van Rootselaar and J. F. Staal, North-Holland, Amsterdam (1968) 145–159.

[10] R. LYNDON, An interpolation theorem in the predicate calculus, *Pacif. J. Math.* **9** (1959) 129–142.

[11] K. SCHÜTTE, *Beweistheorie*, Springer, Berlin (1960).

[12] W. W. TAIT, Applications of the cut-elimination theorem to some subsystems of analysis, these proceedings 475–488.

[13] G. TAKEUTI, Ordinal diagrams II, *J. Math. Soc. Japan* **12** (1960) 385–391.

[14] G. TAKEUTI, On the inductive definition with quantifiers of second order, *J. Math. Soc. Japan* **13** (1961) 333–341.

[15] G. TAKEUTI, Consistency proofs of subsystems of classical analysis, *Ann. Math.* **82** (1967) 299–348.

[16] A. TARSKI, A. MOSTOWSKI and R. M. ROBINSON, *Undecidable theories*, North-Holland, Amsterdam (1953).

BROUWER'S BAR THEOREM AND A SYSTEM OF ORDINAL NOTATIONS

HARVEY GERBER*

In [3] Gödel proves the consistency of arithmetic by using computable functionals of finite type. Spector [6] extends Gödel's proof to a consistency proof of analysis by introducing a new definition, bar recursion, and a corresponding principle of proof, bar induction. Bar induction is a generalization of Brouwer's bar theorem [1] (bar induction of type 0) to higher types. The problem still remains of obtaining a proof of the consistency of analysis by using the constructive theory of ordinals.

In § 1 we construct a system of ordinal notations based upon the work done in [2]. This system of notations has been used by Wm. Howard (unpublished) to prove the consistency of the formal system obtained by adjoining the axiom of bar induction of type 0 to elementary intuitionistic analysis.

In § 2 we prove the well-ordering of any proper segment of our notations, but not the whole segment itself, using Brouwer's bar theorem formulated in the form of $\mathrm{TI_D}$, 'the axiom of transfinite induction' for decidable relations ρ.

§ 1. A system of ordinal notations. The terms $\mathbf{0}$, Ω^0, $\Omega^0[\alpha, a]$ defined below can be interpreted as the ordinal numbers 0, 1, $\varphi\alpha^* a^*$ respectively (of [2]), provided that the terms α, a are interpreted as the ordinal numbers α^*, a^* (also of [2]). We recall that $\varphi 0$ is any normal function whose range consists of limit ordinals.

DEFINITION 1. *Terms* and *class* Cl *of terms* of the system T.

1.1. $\mathbf{0}$ is a term and $Cl(\mathbf{0}) = 2$.

* The author is grateful to the National Research Council of Canada (Grant # A-3723) for financial assistance. The author also wishes to thank Professor William Howard for his many helpful suggestions.

1.2. If α is a term then Ω^α is a term and

$$Cl(\Omega^\alpha) = \begin{cases} 2 & \text{if } \alpha = \mathbf{0}, \\ 3 & \text{otherwise.} \end{cases}$$

1.3. If α, β, b are terms and $Cl(b) = 2$ then $\Omega^\alpha[\beta, b]$ is a term and

$$Cl(\Omega^\alpha[\beta, b]) = \begin{cases} 2 & \text{if } \alpha = \mathbf{0}, \\ 3 & \text{otherwise.} \end{cases}$$

1.4. If α, β are terms, then $\alpha \# \beta$ is a term and

$$Cl(\alpha \# \beta) = \max\{Cl(\alpha), Cl(\beta)\}.$$

1.5. If α is a term then $\Omega^\alpha\mathbf{0}$ is a term and $Cl(\Omega^\alpha\mathbf{0}) = 2$.

Intuitively, $Cl(\alpha) = 2$ (resp. $Cl(\alpha) = 3$) says that the ordinal which α denotes is in the second (resp. third) number class. This concept is needed in order to provide the restriction in 1.3 above which corresponds to the restriction in [**2**], that the function $\varphi\beta$ is defined only for arguments b such that b is in the second number class. We call the terms of the form Ω^α or $\Omega^\alpha[\beta, b]$ the *principal terms*

Let $*$, $\langle\ \rangle$ be defined as in [**4**].

Definition 2. We define the *sequence of summands* of a term α, written $S(\alpha)$, as follows:

2.1. If α is a principal term or $\mathbf{0}$ then $S(\alpha) = \langle\alpha\rangle$.

2.2. If $\alpha = \beta \# \gamma$ then $S(\alpha) = S(\beta) * S(\gamma)$.

If $S(\alpha) = \langle\alpha_1, \ldots, \alpha_n\rangle$ then we say that each α_i $(1 \leqslant i \leqslant n)$ is a summand of α.

Definition 3. *Degree* of terms:

3.1. $D(\mathbf{0}) = 0$,

3.2. $D(\Omega^\alpha) = D(\alpha)+1$,

3.3. $D(\Omega^\alpha[\beta, b]) = D(\alpha)+D(\beta)+D(b)+1$,

3.4. $D(\alpha \# \beta) = D(\alpha)+D(\beta)$.

Definition 4. Let t be a principal term. We define the *exponent* and the *coefficient* of t, written $E(t)$ and $K(t)$ respectively as follows:

4.1. $E(\Omega^\alpha) = \alpha$, $K(\Omega^\alpha) = \Omega^\mathbf{0}$

4.2. $E(\Omega^\alpha[\beta, b]) = \alpha$, $K(\Omega^\alpha[\beta, b]) = \Omega^\mathbf{0}[\beta, b]$.

DEFINITION 5. We define the relation $C(x, t)$ read 'x is a *constituent* of t' as follows:

5.1. If $t = \mathbf{0}$ then $C(x, t)$ iff $x = \mathbf{0}$.

5.2. Let $t = t_1 \# \dots \# t_n$ where t_i is either a principal term or $\mathbf{0}$ for $1 \leqslant i \leqslant n$. Then $C(x, t)$ iff $x = K(t_i)$ or $C(x, E(t_i))$ for some i if $t_i \neq \mathbf{0}$, or $x = \mathbf{0}$ if $t_i = \mathbf{0}$.

DEFINITION 6. We define the relation $P(x, \alpha, a)$ read 'x is a *part* of $\Omega^{\mathbf{0}}(\alpha, a)$' as follows:

$$P(x, \alpha, a) \quad \text{iff} \quad C(x, \alpha) \vee x = a.$$

Before defining the $<$-relation and the $\equiv$-relation we introduce the following abbreviations. We abbreviate $a < b \vee a \equiv b$ by $a \leqslant b$, $\neg (a \equiv b)$ by $a \not\equiv b$ and $a < b$ by $b > a$. Let $t = t_1 \# \dots \# t_n$ where each t_i is either a principal term or $\mathbf{0}$ (we call such a representation the *normal form representation* (n.f.r.) for t) and at least one of the t_i is different from $\mathbf{0}$. Let $L(t)$ denote the summand $t_i \neq \mathbf{0}$ of t, of largest index i, such that $E(t_i) \leqslant E(t_j)$ for all j $(1 \leqslant j \leqslant n)$ where $t_j \neq \mathbf{0}$ and such that $K(t_i) \leqslant K(t_m)$ for all m $(1 \leqslant m \leqslant n)$, where $E(t_i) \equiv E(t_m)$. We write $[\alpha, a]$, $\mathbf{1}$, Ω etc., instead of $\Omega^{\mathbf{0}}[\alpha, a]$, $\Omega^{\mathbf{0}}$, $\Omega^{\Omega^{\mathbf{0}}}$, etc.

Assume that $\alpha \not\equiv \mathbf{0} \vee a \not\equiv \mathbf{0}$. Let $\mathrm{DP}(\alpha, a)$ denote the term a if $a \not\equiv \mathbf{0}$. If $a \equiv \mathbf{0}$ and $K(L(t)) \not\equiv \mathbf{1}$ or $E(L(t)) \equiv \mathbf{0}$ then $\mathrm{DP}(\alpha, a)$ denotes $K(L(t))$. If $a \equiv \mathbf{0}$ and $E(L(t)) \not\equiv \mathbf{0}$ and $K(L(t)) \equiv \mathbf{1}$ then $\mathrm{DP}(\alpha, a)$ denotes $\mathrm{DP}(E(L(t)), a)$. We write $x = \mathrm{DP}(\alpha, a)$ and say 'x is the *distinguished part* of (α, a)'.

One final abbreviation. Assume that $a \not\equiv \mathbf{0} \vee \Omega \leqslant \alpha$. Let $t = t_1 \# \dots \# t_n$ be the n.f.r. for t. If $a \not\equiv \mathbf{0}$ then we write $x \in \mathrm{ND}(t, a)$ iff $C(x, t)$. If $a \equiv \mathbf{0}$ and $K(L(t)) \not\equiv 1$ and $\Omega < t$ then we write $x \in \mathrm{ND}(t, a)$ iff $C(x, t_1 \# \dots \# L(t)^* \# \dots \# t_n)$ where $L(t)^*$ is obtained by replacing $L(t) = \Omega^{\alpha}[\beta, b]$ by Ω^{α}. If $a \equiv \mathbf{0}$, $E(L(t)) \equiv \mathbf{0}$ then we write $x \in \mathrm{ND}(t, a)$ iff $C(x, t_1 \# \dots \# L(t)^* \# \dots \# t_n)$ where $L(t)^*$ is obtained by replacing $L(t)$ by $\mathbf{0}$. Finally, if $a \equiv \mathbf{0}$, $E(L(t)) \not\equiv \mathbf{0}$ and $K(L(t)) \equiv \mathbf{1}$ then we write $x \in \mathrm{ND}(t, a)$ iff $C(x, t_1 \# \dots \# L(t)^* \# \dots \# t_n)$, where $L(t)^*$ is obtained by replacing $L(t)$ by $\mathbf{0}$ or $x \in \mathrm{ND}(E(L(t)), a)$. We say '$x$ is a *non-distinguished part* of (α, a)' if $x \in \mathrm{ND}(\alpha, a)$.

The following definition is a definition by induction on the total number of components and parts of the two terms involved. Hence this definition gives an effective ordering of the terms.

DEFINITION 7. Inductive definition of the $\equiv$-relation and $<$-relation on T:

7.1. $\mathbf{0} \equiv \mathbf{0}$, $\mathbf{0} < a$ for all $a \not\equiv \mathbf{0}$, and $\Omega^{\alpha}\mathbf{0} \equiv \mathbf{0}$ for all α.

7.2. Let $t_1 = \Omega^{\alpha}$ and $t_2 = \Omega^{\beta}$. If $\alpha \equiv \beta$, then $t_1 \equiv t_2$.

7.3. Let $t_1 = \Omega^{\alpha}[\alpha_1, a_1]$, $t_2 = \Omega^{\beta}[\alpha_2, a_2]$ with $\alpha \equiv \beta$.

7.3.1. If $\alpha_1 \equiv \alpha_2$ and $a_1 \equiv a_2$, then $t_1 \equiv t_2$.

7.3.2. If $\alpha_1 < \alpha_2$ and $[\alpha_2, a_2] \equiv \mathrm{DP}(\alpha_1, a_1)$ and

$$\bigwedge x[x \in \mathrm{ND}(\alpha_1, a_1) \to x < [\alpha_2, a_2]],$$

then $t_1 \equiv t_2$.

7.3.3. If $\alpha_2 < \alpha_1$ and $[\alpha_1, a_1] \equiv \mathrm{DP}(\alpha_2, a_2)$ and

$$\bigwedge x[x \in \mathrm{ND}(\alpha_2, a_2) \to x < [\alpha_1, a_1]],$$

then $t_1 \equiv t_2$.

7.4. Let $S(\alpha) = \langle \alpha_1, \ldots, \alpha_k \rangle$ and $S(\beta) = \langle \beta_1, \ldots, \beta_n \rangle$. If $k = n$ and there is a permutation $(l_1, \ldots, l_k)$ of $(1, \ldots, k)$ such that $\alpha_i \equiv \beta_{l_i}$ for each $i = 1, \ldots, k$, then $\alpha \equiv \beta$. If $k < n$ (resp. $n < k$) and there is a permutation $(l_1, \ldots, l_n)$ of $(1, \ldots, n)$ (resp. a permutation $(l_1, \ldots, l_k)$ of $(1, \ldots, k)$) such that $\alpha_m \equiv \beta_{l_m}$ for $1 \leqslant m \leqslant k$ and $\beta_{l_m} = \mathbf{0}$ for $k < m \leqslant n$ (resp. $\alpha_{l_m} \equiv \beta_m$ for $1 \leqslant m \leqslant n$ and $\alpha_{l_m} = \mathbf{0}$ for $n < m \leqslant k$), then $\alpha \equiv \beta$.

7.5. If t_1, t_2 are principal terms and if $E(t_1) < E(t_2)$, then $t_1 < t_2$.

7.6. If $t_1 = \Omega^{\alpha}$, $t_2 = \Omega^{\beta}[\gamma, a]$ and if $\alpha \equiv \beta$, then $t_1 < t_2$.

7.7. Let $t_1 = \Omega^{\alpha}[\alpha_1, a_1]$, $t_2 = \Omega^{\beta}[\alpha_2, a_2]$ with $\alpha \equiv \beta$.

7.7.1. If $\alpha_1 \equiv \alpha_2$ and $a_1 < a_2$, then $t_1 < t_2$.

7.7.2. If $\alpha_1 < \alpha_2$ and $\bigwedge x\{P(x, \alpha_1, a_1) \to x < [\alpha_2, a_2]\}$, then $t_1 < t_2$.

7.7.3. If $\bigvee x\{P(x, \alpha_2, a_2) \wedge [\alpha_1, a_1] < x\}$, then $t_1 < t_2$.

7.7.4. If $\bigvee x[x \in \mathrm{ND}(\alpha_2, a_2) \wedge x \equiv [\alpha_1, a_1]]$, then $t_1 < t_2$.

7.8. Let β be a principal term, then if $\beta_1, \ldots, \beta_m < \beta$ we have $\beta_1 \# \ldots \# \beta_m < \beta$.

7.9. Let $\alpha, \beta_1, \ldots, \beta_m$ be principal terms, $m > 1$. If $\alpha \leqslant \beta_k$ for some k $(1 \leqslant k \leqslant m)$, then $\alpha < \beta_1 \# \ldots \# \beta_m$.

7.10. Let $\alpha = \alpha_1 \# \ldots \# \alpha_m$, $\beta = \beta_1 \# \ldots \# \beta_n$ be the n.f.r. for α, β resp. where $n > 1$, $m > 1$. If there exist α_l $(1 \leqslant l \leqslant m)$, β_k $(1 \leqslant k \leqslant n)$ such that $\alpha_l = \beta_k$ and

$$\alpha_1 \# \ldots \# \alpha_{l-1} \# \alpha_{l+1} \# \ldots \# \alpha_m < \beta_1 \# \ldots \# \beta_{k-1} \# \beta_{k+1} \# \ldots \# \beta$$

then $\alpha < \beta$.

Associativity and commutativity follow trivially from def. 7.4. We see from def. 1.3 that $b < \Omega$ in the term $\Omega^\alpha[\beta, b]$. The following theorems show that $\equiv$ is an equivalence relation, the $<$-relation is compatible with $\equiv$, and that the system T is linearly ordered.

THEOREM 1.1. *Let a and b be any terms; then*

(i) $a \equiv a$ *and* $\neg\,(a < a)$.

(ii) *If* $a \equiv b$, *then* $b \equiv a$.

(iii) *One and only one of the following hold:*

$$a < b,\ a \equiv b,\ b < a.$$

PROOF. We prove (i) by induction on $D(a)$, and we prove (ii) and (iii) by induction on $D(a)+D(b)$.

THEOREM 1.2. *Let a, b, c be any terms, then*

(i) $a \equiv b \wedge b \equiv c \rightarrow a \equiv c$,

(ii) $a < b \wedge b < c \rightarrow a < c$,

(iii) $a \equiv b \wedge b < c \rightarrow a < c$,

(iv) $a \equiv b \wedge c < b \rightarrow c < a$.

PROOF. We prove the conjunction of (i)–(iv) by induction on $D(a)+D(b)+D(c)$. Namely, if a', b', c' are any terms such that $D(a')+D(b')+D(c') < D(a)+D(b)+D(c)$ and if a', b', c' satisfy the premise of (i), (ii), (iii) or (iv) then the conclusion follows. Let us assume that $a = [\alpha_1, a_1]$, $b = [\alpha_2, a_2]$, $c = [\alpha_3, a_3]$, where $\alpha_1 \equiv \alpha_2$, $a_1 \equiv a_2$, $\alpha_2 < \alpha_3$, $[\alpha_3, a_3] \equiv \mathrm{DP}(\alpha_2, a_2)$ and $\bigwedge x[x \in \mathrm{ND}(\alpha_2, a_2) \rightarrow x < [\alpha_3, a_3]]$. By the induction hypothesis $\alpha_1 \equiv \alpha_2$ and $\alpha_2 < \alpha_3$ imply $\alpha_1 < \alpha_3$. Since $\alpha_1 \equiv \alpha_2$ and $a_1 \equiv a_2$, it is easy to see that $\mathrm{DP}(\alpha_2, a_2) \equiv \mathrm{DP}(\alpha_1, a_1)$, and that if $y \in \mathrm{ND}(\alpha_1, a_1)$ with $y \not\equiv \mathbf{0}$, then there is an $x \in \mathrm{ND}(\alpha_2, a_2)$ such that $y \equiv x$. Thus by the induction assumption $\mathrm{DP}(\alpha_1, a_1) \equiv [\alpha_3, a_3]$ and $\bigwedge x[x \in \mathrm{ND}(\alpha_1, a_1) \rightarrow x < [\alpha_3, a_3]]$. Thus $[\alpha_1, a_1] \equiv [\alpha_3, a_3]$. The other case are similar.

We can now easily show that if $b < a \# 1$ then $b \leqslant a$.

THEOREM 1.3. $\bigwedge x\{P(x, \alpha, a) \rightarrow x \leqslant [\alpha, a]\}$.

PROOF. By induction on $D([\alpha, a])$. Let p be the maximum part of (α, a). We can assume that $p = \mathrm{DP}(\alpha, a)$ and all other parts of (α, a) are less than p, for otherwise $p < [\alpha, a]$. Let $p = [\beta, b]$. If $\alpha < \beta$, then $[\alpha, a] \equiv$ $\equiv [\beta, b]$. If $\alpha \equiv \beta$ and $a = [\beta, b]$, then $b \leqslant [\beta, b]$ by the induction hypothesis and hence $[\beta, b] \equiv [\alpha, b] \leqslant [\alpha, [\beta, b]] = [\alpha, a]$. If $a \equiv \mathbf{0}$ then p is a constituent of α. Since $\alpha \equiv \beta$ there is a constituent q of β such that $p \equiv q$.

If $b \equiv \mathbf{0}$, then $p \equiv [\alpha, a]$. If $b > \mathbf{0}$ then $[\beta, b] > q \equiv [\beta, b]$ which contradicts theorem 1.1.

Now assume that $\beta < \alpha$ and $a \equiv \mathbf{0}$. Let $P(r, \beta, b)$ with $r > [\alpha, a]$. Let α^* be obtained by replacing p by r in α. Then, since $[\beta, b] \geqslant r$, we have $r \leqslant [\alpha^*, \mathbf{0}] \leqslant [\alpha, \mathbf{0}] < r$, a contradiction. If there is an $r \in \mathrm{ND}(\beta, b)$ such that $r \equiv [\alpha, a]$ then, since $[\beta, b] > r$, we have $r \leqslant [\alpha^*, \mathbf{0}] < [\alpha, \mathbf{0}] \equiv r$, again a contradiction. If $P(r, \beta, b)$ implies $r < [\alpha, a]$ then $[\beta, b] < [\alpha, a]$. If $r \in \mathrm{ND}(\beta, b) \to r < [\alpha, a]$ and $p \equiv [\alpha, \mathbf{0}]$ where $p = \mathrm{DP}(\beta, b)$ then $[\alpha, a] \equiv [\beta, b]$. The case when $a \not\equiv \mathbf{0}$ and $\beta < \alpha$ is similar.

It is easy to see that if $p \equiv \mathbf{0}$, $p = \Omega^{\mathbf{0}}$ or $p = t_1 \# \ldots \# t_n$, then the theorem holds.

§ 2. Well-foundedness. In this section it is useful to alter the definition of term by writing $\Omega^{\beta}(a_1 \# \ldots \# a_n)$ for $\Omega^{\beta} a_1 \# \ldots \# \Omega^{\beta} a_n$ where $Cl(a_i) = 2$ $(1 \leqslant i \leqslant n)$. Thus, for example, we write $\Omega^{\Omega([\mathbf{0}, \mathbf{0}] \# \mathbf{1})} \# \# \Omega[\mathbf{0}, \mathbf{0}] \# 1)$ instead of $\Omega^{\Omega[\mathbf{0}, \mathbf{0}] \# \Omega} \# \Omega[\mathbf{0}, \mathbf{0}] \# \Omega$. If $\mathbf{1}$ is a summand of t, then we write $t = \alpha \# \mathbf{1}$. If $t = \alpha \# \mathbf{1}$ then the term $t^* = \alpha$ is defined inductively in the obvious way. If it is not the case that either $t = \mathbf{0}$ or $t = \alpha \# \mathbf{1}$ then we write $t \in \mathrm{Lim}$.

LEMMA 2.1

(i). *Suppose* $[\alpha \# \mathbf{1}, \mathbf{0}] > [\beta, b]$. *Then there exists a* k *such that* $g(k) > [\beta, b]$, *where* $g(1) = [\alpha, \mathbf{0}]$, $g(n+1) = [\alpha, g(n)]$.

(ii). *Suppose* $[\alpha \# \mathbf{1}, a \# \mathbf{1}] > [\beta, b]$. *Then there exists a* k *such that* $g(k) > [\beta, b]$ *where* $g(1) = [\alpha \# \mathbf{1}, a] \# \mathbf{1}$, $g(n+1) = [\alpha, g(n)]$.

PROOF. We prove (i) by induction on $D([\beta, b])$. It is easy to see that $\alpha \# \mathbf{1} \not\equiv \beta$. Assume that $\alpha \# \mathbf{1} > \beta$ and $[\alpha \# \mathbf{1}, \mathbf{0}] > p$ where p is the maximum part of (β, b). By the induction assumption there is a k such that $g(k) > q$, where q is the maximum summand of p. Thus $g(k) > p$. If $\alpha > \beta$, then $g(k) > [\beta, b]$. If $\alpha \equiv \beta$, then $g(k) > b$ and thus $g(k+1) = [\alpha, g(k)] > [\beta, b]$.

If there is a part of $(\alpha \# \mathbf{1}, \mathbf{0})$ which is greater than $[\beta, b]$, then there is a part of $(\alpha, \mathbf{0})$ which is greater than $[\beta, b]$. Thus $g(1) > [\beta, b]$. If there is a $p \in \mathrm{ND}(\alpha \# \mathbf{1}, \mathbf{0})$ such that $p \equiv [\beta, b]$, then there is a part of $(\alpha, \mathbf{0})$ which is equal to $[\beta, b]$. Thus $g(2) > g(1) \geqslant [\beta, b]$.

We also prove (ii) by induction on $D([\beta, b])$.

Let $\alpha \not\equiv \mathbf{0}$ be any term. If $K(L(\alpha)) \not\equiv \mathbf{1}$ or $E(L(\alpha)) \equiv \mathbf{0}$, then $\alpha(c)$ is the term obtained by replacing the summand $L(\alpha)$ of α by the term $\Omega^{E(L(\alpha))}c$.

If $K(L(\alpha)) \equiv \mathbf{1}$ and $E(L(\alpha)) \not\equiv \mathbf{0}$, then $\alpha(c)$ is obtained by replacing $L(\alpha)$ by $\Omega^{\beta(c)}$ where $\beta = E(L(\alpha))$. Let $t = [\alpha, a] \not\equiv [\mathbf{0}, \mathbf{0}]$, then $t\{c\} = [\alpha, c]$ if $a \not\equiv \mathbf{0}$ and $t\{c\} = [\alpha(c), a]$ if $a \equiv \mathbf{0}$. We see that $t\{c\}$ is obtained by replacing the distinguished part of (α, a) by c only at $\mathrm{DP}(\alpha, a)$.

LEMMA 2.2. *If* $t = [\alpha, a] > [\beta, b]$ *and if* $\mathrm{DP}(\alpha, a) \in \mathrm{Lim}$ *then there is a* $c < \mathrm{DP}(\alpha, a)$ *such that* $t\{c\} > [\beta, b]$.

PROOF. By induction on $D([\beta, b])$. If $\alpha \equiv \beta$ and $a > b$ then $a \in \mathrm{Lim}$ thus choose $c = b \# \mathbf{1}$. If $\alpha > \beta$ and all parts of (β, b) are less than $[\alpha, a]$, then by the induction hypothesis there is a c such that $t\{c\} > p$ where p is any part of (β, b). Note that $\alpha(c) > \beta$. Thus $t\{c\} > [\beta, b]$.

Assume that there is a part p of (α, a) such that $p > [\beta, b]$. If $p = \mathrm{DP}(\alpha, a)$, then set $c = [\beta, b] \# \mathbf{1}$; if $p \neq \mathrm{DP}(\alpha, a)$, then set $c = \mathbf{1}$. If $q \in \mathrm{ND}(\alpha, a)$ and $q \equiv [\beta, b]$, then choose $c = \mathbf{1} \# \mathbf{1}$.

LEMMA 2.3. *Let* $[\alpha, a \# \mathbf{1}] > [\beta, b]$. *If* $\mathrm{DP}(\alpha, \mathbf{0}) \in \mathrm{Lim}$ *then either* $[\alpha, a] > [\beta, b]$ *or there is a* $c < \mathrm{DP}(\alpha, \mathbf{0})$ *such that* $[\alpha(c), [\alpha, a] \# \mathbf{1}] > [\beta, b]$.

PROOF. By induction on $D([\beta, b])$. If $\alpha \equiv \beta$ then $a \# \mathbf{1} > b$ and hence $a \geqslant b$. If $a > b$ then $[\alpha, a] > [\beta, b]$ and if $a \equiv b$ then $[\alpha(c), [\alpha, a] \# \mathbf{1}] > [\beta, b]$ with $c = \mathbf{1}$. Assume that $\alpha > \beta$ and all parts of (β, b) are less than $[\alpha, a \# \mathbf{1}]$. Let q be the maximum summand of the maximum part p of $[\beta, b]$. Then either $[\alpha, a] > q$ and hence $[\alpha, a] > [\beta, b]$, or there is a $c_1 < \mathrm{DP}(\alpha, \mathbf{0})$ such that $[\alpha(c_1), [\alpha, a] \# \mathbf{1}] > q$. Since $\alpha > \beta$ there is a $c_2 < \mathrm{DP}(\alpha, \mathbf{0})$ such that $\alpha(c_2) > \beta$. The lemma holds taking $c_3 = \max(c_1, c_2)$.

If there is a part $p \neq a \# \mathbf{1}$ of $(\alpha, a \# \mathbf{1})$ such that $p > [\beta, b]$ then $[\alpha, a] > [\beta, b]$. If $p = a \# \mathbf{1}$ then $[\alpha, a] \# \mathbf{1} > [\alpha, a] \geqslant [\beta, b]$. Thus the lemma holds taking $c = \mathbf{1}$. Similarly, if $p \in \mathrm{ND}(\alpha, a \# \mathbf{1})$ and $p \equiv [\beta, b]$, then since $a \# \mathbf{1} \not\equiv [\beta, b]$ we have $[\alpha, a] \# \mathbf{1} > [\alpha, a] \geqslant [\beta, b]$. Thus choose $c = \mathbf{1}$.

Let $\alpha \not\equiv \mathbf{0}$ be any term such that $\mathrm{DP}(\alpha, \mathbf{0}) = \mathbf{1}$ and $\alpha \neq \gamma \# \mathbf{1}$. If $E(L(\alpha)) = \beta \# \mathbf{1}$, then $\alpha[c]$ is the term obtained by replacing the summand $L(\alpha)$ of α by the term $\Omega^{\beta}c$. If $E(L(\alpha)) \neq \beta \# \mathbf{1}$ then $a[c]$ is obtained by replacing $L(\alpha)$ by $\Omega^{\beta[c]}$ where $\beta = E(L(\alpha))$. We see that if $\alpha > \beta$ and c is greater than any constituent of β then $\alpha[c] > \beta$.

LEMMA 2.4. *Let* $[\alpha, \mathbf{0}] > [\beta, b]$ *where* $\alpha \not\equiv \mathbf{0}$, $\mathrm{DP}(\alpha, \mathbf{0}) = \mathbf{1}$. *If* $\alpha \neq \gamma \# \mathbf{1}$, *then there exists an* n *such that* $g(n) > [\beta, b]$, *where* $g(1) = [\alpha[\mathbf{1}], \mathbf{0}]$, $g(n+1) = [\alpha[g(n)], \mathbf{0}]$.

PROOF. By induction on $D([\beta, b])$. It is easy to see that $\alpha \not\equiv \beta$. Assume

$\alpha > \beta$ and all parts of (β, b) are less than $[\alpha, \mathbf{0}]$. Then there is an m such that $g(m) > p$ where p is the maximum summand of $[\beta, b]$. Hence $\alpha[g(m)] > \beta$ and thus $g(m+1) > [\beta, b]$.

Assume that there is a part p of $(\alpha, \mathbf{0})$ such that $p > [\beta, b]$. Then p is a part of $g(1)$ and hence $g(1) > [\beta, b]$. Similarly any non-distinguished part of $(\alpha, \mathbf{0})$ is a non-distinguished part of $g(2)$, thus $g(2) > [\beta, b]$.

LEMMA 2.5. *Let* $[\alpha, a \# \mathbf{1}] > [\beta, b]$ *and let* α *be as in lemma* 2.4 *with* $\alpha \neq \gamma \# \mathbf{1}$. *Then there is an n such that* $g(n) > [\beta, b]$ *where* $g(1) = [\alpha, a] \# \mathbf{1}$, $g(n+1) = [\alpha[g(n)], \mathbf{0}]$.

PROOF. By induction on $D([\beta, b])$.

Note that lemmas 2.1–2.5 hold when $[\beta, b]$ is replaced by an arbitrary term t^*. Simply take S to be the maximum summand of t^*, and apply the restricted result.

Before proceeding to a proof of the well-foundedness of any proper segment of our notations we need the following definitions. We assume that the reader is familiar with the formalization of H (elementary intuitionistic analysis) as given in [**4**]. Let Q be any property, and ρ any relation definable in H.

DEFINITION 8. Q is *progressive with respect to* ρ, written Prog (Q, ρ), if

$$\bigwedge x\{\bigwedge y[x\rho y \to Q(y)] \to Q(x)\}.$$

The principle of *proof by transfinite induction* with respect to ρ up to a, written $\mathrm{I}(\rho, a)$, is

$$\bigwedge Q\{\mathrm{Prog}\,(Q, \rho) \to \bigwedge y[a\rho y \to Q(y)]\}.$$

DEFINITION 9. The relation ρ is *well-founded up to a*, written WF (ρ, a) if given any free choice sequence f, if $a\rho f(0)$ then

$$\bigvee n \neg [f(n)\rho f(n+1)].$$

Finally by the *axiom of transfinite induction* for a given relation ρ up to a, written $\mathrm{TI}(\rho, a)$ is meant the axiom scheme

$$\mathrm{WF}(\rho, a) \to \mathrm{I}(\rho, a).$$

We shall be using only one order relation $>$ thus we will write Prog (Q) for Prog $(Q, >)$ etc.

As in [**5**], p. 29 we can find a one to one mapping ψ from our notations into the natural numbers. Let us assume that this has been shown. In what follows we identify the notation with the natural number given by ψ.

Let

$$T_1(\alpha_1, z, x) = \alpha_1 \# \Omega^z x$$

and

$$T_{k+1}(\alpha_1, \ldots, \alpha_{k+1}, z, x) = \alpha_1 \# \Omega^{T_k(\alpha_2, \ldots, \alpha_{k+1}, z, x)}.$$

Note that, for example, $T_1(\alpha_1, z, \mathbf{1}) = \alpha_1 \# \Omega^z$, $T_1(\alpha_1, z, \mathbf{0}) \equiv \alpha_1$ and $T_1(\alpha_1, z, y \# \mathbf{1}) = T_1(\alpha_1 \# \Omega^z y, z, \mathbf{1})$. We define

$$S_k(\alpha_1, \ldots, \alpha_k, z, x, a) = [T_k(\alpha_1, \ldots, \alpha_k, z, x), a].$$

Let $U_1(\alpha_1, z)$ denote

$$\alpha_1 \not\equiv \mathbf{0} \to E(L(\alpha_1)) \geqslant z$$

and $U_{n+1}(\alpha_1, \ldots, \alpha_{n+1}, z)$ denote

$$[\alpha_1 \not\equiv \mathbf{0} \to E(L(\alpha_1)) \geqslant T_n(\alpha_2, \ldots, \alpha_n, z, \mathbf{1})] \wedge U_n(\alpha_2, \ldots, \alpha_{n+1}, z).$$

Let $P_n(\alpha_1, \ldots, \alpha_n, z, x)$ denote

$$\bigwedge b\{\mathrm{WF}(b) \to \mathrm{WF}(S_n(\alpha_1, \ldots, \alpha_n, z, x, b))\};$$

e.g. $P_2(\alpha_1, \alpha_2, z, x)$ denotes $\bigwedge b\{\mathrm{WF}(b) \to \mathrm{WF}([\alpha \# \Omega^{\alpha_2 \# \Omega^z x}, b]$. Finally let $Q_n(z, x)$ denote

$$(\bigwedge \alpha_1) \ldots (\bigwedge \alpha_n)\{U_n(\alpha_1, \ldots, \alpha_n, z) \wedge P_n(\alpha_1, \ldots, \alpha_n, z, \mathbf{0}) \to P_n(\alpha_1, \ldots, \alpha_n, z, x)\}$$

and

$$\alpha_n \not\equiv \mathbf{0} \wedge E(L(\alpha_n)) \equiv z \to K(L(\alpha_n)) \geqslant x.$$

LEMMA 2.6. If

$$\mathrm{WF}(S_n(\alpha_1, \ldots, \alpha_n, z, x, \mathbf{0})) \tag{1}$$

and

$$\bigwedge a[\mathrm{WF}(a) \to \{\mathrm{WF}S_n(\alpha_1, \ldots, \alpha_n, z, x, a) \to \mathrm{WF}S_n(\alpha_1, \ldots, \alpha_n, z, x, a \# \mathbf{1})\}], \tag{2}$$

then $P_n(\alpha_1, \ldots, \alpha_n, z, x)$.

PROOF. We will get $P_n(\alpha_1, \ldots, \alpha_n, z, x)$ from TI by showing Prog λb $\mathrm{WF}S_n(\alpha_1, \ldots, \alpha_n, x, b)$. In view of (1) and (2) the only case to consider is when $b \in \mathrm{Lim}$. Prog λb. $\mathrm{WF}S_n(\alpha_1, \ldots, \alpha_n, x, b)$ then follows from lemma 2.2.

LEMMA 2.7. *Suppose* $x \in \text{Lim}$, $x < \Omega$ *and* $(\bigwedge y < x)P_n(\alpha_1, \ldots, \alpha_n, z, y)$. *Then* $P_n(\alpha_1, \ldots, \alpha_n, z, x)$.

PROOF. We establish (1) and (2) of lemma 2.6. To get (1) observe that the hypothesis implies

$$(\bigwedge y < x)\text{WF}(S_n(\alpha_1, \ldots, \alpha_n, z, y, \mathbf{0}));$$

hence $S_n(\alpha_1, \ldots, \alpha_n, z, x, \mathbf{0})$ by lemma 2.2. To prove (2) let θxb denote $S_n(\alpha_1, \ldots, \alpha_n, z, x, b)$. Then

$$\theta x(a \mathbin{\#} \mathbf{1}) = \lim_{y<x} \theta y((\theta xa) \mathbin{\#} \mathbf{1}) \tag{3}$$

by lemma 2.3. Assume WF(a) and WF(θxa) (so WF((θxa) $\#$ **1**)). Hence from $(\bigwedge y < x)P_n(\alpha_1, \ldots, \alpha_n, z, y)$ we conclude $(\bigwedge y < x)\text{WF}(\theta y((\theta xa) \mathbin{\#} \mathbf{1}))$. Thus $\text{WF}(\theta x(a \mathbin{\#} \mathbf{1}))$ by (3).

THEOREM 2.1. If $Q_n(z, \mathbf{1})$ *then* Prog $\lambda x \,.\, Q_n(z, x)$ for all $x < \Omega$.

PROOF. $Q_n(z, \mathbf{0})$ is obvious. $\bigwedge x\{Q_n(z, x) \to Q_n(z, x \mathbin{\#} \mathbf{1})\}$ follows from $Q_n(z, \mathbf{1})$ because $P_n(\alpha_1, \ldots, \alpha_n, z, x \mathbin{\#} \mathbf{1})$ is just $P_n(\alpha_1, \ldots, \alpha_n \mathbin{\#} \Omega^z, z, x)$. It remains to prove, for $x \in \text{Lim}$, $x < \Omega$, that $Q_n(z, x)$ if $(\bigwedge y < x)Q_n(z, y)$. This follows from lemma 2.7.

COROLLARY 1. $Q_n(z, \mathbf{1}) \to Q_n(z \mathbin{\#} \mathbf{1}, \mathbf{1})$.

PROOF. Assume $Q_n(z, \mathbf{1})$. Then $\bigwedge x\{\text{WF}(x) \to Q_n(z, x)\}$ by theorem 2.1 and TI. Assume $U_n(\alpha_1, \ldots, \alpha_n, z \mathbin{\#} \mathbf{1})$ and $P_n(\alpha_1, \ldots, \alpha_n, z \mathbin{\#} \mathbf{1}, \mathbf{0})$; we must prove $P_n(\alpha_1, \ldots, \alpha_n, z \mathbin{\#} \mathbf{1}, \mathbf{1})$. By lemma 2.6 it suffices to prove

$$\text{WF}S_n(\alpha_1, \ldots, \alpha_n, z \mathbin{\#} \mathbf{1}, \mathbf{0}) \tag{4}$$

and

$$\bigwedge a[\text{WF}(a) \to \{\text{WF}(S_n(\alpha_1, \ldots, \alpha_n, z \mathbin{\#} \mathbf{1}, \mathbf{1}, a)) \to \text{WF}(S_n(\alpha_1, \ldots, \alpha_n, z \mathbin{\#} \mathbf{1}, \mathbf{1}, a \mathbin{\#} \mathbf{1}))\}]. \tag{5}$$

From $\bigwedge x[\text{WF}(x) \to Q_n(z, x)]$, $U_n(\alpha_1, \ldots, \alpha_n, z \mathbin{\#} \mathbf{1})$ and $P_n(\alpha_1, \ldots, \alpha_n, z \mathbin{\#} \mathbf{1}, \mathbf{0})$ we conclude

$$\bigwedge x[\text{WF}(x) \to P_n(\alpha_1, \ldots, \alpha_n, z, x)]. \tag{6}$$

Hence $\bigwedge x[\text{WF}(x) \to \text{WF}(S_n(\alpha_1, \ldots, \alpha_n, z, x, \mathbf{0}))]$. Hence (4) follows from lemma 2.4. To prove (5) let $g(n)$ be as in lemma 2.5. Hence, assuming WF(a) and $\text{WF}(S_n(\alpha_1, \ldots, \alpha_n, z \mathbin{\#} \mathbf{1}, \mathbf{1}, a))$, we conclude $\bigwedge n\text{WF}(g(n))$ with the help of $\bigwedge x(\text{WF}(x) \to \text{WF}S_n(\alpha_1, \ldots, \alpha_n, z, x, \mathbf{0}))$ proved above.

But

$$S_n(\alpha_1, \ldots, \alpha_n, z \# \mathbf{1}, \mathbf{1}, a \# \mathbf{1}) = \lim_{n\to\infty} g(n)$$

by lemma 2.5. Hence $\mathrm{WF}(S_n(\alpha_1, \ldots, \alpha_n, z \# \mathbf{1}, \mathbf{1}, a \# \mathbf{1}))$. Thus (5) is proven.

COROLLARY 2. $Q_n(\mathbf{0}, \mathbf{1})$.

PROOF. If $n > 1$, then $Q_n(\mathbf{0}, \mathbf{1})$ is $\bigwedge z(Q_{n-1}(z, \mathbf{1}) \to Q_{n-1}(z \# \mathbf{1}, \mathbf{1}))$, so $Q_n(\mathbf{0}, \mathbf{1})$ from corollary 1. We must prove $Q_1(\mathbf{0}, \mathbf{1})$ separately. This proof is similar to the last part of the proof of corollary 1, a function g being constructed by use of lemma 2.1 and an appeal being made to lemma 2.6 (for S_1 and P_1).

We define Ω_n for all $n < w$ inductively as follows:

$$\Omega_0 = \Omega,$$

$$\Omega_{n+1} = \Omega^{\Omega_n}.$$

COROLLARY 3. For all k, $\mathrm{WF}([\Omega_k, \mathbf{0}])$.

PROOF. We first prove $(\bigwedge b)\{\mathrm{WF}(b) \to \mathrm{WF}([\mathbf{0}, b])\}$. Assume $\mathrm{WF}([\mathbf{0}, a])$ for all $a < b$. Let f generate a descending chain, where $f(0) < [\mathbf{0}, b]$. Then $f(0) = k[\mathbf{0}, a_1] \# \beta$ where k is an integer, $a_1 < b$ and $\beta < [\mathbf{0}, a_1]$. Since $\beta < [\mathbf{0}, a_1]$ we can apply the hypothesis of transfinite induction and conclude that there is an n such that $f(0) > \ldots > f(n) = j[\mathbf{0}, a_1] \# \gamma$, where $j < k$ and $\gamma < [\mathbf{0}, a_1]$. After finitely many applications of this argument we get p such that $f(p) = \delta$, where $\delta < [\mathbf{0}, a_1]$, so we can apply the hypothesis of transfinite induction once more to get q such that $\neg\, [f(p) > f(q+1)]$. Now set $\alpha_1 = \ldots = \alpha_n = z = \mathbf{0}$ in corollary 2 and get

$$\bigwedge b\{\mathrm{WF}(b) \to \mathrm{WF}([\underbrace{\Omega^{\cdot^{\cdot^{\Omega^{\mathbf{0}}\mathbf{0}}}}}_{n}, b])\} \to \bigwedge b\{\mathrm{WF}(b) \to \mathrm{WF}([\underbrace{\Omega^{\cdot^{\cdot^{\Omega^{\mathbf{0}}\mathbf{1}}}}}_{n}, b])\}.$$

Hence from $\bigwedge b\{\mathrm{WF}(b) \to \mathrm{WF}([\mathbf{0}, b])\}$ and $Q_1(\mathbf{0})$ and $\ldots$ and $Q_n(\mathbf{0})$ we get

$$\mathrm{WF}([\underbrace{\Omega^{\cdot^{\cdot^{\Omega}}}}_{n-1}, \mathbf{0}]).$$

COROLLARY 4. *Let* $T^* = \{\alpha: \alpha \in T \wedge \alpha < \Omega\}$. *Any proper segment of* T^* *is well-ordered.*

PROOF. From corollary 3.

From theorem 1.1 we see that the relation $<$ is decidable. Thus we have proven the well-ordering of any proper segment of our notations less than Ω by using TI_D.

Simon Fraser University

REFERENCES

[1] L. E. J. BROUWER, Über Definitionsbereiche von Funktionen, *Math. Ann.* **97** (1927) 60–76.

[2] H. GERBER, An extension of Schütte's klammersymbols, *Math. Ann.* **174** (1967) 203–216.

[3] K. GÖDEL, Über eine bisher noch nicht benutze Erweiterung des finiten Standpunktes, *Dialectica* **12** (1958) 280–287.

[4] W. A. HOWARD and G. KREISEL, Transfinite induction and bar induction of types zero and one, and the role of continuity in intuitionistic analysis , *J. Symb. Logic.* **31** (1966) 325–358.

[5] K. SCHÜTTE, Kennzeichnung von Ordnungszahlen durch rekursiv erklärte Funktionen, *Math. Ann.* **127** (1954) 15–32.

[6] C. SPECTOR, Provably recursive functionals of analysis: a consistency proof of analysis by an extension of principles formulated in current intuitionistic mathematics, *Proc. Symp. in Pure Mathematics, Am. Math. Soc., Providence* **5** (1962) 1–27.

REGULAR ORDINALS AND NORMAL FORMS

DAVID ISLES

1. Introduction. The ordinary Cantor normal form for countable ordinals θ employs the ordinal functions of addition, multiplication and exponentiation (based on ω) to express θ in the form $\omega^{\theta_1}n_1 + \ldots + \omega^{\theta_k}n_k$; if θ is not a fixed point of the normal function $\lambda x\omega^x$, the ordinals θ_i, n_i are all $< \theta$. In as much as the fixed points of any normal function f are themselves the range of a normal function (called the derivative of f; see theorem 2.1), one can define a sequence of normal functions $\{f_\beta\}$ where f enumerates the fixed points of f_α for $\alpha < \beta$. This sequence can be used to obtain normal forms for an initial segment of the second number class in which many of the fixed points of $\lambda x\omega^x$ are included. The length of this segment depends on the size of the collection $\{f_\beta\}$. Starting with work of Veblen [7], Bachmann in [**1**] showed how to use normal functions of the third number class in defining the set $\{f_\beta\}$; this procedure was later continued by Gerber [**4**] several of whose ideas occur here. In this paper, the process is generalized to allow the use of the αth number class for certain transfinite α.

Let $G = G_1$ be the normal function which enumerates the closure under limits of the class of regular ordinals (def. 2.2). In section 3 we employ the sequence $\{G_\beta\}$, where G_β enumerates the fixed points of G_α for $\alpha < \beta$, in defining normal forms for all regular ordinals $\delta < G_I(1)$ where I is the first regular fixed point of G. Normal forms for ordinals a, $G(p) < a < G(p+1)$ are obtained by constructing sets of ordinals $\mathrm{Or}(p) \subseteq G_I(1)+1$ and then generating the derivatives φ_α of the function $\lambda x G(p)^x$ (exponentiation) for $\alpha \in \mathrm{Or}(p)$. In section 6 we define the sets $\mathrm{Or}(p)$ by induction on $\alpha < G_I(1)$: if $\alpha < G(p+1)$, then $\alpha \in \mathrm{Or}(p)$; if $G(p+1) < \alpha$ and $\alpha \in \mathrm{Or}(q)$ $(p+1 \leqslant q)$ then, roughly speaking, $\alpha \in \mathrm{Or}(p)$ only if it is possible to define a normal form for α in which all of the ordinals occurring are $\leqslant G(p+1)$. Details of the procedure whereby a normal form for $\alpha \in \mathrm{Or}(q)$ can be constructed are given in sections 4, 5 and 7.

We conclude this paper first by demonstrating that the normal forms developed include those of Bachmann and yield a recursive ordering for a segment of the countable ordinals, and then by indicating how they can be used to replace ordinal diagrams in some of Takeuti's work. Most proofs are omitted.

2. Bachmann collections of ordinals. In what follows we will consider an ordinal number to be the set of its predecessors. A normal function is an increasing continuous ordinal function; 0 will not in general be included in the domain of the normal functions discussed here. If f is any ordinal function and θ an ordinal, $\mathrm{V}f$ will denote the range of f, $f\upharpoonright\theta$ the restriction of f to θ, $\mathrm{Suc}(\theta)$ that θ is a successor, and $\mathrm{Lim}(\theta)$ that θ is a limit.

DEFINITION 2.1. A limit ordinal ∂ is *regular* if there is no $\theta < \partial$ and function $f\colon \theta \to \partial$ such that $\partial = \mathrm{lub}\,\{f(\alpha)+1 | \alpha < \theta\}$.

To secure the existence of regular ordinals we add to the usual axioms of set theory (not including the axiom of choice) the following axiom.

AXNORM. Every normal function defined for all ordinals has arbitrarily great regular fixed points.

Applying it to the identity function, we obtain an enumeration of the closure under limits of the regular ordinals.

DEFINITION 2.2. $G(1) = \omega$.
$G(\theta+1) =$ least regular ordinal greater than $G(\theta)$.
$\mathrm{Lim}(\mu) \Rightarrow G(\mu) = \mathrm{lub}\{G(\theta) | \theta < \mu\}$.

In what follows up through theorem 2.5 we will suppose that f is a normal function on the regular ordinal ∂.

DEFINITION 2.3. The mth iterations of f are the normal functions $f^m(x)$ where $f^0(x) = x$ and $f^{n+1}(x) = f(f^n(x))$.

THEOREM 2.1 (Veblen [7]). *The set of fixed points of f is order isomorphic to ∂. The order isomorphism f' is a normal function on ∂ (called the derivative of f).*

THEOREM 2.2. (1). $f'(1) = \mathrm{lub}\,\{f^n(1) | 1 \leqslant n < \omega\}$,
(2). $f'(x+1) = \mathrm{lub}\,\{f^n(f'(x)+1) | 1 \leqslant n < \omega\}$.

Both of the given sequences are fundamental.

Let $\{f_\theta | 1 \leqslant \theta < \mu, \mathrm{Lim}(\mu), \mu < \partial\}$ be a sequence of normal functions on ∂.

THEOREM 2.3. (Veblen [7]). *Suppose that if* $1 < \theta < \mu$ *then* $Vf_\theta \subseteq Vf'_\nu$ *for* $1 \leqslant \nu < \theta$. *Then* $\bigcap \{Vf_\theta | \ 1 \leqslant \theta < \mu\}$ *is order isomorphic to* ∂ *and the order isomorphism* φ *is a normal function on* ∂.

THEOREM 2.4. (notation from theorem 2.3). *Let*

$$\mu = \text{lub}\{\mu(i) | 1 \leqslant i < \pi, \ \text{Lim}(\pi), \pi \leqslant \mu\}.$$

Then

$$\varphi(1) = \text{lub}\{f_{\mu(i)}(1) | 1 \leqslant i < \pi\}$$

and

$$\varphi(x+1) = \text{lub}\{f_{\mu(i)}(\varphi(x)+1) | 1 \leqslant i < \pi\}.$$

All of the given sequences are fundamental.

$\{f_\theta | 1 \leqslant \theta < \partial\}$ is a sequence of normal functions on ∂.

THEOREM 2.5 (Veblen [7]). *If for every* θ, $1 \leqslant \theta < \partial$,

(1). $Vf_\theta \subseteq Vf'_\nu$, $1 \leqslant \nu < \theta$

and

(2). $\text{Lim}(\theta) \Rightarrow Vf_\theta = \bigcap \{Vf_\nu | 1 \leqslant \nu < \theta\}$,

then the function $\lambda x f_x(1)$ *is a normal function on* ∂.

The sets $\text{Or}(p)$ mentioned in the introduction will be unions of sets of the following sort:

DEFINITION 2.4. Suppose $\text{Lim}(\mu)$. A Bachmann collection of ordinals of type $\leqslant \mu$ and bounded by π, $\mathfrak{B}(\pi, \mu)$ is a set of ordinals such that:

B1. $\theta \in \mathfrak{B}(\pi, \mu) \Rightarrow \theta \leqslant \pi$,

B2. $1 \in \mathfrak{B}(\pi, \mu)$; $\theta < \pi \ \Rightarrow \ \theta \in \mathfrak{B}(\pi, \mu)$ iff $\theta+1 \in \mathfrak{B}(\pi, \mu)$.

B3. If $\theta \in \mathfrak{B}(\pi, \mu)$ and $\text{Lim}(\theta)$, there is defined a fundamental sequence $\text{DS}[\theta]$ (the 'distinguished sequence' of θ) such that:

(a). Domain of $\text{DS}[\theta] = \text{T}(\theta) \leqslant \mu$.

(b). $\text{DS}[\theta](\text{i}) \in \mathfrak{B}(\pi, \mu)$, $1 \leqslant i < \text{T}(\theta)$; $\theta = \text{lub in } \mathfrak{B}(\pi, \mu)\{\text{DS}[\theta](i)\}$.

(c). If $1 < d < \text{T}(\theta)$, $d = d'+1$ and $\text{Suc}(\text{DS}[\theta](d))$, then $\text{DS}[\theta](d) = \text{DS}[\theta](d')+1$.

(d). $\text{Lim}(e)$ and $e < \text{T}(\theta) \Rightarrow \text{Lim}(\text{DS}[\theta](e))$, $\text{T}(\text{DS}[\theta](e)) = e$ and $\text{DS}[\text{DS}[\theta](e)] = \text{DS}[\theta] \upharpoonright e$,

(e). ('Nesting property'). If $\text{Lim}(\delta)$, $\delta \in \mathfrak{B}(\pi, \mu)$ and $\text{DS}[\theta](i) < \delta \leqslant \text{DS}[\theta](i+1)$, then $\text{DS}[\theta](i) \leqslant \text{DS}[\delta](1)$.

$\text{DS}[\theta](i)$ will often be abbreviated $\theta(i)$.

If $\{f_\alpha | 1 \leqslant \alpha \leqslant \theta\}$ is a set of ordinal functions then if $\beta < \alpha \leqslant \theta$, $\beta \rightarrow \alpha$ means $Vf_\sigma \subseteq Vf_\beta$, $\beta \leqslant \sigma \leqslant \alpha$.

THEOREM 2.6 (Bachmann [**1**]). *Let F be a normal function and ∂ a regular fixed point of F. Given $\mathfrak{B}(\pi, \partial)$ there is a set of normal functions $\{F(\theta, -) | \theta \in \mathfrak{B}(\pi, \partial)\}$ such that:*

(1). *Domain of* $F(\theta, -) = \partial$;

(2). $F(1, -) = F \restriction \partial$;

(3). $F(\theta+1, -) = F(\theta, -)'$;

(4). *if* $\mathrm{Lim}(\theta)$, $\mathrm{T}(\theta) < \partial$, *then* $\mathrm{V}F(\theta, -) = \bigcap \{\mathrm{V}F(\mathrm{DS}[\theta](i), -) | 1 \leqslant i < T(\theta)\}$;

(5). *if* $\mathrm{Lim}(\theta)$, $\mathrm{T}(\theta) = \partial$, *then* $F(\theta, -) = [\lambda i F(\mathrm{DS}[\theta](i), 1)]'$.

Furthermore, in cases 4 *and* 5

(6). $\mathrm{DS}[\theta](d)+1 \rightarrow \mathrm{DS}[\theta](d+1)$.

PROOF. See Bachmann [**1**], p. 130.

The family $\{F(\theta, -) | \theta \in \mathfrak{B}(\pi, \partial)\}$ will be said to be 'based on' $\mathfrak{B}(\pi, \partial)$.

LEMMA 2.7 *Suppose $\pi \in \mathfrak{B}(\pi, \partial)$ and $1 < F(1)$. If $a \in \mathrm{V}F(1, -)$ there is a last $\beta^* \in \mathfrak{B}(\pi, \partial)$ such that $a \in \mathrm{V}F(\beta^*, -)$. If $a < F(\pi+1,1)$, then $a = F(\beta^*, b)$ where $b < a$.*

PROOF. See Bachmann [**1**], Satz 1, p. 138.

This lemma will be basic in our construction of normal forms. Although the normal forms will be defined in terms of normal functions based on Bachmann collections, they will be expressible as finite ordered sets of ordinals. In order to develop these normal forms, we will consider Bachmann collections with each member θ of which will be associated finite sets of ordinals called the 'parts' of θ. These finite sets will include the ordinals occurring in the normal form of θ.

Notation. If Q is a set of ordinals and θ an ordinal, then $Q \leqslant \theta$ (or $Q < \theta$) is an abbreviation for $(x)[x \in Q \Rightarrow x \leqslant \theta$ (or $x < \theta)]$ and $\theta \leqslant Q$ (or $\theta < Q$) abbreviates $(\mathrm{E}x)[x \in Q$ and $\theta \leqslant x$ (or $\theta < x)]$.

DEFINITION 2.5. A Bachmann notational collection of type $\leqslant \partial$, bounded by π, $\mathfrak{B}^*(\pi, \partial)$ is a Bachmann collection with each member of which is associated two finite sets of ordinals $P[\theta]$ and $\mathrm{ND}[\theta]$ ('parts' of θ and 'non-distinguished parts' of θ) and an ordinal $\mathrm{D}[\theta]$('distinguished part' of θ) such that:

P1. $x \in \mathrm{P}[\theta] \cup \mathrm{ND}[\theta] \cup \{\mathrm{D}[\theta]\} \Rightarrow x \in \mathfrak{B}^*(\pi, \partial)$, $x \leqslant \theta$, $x < \partial$ and, if $\omega < x$, x is unequal to any regular ordinal.

P2. (a). $\mathrm{P}[\theta] = \mathrm{ND}[\theta] \cup \{\mathrm{D}[\theta]\}$;

(b). $\mathrm{P}[\mathrm{P}[\theta]] = \bigcup \{\mathrm{P}[x] | x \in \mathrm{P}[\theta]\} = \mathrm{P}[\theta]$,

$\mathrm{D}[\mathrm{D}[\theta]] = \mathrm{D}[\theta]$.

Let e be a limit, $e < \mathrm{T}(\theta)$.

P3. $\mathrm{ND}[\mathrm{DS}[\theta](e)] = \mathrm{ND}[\theta]$.

P4. $\mathrm{D}[\theta(e)] \in \mathrm{ND}[\theta(e+k)]$, $1 \leqslant k < \omega$.

P5 (a). $\mathrm{P}[\theta(1)] = \mathrm{ND}[\theta]$;

(b). $\mathrm{P}[\theta(d+k)] = \mathrm{P}[\theta(d)]$, where $d = 1$ or $\mathrm{Lim}(d)$ and $0 \leqslant k < \omega$.

P6. If $\theta(e+i) < \sigma \leqslant \theta(e+i+1)$ and $\sigma \in \mathfrak{B}^*(\pi, \partial)$, then $\mathrm{D}[\theta(e)] \in \mathrm{ND}[\sigma]$, $1 \leqslant i < \omega$.

Notation: If we wish to emphasize that $\mathfrak{B}(\pi, \partial)$ (or $\mathfrak{B}^*(\pi, \partial)$) is a segment we will write $B(\pi, \partial)$ (or $B^*(\pi, \partial)$). In the course of this paper several different Bachmann notational collections will occur; the associated parts and sequences will be variously indicated by $\mathrm{P}[\mathrm{I}; \theta]$, $\mathrm{P}[q; \theta]$, $\mathrm{P}^*[< q; \theta]$, $\mathrm{DS}^*\ [< q; \theta]$ etc.

3. Normal forms for regular ordinals

DEFINITION 3.1. I is the first regular fixed point of G.

The existence of I is guaranteed by AxNorm. Notice that if the axiom of choice is assumed, I is just the first weakly inaccessible ordinal. $\{\theta | 1 \leqslant \theta \leqslant I\}$ is a trivial example of a Bachmann collection of type $\leqslant I$, bounded by I (let $\mathrm{DS}[\theta] = \lambda i[i < \theta]$). Thus we can apply theorem 2.6 to $B(I, I)$ and obtain $\{G(\theta, -) | 1 \leqslant \theta \leqslant I\}$ where $G(1, -) = G \restriction I$.

DEFINITION 3.2. $\mathrm{NF}(I, \theta)$, the Cantor normal form (relative to $\{G(\theta, -) | 1 \leqslant \theta \leqslant I\}$) for ordinals θ, $1 \leqslant \theta < G(I+1, 1)$.

(1). If $\theta = \theta' + k$ where $\mathrm{Lim}(\theta')$, $1 \leqslant k < \omega$,

$$\mathrm{NF}(I; \theta) = \mathrm{NF}(I; \theta') + 1 + \ldots + 1, \ (k \text{ ones}).$$

(2). If $G(p) < \theta < G(p+1)$, $\mathrm{NF}(I; \theta) = \langle \theta \rangle$, $\mathrm{Lim}(\theta)$.

(3). If $\theta \in \mathrm{V}G(1, -)$, β^* is the ordinal given by lemma 2.7 and $\theta = G(\beta^*, b)$, then $\mathrm{NF}(I; \theta) = \langle \beta^*, b \rangle$.

Notation. $\mathrm{NF}(I; \theta) \equiv G(\beta^*, b)$ will mean $\mathrm{NF}(I; \theta) = \langle \beta^*, b \rangle$. Thus $\theta = G(\beta_1^*, b_1) = G(\beta_2^*, b_2)$ is possible although $\mathrm{NF}(I; \theta) \equiv G(\beta_1^*, b_1)$ and $\mathrm{NF}(I; \theta) \not\equiv G(\beta_2^*, b_2)$.

By defining suitable distinguished sequences and parts, we can show that $\{\theta | \theta \leqslant G(1, p+1) < G(I, 1)\}$ is a Bachmann notational segment of type $\leqslant G(1, p+1)$, bounded by $G(1, p+1)$ i.e.

$$\{\theta | \theta \leqslant G(1, p+1)\} = B^*(G(1, p+1), G(1, p+1)).$$

I-distinguished sequences and I-types, $\mathrm{DS}[I;\theta]$ and $\mathrm{T}(I;\theta)$, can be defined inductively for all $\theta < G(I+1, 1)$ by considering NF(I; θ). Except for the cases $G(p) < \theta \leqslant G(p+1)$ and $\mathrm{NF}(I;\theta) \equiv G(I, 1)$ the cases of the definition are almost identical to those of def. 4.5 and will be omitted. If $G(p) < \theta \leqslant G(p+1)$ and $\theta = G(p)+\theta'$, we set $\mathrm{DS}[I;\theta] = \lambda i[G(p)+i]$ and $\mathrm{T}(I;\theta) = \theta'$; if $\theta = G(I, 1)$ we set $\mathrm{T}(I;\theta) = \omega$ and $\mathrm{DS}[I;\theta] = \lambda n s(n)$ where $s(1) = G(1, 1)$ and $s(n+1) = G(s(n), 1)$. The definition of I-parts, $\mathrm{P}[I;\theta]$, $\mathrm{ND}[I;\theta]$ and $\mathrm{D}[I;\theta]$, coincides with def. 4.6 except where $G(p) < \theta \leqslant \leqslant G(p+1)$ or $\theta = G(I, 1)$. If $\theta = G(p)+\theta' < G(p+1)$ we let $\mathrm{P}[I;\theta] = = \mathrm{P}[I;G(p)]\cup\{\theta\}$, $\mathrm{ND}[I;\theta] = \mathrm{P}[I;G(p)]$ and $\mathrm{D}[I;\theta] = \theta$. If $\theta = G(I, 1)$ then $\mathrm{P}[I;\theta] = \mathrm{ND}[I;\theta] = \{1, \omega\}$ and $\mathrm{D}[I;\theta] = \omega$. If $\theta = G(p+1)$ then $\mathrm{P}[I;\theta] = \mathrm{ND}[I;\theta] = \mathrm{P}[I;G(p)]$ and $\mathrm{D}[I;\theta] = \omega$.

By induction on $\{\theta | \theta < G(I+1, 1)\}$ while considering cases arising from $\mathrm{NF}(I;\theta)$ one can establish properties B3(d), B3(e) and P1–P6 (def. 2.5). In the proof of B3(e) and P6 one makes use of the recursion relations:

$$G(s, u) < G(s', u') \text{ iff (a) } s < s' \text{ and } u < G(s', u'),$$
$$\text{or (b). } s = s' \text{ and } u < u',$$
$$\text{or (c). } s' < s \text{ and } G(s, u) < u'.$$

The following properties of I-parts (needed later) can also be derived:

P2(c). $\mathrm{P}[I;\mathrm{ND}[I;\theta]] = \mathrm{ND}[I;\theta]$;
$\mathrm{ND}[I;\mathrm{D}[I;\theta]] \subseteq \mathrm{ND}[I;\theta]$.

P7(a). $\mathrm{Suc}(\theta)$ iff $\mathrm{D}[I;\theta] = 1$,
(b)(i). $\mathrm{D}[I;\theta] = \omega \Rightarrow \mathrm{T}(I;\theta) = \omega$ or $\mathrm{T}(I;\theta) = G(q+1)$.
(ii). $\mathrm{D}[I;\theta] \neq \omega \Rightarrow (\mathrm{E}!q)[G(q) < \mathrm{D}[I;\theta] < G(q+1)$ and $\mathrm{D}[I;\theta] = G(q)+\mathrm{T}(I;\theta)]$.

In both cases if $\mathrm{Lim}(e)$, $e < T(I;\theta)$, then $\mathrm{D}[I;\theta(e)] = G(q)+e$.

P8. If either $\mathrm{D}[I;\theta] = \omega$ and $\mathrm{T}(I;\theta) = G(q+1)$, or $\mathrm{D}[I;\theta] = G(q)+ \mathrm{T}(I;\theta)$, then $\mathrm{P}[I;G(q)] \subseteq \mathrm{ND}[I;\theta]$.

Lemma 3.1 guarantees that in certain circumstances the distinguished sequence of an ordinal can be extended. This 'extension property' will be possessed by the Bachmann collections which we discuss in section 4. If a and b are ordinals, $a < b$, $[a, b] = \{e | a \leqslant e < b\}$.

LEMMA 3.1. *Suppose* $\mathrm{Lim}(\theta)$, $\theta < \beta < G(I+1, 1)$. *Let* $d = \mathrm{T}(I;\theta) = \mathrm{D}[I;\theta]$ *and assume* $G(q) < d < d^* \leqslant G(q+1)$ *where* $d^* \leqslant \beta$ *and* $d^* \leqslant \mathrm{T}(I;\beta)$ *if* $\theta = \mathrm{DS}[I;\beta](d)$. *Then if* $\mathrm{ND}[I;\theta]\cup\mathrm{ND}[I;\beta]\cap[d, d^*) = \emptyset$, *there is an ordinal* θ^*, $\theta^* \leqslant \beta$ *such that* $\mathrm{T}(I;\theta^*) = d^*$, $\mathrm{DS}[I;\theta] = \mathrm{DS}[I;\theta^*]\restriction d$ *and* $\theta = \mathrm{DS}[I;\theta^*](d)$.

PROOF. We use a double induction on β and θ. Notice that if we establish the existence of a suitable θ^*, then $\theta^* \leqslant \beta$. For if $\theta = \theta^*(d) < \beta < \theta^*$ we could conclude that either $\beta = \theta^*(q)$, Lim (q), $d < q = \mathrm{T}(I; \beta) < d^*$, or $\mathrm{D}[I; \theta^*(k)] \in \mathrm{ND}[I; \beta]$, where $d \leqslant k < d^*$. Since $\mathrm{D}[I; \theta^*(d)] = G(q)+\mathrm{T}(I; \theta) = d$, it follows $\mathrm{D}[I; \theta^*(k)] = G(q)+k = k$. Both cases are impossible.

We may assume $\theta \neq \beta(d)$ for if it did simply let $\theta^* = \beta$ if $d^* = \mathrm{T}(I; \beta)$ or $\theta^* = \beta(d^*)$ if $d^* < \mathrm{T}(I; \beta)$. If $G(q) < \theta < G(q+1)$ we would have $\theta = d$ and could take $\theta^* = d^* \leqslant G(q+1)$. There are two cases left to consider: $\mathrm{NF}(I; \theta) \equiv G(\gamma, \mu)$ and $\mathrm{NF}(I; \theta) \equiv G(\mu, b+1)$, where $\mathrm{Lim}(\mu)$. In both cases $\mu < \theta$ and $\mathrm{ND}[I; \mu] \subseteq \mathrm{ND}[I; \theta]$ implies the existence of μ^* with $\mathrm{DS}[I; \mu] = \mathrm{DS}[I; \mu^*] \restriction d$. In the first case, we let $\theta^* = G(\gamma, \mu^*)$ after observing that μ and μ^* must lie between the same consecutive fixed points of $G(\gamma, -)$. In the second case, we let $\theta^* = G(\mu^*, 1)$ if $b = 0$.

$b < G(\mu, b)$ is impossible for that would mean $d = \mathrm{D}[I; \mu] \in \mathrm{P}[I; \mu] \subseteq \mathrm{P}[I; G(\mu, b)] \subseteq \mathrm{ND}[I; \theta]$ (def. 4.6(6)). The remaining possibility is $G(\mu, b) = b$; hence $\mathrm{NF}(I; b) \equiv G(\pi, e)$ for $\mu < \pi$. If $\mu < \pi = \mu^*$, let $\theta^* = G(\mu^*, e+1)$ and if $\mu < \mu^* < \pi$ let $\theta^* = G(\mu^*, b+1)$. $\mu < \pi < \mu^*$ is impossible since this would imply $v \in \mathrm{P}[I; \pi] \subseteq \mathrm{P}[I; b] \subseteq \mathrm{ND}[I; \theta]$ where $\mathrm{Lim}(v)$, $d \leqslant v < d^*$.

Replacing $\mathrm{NF}(I; \theta)$ by $\mathrm{NF}^+(I; \theta)$ in def. 3.2 and changing clause 3 to read $\mathrm{NF}^+(I; \theta) = \langle \mathrm{NF}^+(I; \beta^*), \mathrm{NF}^+(I; b)\rangle$ we can define the extended Cantor normal form of θ (relative to $\{G(\beta, -)\}$).

Remark 1. If $S(I; \theta)$ is the set of ordinals which occur in $\mathrm{NF}^+(I; \theta)$, then $\mathrm{S}(I; \theta) \subseteq \mathrm{P}[I; \theta] \cup \{I\}$.

4. Properties of Bachmann notational collections. Any ordinal θ lying between consecutive values of G has no interesting normal form $\mathrm{NF}^+(I, \theta)$. In this paper we will show how a large number of such ordinals $\leqslant G(I, 1)$ can be assigned a normal form in terms of normal functions and smaller ordinals. In section 6 Bachmann notational collections of type $\leqslant G(p+1)$ will be defined for each $p+1 < G(I, 1)$; these collections will then be used as in theorem 2.6 to derive the set of normal functions which enter into the normal forms. This section and the next will be spent establishing those properties of Bachmann collections which will be needed in their definition.

We will use the abbreviation $\mathfrak{B}(\pi, p)$ to stand for the Bachmann collection $\mathfrak{B}(\pi, G(p+1))$ where $\pi \leqslant G(I, 1)$ and $G(p+1) < G(I, 1)$; distinguished sequences and types of its members will be denoted by $\mathrm{DS}[p; \theta]$ and

$T(p; \theta)$. In addition to B1–B3 we will assume that the following are true of $\mathfrak{B}(\pi, p)$:

B4. If $\theta \leqslant G(p)$ and $\theta \in \mathfrak{B}(\pi, p)$, then $\{\alpha | \alpha \leqslant \theta\} \subseteq \mathfrak{B}(\pi, p)$.

B5. If $\theta \in \mathfrak{B}(\pi, p)$ and $\theta \leqslant G(p+1)$, then $DS[p; \theta] = DS[I; \theta]$ and $T(p; \theta) = T(I; \theta)$.

If the Bachmann collection $\mathfrak{B}(\pi, p)$ is, in fact, a Bachmann notational collection $\mathfrak{B}^*(\pi, p)$, the parts of $\theta \in \mathfrak{B}^*(\pi, p)$ will be denoted by $P[p; \theta]$, $ND[p; \theta]$ and $D[p; \theta]$. In addition to P1–P6 (def. 2.5) and P7, P8 (with p replacing I), the following is assumed to hold for $\mathfrak{B}^*(\pi, p)$:

P9. If $\theta \in \mathfrak{B}^*(\pi, p)$ and $\theta \leqslant G(p+1)$, then $P[p; \theta] = P[I; \theta]$, $ND[p; \theta] = ND[I; \theta]$ and $D[p; \theta] = D[I; \theta]$.

Given $\mathfrak{B}^*(\pi, p)$ we employ theorem 2.6 to generate $\{F^p(\theta; -) | \theta \in \mathfrak{B}^*(\pi, p)\}$ where $F^p(1, -) = \lambda x G(p)^x \upharpoonright G(p+1)$.

We first establish that recursion relations similar to those for $\{G(\beta, -)\}$ hold for $\{F^p(\theta, -)\}$. This is accomplished by a series of lemmas of which the most important is

LEMMA 4.1. *If* $\theta < \gamma$ *and either*

(1). $a = 1$ *and* $ND[p; \theta] < F^p(\gamma, c) = D[p; \theta]$

or

(2). $P[p; \theta] < F^p(\gamma, c) = a$,

then $F^p(\theta, a) = F^p(\gamma, c)$.

THEOREM 4.2 (Recursion relations; Gerber [**4**]). $F^p(\theta, a) < F^p(\gamma, c)$ *iff one of the following conditions holds*:

(1). $\theta < \gamma$ *and* $P[p; \theta] \cup \{a\} < F^p(\gamma, c)$,

(2). $\theta = \gamma$ *and* $a < c$,

(3). $\gamma < \theta$ *and* $F^p(\theta, a) < P[p; \gamma] \cup \{c\}$,

(4). $\gamma < \theta$ *and* $(Ex)[\{(x \in P[p; \gamma]$ *and* $1 < c)$ *or* $(x \in ND[p; \gamma]$ *and* $1 = c)\}$ *and* $x = F^p(\theta, a)]$.

COROLLARY 4.2.1. $F^p(\theta, a) = F^p(\gamma, c)$ *iff one of the following conditions holds*:

(1). $\theta < \gamma$ *and either*

(a). $1 < a$, $a = F^p(\gamma, c)$ *and* $P[p; \theta] < F^p(\gamma, c)$,

or

(b). $1 = a$, $D[p; \theta] = F^p(\gamma, c)$ *and* $ND[p; \theta] < F^p(\gamma, c)$.

(2). *Reverse roles of* θ *and* γ, a *and* c *in* (1).

(3). $\theta = \gamma$ *and* $a = c$.

DEFINITION 4.1. Suppose $\pi \in \mathfrak{B}^*(\pi, p)$. We define by induction on $a < G(p+1)$ the Cantor normal form of a relative to $\{F^p(\theta, -)|\theta \in \mathfrak{B}^*(\pi, p)\}$, $\mathrm{NF}(\pi, p; a)$:

(1). If $a \leqslant G(p)$, $\mathrm{NF}(\pi, p; a) = \mathrm{NF}(I, a)$.

(2). If $a \in \mathrm{V}F^p(1, -)$ let α be the last member of $\mathfrak{B}^*(\pi, p)$ such that $a \in \mathrm{V}F^p(\alpha, -)$; $a = F^p(\alpha, b)$. Then $\mathrm{NF}(\pi, p; a) = \langle \mathrm{NF}(I; G(p))\rangle \langle \alpha, b\rangle$. (This will often be abbreviated as $\mathrm{NF}(\pi, p; a) \equiv F^p(\alpha, b)$).

(3). If $G(p) < a < G(p+1)$ and $a \notin \mathrm{V}F^p(1, -)$ then a can be written $\sum_{i=1}^k F^p(\alpha_i, b_i)m_i + m_{k+1}$ where $m_i < G(p)$ (and the summands are decreasing). Then

$$\mathrm{NF}(\pi, p; a) = \langle\langle \mathrm{NF}(\pi, p; F^p(\alpha_1, b_1))\rangle, \langle \mathrm{NF}(I; m_1)\rangle + \ldots + \mathrm{NF}(I; m_{k+1})\rangle.$$

Remark 2. If $\mu < \pi$, $\mathfrak{B}^*(\mu, p)$ is also a Bachmann notational collection. Suppose $\mu \in \mathfrak{B}^*(\mu, p)$ and $\mathrm{NF}(\mu, p; a) \equiv F^p(\theta, b)$ where $\mathrm{P}[p; \theta] \cup \{b\} < a$, by corollary 4.2.1 it then follows that $\mathrm{NF}(\pi, p; a) \equiv F^p(\theta, b)$.

Using $\mathfrak{B}^*(\pi, p)$ as we used $\{\theta | \theta \leqslant I\}$, we now define the analogous set to $B^*(G(p+1), G(p+1))$.

DEFINITION 4.2. $B^*(\pi, p)$ is the set defined as follows:

(1). If $\pi \leqslant G(p)$, then $B^*(\pi, p) = \{a | a \leqslant \pi\}$;

otherwise,

(2). $a \leqslant G(p) \Rightarrow a \in B^*(\pi, p)$;

(3). if $\mathrm{NF}(\pi, p; a) \equiv F^p(\theta, b)$, $\mathrm{P}[p; \theta] \cup \{b\} < a$ and $\mathrm{P}[p; \theta] \cup \{b\} \subseteq B^*(\pi, p)$, then $a \in B^*(\pi, p)$;

(4). if $\mathrm{NF}(\pi, p; a) \equiv \sum F^p(\theta_i, b_i)m_i + m$ then $a \in B^*(\pi, p)$ if $\{F^p(\theta_i, b_1)\} \subseteq B^*(\pi, p)$.

Members of $B^*(\pi, p)$ will be indicated by a, b, c, etc. From remark 2 it follows that $B^*(\mu, p) \subseteq B^*(\pi, p)$ if $\mu < \pi$ and $\mu \in \mathfrak{B}^*(\pi, p)$. We will show $B^*(\pi, p) = B^*(F^p(\pi+1, 1), G(p))$, a Bachmann notational segment of type $\leqslant G(p)$, bounded by $F^p(\pi+1, 1)$. The next theorem and its corollaries show that $B^*(\pi, p)$ is, in fact, a segment.

DEFINITION 4.3. Suppose $\{\theta, \beta\} \subseteq \mathfrak{B}^*(\pi, p)$ and $\theta < \beta$. Further suppose $d = \mathrm{T}(p; \theta) = \mathrm{D}[p; \theta]$ and that d^* is an ordinal such that $G(q) < d < d^* \leqslant G(q+1) \leqslant G(p+1)$ where $d^* \leqslant \beta$ and $d^* \leqslant \mathrm{T}(p; \beta)$ if $\theta = \mathrm{DS}[p; \beta](d)$. Finally suppose $(\mathrm{ND}[p; \theta] \cup \mathrm{ND}[p; \beta]) \cap [d, d^*) = \emptyset$. If whenever these conditions hold there is an ordinal $\theta^* \in \mathfrak{B}^*(\pi, p)$, such that $\theta^* \leqslant \beta$,

$T(p;\ \theta^*) = d^*$, $DS[p;\ \theta] = DS[p;\ \theta^*]\restriction d$, and $\theta = DS[p;\ \theta^*](d)$, then $\mathfrak{B}^*(\pi, p)$ is said to have the extension property (EP).

THEOREM 4.3. *If* $\mathfrak{B}^*(\pi, p)$ *has* EP *and* $a \in B^*(\pi, p)$, *then* $b < a$ *implies* $b \in B^*(\pi, p)$.

PROOF. Suppose the theorem were false and let $\langle a, b\rangle$ be the smallest pair (lexicographically ordered) for which it is false. By using theorem 4.2 and the definition of $B^*(\pi, p)$ one can show $b = F^p(\partial, 1) = D[p, \partial]$. Next consider $NF(\pi, p; a) \equiv F^p(\theta, c)$. Application of the recursion relations to $b < a$ yields several possibilities. If $\theta < \partial$ there must be $x_0 \in P[p;\ \theta]\cup\{c\} \subseteq B^*(\pi, p)$ with $b \leqslant x_0 < a$. No $\theta = \partial$ is impossible since $b = D[p;\ \partial] \in P[p;\ \theta] \subseteq B^*(\pi, p)$. Hence $\partial < \theta$ and $P[p;\ \theta]\cup\{c\} < b$. From the latter inequality follows $ND[p;\ \theta]\cap[b, G(p+1)) = \emptyset$; since $ND[p;\ \partial] < b$ we have $ND[p;\ \partial]\cap[b, G(p+1)) = \emptyset$. Suppose $\partial = DS[p;\ \theta](b)$ where $b < T(p;\ \theta)$; if $T(p;\ \theta) \neq G(p+1)$ then, since $b = F^p(\partial, 1)$, $T(p;\ \theta) = D[p;\ \theta] \in P[p;\ \theta] < b$. Thus $T(p;\ \theta) = G(p+1)$ which has as a consequence that $b = F^p(\theta(b);\ 1) \in VF^p(\theta;\ -)$, i.e. $NF(\pi, p;\ b) \not\equiv F^p(\partial, 1)$. The only option left is that $\partial \neq \theta(b)$. But then since $\mathfrak{B}^*(\pi, p)$ has EP there is an ordinal $\partial^* \leqslant \theta$ such that $T(p;\ \partial^*) = G(p+1)$ and $DS[p;\ \partial^*](b) = \partial$. This means $b = F^p(\partial(b), 1) \in VF^p(\partial^*, -)$ and contradicts the fact that $NF(\pi, p; b) \equiv F^p(\partial, 1)$.

COROLLARY 4.3.1. *If* $\mathfrak{B}^*(\pi, p)$ *has* EP *and* $P[p;\ \pi] \subseteq B^*(\pi, p)$, *then* $B^*(\pi, p) = \{a | a < F^p(\pi+1, 1)\}$.

The next lemma and theorem will be used in the inductive definition of Bachmann collections (section 6). Recall that if $\mathfrak{B}^*(\pi, p)$ is a Bachmann notational collection, so is $\mathfrak{B}^*(DS[p;\ \pi](i), p)$, and $NF(DS[p;\ \pi](i), p; a)$ is the Cantor normal form of a relative to $\{F^p(\theta, -) | \theta \in \mathfrak{B}^*(\pi(i), p)\}$.

LEMMA 4.4. *Consider* $DS[p;\ \pi](i)$ *where* $1 \leqslant i < T(p;\ \pi)$ *if* $T(p;\ \pi) < G(p+1)$, *and* $1 \leqslant i < F^p(\pi, 1)$ *if* $T(p;\ \pi) = G(p+1)$. *Then if* $a \leqslant P[p;\ \pi(i)]$ *and* $NF(\pi(i),\ p;\ a) \equiv F^p(\theta,\ 1) = T(p;\ \theta)$, *it follows that* $NF(\pi, p; a) \equiv F^p(\theta, 1)$.

DEFINITION 4.4. $A_{\pi,p}(a)$, the ancestors of a (relative to $\{F^p(\beta, -) | \beta \in \mathfrak{B}^*(\pi, p)\}$) for $a < G(p+1)$:

(1). If $a \leqslant G(p)$, $A_{\pi,p}(a) = \{a\}$.

(2). If $P[p;\ \theta]\cup\{b\} < F^p(\theta, b) \equiv NF(\pi, p; a)$, then

$$A_{\pi,p}(a) = A_{\pi,p}(P[p;\ \theta]) \cup A_{\pi,p}(b) \cup P[p;\ \theta] \cup \{b\}.$$

If $F^p(\theta, b) \leqslant P[p; \theta] \cup \{b\}$, $A_{\pi,p}(a) = \emptyset$.

(3). If $\mathrm{NF}(\pi, p; a) \equiv \sum F^p(\theta_i, b_i)m_i + m$ then

$$A_{\pi,p}(a) = \bigcup A_{\pi,p}(F^p(\theta_i, b_i)) \cup \{m_1, \ldots, m\}.$$

Remark 3. Notice that $a \in B^*(\pi, p)$ iff $A_{\pi,p}(a) \neq \emptyset$ and $A_{\pi,p}(a) \subseteq B^*(\pi, p)$.

THEOREM 4.5. *Suppose* $\mathfrak{B}^*(\pi, p)$ *has* EP *and* $P[p; \pi] \subseteq B^*(\pi, p)$. *Then*

(1). *if* $\mathrm{T}(p; \pi) < G(p+1)$, $\mathrm{P}[p; \pi(i)] \subseteq B^*(\pi(i), p)$, $1 \leqslant i < \mathrm{T}(p; \pi)$, *and if* $\mathrm{T}(p; \pi) = G(p+1)$, *then* $\mathrm{P}[p; \pi(i)] \subseteq B^*(\pi(i), p)$ *for* $1 \leqslant i < F^p(\pi, 1)$;

(2). *if* $\mathrm{T}(p; \pi) = G(p+1)$, *then* $(\theta)[\theta \in \mathfrak{B}^*(\pi, p)$ *and* $\mathrm{DS}[p; \pi](F^p(\pi, 1)) \leqslant \theta < \pi \Rightarrow \mathrm{P}[p; \theta] \nsubseteq B^*(\theta, p)]$.

PROOF. (1). Suppose $x_0 \in \mathrm{P}[p; \pi(i)]$ and $x_0 \notin B(\pi(i), p)$. By remark 3 there is some smallest ancestor $a \leqslant x_0$ such that $a \notin B^*(\pi(i), p)$. Hence $\mathrm{NF}(\pi(i), p; a) \equiv F^p(\partial, a)$ or $\mathrm{NF}(\pi(i), p; a) \equiv F^p(\partial, 1) = \mathrm{D}[p; \partial] = a$, (corollary 4.2.1). In the first case $a \leqslant \mathrm{P}[p; \pi(i)] \leqslant F^p(\pi(i), 1) \Rightarrow a \in \mathrm{V}F^p(\partial+1, -)$. No. Using lemma 4.4 in the second case, one derives $\mathrm{NF}(\pi, p; a) \equiv F^p(\partial, 1) = \mathrm{D}[p; \partial]$ i.e. $a \notin B^*(\pi, p)$. By using properties P1–P7 (def. 2.5) one sees $a \leqslant \mathrm{P}[p; \pi(i)] \leqslant \mathrm{P}[p; \pi] \cup \{F^p(\pi, 1)\}$.
As $\mathrm{P}[p; \pi] \cup \{F^p(\pi, 1)\} \subseteq B^*(\pi, p)$ the contradiction $a \in B^*(\pi, p)$ follows from theorem 4.3.

(2). $\mathrm{NF}(\pi(F^p(\pi, 1)), p; F^p(\pi, 1)) \equiv F^p(\pi(F^p(\pi, 1)), 1) = F^p(\pi, 1) = \mathrm{D}[p; \pi(F^p(\pi, 1))]$ implies $\mathrm{P}[p; \pi(F^p(\pi, 1))] \nsubseteq B^*(\pi(F^p(\pi, 1)), p)$. Suppose $F^p(\pi, 1) \in \mathrm{V}F^p(\theta, -)$ for some smallest θ, $\pi(F^p(\pi, 1)) < \theta < \pi$. Then $\mathrm{T}(p; \theta) = G(p+1)$ and $F^p(\pi, 1) = F^p(\theta(F^p(\pi, 1)), 1)$. $F^p(\pi, 1) \in \mathrm{V}F^p(\theta(F^p(\pi, 1)), -)$ implies $\theta(F^p(\pi, 1)) \leqslant \pi(F^p(\pi, 1)) < \theta < \pi$. Application of the nesting property yields the contradiction $\theta(F^p(\pi, 1)) \leqslant \pi(F^p(\pi, 1)) \leqslant \theta(1)$. Thus $F^p(\pi, 1) \notin \mathrm{V}F^p(\theta, -)$ and hence $\mathrm{NF}(\theta, \mathrm{p}; F^p(\pi, 1)) \equiv F^p(\pi(F^p(\pi, 1)), 1) = \mathrm{D}[p; \pi(F^p(\pi, 1))]$, i.e. $F^p(\pi, 1) \notin B^*(\theta, p)$ for $\pi(F^p(\pi, 1)) < \theta < \pi$. But $\pi(F^p(\pi, 1)) < \theta < \pi$ implies either $\theta = \pi(e)$ where $\mathrm{Lim}(e)$ and $F^p(\pi, 1) < e$ or $\pi(e+k) < \theta \leqslant \pi(e+k+1)$, $\mathrm{Lim}(e)$ and $F^p(\pi, 1) \leqslant e$. In the first case $e = \mathrm{D}[p; \theta]$ and in the latter $e \in \mathrm{ND}[p; \theta]$. But this means $\mathrm{P}[p; \theta] \nsubseteq B^*(\theta, p)$, for as $\mathfrak{B}^*(\pi, p)$ has EP, so does $\mathfrak{B}^*(\theta, p)$ and thus (theorem 4.3) $e \in B^*(\theta, p)$ would imply $F^p(\pi, 1) \in B^*(\theta, p)$.

For the rest of this section we shall assume that $\mathfrak{B}^*(\pi; p)$ has EP, $\pi \in \mathfrak{B}^*(\pi, p)$, and $\mathrm{P}[p; \pi] \subseteq B^*(\pi, p)$. We first show that the segment $B^*(\pi, p)$ is a Bachmann collection by defining sequences of length $\leqslant G(p)$.

DEFINITION 4.5. We define $\mathrm{DS}^*[<p; a]$ and $\mathrm{T}^*(<p; a)$ inductively for $a \in B^*(\pi, p)$:

(1). If $a \leqslant G(p)$, $\mathrm{DS}^*[<p; a] = \mathrm{DS}[I; a]$ and $\mathrm{T}^*(<p; a) = \mathrm{T}(I; a)$.

(2). (i). $\mathrm{NF}(\pi, p; a) \equiv F^p(\theta, b)m \Rightarrow \mathrm{DS}^*[<p; a] = F^p(\theta, b)\mathrm{DS}[I; m]$, and $\mathrm{T}^*(<p; a) = \mathrm{T}(I; m)$.

(ii). $\mathrm{NE}(\pi, p; a) \equiv F^p(1, b+1) \Rightarrow \mathrm{DS}^*[<p; a] = F^p(1, b)\mathrm{DS}[I; G(p)]$, and $\mathrm{T}^*(<p; a) = \mathrm{T}(I; G(p))$.

(iii). $\mathrm{NF}(\pi, p; a) \equiv \sum F^p(\theta_i, b_i)m_i + \partial \Rightarrow$

$$\mathrm{DS}^*[<p; a] = \sum F^p(\theta_i, b_i)m_i + \mathrm{DS}^*[<p; \partial],$$

and $\mathrm{T}^*(<p; a) = \mathrm{T}^*(<p; \partial)$.

(3). If $\mathrm{NF}(\pi, p; a) \equiv F^p(\theta+1, b+1)$, $0 \leqslant b$ and $1 \leqslant \theta$, then

$$\mathrm{DS}^*[<p; a] = \lambda n g(n),$$

where

$$g(1) = F^p(\theta, 2) \text{ if } b = 0,$$
$$g(1) = F^p(\theta, F^p(\theta+1, b)+1) \text{ if } 0 < b,$$
$$g(n+1) = F^p(\theta, g(n)),$$

and $\mathrm{T}^*(<p; a) = \omega$.

(4). If $\mathrm{NF}(\pi, \mathrm{p}; a) \equiv F^p(\theta, b)$ with $\mathrm{Lim}(b)$, let $b = f+e$ where f is the last fixed point of $F^p(\theta, -)$ preceding b, $0 < e \leqslant b < a$. As $B^*(\pi, p)$ is a segment, $e \in B^*(\pi, p)$. Then

$$\mathrm{DS}^*[<p; a] = F^p(\theta, 1+f+\mathrm{DS}^*[<p; e]),$$

and $\mathrm{T}^*(<p; a) = \mathrm{T}^*(<p; e)$.

(5). $\mathrm{NF}(\pi, p; a) \equiv F^p(\theta, b+1)$ where $0 \leqslant b$, $\mathrm{Lim}(\theta)$, and $\mathrm{T}(p; \theta) = G(p+1)$, then

$$\mathrm{DS}^*[<p; a] = \lambda n h(n),$$

where

$$h(1) = F^p(\theta(2), 1) \text{ if } b = 0,$$
$$h(1) = F^p(\theta(F^p(\theta, b)+1), 1) \text{ if } 0 < b,$$
$$h(n+1) = F^p(\theta(h(n)), 1),$$

and $\mathrm{T}^*(<p; a) = \omega$.

(6). $\mathrm{NF}(\pi, p; a) \equiv F^p(\theta, b+1)$ where $\mathrm{Lim}(\theta)$ and $\mathrm{T}(p, \theta) < G(p+1)$. If $\mathrm{D}[p; \theta] = \omega$ (so $\mathrm{T}(p; \theta) = \omega$ or $\mathrm{T}(p; \theta) = G(q+1) \leqslant G(p)$) or if $\omega \neq \mathrm{D}[p; \theta] < G(p)$, we let

$$\mathrm{DS}^*[<p; a] = \lambda i F^p(\theta(1+i), F^p(\theta, b)+1),$$

and $\mathrm{T}^*(<p; a) = \mathrm{T}(p; \theta)$.

Else $D[p;\theta] = G(p) + T(p;\theta)$ and $T(p;\theta) \in B^*(\pi, p)$. If $0 < b$, let

$$DS^*[<p;a] = F^p(\theta(1 + DS^*[<p; T(p;\theta)]), F^p(\theta, b)+1)$$

and

$$T^*(<p;a) = T^*(<p; T(p;\theta)).$$

If $b = 0$ let f be the last fixed point of the normal function $\lambda i F^p(\theta(i), 1)$ preceding $T(p;\theta)$, thus $T(p;\theta) = f + e$ where $e \leqslant T(p;\theta)$ and $e \in B^*(\pi, p)$. Then

$$T^*(<p;a) = T^*(<p;e).$$

and

$$DS^*[<p;a] = F^p(\theta(1 + f + DS^*[<p;e]), 1)$$

Notation: $DS[<p;a](i)$ will often be written $a(i)$. Note that $a = \text{lub}\ \{a(i) | 1 \leqslant i < T^*(<p;a)\}$.

Lemmas 4.6 and 4.7 are used in establishing that $NF(\pi, p; a(i)) \equiv a(i)$, a fact needed in the proofs of theorems 4.8 and 4.9.

LEMMA 4.6. (1). *If* $NF(\pi, p; a) \equiv F^p(\alpha, b)$, $\text{Lim}(b)$, *and* $b(1) \leqslant c \leqslant b$, *then* $c < F^p(\alpha, c)$.

(2). *If* $NF(\pi, p; a) \equiv F^p(\alpha, 1)$, $\text{Lim}(\alpha)$, $D[p;\alpha] = G(p) + T(p;\alpha)$, *and* $T(p;\alpha)(1) \leqslant c \leqslant T(p;\alpha)$, *then* $c < F^p(\alpha(c), 1)$.

LEMMA 4.7. (1). *If* $a = F^p(\alpha, \beta)$ *and* $1 < b < F^p(\alpha+1, 1)$ *or* $F^p(\alpha+1, d) < b < F^p(\alpha+1, d+1)$, *then* $a \notin VF^p(\theta, -)$ for $\alpha < \theta \leqslant \pi$, $\theta \in \mathfrak{B}^*(\pi, p)$.

(2). *If* $a = F^p(\alpha(e), 1)$ *where* $1 < e < T(p;\alpha)$ *and* $e < F^p(\alpha(e), 1)$, *then* $a \notin VF^p(\theta), -)$ *for* $\alpha < \theta \leqslant \pi$, $\theta \in \mathfrak{B}^*(\pi, p)$.

COROLLARY 4.7.1. *If* $a \in B^*(\pi, p)$, $NF(\pi, p; a) \equiv F^p(\alpha, b)$ *and either* $1 < \alpha$ *or* $1 = \alpha$ *and* $\text{Lim}(b)$, *then* $NF(\pi, p; a(i)) \equiv a(i)$.

We now use these lemmas to prove that properties B3(d) and B3(e) hold for $B^*(\pi, p)$ and hence that $B^*(\pi, p)$ is a Bachmann collection of type $\leqslant G(p)$.

THEOREM 4.8. *Suppose* $a \in B^*(\pi, p)$ *and* e *is a limit*, $e < T^*(<p;a)$, *then* $\text{Lim}(DS^*[<p;a](e))$, $T^*(<p;a(e)) = e$, *and* $DS^*[<p;a(e)] = DS^*[<p;a]{\restriction}e$.

PROOF. By induction on $B^*(\pi, p)$ using the preceding corollary.

THEOREM 4.9. (nesting theorem). *Suppose* a, d *are limits*, $\{a, d\} \subseteq B^*(\pi, p)$, *and* $a(u) < d \leqslant a(u+1)$ *where* $1 \leqslant u < T^*(< p; a)$; *then* $a(u) \leqslant d(1)$.

PROOF. The structure of the proof is a double transfinite induction: the primary induction is on $\{a | \mathrm{Lim}(a) \text{ and } a \in B^*(\pi, p)\}$ and the secondary induction on $\{d | a(u) < d \leqslant a(u+1) \text{ and } \mathrm{Lim}(d)\}$. Occasionally a subsidiary induction on u is needed. It is a consequence of theorem 4.2 that the inequalities $a(u) < d \leqslant a(u+1)$ can arise only because of certain ordering relations between the p-parts and the arguments of the normal forms of $a(u)$, d, and $a(u+1)$. The proof of the theorem as one considers each of these several possibilities is tedious but not difficult. Full use is made of lemma 4.6, corollary 14.7.1 and of the properties P1–P9 for p-parts.

To complete the task of demonstrating that $B^*(\pi, p)$ is a Bachmann notational segment, we now define parts for $a \in B^*(\pi, p)$ and show that analogues of P1–P9 hold for them.

DEFINITION 4.6. We define inductively $\mathrm{P}^*[< p; a]$, $\mathrm{ND}^*[< p; a]$ and $\mathrm{D}^*[< p; a]$ for $a \in B^*(\pi, p)$:

(1) (i). $a = a'+1 \Rightarrow \mathrm{P}^*[< p; a] = \mathrm{ND}^*[< p; a] = \mathrm{P}^*[< p; a']$, and $\mathrm{D}^*[< p; a] = 1$.

(ii). $a \leqslant G(p) \Rightarrow \mathrm{P}^*[< p; a] = \mathrm{P}[I; a]$, $\mathrm{ND}^*[< p; a] = \mathrm{ND}[I; a]$, and $D^*[< p; a] = \mathrm{D}[I; a]$.

If $G(p) < a$, $\mathrm{P}[I; G(p)]$ will always be included in $\mathrm{P}^*[< p; a]$ and $\mathrm{ND}^*[< p; a]$.

(2) (i). $\mathrm{NF}(\pi, p; a) \equiv F^p(\theta, b)m \Rightarrow$

$$\mathrm{P}^*[< p; a] = \mathrm{P}^*[< p; F^p(\theta, b)] \cup \mathrm{P}[I; m],$$
$$\mathrm{ND}^*[< p; a] = \mathrm{P}^*[< p; F^p(\theta, b)] \cup \mathrm{ND}[I; m],$$
and $\mathrm{D}^*[< p; a] = \mathrm{D}[I; m]$.

(ii). $\mathrm{NF}(\pi, p; a) \equiv F^p(1, b+1) \Rightarrow$

$$\mathrm{P}^*[< p; a] = \mathrm{P}^*[< p; F^p(1, b)] = \mathrm{ND}^*[< p; a]$$
and $\mathrm{D}^*[< p; a] = \mathrm{D}[I; G(p)]$.

(iii). $\mathrm{NF}(\pi, p; a) \equiv \sum F^p(\theta_i, b_i)m_i + a' \Rightarrow$

$$\mathrm{P}^*[< p; a] = \bigcup \mathrm{P}^*[< p; F^p(\theta_i, b_i)m_i] \cup \mathrm{P}^*[< p; a'],$$
$$\mathrm{ND}^*[< p; a] = \bigcup \mathrm{P}^*[< p; F^p(\theta_i, b_i)m_i] \cup \mathrm{ND}^*[< p; a']$$
$$\mathrm{D}^*[< p; a] = \mathrm{D}^*[< p; a'].$$

(3). $\mathrm{NF}(\pi, p; a) \equiv F^p(\theta+1, b+1), 1 \leqslant \theta \Rightarrow$
$$\mathrm{P}^*[<p; a] = \mathrm{ND}^*[<p; a] = \mathrm{P}^*[<p; \mathrm{P}[p; \theta]] \cup \mathrm{P}^*[<p; F^p(\theta+1, b)],$$
$$\mathrm{D}^*[<p; a] = \omega.$$

(4). $\mathrm{NF}(\pi, p; a) \equiv F^p(\theta, b) > b, \mathrm{Lim}(b) \Rightarrow$
$$\mathrm{P}^*[<p; a] = \mathrm{P}^*[<p; \mathrm{P}[p; \theta]] \cup \mathrm{P}^*[<p; b],$$
$$\mathrm{ND}^*[<p; a] = \mathrm{P}^*[<p; \mathrm{P}[p; \theta]] \cup \mathrm{ND}^*[<p; b],$$
$$\mathrm{D}^*[<p; a] = \mathrm{D}^*[<p; b].$$

(5). $\mathrm{NF}(\pi, p; a) \equiv F^p(\theta, b+1)$, $\mathrm{Lim}(\theta)$ and $\mathrm{T}(p; \theta) = G(p+1) \Rightarrow$
$$\mathrm{P}^*[<p; a] = \mathrm{ND}^*[<p; a] = \mathrm{P}^*[<p; \mathrm{P}[\mathrm{p}; \theta]] \cup \mathrm{P}^*[<p; b],$$
$$\mathrm{D}^*[<p; a] = \omega.$$

(6). $\mathrm{NF}(\pi, p; a) \equiv F^p(\theta, b+1)$, $\mathrm{Lim}(\theta)$ and $\mathrm{T}(p; \theta) < G(p+1) \Rightarrow$
$$\mathrm{P}^*[<p; a] = \mathrm{P}^*[<p; \mathrm{P}[p; \theta]] \cup \mathrm{P}^*[<p; F^p(\theta, b)],$$
$$\mathrm{ND}^*[<p; a] = \mathrm{P}^*[<p; \mathrm{ND}[p; \theta]] \cup \mathrm{ND}^*[<p; \mathrm{D}[p; \theta]] \cup \mathrm{P}^*[<p; F^p(\theta, b)],$$
$$D^*[<p; a] = \mathrm{D}^*[<p; D[p; \theta]].$$

Remark 4. Both this definition and def. 4.5 depend on $\mathrm{NF}(\pi, p; a)$.Remark 2 shows that if $a \in B^*(\pi, p)$ then $\mathrm{NF}(\pi, p; a) \equiv \mathrm{NF}(\beta, p; a)$ for $\pi \leqslant \beta$. Consequently $\mathrm{DS}^*[<p; a]$, $\mathrm{P}^*[<p; a]$, etc. are independent of the ordinal π.

One can now show that properties P1–P9 are true for $\mathrm{P}^*[<p; a]$, $\mathrm{ND}^*[<p; a]$, $\mathrm{DS}^*[<p; a]$ etc. The proofs of all of these except for P6 are straightforward; one inducts on $a \in B^*(\pi, p)$, invoking case analyses according to the possibilities of $\mathrm{NF}(\pi, p; a)$, and employs properties B1–B5 and P1–P9 for $\theta \in \mathfrak{B}^*(\pi, p)$.

5. Redefining sequences and parts of members of $\mathfrak{B}^*(\pi, p)$. We now show how sequences of length $\leqslant G(p)$ and parts $\leqslant G(p)$ can be defined for certain members of $\mathfrak{B}^*(\pi, p)$.

Assume $\mathfrak{B}^*(\pi, p)$ has EP and $\pi \in \mathfrak{B}^*(\pi, p)$.

DEFINITION 5.1. Suppose $\mathrm{P}[p; \pi] \subseteq B^*(\pi, p)$.

(1). $$\mathrm{P}[<p; \pi] = \mathrm{P}^*[<p; \mathrm{P}[p; \pi]],$$
$$\mathrm{ND}[<p; \pi] = \mathrm{P}^*[<p; \mathrm{ND}[p; \pi]] \cup \mathrm{ND}^*[<p; D[p; \pi]],$$
and
$$\mathrm{D}[<p; \pi] = \mathrm{D}^*[<p; \mathrm{D}[p]; \pi]].$$

(2)(a). If $\mathrm{D}[p; \pi] = \omega$, then $\mathrm{T}(p; \pi) = \omega$ or $\mathrm{T}(p; \pi) = G(q+1)$.
If $\mathrm{T}(p; \pi) = \omega$ or $G(q+1) \leqslant G(p)$, then
$$\mathrm{DS}[<p; \pi] = \mathrm{DS}[p; \pi]$$

and

$$T(< p; \pi) = T(p; \pi).$$

If $T(p; \pi) = G(p+1)$, then

$$T(< p; \pi) = \omega$$

and

$$DS[< p; \pi] = \lambda n L(n)$$

where

$$L(1) = DS[p, \pi](2),$$
$$L(n+1) = DS[p; \pi](F^p(L(n); 1)).$$

(b). $D[p; \pi] \neq \omega$ and $D[p; \pi] = G(q)+T(p; \pi)$.

If $q < p$, then

$$T(< p; \pi) = T(p; \pi)$$

and

$$DS[< p; \pi] = DS[p; \pi].$$

If $q = p$, then

$$T(< p; \pi) = T^*(< p; T(p; \pi)) = T^*(< p; D[p; \pi])$$

and

$$DS[< p; \pi] = DS[p, \pi] \circ DS^*[< p; T(p; \pi)].$$

Theorem 4.5.1 says that if $P[p; \pi] \subseteq B^*(\pi, p)$ then $P[p; DS[< p; \pi](i)] \subseteq B^*(DS[< p; \pi](i), p)$, hence

$$DS[< p;\ DS[< p; \pi](i)],\quad P[< p; DS[< [p; \pi](i)], \text{ etc.}$$

are all defined.

As with $P^*[< p; a]$, $DS^*[< p; a]$ etc., one now proves that properties P1–P9 hold for $P[< p; \pi]$, $DS[< p; \pi]$, etc.. The proofs are all straightforward: one examines cases corresponding to those in def. 5.1 and uses the fact that properties B and P hold for $P[p; \pi]$, $DS[p; \pi]$, $P^*[< p; a]$, $DS^*[< p; a]$, etc.. The next lemmas are established in the same way; from them properties B3(d) and B3(e) follow.

LEMMA 5.1. *Suppose* $\mathrm{Lim}(t)$, $t < T(< p; \pi)$, *then* $DS[< p; DS[< p; \pi](t)] = DS[< p; \pi] \restriction t$ *and* $T(< p; DS[p; \pi](t)) = t$.

LEMMA 5.2. *Suppose* $\theta \in \mathfrak{B}^*(\pi, p)$ *and* $P[p; \theta] \subseteq B^*(\pi, \theta)$, *then if* $DS[< p; \pi](c) < \theta < DS[< p; \pi](c+1)$,

$$DS[< p; \pi](c) \leqslant DS[p; \theta](1).$$

The final result of this section states that a uniform bound can be placed on the size of $< p$-parts of $DS[< p; \pi](i)$. This will be used in the inductive definition of the next section.

LEMMA 5.3. $P[< p; DS[< p; \pi](i)] \leqslant P[< p; \pi] \cup \{T(< p; \pi)\}$.

6. Defining a sequence of Bachmann notational collections

THEOREM 6.1. *For each* π, $1 \leqslant \pi < G(I, 1)$, *there is a collection of sets* $\{\mathfrak{B}^*(\pi, k) | 1 \leqslant k < G(I, 1)\}$ *and, if* π *is a limit, a finite sequence of ordinals* $\sum(\pi) = \langle q_1, \ldots, q_{m(\pi)} \rangle$, $1 \leqslant m(\pi) < \omega$. *The collection and sequence have the following properties*:

(1). $\mathfrak{B}^*(\pi, k) \subseteq G(I, 1)$ *and* $\mathfrak{B}^*(\pi, k)$ *is a Bachmann notational collection with* EP *of type* $\leqslant G(k+1)$, *bounded by* π.

(2). $\mathfrak{B}^*(1, k) = \{1\}$, $\mathrm{P}[k; 1] = \mathrm{ND}[k; 1] = \{1\}$ and $\mathrm{D}[k; 1] = 1$.

(3). $\pi \notin \mathfrak{B}^*(\pi, k) \Rightarrow \mathfrak{B}^*(\pi+1, k) = \mathfrak{B}^*(\pi, k)$,
$\pi \in \mathfrak{B}^*(\pi, k) \Rightarrow \mathfrak{B}^*(\pi+1, k) = \mathfrak{B}^*(\pi, k) \cup \{\pi+1\}$,
$\mathrm{P}[k; \pi+1] = \mathrm{ND}[k; \pi+1] = \mathrm{P}[k; \pi]$ and $\mathrm{D}[k; \pi+1] = 1$.

(4). *Suppose* $\mathrm{Lim}(\pi)$ *and* $G(p) < \pi < G(p+1)$:

(a)(i). $q_m < q_{m-1} < \ldots < q_1 = p$

(ii). $\mathrm{P}[q_i; \pi] \subseteq B^*(\pi, q_i)$ *and* $G(q_{i+1}) \leqslant \mathrm{P}[< q_i; \pi] \cup \{\mathrm{T}(< q_i; \pi)\} \leqslant$
$\leqslant G(q_{i+1}+1)$, $1 < i \leqslant m-1$.

(iii). $\mathrm{P}[q_m; \pi] \nsubseteq B^*(\pi; q_m)$ *or* $q_m = 1$.

(b)(i). $k < q_m \Rightarrow \mathfrak{B}^*(\pi, k) = \bigcup_{\theta<\pi} \mathfrak{B}^*(\theta, k)$;
$q_m \leqslant k \Rightarrow \mathfrak{B}^*(\pi, k) = \bigcup_{\theta<\pi} \mathfrak{B}^*(\theta, k) \cup \{\pi\}$.

(ii). $q_1 \leqslant k < G(I, 1) \Rightarrow \mathrm{P}[k; \pi] = \mathrm{P}[I; \pi]$, $\mathrm{ND}[k; \pi] = \mathrm{ND}[I; \pi]$,
$\mathrm{D}[k; \pi] = \mathrm{D}[I; \pi]$, $\mathrm{T}(k; \pi) = \mathrm{T}(I; \pi)$, *and* $\mathrm{DS}[k; \pi] = \mathrm{DS}[I; \pi]$.

(iii). $q_{i+1} \leqslant j < q_i$ *and* $1 \leqslant i \leqslant m-1 \Rightarrow \mathrm{P}[j; \pi] = \mathrm{P}[< q_i; \pi]$,
$\mathrm{ND}[j; \pi] = \mathrm{ND}[< q_i; \pi]$, $\mathrm{D}[j; \pi] = \mathrm{D}[< q_i; \pi]$,
$\mathrm{T}(j; \pi) = \mathrm{T}(< q_i; \pi)$ *and* $\mathrm{DS}[j; \pi] = \mathrm{DS}[< q_i; \pi]$.

(5). $\pi \in \mathfrak{B}^*(\pi, k)$ *only as given by* (2), (3) *or* (4).

PROOF. By induction on π, $1 \leqslant \pi < G(I, 1)$, we shall define the collection $\{\mathfrak{B}^*(\pi, k)\}$. At the πth step in the induction (and only at this step) π will or will not be put into the various $\mathfrak{B}^*(\pi, k)$ depending on whether one of the conditions (2), (3) or (4) is satisfied or not.

Suppose the sets $\{\mathfrak{B}^*(\theta, k) | 1 \leqslant k < G(I, 1)\}$ have been defined for $\theta < \pi$. When $\pi = 1$ or $\pi = \pi'+1$ the definition of $\mathfrak{B}^*(\pi, k)$ is given by (2) and (3). Suppose $\mathrm{Lim}(\pi)$ and $G(p) \leqslant \pi < G(p+1)$. We now proceed to define the sequence $\sum(\pi) = \langle q_1, \ldots, q_m \rangle$ and to prove that the sets

$$\bigcup_{\theta<\pi} \mathfrak{B}^*(\theta, k) \cup \{\pi\} = \mathfrak{B}^*(\pi, k), \quad q_m \leqslant k,$$

are Bachmann notational collections with EP.

Set $q_1 = p$. By induction on $\theta < \pi$ one sees that if $G(r) \leqslant \theta < G(r+1)$ and $r \leqslant k$, then $\theta \in \mathfrak{B}^*(\theta, k)$. Hence $\mathfrak{B}^*(\pi, k) = \{\theta | \theta \leqslant \pi\}$ for $q_1 \leqslant k$. If one defines parts, types, and sequences as in (4b ii), it follows from the results of section 3 that $\mathfrak{B}^*(\pi, k)$ is a Bachmann notational collection with EP of type $\leqslant G(k+1)$, bounded by π.

Suppose $q_1, \ldots, q_t$, and $\mathfrak{B}^*(\pi, k)$ have been defined and shown to have the appropriate properties. Assume that $\mathrm{P}[q_t; \pi] \subseteq B^*(q_t; \pi)$ and that q_{t+1} is that unique ordinal for which $G(q_{t+1}) \leqslant \mathrm{P}[< q_t; \pi] \cup \{T(< q_t; \pi)\} \leqslant \leqslant G(q_{t+1}+1)$. Several lemmas of which the three below are most important, combined with the results of section 6 suffice to prove that if parts and sequences are defined as in (4b iii), $\mathfrak{B}^*(\pi, k)$ is a Bachmann notational collection with EP (of type $\leqslant G(k+1)$, bounded by π) for $q_{t+1} \leqslant k < q_t$. To this end recall from theorem 4.5 that if $v = \mathrm{DS}[< q_t; \pi](\mathrm{i})$ $(1 \leqslant i < \mathrm{T}(< q_t; \pi))$, then $\mathrm{P}[q_t; v] \subseteq B^*(v, q_t)$. Hence $\mathrm{P}[< q_t; v]$, $\mathrm{DS}[< q_t; v]$, etc., are all defined.

LEMMA 6.1.1. *Let* $q_{t+1} \leqslant k < q_t$, *then*

(a). $v \in \mathfrak{B}^*(\pi, k)$.

(b).
$$\mathrm{P}[k; v] = P[< q_t; v],$$
$$\mathrm{ND}[k; v] = \mathrm{ND}[< q_t; v],$$
and $\mathrm{D}[k; v] = \mathrm{D}[< q_t; v]$.

(c). *If* $\mathrm{Lim}(e)$, $e < \mathrm{T}(< q_t; \pi)$ *and* $v = \mathrm{DS}[k; \pi](e) = \mathrm{DS}[< q_t; \pi](e)$, *then* $\mathrm{T}(k; v) = e$ *and* $\mathrm{DS}[k; v] = \mathrm{DS}[k; \pi] \upharpoonright e$.

LEMMA 6.1.2. $\pi = \mathrm{lub}$ *in* $\mathfrak{B}^*(\pi, k)\{\mathrm{DS}[< q_t; \pi](i) | 1 \leqslant i < \mathrm{T}(< q_t; \pi)\}$.

LEMMA 6.1.3. $\mathfrak{B}^*(\pi, k)$ *has* EP *for* $q_{t+1} \leqslant k < q_t$.

PROOF. See def. 4.3 for notation. If $\beta < \pi$, then $\{\theta, \beta\} \subseteq \mathfrak{B}^*(\beta, k)$; by induction, $\mathfrak{B}^*(\beta, k)$ has EP. Thus we can assume $\theta < \beta = \pi$. Further note that as a consequence of lemma 3.1, π, θ can both be taken $\geqslant G(k+1)$. If $\mathrm{Lim}(\pi)$, then $\theta \leqslant \mathrm{DS}[k; \pi](d)$ for some $d < \mathrm{T}(k; \pi)$. The proof is completed by using the induction hypothesis to show that an appropriate $\theta \in \mathfrak{B}^*(\mathrm{DS}[k, \pi](d), k)$.

The definition of the sequence $q_1 > q_2 > \ldots > q_{t+1}$ can be continued, but after a finite number of steps either $q_m = 1$ or $\mathrm{P}[q_m; \pi] \nsubseteq B^*(\pi, q_m)$. For $k < q_m$ set $\mathfrak{B}^*(\pi, k) = \bigcup_{\theta < \pi} \mathfrak{B}^*(\theta, k)$.

Clearly $\bigcup \{\mathfrak{B}^*(\theta, k) | \theta < G(I, 1)\}$ is a Bachmann notational collection with EP for each k, $1 \leqslant k < G(I, 1)$. The collection

$$\mathrm{Or}(k) = \bigcup \{\mathfrak{B}^*(\theta, k) | \theta < G(I, 1)\} \cup \{G(I, 1)\}$$

is also a Bachmann notational collection with EP if we set $\mathrm{DS}[k; G(I, 1)] = \lambda ns(n)$ (see section 3) and $\mathrm{P}[k; G(I, 1)] = \mathrm{ND}[k; G(I, 1)] = \{1, \omega\}$, $\mathrm{D}[k; G(I, 1)] = \omega$.

7. Use of the sets Or(k) to define normal forms

DEFINITION 7.1. Let $\pi \leqslant G(I, 1)$ and $\sum(\pi) = \langle q_1 \ldots, q_s \rangle$; $G(q_1) \leqslant \pi < G(q_1+1)$. For each t, $q_s \leqslant t$, we will define $\mathrm{PNF}^t(\pi)$ (the tth level predicative normal form of π) by induction on π. $\mathrm{PNF}^t(\pi)$ will be an ordered set of ordinals and the ordinals in it form the set $\mathrm{S}(t; \pi)$. We will show that $\mathrm{S}(t; \pi) \subseteq \mathrm{P}[t; \pi] \cup \{I\}$:

(0). $\mathrm{PNF}^t(G(I, 1)) = \langle I, 1 \rangle$ for all t, $1 \leqslant t < G(I, 1)$.

(1). if $q_1 \leqslant t < G(I, 1)$, then

$$\mathrm{PNF}^t(\pi) = \mathrm{NF}^+(I; \pi),$$
$$\mathrm{S}(I; \pi) \subseteq \mathrm{P}[I; \pi] \cup \{I\}$$

(see remark 1).

(2). We can assume PNF^t is defined for $q_i \leqslant t$ and that

$$\mathrm{S}(t, \pi) \subseteq \mathrm{P}[t, \pi] \cup \{I\}.$$

By the main induction if $\theta \in \mathrm{Or}(q_i)$ and $\theta < \pi$, then $\mathrm{PNF}^{q_i}(\theta)$ is defined and

$$\mathrm{S}(q_i; \theta) \subseteq \mathrm{P}[q_i; \theta] \cup \{I\}.$$

Suppose $\mathrm{P}[q_i; \pi] \subseteq B^*(\pi, q_i)$.

(2.1). For each $a \in B^*(\pi, q_i)$ we will define (inductively) $\mathrm{NF}^+(\pi, q_i; a)$; this will be an ordered set of ordinals and the ordinals in $\mathrm{NF}^+(\pi, q_i; a)$ will form the set $\mathrm{S}(q_i; a)$. It will be shown that $\mathrm{S}(q_i; a) \subseteq \mathrm{P}^*[< q_i; a] \cup \{I\}$:

(a). If $a \leqslant G(q_i)$,

$$\mathrm{NF}^+(\pi, q_i; a) = \mathrm{NF}^+(I; a),$$

and

$$\mathrm{S}(q_i; a) = \mathrm{S}(I; a) \subseteq \mathrm{P}[I; a] \cup \{I\}.$$

(b). Suppose $G(q_i) < a < G(q_i+1)$ and $\mathrm{NF}(\pi, q_i; a) \equiv F^p(\theta, b) > b$; by induction $\mathrm{NF}^+(\pi, q_i; b)$ is defined and

$$\mathrm{S}(q_i; b) \subseteq \mathrm{P}^*[< q_i; b] \cup \{I\}.$$

(i). $\theta < a$, $\mathrm{NF}^+(\pi, q_i; \theta)$ is defined and $\mathrm{S}(q_i; \theta) \subseteq \mathrm{P}^*[< q_i; b] \cup \{I\}$. Then

$$\begin{aligned}\mathrm{NF}^+(\pi, q_i; a) &= \langle\langle \mathrm{NF}^+(I; G(q_i))\rangle, \langle \mathrm{NF}^+(\pi, q_i; \theta), \mathrm{NF}^+(\pi, q_i; b)\rangle\rangle,\\ \mathrm{S}(q_i; a) &= \mathrm{S}(I; G(q_i)) \cup \mathrm{S}(q_i; \theta) \cup \mathrm{S}(q_i; b)\\ &\subseteq \mathrm{P}[I; G(q_i)] \cup \mathrm{P}^*[< q_i; \theta] \cup \mathrm{P}^*[< q_i; b] \cup \{I\}\\ &= P^*[< q_i; a] \cup \{I\}.\end{aligned}$$

(ii). $a < \theta$. Let $\mathrm{PNF}^{q_i}(\theta) = h(b_1, \ldots, b_k)$ where

$$\mathrm{S}(q_i; \theta) - \{I\} = \{b_1, \ldots, b_k\} \subseteq \mathrm{P}[q_i; \theta].$$

As $\mathrm{P}[q_i; \theta] < a$ we have $\{b_1, \ldots, b_k\} \subseteq B^*(\pi, q_i)$ and $\mathrm{NF}^+(\pi, q_i; b_j)$ is defined with

$$\mathrm{S}(q_1; b_j) \subseteq \mathrm{P}^*[< q_i; b_j] \cup \{I\}.$$

If we let $\mathrm{NF}^+(\pi, q_i; I) = I$ then

$$\mathrm{NF}^+(\pi, q_i; a) =$$
$$\langle\langle \mathrm{NF}^+(I; G(q_i))\rangle, \langle h(\mathrm{NF}^+(\pi, q_i; b_1), \ldots, \mathrm{NF}^+(\pi, q_i; b_k)), \mathrm{NF}^+(\pi, q_i; b)\rangle\rangle.$$

$$\begin{aligned}\mathrm{S}(q_i; a) &= \mathrm{S}(I; G(q_i)) \cup \mathrm{S}(q_i; b_1) \cup \ldots \cup \mathrm{S}(q_i; b)\\ &\subseteq \mathrm{P}[I; G(q_i)] \cup \mathrm{P}^*[< q_i; b_1] \cup \ldots \cup \mathrm{P}^*[< q_i; b] \cup \{I\}\\ &= \mathrm{P}^*[< q_i; a] \cup \{I\}.\end{aligned}$$

(2.2). For $q_{i+1} \leqslant t < q_t$, $\mathrm{PNF}^t(\pi)$ is defined as follows:

(a). If $i = 1$, i.e. $\pi \in B^*(\pi, q_1)$,

$$\mathrm{PNF}^t(\pi) = \mathrm{NF}^+(q_1; \pi).$$

Clearly

$$\mathrm{S}(t; \pi) \subseteq \mathrm{P}^*[< q_i; \pi] \cup \{I\} = \mathrm{P}[t; \pi] \cup \{I\}.$$

(b). Otherwise let $\mathrm{PNF}^{q_i}(\pi) = v(a_1, \ldots, a_m)$, where

$$\mathrm{S}(q_i; \pi) - \{I\} = \{a_1, \ldots, a_m\} \subseteq P[q_i; \pi].$$

Then

$$\mathrm{PNF}^t(\pi) = v(\mathrm{NF}^+(\pi, q_i; a_1), \ldots, \mathrm{NF}^+(\pi, q_i; a_m))$$

and

$$\begin{aligned}\mathrm{S}(t; \pi) &= \mathrm{S}(q_i; a_1) \cup \ldots \cup \mathrm{S}(q_i; a_m) \cup \{I\} \subseteq\\ &\subseteq \mathrm{P}^*[< q_i; a_1] \cup \ldots \cup \mathrm{P}^*[< q_i; a_m] \cup \{I\} =\\ &= \mathrm{P}[< q_i; \pi] \cup \{I\} = \mathrm{P}[t; \pi] \cup \{I\}\end{aligned}$$

for $q_{i+1} \leqslant t < q_i$.

Remark 5. Notice that if $\{\theta, \pi\} \subseteq \mathrm{Or}(p)$, $\theta < \pi$ and $a \in B^*(\theta, p) \subseteq B^*(\pi, p)$ then $\mathrm{NF}^+(\theta, p; a) = \mathrm{NF}^+(\pi, p; a)$. This is a consequence of the fact, (remark 2) that $\mathrm{NF}(\theta, p; a) = \mathrm{NF}(\pi, p; a)$.

DEFINITION 7.2. Let $\pi \leqslant G(I, 1)$ and $\Sigma(\pi) = \langle q_1, \ldots, q_s \rangle$. The predicative normal form of π (relative to $\{\mathrm{Or}(k) | 1 \leqslant k < G(I, 1)\}$), $\mathrm{PNF}(\pi) = \mathrm{PNF}^{q_s}(\pi)$.

Note that $B^*(G(I, 1), p) = \{a | a < F^p(G(I, 1)+1, 1)\}$ for $1 \leqslant p < G(I, 1)$.

THEOREM 7.1. *If* $a \in B^*(G(I, 1), p) \cup \{F^p(G(I, 1)+1, 1)\}$ *then* a *can be written uniquely as an expression made up from* $\{I, \langle, \rangle, {}^{,}, 1, +\} \cup \{e | \mathrm{Lim}(e)$ *and* $e < G(p)\}$. This will be called $\mathrm{NF}(p; a)$.

PROOF. If $a \leqslant G(p)$, $\mathrm{NF}(p; a) = \mathrm{NF}^+(I; a)$.

$$\mathrm{NF}(p; F^p(G(I, 1)+1, 1)) = \langle\langle \mathrm{NF}(p; G(p))\rangle, \langle\langle I, 1\rangle +1, 1\rangle\rangle.$$

Otherwise suppose

$$\mathrm{NF}(G(I, 1), p; a) \equiv F^p(\theta, b),$$
$$\mathrm{PNF}^p(\theta) = h(b_1, \ldots, b_k)$$

where

$$\mathrm{S}(p; \theta) - \{I\} = \{b_1, \ldots, b_k\} < a.$$

Then

$$\mathrm{NF}(p; a) = \langle\langle \mathrm{NF}(p; G(p))\rangle, \langle h(\mathrm{NF}(p; b_1), \ldots, \mathrm{NF}(p; b_k)), \mathrm{NF}(p; b)\rangle\rangle.$$

One consequence of the recursion relations and the method of definition of the sets $\mathfrak{B}^*(\pi, p)$ is that the ordering $F^1(\alpha, a) < F^1(\beta, b)$ is recursive for countable ordinals $\leqslant F^1(G(I, 1)+1, 1)$. This is a special case of a more general result: The ordering $F^p(\alpha, a) < F^p(\beta, b)$ can be effectively determined relative to the order relations on a finite set of limits $< G(p)$. To get this one shows that if $\theta, \pi \in \mathfrak{B}^*(\pi, p)$ then the relation $\theta < \pi$ can be effectively determined from the order relations of $\mathrm{P}(p; \pi) \cup \mathrm{P}[p; \theta]$ (and the order relations of G).

In concluding this section, we would like to compare our countable limit $F^1(G(I, 1)+1, 1)$ with that of Bachmann,

$$\varphi_{F_{\omega_2+1}(1)}(1)$$

In our notation $F_{\omega_2+1}(1) = F^2(G(1, 3)+1, 1) \in \mathfrak{B}^*(G(I, 1), 1)$ and

$$\varphi_{F_{\omega_2+1}(1)}(1) = F^1(F^2(G(1, 3)+1, 1), 1).$$

From the recursion relations

$$F^1(F^2(G(1,3)+1,1),1) < F^1(G(I,1)+1,1).$$

In the same way, the limit one obtains by generalizing Bachmann's procedure to make use of Ω_n, $n < \omega$, (see for example, Pfeiffer **[5]**) is still $< F^1(G(I,1)+1,1)$.

8. Applications to proof theory. Various consistency proofs and cut elimination theorems are carried through by means of an induction on the ordinal (in some well-defined sense) of the proof tree. Frequently an ordinal is coordinated with a tree by assigning particular ordinals to axioms and then specifiying for each rule of inference a function which determines the ordinal of the conclusion given the premiss and the ordinal of the premiss. In most cases this function can be taken to be one of the functions $F^p(\theta, -)$ described here. For example, consistency of number theory is proved by using $F^1(1, -) \upharpoonright \varepsilon_0$, while to prove consistency of ramified analysis of ramification level $\alpha_0 < \omega_1$, one needs $\{F^1(\beta, -) | \beta < \alpha_0 + 2\}$.

We now briefly indicate how the functions described in this paper also can be used in place of ordinal diagrams to carry out Takeuti's proof of the consistency of the system SINN. Let the definitions of 'semi-isolated', 'grade' and 'proof-figure with degree' be the same as in **[6]**. Consider a Hilbert type second order system containing λ-terms. Axioms are (1) tautologies, quantifier-free verifiable formulas, equality axioms, and λ-axioms $(t \in \lambda x\mathfrak{A}(x) \leftrightarrow \mathfrak{A}(t))$ and (2) $\boldsymbol{E}$-axioms, $\mathfrak{F}(\mathfrak{T}) \Rightarrow \boldsymbol{E}X\mathfrak{F}(X)$, for number and set terms X, $\mathfrak{T}$ where $\mathfrak{T}$ is semi-isolated if $\mathfrak{T}$ is a set term. Rules are induction, modus ponens, the $\boldsymbol{E}$-rule: from $\mathfrak{F}(A) \Rightarrow K$ conclude $\boldsymbol{E}X\mathfrak{F}(X) \Rightarrow K$; and set substitution: from $\mathfrak{F}(A)$ conclude $\mathfrak{F}(\mathfrak{T})$. Takeuti's proof (which, can be easily translated into this formalism) shows how a proof tree with endformula $1 = 0$ could be altered by a succession of reconstructions to yield a proof of $1 = 0$ from tautologies and verifiable formulas. To prove that this procedure terminates, Takeuti assigns ordinal diagrams to the tree and then shows that the reconstructions decrease the ordinal diagrams. Instead of ordinal diagrams, one can assign classical ordinals as follows. Every axiom except the $\boldsymbol{E}$-axioms is assigned 1 or 0; $\mathfrak{F}(\mathfrak{T}) \Rightarrow \boldsymbol{E}X\mathfrak{F}(X)$ is assigned

$$F^\omega(F^\omega(1,1),1).$$

If the premiss of an $\boldsymbol{E}$-rule has ordinal θ, the ordinal of the conclusion is $\theta \oplus 1$; if the major and minor premisses of an induction have ordinals θ, α, the conclusion is assigned $\alpha+\theta\omega$. If the ordinal of $\mathfrak{F}$ is α, $\mathfrak{F} \Rightarrow \mathfrak{G}$ is θ and the grade of $\mathfrak{F} = \partial >$ grade of $\mathfrak{G} = \pi$, then the ordinal of $\mathfrak{G}$ is $F^{\omega}(\partial, \alpha\oplus\theta)$. Finally, if the degree of a substitution is $k < \omega$ and $\mathfrak{F}(A)$ has ordinal α, then $\mathfrak{F}(\mathfrak{T})$ is assigned $F^{\omega}(F^{k}(\alpha, 1), 1)$. The crucial point in checking the correctness of this assignment is to notice that it leads to a decrease of the proof ordinal during Takeuti's 'essential reduction'. This is a consequence of theorem 4.2.

Notice that reference is made only to ordinals $< G(\omega+1)$. By using the regular ordinals $G(1)$, $G(2), \ldots, G(\omega+1)$, one can define the sets $\mathfrak{B}^*(G(\omega+1), k)$, $1 \leqslant k < \omega$; the functions F^k based on these sets would be sufficient to carry out the proof. Thus at least for the purpose of Takeuti's theorem, we do not need the rather strong assumption of the existence of I.

We have succeeded in pushing the construction much 'further along' by making use of Mahlo ordinals (see Gaifman [3]). What is still needed is a reformulation in a more elegant way which eliminates the tedious detail and case analyses. Perhaps the approach to this lies along the lines of Feferman's recent work [2] or in the discovery of a suitable concept of normal form.

REFERENCES

[1] H. Bachmann, Die Normalfunktionen und das Problem der ausgezeichneten Folgen von Ordnungszahlen, *Vierteljahrschr. Naturf. Ges. Zürich* **95** (1950) 5–37.

[2] S. Feferman, Systems of predicative analysis II: Representations of ordinals, *J. Symb. Logic* **33** (1968) 193–220.

[3] H. Gaifman, A generalization of Mahlo's method for obtaining large cardinal numbers, *Israel J. Math.* (July, 1967) 188–199.

[4] H. Gerber, An extension of Schütte's klammersymbols, *Math. Ann.* **174** (1967) 203–216.

[5] H. Pfeiffer, *Ausgezeichnete Folgen für gewisse Abschnitte der zweiten und weiteren Zahlklassen*, thesis, Technische Hochschule Hannover (1964).

[6] G. Takeuti, Consistency proofs of subsystems of classical analysis, *Ann. Math.* **86** (1967) 299–348.

[7] O. Veblen, Continuous increasing functions of finite and transfinite ordinals, *Trans. Amer. Math. Soc.* **9** (1908) 280–292.

FORMALIZATION OF THE THEORY OF ORDINAL DIAGRAMS OF INFINITE ORDER [1]

AKIKO KINO

In this paper we shall develop a formal theory of some systems of ordinal diagrams which have been used to prove the consistency of subsystems of classical analysis. By exhibiting a formal system in which these consistency proofs can be formalized, in particular one which suffices to prove the well-ordering of a given system of ordinal diagrams, one can use Gödel's incompleteness theorem (in the form that no system can prove its own consistency) to form an estimate of what the limits are of the power of such methods. For example, if we construct a formal system **S** in which the well-ordering of ordinal diagrams of finite order can be proved, and if we prove in some subsystem **T** of analysis that **S** is consistent, we know that **T** cannot be proved consistent by ordinal diagrams of finite order.

Takeuti introduced diagrams of finite order in [**5**]. In [**9**] he generalized them to ordinal diagrams constructed from well-ordered sets I, A and S and denoted these by $\mathrm{Od}(I, A, S)$ (or $\mathrm{O}(I, A, S)$ for the system in the narrow sense). It is easily shown (cf. [**4**]) that all systems $\mathrm{Od}(I, A, S)$ (or $\mathrm{O}(I, A, S)$) can be embedded in systems $\mathrm{Od}(I', A', \emptyset)$ with $\emptyset$ empty (or $\mathrm{O}(I', A', \emptyset)$), which we shall henceforth denote by $\mathrm{Od}(I', A')$ (or $\mathrm{O}(I', A')$) simply. In order to give the reader some idea of the strength of these systems $\mathrm{O}(I, A)$ let us recall that $\mathrm{O}(n, \omega)$ corresponds to ordinal diagrams of order n. When I is infinite, even very simple, we get systems of ordinal diagrams sufficient to prove the consistency of a fragment of analysis: for example using the well-ordering of $\mathrm{O}(\omega+1, \omega^3)$ we can prove the consistency of Π^1_1-analysis (cf. Takeuti [**11**]). This motivates us to study how we can formalize, for given primitive recursive I and A, the theory of $\mathrm{Od}(I, A)$ in such a way as to prove

[1] Part of the work herein described was supported by NSF Grant GP-8918. The author would like to thank Professor G. Takeuti for his advice in the preparation of this work and Professor J. Myhill for his stylistic advice.

its well-ordering[2]. In §§ 1 and 2 is given the definition of Od(I, A) and its orderings $<_i (i \in I)$ and a proof of well-ordering which is similar to the one in **[5]** as mentioned in **[4]**.

If a relation $\prec$ orders a set S and $a \in S$, we call a *S-$\prec$- accessible* if the subset $\{b | b \prec a\}$ of S is well-ordered by $\prec$ (in the sense of transfinite induction). Then the following propositions can easily be shown:

PROPOSITION 1. *If every $b \prec a$ is S-$\prec$-accessible, then so is a.*

PROPOSITION 2. *If a is S-$\prec$-accessible, then so is every $b \prec a$.*

PROPOSITION 3. *If a and b are S-$\prec$-accessible, then so is the natural sum $a \# b$ of a and b.*

The purpose of this paper, which is achieved in § 3, is to present a formal system which is in some sense constructive and in which the above mentioned proof of well-ordering of Od(I, A) can be formalized. We begin with intuitionistic arithmetic, i.e. Peano's axioms plus primitive recursive definitions plus the intuitionistic predicate calculus. It is natural to take the notion '$\prec$ is a well-ordering' as a clear and secure one (cf. **[2]**): indeed it is customary to add to intuitionistic arithmetic such a pair of schemata as

$$a \in S \wedge \forall x(x \prec a \rightarrow \mathrm{Ac}(S, \prec, x)) \rightarrow \mathrm{Ac}(S, \prec, a) \tag{1}$$

and

$$\mathrm{Ac}(S, \prec, a) \wedge \forall y(y \in S \wedge \forall x(x \prec y \rightarrow \mathfrak{A}(x)) \rightarrow \mathfrak{A}(y)) \rightarrow \mathfrak{A}(a) \tag{2}$$

where $\prec$ is a decidable relation (in particular a primitive recursive one) and S a decidable set which is the field of $\prec$.

The resulting system is close to the intuitionistic system called **IDK** (cf. **[13]**) but without variables for constructive functions. Only number-variables occur. We know from results of Howard **[14]** and Gerber **[15]** that this system, although much stronger from the point of view of provable well-orderings than intuitionistic arithmetic without the added schema, is not strong enough for the present purpose: for they showed that the primitive

[2] Although only systems of the form O(I, A) are used in consistency-proofs and special cases of the fundamental conjecture of **GLC**, and although also O(I, A), a subsystem of Od(I, A), has a much simpler structure than Od(I, A), we seem nevertheless to be able to develop a formal theory of Od(I, A) in a theory in which a formal theory of O(I, A) can be developed; in other words, Od(I, A) seems not strictly stronger than O(I, A) as far as consistency is concerned. Therefore we only deal with the systems of the form Od(I, A) in the following. The definition of O(I, A) is obtained from the definition of Od(I, A) by restricting α in 1.2 of § 1 to range only over A.

recursive provable well-orderings in that system are a subsystem of O(2) (the system of ordinal diagrams of order 2). The clue is to be found in the transition from propositions 1–3 above with Od(I, A) for S and $<_i$ for $\prec$ which follow immediately from (1) and (2), to those same propositions with N_i for S and $<_i$ for $\prec$. Here N_i is the set of i-normal o.d.'s, a subset of Od(I, A) defined in § 2. (i-normal o.d.'s were called i-fans in **[9]**.)

This suggests that we strengthen (1)–(2) by letting S be not only the whole field of $\prec$, but an arbitrary (not necessarily decidable) subset of that field. It is known[3] that if we strengthen them in this way, allowing only arithmetic formulas for S, the system becomes a little stronger, but no new well-orderings can be obtained. But if we allow inductively defined notions (specifically the notion of an i-normal o.d.) to appear in S, the system becomes strong enough for what we want.

To sum up: the system consists of (I) Heyting arithmetic, (II) the schemata (1)–(2) for *arbitrary* S expressible in the system, and (III) the inductive definition of N_i(cf. N1–N2 in § 3) following Takeuti **[10]**. This is not an inductive definition of the restricted form usual in intuitionistic systems (for example in Troelstra's system), but we still find it sufficiently constructive to be convincing in consistency proofs. In (1) and (2) we put $<_i$ for $\prec$ and Od(I, A) and N_i for S, and the whole proof can be formalized straightforwardly, as will be seen in § 3 below.

Of course we are assuming that I and A are sufficiently small (e.g. $I = \omega+1$, $A = \omega^3$ for Π^1_1-analysis) that their well-orderings can already be proved in Heyting arithmetic. If we want large I and A of course we have to add (IV) axiom schemata expressing the well-ordering of those sets.

§ 1. Definition of Od(I, A) and its linear orderings (cf. [9])

Definition 1. Let I and A be well-ordered sets. If there is no likelihood of confusion we shall use the same symbol $<$ to denote the orderings of I and A; the symbol $<$ as well as $=$ should be understood according to the context. For simplicity let 0 be the first element of I. We call an element of Od(I, A) an *ordinal diagram* (o.d.). The system of ordinal diagrams constructed from I and A is defined recursively as follows:

1. Every element of A is an o.d.
2. If α and β are o.d.'s and $i \in I$, then (i, α, β) is an o.d.
3. If α and β are o.d.'s, then $\alpha \# \beta$ is an o.d.

[3] This was communicated to us by W. Howard.

The *rank* of an o.d. α ($r(\alpha)$) is the number of ('s and #'s occurring in α.

DEFINITION 2. Let α and β be o.d.'s and $i \in I$. $\beta \subset_i \alpha$ (β is an *i-subdiagram* of α) is defined recursively as follows:

1. If $\alpha \in A$, then α has no i-subdiagram for any $i \in I$.

2. If α is of the form (j, α_0, α_1), then $\beta \subset_i \alpha$ if $\beta \subset_i \alpha_1$ and $i < j$, or β is α_1 and $i = j$. α has no i-subdiagram if $j < i$.

3. If α is of the form $\alpha_1 \# \alpha_2$, then $\beta \subset_i \alpha$ if $\beta \subset_i \alpha_1$ or $\beta \subset_i \alpha_2$.

(i-subdiagrams were called i-sections in [**9**]).

DEFINITION 3. An o.d. α is called a *connected ordinal diagram* (c.o.d.) if the operation used in the final step of the construction of α is not #.

DEFINITION 4. Let α be an o.d.. We define the *components* of α recursively as follows:

1. If α is a c.o.d., then α has only one component i.e. α itself.

2. If α is an o.d. of the form $\alpha_1 \# \alpha_2$ and the components of α_1 and α_2 are $\beta_1, \ldots, \beta_k$ and $\gamma_1, \ldots, \gamma_n$ respectively, then the components of $\alpha_1 \# \alpha_2$ are $\beta_1, \ldots, \beta_k, \gamma_1, \ldots, \gamma_n$.

DEFINITION 5. Let α and β be o.d.'s. We define $\alpha = \beta$ recursively as follows:

1. If $\alpha \in A$, then $\alpha = \beta$ is the same as equality in A.

2. If α is of the form (i, α_0, α_1), then $\alpha = \beta$ if β is of the form (j, β_0, β_1), with $i = j$, $\alpha_0 = \beta_0$ and $\alpha_1 = \beta_1$.

3. If α is a non-connected o.d. with k components $\alpha_1, \ldots, \alpha_k$, then $\alpha = \beta$ if β has the same number of components $\beta_1, \ldots, \beta_k$ and there exists a permutation $(l_1, \ldots, l_k)$ of $(1, \ldots, k)$ such that $\alpha_n = \beta_{l_m}$ for $m = 1, \ldots, k$.

DEFINITION 6. Let α be an o.d. and let $i \in I$. Then i is called an *index* of α if α has an i-subdiagram.

DEFINITION 7. Let α and β be o.d.'s and let $i \in I$. We define the relations $\alpha <_i \beta$ and $\alpha <_\infty \beta$ recursively as follows:

1. If $\alpha, \beta \in A$, then $\alpha <_i \beta$ and $\alpha <_\infty \beta$ mean $\alpha < \beta$ in A.

2. Let the components of α and β be $\alpha_1, \ldots, \alpha_k$ and $\beta_1, \ldots, \beta_h$ respectively. $\alpha <_i \beta$ ($i \in I$ or i is ∞) holds if one of the following conditions is satisfied:

2.1. There exists a β_m ($1 \leqslant m \leqslant h$) such that for every l ($1 \leqslant l \leqslant k$) $\alpha_l <_i \beta_m$ holds.

2.2. $k = 1$, $h > 1$ and $\alpha_1 = \beta_m$ for some m ($1 \leqslant m \leqslant h$).

2.3. $k > 1, h > 1$ and there exist an α_l $(1 \leqslant l \leqslant k)$ and a β_m $(1 \leqslant m \leqslant h)$ such that $\alpha_l = \beta_m$ and

$$\alpha_1 \# \cdots \# \alpha_{l-1} \# \alpha_{l+1} \# \cdots \# \alpha_k <_i \beta_1 \# \cdots \# \beta_{m-1} \# \beta_{m+1} \# \cdots \# \beta_h .$$

3. Let α and β be c.o.d.'s and $i \in I$. If there exists no index of α or β greater than i we define $\tilde{\imath}$ to be ∞, and if there exists any such indices we define $\tilde{\imath}$ to be the minimum of them. Then $\alpha <_i \beta$ if one of the following conditions is satisfied:

3.1. There exists an i-subdiagram β_0 of β such that $\alpha \leqslant_i \beta_0$.

3.2. $\alpha_0 <_i \beta$ for every i-subdiagram α_0 of α and $\alpha <_{\tilde{\imath}} \beta$.

4. Let α and β be c.o.d.'s of the form (i, α_0, α_1) and (j, β_0, β_1) respectively. $\alpha <_\infty \beta$ if one of the following conditions is satisfied:

4.1. $\alpha_1 <_0 \beta_0$.

4.2. $\alpha_0 = \beta_0$ and $i < j$.

4.3. $\alpha_0 = \beta_0, i = j$ and $\alpha_1 <_i \beta_1$.

5. $(i, \alpha_0, \alpha_1) <_\infty a$ if $\alpha_0 <_0 a$. $a <_\infty (i, \alpha_0, \alpha_1)$ if $a \leqq_0 \alpha_0$.

The following propositions can be easily shown:

PROPOSITION 1. $=$ *is an equivalence relation.*

PROPOSITION 2. *If* $\alpha_1 = \beta_1$, $\alpha_2 = \beta_2$, *then* $\alpha_1 \# \alpha_2 = \beta_1 \# \beta_2$ *and* $(i, \alpha_1, \alpha_2) = (i, \beta_1, \beta_2)$.

PROPOSITION 3. *If* $\alpha_1 = \beta_1, \alpha_2 = \beta_2$ *and* $\alpha_1 <_i \alpha_2$, *then* $\beta_1 <_i \beta_2$.

PROPOSITION 4. *Every relation* $<_i$ $(i \in I$ *or* $i = \infty)$ *is a linear ordering of* Od(I, A).

§ 2. Informal proof of well-ordering

DEFINITION 1. If a relation $\prec$ orders a set S, and $a \in S$, we call *a S-$\prec$-accessible* if the set of all $b \in S$, $b \prec a$ is well-ordered by $\prec$. Here 'well-ordered' is to be taken in the sense of transfinite induction (not well-foundedness). So what we have to prove is that every element of Od(I, A) is Od(I, A)-$<_i$-accessible for every $i \in I$.

DEFINITION 2. We define 'an o.d. β is an *exponent* of an o.d. α' (denoted $\beta \lessdot \alpha$) recursively as follows:

1. If $\alpha \in A$, α has no exponent.

2. If α is of the form $\alpha_1 \# \ldots \# \alpha_m$, where $\alpha_1, \ldots, \alpha_m$ are c.o.d.'s, then $\beta \lessdot \alpha$ if $\beta \lessdot \alpha_i$ for some i $(1 \leqslant i \leqslant m)$.

3. If α is of the form (i, α_0, α_1), then $\beta \lessdot \alpha$ if β is α_0 or $\beta \lessdot \alpha_0$ or $\beta \lessdot \alpha_1$. (Exponents were called 'values' in [**9**].)

PROPOSITION 0. (Proposition 2 of § **3** of [**8**]). *If* $\beta \lessdot \alpha$, *then* $\beta <_0 \alpha$.

The proof is omitted here. It should be noticed that it does not involve the notion of accessibility of o.d.'s.

DEFINITION 3. The set N_i of *i-normal* o.d.'s (called *i*-fans in [**9**]; this is the central notion of the proof) is defined as follows by transfinite induction on I:

1. Every o.d. every exponent of which is $\mathrm{Od}(I, A)$-$<_0$-accessible is a 0-normal o.d.

2. If i' is the successor of i in I, then α is an i'-normal o.d. if α is an i-normal o.d. and every i-subdiagram of α is N_i-$<_i$-accessible.

3. If i is a limit number of I, then α is an i-normal o.d. if α is a j-normal o.d. for every $j < i$ in I.

4. α is called an ∞-normal o.d. if α is an i-normal o.d.for every $i \in I$.

The following propositions are immediate:

PROPOSITION 1. *If every o.d.* $\beta <_i \alpha$ *is* $\mathrm{Od}(I, A)$-$<_i$*-accessible, so is* α. *Here* $i \in I$ *or* $i = \infty$.

PROPOSITION 2. *If* α *is* $\mathrm{Od}(I, A)$-$<_i$*-accessible, so is every* $\beta <_i \alpha$. *Here* $i \in I$ *or* $i = \infty$.

PROPOSITION 3. *If* $\alpha_1, \ldots, \alpha_m$ *are* $\mathrm{Od}(I, A)$-$<_i$*- accessible, so is* $\alpha_1 \# \ldots \# \alpha_m$.

These propositions hold also when we replace $\mathrm{Od}(I, A)$-$<_i$-accessibility by N_i-$<_i$-accessibility (called *i*-accessibility in [**4**]), where N_i is the set of *i*-normal o.d.'s.

This induction on a set we don't know to be decidable will turn out to have importance for the axiom system in which we later formalize this proof.

By propositions 1*–3* we denote propositions like 1–3 except that they refer to N_i-$<_i$-accessibility instead of $\mathrm{Od}(I, A)$-$<_i$-accessibility.

PROPOSITION 4. *If* α *is* $N_{i'}$-$<_{i'}$*-accessible, it is* N_i-$<_i$*-accessible, where* i' *denotes the successor of* i *in* I.

PROOF. We prove this by double induction on $<_{i'}$ among $N_{i'}$-$<_{i'}$-

accessible o.d.'s and on the rank of an o.d. Let α be $N_{i'}$-$<_{i'}$-accessible and assume as the inductive hypothesis on $<_{i'}$:

(1). For every $N_{i'}$-$<_{i'}$-accessible o.d. β such that $\beta <_{i'} \alpha$, β is N_i-$<_i$-accessible.

We claim α is N_i-$<_i$- accessible. For this we shall show that every i-normal o.d. $\beta <_i \alpha$ is an i'-normal o.d. and is N_i-$<_i$-accessible by induction on the rank of β. Let β be an i-normal o.d. such that $\beta <_i \alpha$ and assume as the inductive hypothesis on the rank of β:

(2). Every i-normal o.d. γ such that $\gamma <_i \alpha$ and $r(\gamma) < r(\beta)$ is an i'-normal o.d. and is N_i-$<_i$-accessible.

For any i-subdiagram β_0 of β, β_0 is an i-normal o.d. and is $<_i \alpha$. So β_0 is an i'-normal o.d. and is N_i-$<_i$-accessible by the inductive hypothesis (2). So β is an i'-normal o.d. Since $\beta <_i \alpha$ by assumption, one of two cases holds:

Case 1. $\beta <_{i'} \alpha$. Then β is $N_{i'}$-$<_{i'}$-accessible by proposition 2* and so is N_i-$<_i$-accessible by (1).

Case 2. There exists an i-subdiagram α_0 of α such that $\beta \leqslant_i \alpha_0$. Since α_0 is N_i-$<_i$-accessible and β is i-normal by assumption, β is N_i-$<_i$-accessible by proposition 2*.

Thus by proposition 1*, α is N_i-$<_i$-accessible.

PROPOSITION 5. *If α is N_i-$<_i$-accessible, then α is N_j-$<_j$-accessible for every $j < i$.*

PROOF. This is easily seen from the following lemmas 1–3.

LEMMA 1. *Let i be a limit element of I such that the following condition is satisfied*:

(3). *For any j, k such that $j < k < i$, every N_k-$<_k$-accessible i-normal o.d. is N_j-$<_j$-accessible.*

Then for every $j < i$, α is N_j-$<_j$-accessible if it is N_i-$<_i$-accessible.

PROOF. Let α be N_i-$<_i$-accessible. Let i_0 be the successor of the greatest index of α less than i. We should note that $\beta <_i \alpha$ if $\beta <_{i_0} \alpha$ and so α is N_{i_0}-$<_{i_0}$-accessible. Hence if $j < i_0$ then α is N_j-$<_j$-accessible by assumption (3).

In order to consider the case $i_0 \leqslant j < i$ we introduce an auxiliary notion 'γ is an nth j-branch of β w.r.t. k_0 and k_1' (where k_0 and k_1 are arbitrary fixed elements in I such that $k_0 < k_1$) defined recursively as follows:

(i). If $k_0 \leqslant j \leqslant k_1$ and $\gamma \subset_j \beta$, γ is a first j-branch of β w.r.t. k_0 and k_1.

(ii). If $\gamma \subset_j \delta$ and δ is an nth k-branch of β w.r.t. k_0 and k_1, γ is an nth

j-branch of β w.r.t. k_0 and k_1 if $k_0 \leqslant j < k$; and γ is an $(n+1)$st j-branch of β w.r.t. k_0 and k_1 if $k \leqslant j < k_1$.

We prove lemma 1 by transfinite induction on $<_i$ among N_i-$<_i$-accessible o.d.'s, using also induction on the number of branches w.r.t. i_0 and i. Let α be N_i-$<_i$-accessible and assume as the inductive hypothesis on $<_i$:

(4) Every i-normal o.d. $\beta <_i \alpha$ is N_k-$<_k$-accessible for every $k < i$. Since for every $j < i_0$ lemma 1 has been proved, it is enough to show that α is N_j<$_j$-accessible for every j such that $i_0 \leqslant j < i$.

Let $i_0 \leqslant j < i$, $\beta <_j \alpha$ and let β be a j-normal o.d. We shall prove that β is an i-normal o.d. and N_l-$<_l$-accessible for every l such that $i_0 \leqslant l < i$, by induction on the number of branches of β w.r.t. j and i.

Let $j \leqslant k < i$ and let β_0 be any k-branch of β. By the inductive hypothesis on the number of branches, β_0 is i-normal and N_k-$<_k$-accessible. Hence β is an i-normal o.d. and $\beta <_i \alpha$ because $\beta <_j \alpha$. So β is N_k-$<_k$-accessible for every k such that $k < i$ by assumption (4).

Thus α is N_k-$<_k$-accessible for every $k < i$.

By proposition 4 and lemma 1 we have

LEMMA 2. *For every* $i \in I$ *such that* (3) *holds and for every* $j < i$, *if* α *is* N_i-$<_i$-*accessible, then it is* N_j-$<_j$-*accessible.*

LEMMA 3. *For every* $i \in I$, (3) *holds.*

PROOF. By transfinite induction on I using lemma 2.

PROPOSITION 6. *If* α *is* N_∞-$<_\infty$-*accessible, it is* N_i-$<_i$-*accessible for every* $i \in I$.

PROOF. Similar to the proof of proposition 5 using

LEMMA 4. *For every pair* j *and* k *in* I *such that* $j < k$, *every* N_k-$<_k$-*accessible* ∞-*normal o.d. is* N_j-$<_j$-*accessible.*

PROOF. Similar to the proof of lemma 1.

PROPOSITION 7. *Every* ∞-*normal o.d. is* N_∞-$<_\infty$-*accessible.*

PROOF. The proof of this proposition is not difficult but rather laborious. We shall give a very brief outline, referring the reader to proposition 14 in [7].

Let sup(α) denote the successor of the maximal element of A occurring in α. Then one easily obtains

LEMMA 5. $\alpha \lessdot_i$ *sup* (α) *for all o.d.'s* α, *and for all* $i \in I$ *and for* $i = \infty$.

So by proposition 2* it suffices to prove

LEMMA 6. *If* $a \in A$, *then* a *is* N_∞-$<_\infty$-*accessible.*

This is proved by showing that every c.o.d. α such that $\alpha <_\infty a$ is N_∞-$<_\infty$-

accessible (considering all possible cases) and applying propositions 3* and 1*.

By propositions 6 and 7 we immediately have

PROPOSITION 8. *Every* ∞*-normal o.d. is* N_i-$<_i$*-accessible for all* $i \in I$.

PROPOSITION 9. *Every* 0*-normal o.d. is* N_i-$<_i$*-accessible for all* $i \in I$ *and for* $i = \infty$.

PROOF. This will follow from the following lemmas 7 and 8.

LEMMA 7. *Every i-normal o.d. is* N_i-$<_i$*-accessible.*

PROOF. By lemma 5 and propositions 8 and 2*.

LEMMA 8. *Every* 0*-normal o.d. is i-normal for all* $i \in I$ *and for* $i = \infty$.

PROOF. By induction on I using lemma 7.

LEMMA 9. *If* α *is an o.d. which is not* 0*-normal, then there is a* 0*-normal o.d.* β *such that* $\beta <_0 \alpha$ *and* β *is not* N_0-$<_0$*-accessible.*

PROOF. By induction on the rank of α using proposition 0.

From this we have

PROPOSITION 10. *Every* 0*-normal o.d. is* N_0-$<_0$*-accessible.*

PROPOSITION 11. *Every o.d. is* 0*-normal.*

By this and lemma 8 we have

COROLLARY. $N_i = \mathrm{Od}(I, A)$ *for all* $i \in I$ *and for* $i = \infty$.

By propositions 10 and 11 we have

PROPOSITION 12. *Every o.d. is* $\mathrm{Od}(I, A)$-$<_0$*-accessible.*

THEOREM. *Every o.d. is* $\mathrm{Od}(I, A)$-$<_i$*-accessible for all* $i \in I$ *and for* $i = \infty$.

PROOF. By the corollary of proposition 11 and proposition 9.

§ 3. **Formal theory of** $\mathrm{Od}(I, A)$. In this section we shall give details of the formalization of the argument of § 2.

Let I and A be primitive recursive sets of numbers and $<_I$ and $<_A$ be primitive recursive predicates which well-order I and A respectively. We recall the definition of $\mathrm{Od}(I, A)$ and the accessibility-proof of $\mathrm{Od}(I, A)$ (§§ 1–2), and try to formalize it as described in the introduction.

For the sake of convenience let $I(a)$ and $A(a)$ be the characteristic predicates of the sets I and A respectively; obviously they are primitive recursive: let o be the first element of I w.r.t. $<_I$. We are interested in the arithmetization of $\mathrm{Od}(I, A)$ and shall not always make distinction between notions and their arithmetizations.

1. *Definition of* Od(I, A) *and its linear orderings* $<_i$. We have introduced primitive recursive predicates I, A, $<_I$, $<_A$ and a constant o. Let us fix another constant ∞ for which $\neg I(\infty)$ and define $a \gtrsim b$ by $a <_I b \vee (I(a) \wedge b = \infty)$, and $\tilde{I}(i)$ by $I(i) \vee i = \infty$. It is easily seen that the notions 'a is an ordinal diagram (o.d.)' (denoted $O(a)$), 'a equals b in o.d.'s' '(denoted $=(a, b)$) and the linear orderings $a <_i b$ (denoted $<(i, a, b)$ for uniformity of notation) for each i ($I(i)$ or $i = \infty$) can be introduced in a primitive recursive manner in Heyting (intuitionistic first order) arithmetic (cf. [7]).

To be more precise let us fix a basic formal theory which we shall later extend to a system containing new axioms and axiom schemata concerning accessibility. For the sake of technical convenience we choose a slight modification of Gentzen's **LJ**(first order intuitionistic predicate calculus [**1**]), enriched by arithmetical axioms and induction: A sequent $\Gamma \Rightarrow \Delta$ is called *admissible* if at most one formula in Δ contains quantifiers (so that all the other formulas in Δ are decidable). The basic system is obtained from Gentzens's **LK** ([**1**]) by requiring that every sequent in a proof be admissible and allowing sequents of the following forms as initial sequents (axiom schemata):

1.1. Logical initial sequent:

$$\mathfrak{D} \Rightarrow \mathfrak{D}.$$

1.2. Axiom schemata for equality:

$$\Rightarrow a = a,$$
$$a = b, \mathfrak{A}(a) \Rightarrow \mathfrak{A}(b).$$

1.3. Mathematical axioms (mathematische Grundsequenz in [**3**]), i.e., a sequent $\Gamma \Rightarrow \Delta$ with the following properties; every formula of Γ and Δ is primitive recursive and contains no logical symbol, and every sequent obtained from $\Gamma \Rightarrow \Delta$ by replacing all free variables in Γ and Δ by arbitrary natural numbers (i.e. numerals) is true.

1.4. Course-of-values induction:

$$\forall x(\forall y(y < x \rightarrow \mathfrak{A}(y)) \rightarrow \mathfrak{A}(x)) \Rightarrow \mathfrak{A}(a).$$

In order to introduce primitive recursive predicates $O(s)$, $=(a, b)$ and $<(i, a, b)$, several primitive recursive functions and predicates are used; among them $a \subset_i b$ (denoted $\subset(i, a, b)$) is important. We assume that any desirable properties of these primitive recursive functions and predicates are listed in the mathematical axioms (cf. [7] for examples of such axioms).

2. *Accessibility of* Od(I, A). We wish to add further notions to the basic system so that the system so obtained is strong enough to establish the accessibility of Od(I, A).

Since we know as part of our assumption that I and A are well-ordered by $<_I$ and $<_A$ respectively, we can introduce accessibility of I w.r.t. $<_I$ and of A w.r.t. $<_A$ as axiom schemata (new initial sequents):

For any formula $\mathfrak{A}(a)$

AI. $I(a), \forall x(I(x) \wedge \forall y(y <_I x \rightarrow \mathfrak{A}(y)) \rightarrow \mathfrak{A}(x)) \Rightarrow \mathfrak{A}(a)$.

AA. $A(a), \forall x(A(x) \wedge \forall y(y <_A x \rightarrow \mathfrak{A}(y)) \rightarrow \mathfrak{A}(x)) \Rightarrow \mathfrak{A}(a)$.

Let us now follow closely the accessibility proof in § 2. It is again clear that the notion $a \lessdot b$ (a is an exponent of b) can be added in a primitive recursive manner to the basic system. Thus we are in a position to formalize the two simultaneously defined notions 'a is an i-normal o.d.' and 'an i-normal o.d. a is N_j-$<_j$-accessible'. Now let us recall (1) and (2) in the introduction, to see how to introduce the notion of an element s of S linearly ordered by $\prec$ being accessible in S w.r.t. $\prec$ (denoted $Ac(S, \prec, s)$).

To this end, it is convenient to introduce the abstraction operator $\{\ \}$ into the system as well as a new higher order predicate constant $Ac(*_0, *_1, *_2)$: For any formula $\mathfrak{A}(a_1, \ldots, a_n)$, which may contain other free variables, $\{x_1, \ldots, x_n\}\ \mathfrak{A}(x_1, \ldots, x_n)$ is called *an abstract with n argument-places*. $Ac(\{x\}\mathfrak{A}(x), \{x, y\}\mathfrak{B}(x, y), a)$ is a formula if $\{x\}\mathfrak{A}(x)$ and $\{x, y\}\mathfrak{B}(x, y)$ are abstracts with one and two argument places respectively. We use the following abbreviations:

$$Ac(\{x\}\mathfrak{A}(x), a, b) \quad \text{for} \quad Ac(\{x\}\mathfrak{A}(x), \{x, y\} < (a, x, y), b)$$

and

$$Ac(a, b) \quad \text{for} \quad Ac(\{x\}O(x), a, b).$$

The latter will mean that an o.d. b is accessible in Od(I, A) w.r.t. $<_a$. Since $O(a)$, $I(a)$ and $<(a, b, c)$ are primitive recursive, we can introduce Od(I, A)-$<_j$-accessibility by

AO1. $\tilde{I}(j), O(a), \forall x(<(j, x, a) \rightarrow Ac(j, x)) \Rightarrow Ac(j, a)$,

AO2. $\tilde{I}(j), O(a), Ac(j, a), \forall x(O(x) \wedge \forall y(<(j, y, x) \rightarrow \mathfrak{A}(y)) \rightarrow \mathfrak{A}(x)) \Rightarrow \mathfrak{A}(a)$,

where $\mathfrak{A}(a)$ is an arbitrary formula.

We are now ready to introduce the central notion 'a is an i-normal o.d.' ($N(i, a)$) by an inductive definition w.r.t. $\precsim$. To formalize this, let $\tilde{O}(b)$ be

$$O(b) \wedge \forall x(\lessdot(x, b) \rightarrow Ac(o, x)),$$

and let $G(\{x, y\}\mathfrak{A}(x, y), a, b)$ be

$$\tilde{O}(b) \wedge ((I(a) \wedge \forall x(x \precsim a \rightarrow \mathfrak{A}(x, b) \wedge \forall y(\subset(x, y, b) \rightarrow \mathfrak{A}(x, y) \wedge Ac(\{z\}\mathfrak{A}(x, z), x, y))) \vee (a = \infty \wedge \forall x(x \precsim a \rightarrow \mathfrak{A}(x, b))).$$

Then we can introduce a new predicate constant $N(i, a)$ using Takeuti's kind of inductive definition in **[10]** (though our system does not contain second order quantifiers).

N1. $\tilde{I}(a), N(a, b) \Rightarrow G(\{x, y\}(N(x, y) \wedge x \precsim a), a, b)$

N2. $\tilde{I}(a), G(\{x, y\}(N(x, y) \wedge x \precsim a), a, b) \Rightarrow N(a, b)$.

Let $Ac(a, b, c)$ be $Ac(\{x\}N(b, x), a, c)$ (which will mean c is N_b-$<_a$-accessible) and introduce the axiom and axiom schema for N_i-$<_j$- accessibility.

AN1. $N(i, a), \forall x(N(i, x) \wedge <(j, x, a) \rightarrow Ac(j, i, x)) \Rightarrow Ac(j, i, a)$

AN2. $\tilde{I}(j), Ac(j, i, a), \forall x(N(i, x) \wedge \forall y(N(i, y) \wedge <(j, y, x) \rightarrow \mathfrak{A}(y)) \rightarrow \mathfrak{A}(x)) \Rightarrow \mathfrak{A}(a)$

where $\mathfrak{A}(a)$ is an arbitrary formula.

Naturally the notion of formula should be extended to include new predicates in the axiom schemata (initial sequents) of the basic system, and the definition of a sequent being admissible should read: A sequent $\Gamma \Rightarrow \Delta$ is called *admissible* if at most one formula in Δ contains quantifiers, the predicate N or Ac. (Thus the other formulas in Δ are all decidable.) Finally for technical reasons we need an additional axiom schema concerning Ac.

EA. $\forall x(\mathfrak{A}(x) \leftrightarrow \mathfrak{B}(x)) \Rightarrow Ac(\{x\}\mathfrak{A}(x), a, b) \leftrightarrow Ac(\{x\}\mathfrak{B}(x), a, b)$,

where $\mathfrak{A}(a)$ and $\mathfrak{B}(a)$ are arbitrary formulas and $\mathfrak{A} \leftrightarrow \mathfrak{B}$ denotes $(\mathfrak{A} \rightarrow \mathfrak{B}) \wedge (\mathfrak{B} \rightarrow \mathfrak{A})$.

3. *Outline of the formal proof of accessibility.* After the above preparation it is rather routine to carry out the formal proof of the accessibility of Od(I, A), though writing it down in full detail is naturally laborious. We have no essential difficulty in changing the formal accessibility proof in

[**4**] § 4 into a formal proof of accessibility in the present system. Instead of giving technical details we make a few remarks to give the reader some idea of how the proof can be carried out, referring him to [7] and [**4**] § 4 for the details.

First, we can use properties of primitive recursive functions and predicates freely in terms of mathematical axioms as in [7] (though we need more mathematical axioms than those required in [7]).

Secondly, we can see as follows that no second order quantification takes place in the present proof: In [**4**] § 4 we presented a formal theory of $\mathrm{Od}(I, A)$ in which the notion of accessibility was introduced by making use of such second order quantifications as

$$\mathrm{A}(i, \alpha, a) \text{ (to mean `a is accessible w.r.t. $<_i$ in $\{x|\alpha[x]\}$')}$$
$$\underset{\text{def}}{\leftrightarrow} \forall\varphi(\forall x(\alpha[x] \wedge \forall y(\alpha[y] \wedge <(i, y, x) \rightarrow \varphi[y]) \rightarrow \varphi[x]) \rightarrow \varphi[a]),$$

We also introduce the notion 'a is an i-normal o.d.' (there called i-fan) using inductive definition with second order quantifiers following [**10**]. Those quantifiers were required essentially only in order to express these two notions. We introduced the inference schema $\forall$ elimination for a predicate variable.

$$\frac{\mathfrak{F}(\mathrm{V}), \Gamma \Rightarrow \Delta}{\forall\varphi\mathfrak{F}(\varphi), \Gamma \Rightarrow \Delta}$$

under the restriction that $\mathfrak{F}(\alpha)$ contained no second order quantifiers. By going over the actual proof outlined in § 2, we verify that any principal formula of an $\forall$ elimination for a predicate variable $\mathfrak{J}$ occurring in the proof is of the form $\mathrm{A}(i, \{x\}\mathfrak{A}(x), a)$, where $\mathfrak{A}(b)$ is $O(b)$ or $F(j, b)$. In other words, since here we have the predicate Ac expressing accessibility, we can obtain the lower sequent of $\mathfrak{J}$ by reading Ac for A there and by making use of either AO2 or AN2 with other minor changes.

REFERENCES

[1] G. Gentzen, Untersuchungen über das logische Schliessen, I, II, *Math. Z.* **39** (1935) 176–210, 405–431.

[2] G. Gentzen, Die Widerspruchsfreiheit der reinen Zahlentheorie, *Math. Ann.* **112** (1936) 493–565.

[3] G. Gentzen, Neue Fassung des Widerspruchsfreiheitsbeweises für reinen Zahlentheorie, *Forschung zur Logik und Grundlegung der exakten Wissenschaften*, Neue Folge **4**, Leipzig (1938) 19–44.

[4] A. Kino, On ordinal diagrams, *J. Math. Soc. Japan* **13** (1961) 346–356.

[5] G. TAKEUTI, Ordinal diagrams, *J. Math. Soc. Japan* **9** (1957) 386–394.

[6] G. TAKEUTI, On the fundamental conjecture V, *J. Math. Soc. Japan* **10** (1958) 121–134.

[7] G. TAKEUTI, On the formal theory of the ordinal diagrams, *Ann. Japan Assoc. Philos. Sci.* **3** (1958) 151–170.

[8] G. TAKEUTI, On the fundamental conjecture VI, *Proc. Japan Academy* **37** (1961) 437–439.

[9] G. TAKEUTI, Ordinal diagrams II, *J. Math. Soc. Japan* **12** (1960) 385–391.

[10] G. TAKEUTI, On the inductive definition with quantifiers of second order, *J. Math. Soc. Japan* **13** (1961) 333–341.

[11] G. TAKEUTI, Consistency proofs of subsystems of classical analysis, *Ann. Math.* **86** (1967) 299–348.

[12] G. TAKEUTI, On a generalized logic calculus, *Japan J. Math.* **23** (1953) 39–96. Errata to 'On a generalized logic calculus', *Japan J. Math.* **24** (1954) 149–156.

[13] A. S. TROELSTRA, The theory of choice sequences, in *Logic, methodology and philosophy of science III*, North-Holland, Amsterdam (1968) 201–223.

[14] W. A. HOWARD and G. KREISEL, Transfinite induction and bar induction of type zero and one, and the role of continuity in intuitionistic analysis, *J. Symb. Logic* **31** (1966) 325–358.

[15] H. GERBER, Brouwer's bar theorem and a system of ordinal notations, these proceedings, 327–338.

ON THE RELATIONSHIP BETWEEN TAKEUTI'S ORDINAL DIAGRAMS $O(n)$ AND SCHÜTTE'S SYSTEM OF ORDINAL NOTATIONS $\Sigma(n)$

HILBERT LEVITZ*

1. Introduction. In connection with his proof theoretical investigations [**13**] Takeuti defined for each positive integer n a system $O(n)$ which consists of formal expressions called 'ordinal diagrams' together with $n+1$ well-orderings of these expressions [**12**]. He showed the consistency of a certain subsystem of formal simple type theory by assigning ordinal diagrams to the proof figures and by arguing by transfinite induction on these ordinal diagrams that cuts can be eliminated from the proofs. He then went on to prove the consistency of even more extensive subsystems [**16**] by using 'ordinal diagrams of infinite order' developed in [**14**].

In this exposition we use $O(n)$ to denote the *set* of ordinal diagrams of order n, and $\langle O(n), <_i\rangle$ for $0 \leqslant i \leqslant n$ to denote the structure consisting of the set $O(n)$ ordered by $<_i$. If a set A is well-ordered by a relation $<$, then $||u \in \langle A, <\rangle||$ will be used to denote the ordinal number corresponding to $u \in A$ when $\langle A, <\rangle$ is mapped by its ordering function onto an initial segment of the ordinals; $||\langle A, <\rangle||$ will denote the order type of $\langle A, <\rangle$.

In the author's doctoral dissertation [**5**] it was shown that $||\langle O(1), <_1\rangle||$ is the least ω-critical number (cf. [**10**]). This ordinal appears in Bachmann's hierarchy of normal functions as $\varphi_\omega(1)$ (Bachmann's functions have 1, not 0, as the least element of their domain of definition). We also located Veblen's least E-number ([**9**], [**17**]) within $\langle O(2), <_2\rangle$. Under the assumption that Bachmann's hierarchy satisfies certain closure, representation, and recursion conditions we showed that $||2 \in \langle O(2), <_2\rangle||$ equals Bachmann's $\varphi_{\varepsilon_\Omega+1}(1)$.

* The author wishes to thank Professors K. Schütte and W. A. Howard for their encouragement.

This work was supported by a grant from the Office of Scientific Research of the United States Air Force.

Gerber [2] has shown that Bachmann's hierarchy does indeed have these properties.

Schütte [11] has developed for each n a system of terms $\Sigma(n)$ and an ordering $<$ of these terms so that $\langle \Sigma(n), <\rangle$ is a well-ordered structure. $\langle \bigcup_{n<\omega} \Sigma(n), <\rangle$ is not a well-ordered structure, but it does have a largest well-ordered initial segment $\langle \Sigma_0, <\rangle$. The principal result of this investigation is that

$$\lim_{n<\omega} \|\langle O(n), <_n\rangle\| = \|\langle \Sigma_0, <\rangle\|.$$

Pfeiffer [8] has shown how to delete terms from $\bigcup_{n<\omega} \Sigma(n)$ (by means of a restriction on the term formation rules) so that the resulting set Σ is well-ordered by $<$, and $\langle \Sigma_0, <\rangle$ is an initial segment of $\langle \Sigma, <\rangle$. He has also shown that $\|\langle \Sigma_0, <\rangle\| = \alpha_*^0$ where α_*^0 is the 'Grenzzahl' of his own extended version of Bachmann's hierarchy [7]. In this extended version the initial ordinals ω_n $(n < \omega)$ play a role.

Isles [3], working independently of Pfeiffer, has developed an extended version of Bachmann's hierarchy in which initial ordinals even greater than ω_ω play a role.

2. The system $P^*(n)$. In [6] we described a system $O^*(n)$ which differed from $O(n)$ in inessential respects, and for which $\|\langle O^*(n), <_i\rangle\| = \|\langle O(n), <_i\rangle\|$ when $0 \leqslant i \leqslant n$. We then described a system $P^*(n)$ such that $\langle P^*(n), <_n\rangle$ is an initial segment of $\langle O^*(n), <_n\rangle$ which in turn is order isomorphic to an initial segment of $\langle P^*(n+1), <_{n+1}\rangle$, the latter initial segment being the one determined by $[1, [1, 1]] \in P^*(n+1)$†. We find it more convenient to work with the system $P^*(n)$ because its members are built up using two place expressions [,] as opposed to the three place expressions [; ,] used in $O(n)$. Below we show how $P^*(n)$ is defined. In addition we state some lemmas about $P^*(n)$ which will be needed in relating $P^*(n+1)$ to $\Sigma(n)$. For the proofs of these lemmas the reader should consult [6].

DEFINITION 2.1.
(a). Let n be a fixed positive integer. The expressions in $P^*(n)$ are called *ordinal diagrams* and are generated by means of the two operations $\#$ and [,] as follows (for brevity we call a member of $P^*(n)$ an o.d.):

† In [6] we used the notation (1, (1, 1)) instead of [1, [1, 1]]; we prefer to use square brackets here because round brackets are used in forming the members of $\Sigma(n)$.

E1.1. $0 \in P^*(n)$.

E1.2. If $u \in P^*(n)$ and i is an integer such that $1 \leqslant i \leqslant n$, then $[i, u] \in P^*(n)$. i is called the *index* of the o.d.

E1.3. If $u, v \in P^*(n)$, then so is $u \# v$.

(b). An ordinal diagram u is called *connected* if the operation used last in the construction of u is not $\#$. That is, u is 0 or u is $[i, v]$.

(c). The notion of *component* is defined recursively as follows:

E2.1. If u is connected then u has for its components only u itself and 0.

E2.2. If u is of the form $u_1 \# u_2$ and the components of u_1 and u_2 are $x_1, x_2, \ldots, x_s$ and $y_1, y_2, \ldots, y_t$ respectively, then the components of u are $x_1, x_2, \ldots, x_s, y_1, y_2, \ldots, y_t$.

DEFINITION 2.2. We define the notion of *equality* recursively as follows:

E3.1. If all of the components of u are 0, then $u = v$ if and only if all of the components of v are 0.

E3.2. If u has a component different from 0, and if $u_1, \ldots, u_s$ are the components of u which are different from 0, then $u = v$ if and only if among the components of v there are precisely s of them $v_1, \ldots, v_s$ which are different from 0 and there exists a permutation $(t_1, \ldots, t_s)$ of $(1, \ldots, s)$ such that $u_m = v_{t_m}$ for $m = 1, \ldots, s$.

E3.3. $i = j$ and $x = y$ imply $[i, x] = [j, y]$.

DEFINITION 2.3. If u and v are o.d.'s and i is an integer satisfying $1 \leqslant i \leqslant n$, we define the relation $u \subset_i v$ recursively as follows:

E4.1. If v is 0 then $u \subset_i v$ does not hold.

E4.2. Let v be of the form $[j, v_0]$:

E4.2.1. If $j < i$, then $u \subset_i v$ holds if and only if $u \subset_i v_0$ holds.

E4.2.2. If $j = i$, then $u \subset_i v$ holds if and only if u is v_0.

E4.2.3. If $j > i$, then $u \subset_i v$ never holds.

E4.3. Let v be of the form $v_1 \# v_2$. Then $u \subset_i v$ if and only if $u \subset_i v_1$ or $u \subset_i v_2$.

DEFINITION 2.4. We define the relations $u <_i v$ $(0 \leqslant i \leqslant n)$ recursively as follows:

E5.1. Let the components of u and v be $u_1, \ldots, u_k$ $(k \geqslant 1)$ and $v_1, \ldots, v_h$ $(h \geqslant 1)$ respectively. $u <_i v$ holds if and only if one of the following conditions is fulfilled:

E5.1.1. There exists v_m $(1 \leqslant m \leqslant h)$ such that for every s $(1 \leqslant s \leqslant k)$ $u_s <_i v_m$.

E5.1.2. $k = 1$, $h > 1$, $u_1 = v_m$ for a suitable m ($1 \leqslant m \leqslant h$), and $v_t \neq 0$ for some $t \neq m$.

E5.1.3. $k > 1$, $h > 1$, and there exists u_s ($1 \leqslant s \leqslant k$) and v_m($1 \leqslant m \leqslant h$) such that $u_s = v_m$ and $u_1 \# \ldots \# u_{s-1} \# u_{s+1} \# \ldots \# u_k <_i v_1 \# \ldots \# \# v_{m-1} \# v_{m+1} \# \ldots \# v_h$.

E5.2. Let u, v be c.o.d.'s. Then $u <_i v$ ($i = 1, \ldots, n$) if and only if one of the following conditions is fulfilled:

E5.2.1. There exists z such that $u \leqslant_i z \subset_i v$.

E5.2.2. $u <_{i-1} v$ and $z \subset_i u$ implies $z <_i v$.

E5.3. If v has the form $[j, y]$, then $0 <_0 v$ holds. If u has the form $[i, x]$, then $u <_0 0$ does not hold.

E5.4. Let u and v be c.o.d.'s of the form $[i, x]$ and $[j, y]$ respectively. $u <_0 v$ if and only if one of the following is fulfilled:

E5.4.1. $i > j$.

E5.4.2. $i = j$ and $x <_i y$.

DEFINITION 2.5. We assign to each $u \in P^*(n)$ a non-negative integer called the *length* of u and we denote it by Lu:

E6.1. $L0 = 0$.

E6.2. $L(u \# v) = Lu + Lv$.

E6.3. $L[i, x] = Lx + 1$.

DEFINITION 2.6. In the system $P^*(n)$ we define the notation l_m recursively as follows: $l_0 = 0$, $l_{m+1} = l_m \# [n, 0]$. Usually we write 1 instead of l_1.

LEMMA 2.7. ([**6**], lemma 3.3). *If* $0 < i \leqslant k \leqslant n$, *then* $x <_k [i, x]$.

LEMMA 2.8 ([**6**], lemma 3.4). $[i, x] <_k [j, y]$ *if and only if at least one of the following holds*:

(a). $k = 0 \wedge (j < i \vee (j = i \wedge x <_i y))$.

(b). $k > 0 \wedge ([i, x] <_{k-1} [j, y] \wedge (i > k \vee (i \leqslant k \wedge x <_k [j, y])))$.

(c.) $k > 0 \wedge j \leqslant k \wedge [i, x] \leqslant_k y$.

LEMMA 2.9 ([**6**], lemmas 3.5, 3.6])

(a). $0 \leqslant k \leqslant i \leqslant n$, $1 \leqslant i$, *and* $x <_i y$ *imply* $[i, x] <_k [i, y]$.

(b). $0 \leqslant k < i \leqslant n$, *and* $0 < j < i$ *imply* $[i, x] <_k [j, y]$.

DEFINITION 2.10. We define the functions f_k for $1 \leqslant k \leqslant n$ as follows:

(1). $f_k 0 = 0$,

(2). $f_k(u_1 \# \ldots \# u_s) = f_k u_1 \# \ldots \# f_k u_s$ if u_i is connected for $1 \leqslant i \leqslant s$.

$$(3).\ f_k[j, x] = \begin{cases} [k, [j, x]] & \text{if } 1 \leqslant j < k, \\ [k, x \# 1] & \text{if } k = j \text{ and } x = [p, y] \# l_m \text{ where } p < k, \\ [j, x] & \text{otherwise.} \end{cases}$$

LEMMA 2.11 ([**6**], lemma 3.8]). *If* $1 \leqslant k \leqslant n$, *and* $0 \leqslant p \leqslant k$, *then* $u <_k v$ *implies that* $f_k u <_p f_k v$.

DEFINITION 2.12. For $1 \leqslant k \leqslant n$ we define the functions F_k as follows:

(1). $F_k 0 = 0$

(2). $F_k(u_1 \# \ldots \# u_s) = F_k u_1 \# \ldots \# F_k u_s$ if u_i is connected for $1 \leqslant i \leqslant s$.

$$(3).\ F_k[j, x] = \begin{cases} 0 & \text{if } j < k, \\ x & \text{if } j = k \text{ and } x = [p, y] \text{ where } p < k, \\ [k, [p, y] \# l_m] & \text{if } k = j \text{ and } x = [p, y] \# l_{m+1} \\ & \qquad \text{where } p < k, \\ [j, x] & \text{otherwise.} \end{cases}$$

LEMMA 2.13.

(a). $F_k f_k x = x$

(b). $f_k F_k x = x$ *provided each non-zero component of* x *has index equal or greater than* k.

(c). *If* $1 \leqslant k \leqslant n$, *then* $u <_{k-1} v$ *implies* $F_k u <_k F_k v$ *provided each non-zero component of* u, v *has index equal or greater than* k.

PROOF.

(a), (b), Immediate from defs. 2.10. 2.12.

(c). Suppose not, then $F_k v \leqslant_k F_k u$. But then using part (b) of this lemma together with lemma 2.11 we get $v = f_k F_k v \leqslant_{k-1} f_k F_k u = u$, contradiction.

3. The system $\Sigma^*(n)$. The system $\Sigma(n)$ does not have an identity element with respect to the operation $\#$. Below we describe a system $\Sigma^*(n)$ which has such an identity. In doing so it will be necessary to modify certain clauses in the definition of $\Sigma(n)$ which are not compatible with the presence of an identity. Failure to make these modifications would result in $u < u \# 0$.

DEFINITION 3.1 (a). Let n be a fixed positive integer. The members of $\Sigma^*(n)$ will be *terms* defined recursively as follows:

G1.1. The symbols $\Omega_0, \Omega_1, \ldots, \Omega_n$ are terms.

G1.2. If u and v are terms then so are (u, v) and $u \# v$.

We sometimes write 0 instead of Ω_0.

(b). Terms of the form Ω_i and of the form (u, v) are called *connected*. The notion of component is defined exactly as in clauses E2.1 and E2.2 of § 2.

DEFINITION 3.2. To each term u we assign a non-negative integer called the *length* of u (denoted by Lu) and a non-negative integer called the *level* of u (denoted by Su) recursively as follows:

G2.1. $L0 = 0$.

G2.2. $L\Omega_i = 1$ for $1 \leqslant i \leqslant n$.

G2.3. $L(u, v) = Lu+Lv+1$.

G2.4. $L(u_1 \# \dots \# u_k) = Lu_1 \# \dots \# Lu_k$ for connected terms $u_1, \dots, u_k$ $(k > 1)$.

G2.5. $S\Omega_i = i$ $(i = 0, 1, \dots, n)$.

G2.6. $S(u, v) = Sv$.

G2.7. $S(u_1 \# \dots \# u_k) = \max\{Su_1, \dots, Su_k\}$ for connected terms $u_1, \dots, u_k$ $(k > 1)$.

DEFINITION 3.3. We define *equality* among terms recursively as follows:

G3.1. $\Omega_i = \Omega_i$ $(i = 0, 1, \dots, n)$.

G3.2. $u_1 = v_1$ and $u_2 = v_2$ imply $(u_1, u_2) = (v_1, v_2)$.

G3.3. Same as E3.1. of § 2.

G3.4. Same as E3.2. of § 2.

DEFINITION 3.4. We define the set of *i-coefficients* $K_i u$ of a term u recursively as follows:

G4.1. If u is connected and $Su \leqslant i$, then $K_i u = \{0, u\}$.

G4.2. If $0 \leqslant i < k \leqslant n$, then $K_i \Omega_k = \{0\}$, that is the set whose only member is the symbol 0.

G4.3. If $i < Sv$, then $K_i(u, v) = K_i u \cup K_i v$

G4.4. $K_i(u_1 \# \dots \# u_k) = K_i u_1 \cup \dots \cup K_i u_k$ for $u_1, \dots, u_k$ connected $(k > 1)$.

DEFINITION 3.5. We define the relation $<$ on $\Sigma^*(n)$ recursively as follows:

G5.1. If $i \leqslant Sv$ $(i = 0, 1, \dots, n)$, then $\Omega_i < (u, v)$.

G5.2. If u is connected and $Su < i$ $(i = 1, \dots, n)$, then $u < \Omega_i$.

G5.3. If $u_1 < v_1$, $Su_2 = i$, and $x \in (K_i u_1 \cup \{u_2\})$ implies $x < (v_1, v_2)$, then $(u_1, u_2) < (v_1, v_2)$.

G5.4. If $u_1 = v_1$ and $u_2 < v_2$, then $(u_1, u_2) < (v_1, v_2)$.

G5.5. If $v_1 < u_1$, $Sv_2 = i$, and $(u_1, u_2) \leqslant x$ for some $x \in (K_i v_1 \cup \{v_2\})$, then $(u_1, u_2) < (v_1, v_2)$.

G5.6. Same as clause E5.1. of § 2, reading $<$ instead of $<_i$.

DEFINITION 3.6. We define the expression l_m and the functions $1+x$, $-1+x$, and Ω_i+x for $0 \leqslant i \leqslant n$ as follows:

(1). $l_0 = 0$. $l_{m+1} = l_m \# (0,0)$. We will normally write 1 instead of l_1.

(2). $$1+x = \begin{cases} x \# 1 & \text{if } x = l_m \text{ for some } m, \\ x & \text{otherwise.} \end{cases}$$

(3). $$-1+x = \begin{cases} l_m & \text{if } x = l_{m+1}, \\ x & \text{otherwise.} \end{cases}$$

(4). $$\Omega_i+x = \begin{cases} x & \text{if } x \text{ has a component } (u,v) \text{ where } Sv \geqslant i, \\ \Omega_i \# x & \text{otherwise.} \end{cases}$$

The following lemma states some elementary consequences of definition 3.6.

LEMMA 3.7.
(a). *$Sx = i$ implies $x = \Omega_i+y$ for some y.*
(b). *$x < y$ implies $\Omega_i+x < \Omega_i+y$.*

DEFINITION 3.8. We define the sets C_i and the functions h_i for $0 \leqslant i \leqslant n$ as follows:

(1). $x \in C_i$ if and only if $x = \Omega_j$ where $0 < j \leqslant i$ or $x = (u, v)$ where $u \neq 0$ and $Sv < i$.

(2). $$h_i x = \begin{cases} x & \text{if } x \in C_i, \\ (0, y \# l_m) & \text{if } x = y \# l_{m+1} \text{ and } y \in C_i, \\ (0, x) & \text{otherwise.} \end{cases}$$

LEMMA 3.9 (Simple consequences of def. 3.8).
(a). *$h_i x$ is a strictly increasing function of x.*
(b). *For a given i, $(0, x) = h_i y$ where $y = x$ or $y = x \# 1$.*
(c). *If $Sw \leqslant i$, then $w = u \# v$ where each non-zero component of u is of the form $h_i z$ for some z, and each non-zero component of v is of the form (x, y) where $x \neq 0$ and $Sy = i$.*
(d). *$x < (1+u, v)$ implies $h_i(x) < (1+u, v)$.*
(e). *$x \leqslant h_i x$.*
(f). *If $u \neq 1$ and $Sx > k$, then $u \in K_k x$ implies $u \in K_k h_i x$.*
(g). *$h_i x \leqslant (0, h_j x)$ for any i, j.*
(h). *$i \geqslant j$ implies $h_i x \leqslant h_j x$.*

LEMMA 3.10.
(a). *$v < (u, v)$.*
(b). *$Sv = i$ and $x \in K_i u$ imply $x < (u, v)$.*

PROOF (Cf. **[11]**, lemma 9.). The proof given there is for $\Sigma(n)$, but it applies also to $\Sigma^*(n)$.

The following recursively defined mapping $'$ maps $\Sigma(n)$ onto $\{x | x \in \Sigma^*(n) \wedge \wedge x \neq 0\}$, and preserves order:

(1). $(u_1 \# \ldots \# u_s)' = u_1' \# \ldots \# u_s'$ if u_i connected for $1 \leqslant i \leqslant s$.
(2). $1' = (0, 0)$.
(3). $\Omega_i' = \Omega_i$ for $i \geqslant 1$.
(4). $(1, x)' = (0, x')$.
(5). $(x, y)' = (-1+x', -1+y')$ if $x \neq 1$.

4. The principal mappings. In this section we describe an order preserving mapping from $\langle P^*(n+1), <_{n+1}\rangle$ onto an initial segment of $\langle \Sigma^*(n), <\rangle$.

DEFINITION 4.1. For $0 \leqslant k \leqslant n+1$ we define the mapping B_k from $P^*(n+1)$ into $\Sigma^*(n)$ as follows:

$$B_k x = \begin{cases} 1 & \text{if } x = [i, y] \# l_m \text{ where } i < k-1, \\ 0 & \text{otherwise.} \end{cases}$$

DEFINITION 4.2. For $0 \leqslant k \leqslant n+1$ we define recursively the mappings g_k and H_k from $P^*(n+1)$ into $\Sigma^*(n)$ as follows:

(1). $g_k(0) = H_k(0) = 0$.
(2). $g_k(u_1 \# u_2 \# \ldots \# u_s) = g_k u_1 \# g_k u_2 \# \ldots \# g_k u_s$,
$H_k(u_1 \# u_2 \# \ldots \# u_s) = H_k u_1 \# H_k u_2 \# \ldots \# H_k u_s$ if u_i is connected for $1 \leqslant i \leqslant s$.

(3). $$H_k[i, x] = \begin{cases} 0 & \text{if } i \geqslant k, \\ h_{n+1-(k-1)}(g_{k-1}x) & \text{if } i = k-1, \\ g_{k-1}[i, x] & \text{if } i < k-1. \end{cases}$$

$$g_k[i, x] = \begin{cases} h_{n+1-k}(\Omega_{n+1-i}+g_i x) & \text{if } i \geqslant k, \\ (1+H_k x, \Omega_{n+1-k}+(B_k x \# g_k F_k x)) & \text{if } i = k-1, \\ (H_k[i, x], \Omega_{n+1-k}) & \text{if } i < k-1. \end{cases}$$

It will be seen later on that g_{n+1} is the order preserving mapping referred to in the opening remark of this section.

LEMMA 4.3. *Assume* $0 \leqslant k \leqslant n+1$, *then*:

(a). $Sg_k[i, x] = n+1-\max\{k, i\}$.
(b). $\Omega_{n+1-k} < g_k[i, x]$ *provided* $1 \leqslant i < k$.
(c). *If* $i \geqslant k$ *and* $g_k[i, x] = (u, v)$, *then* $u = 0$ *or* $S(u, v) < n+1-k$.
(d). *If* $u = g_{n+1-k}(v)$, *then if* $k^* \leqslant k$, *there exists* v^* *such that* $u = g_{n+1-k^*}(v^*)$.
(e). $s \geqslant i$ *and* $s \geqslant k$ *imply* $g_k[s, v] \leqslant (0, g_i[s, v])$.

(f). *$s > i$ and $s > j$ imply* $g_i[s, x] = g_j[s, x]$.
(g). *$i \leqslant j \leqslant s$ implies* $g_i[s, y] \leqslant g_j[s, y]$.

PROOF.

(a). By induction on $Lg_k[i, x]$.
(b). Immediate from part (a) together with def. 3.5.
(c). Immediate from def. 3.8.
(d). We can assume that v is connected. If $v = 0$, then trivial, so we can further assume that v has the form $[j, t]$.

(d1). $k = k^*$. Then trivial.

(d2). $k^* < k$:

(d2.1). $j < n+1-k^*$. Then using def. 3.8 and lemma 4.3(a) we see that $g_{n+1-k^*}[j, t] = h_k(\Omega_{k^*} + g_{n+1-k^*}[j, t]) = g_{n+1-k}[n+1-k^*, [j, t]]$.

(d2.2). $j \geqslant n+1-k^*$. Then $k > k^* \geqslant n+1-j$:

(d2.2.1). $g_j t$ is of the form $(p, q) \# l_m$ where $p \neq 0$, $S(p, q) = k^*$. Then using def. 3.8 along with the fact that $g_j(t \# 1) = g_j t \# 1$ we get $g_{n+1-k^*}[j, t] = h_{k^*}(\Omega_{n+1-j} + g_j t) = h_k(\Omega_{n+1-j} + g_j t \# 1) = g_{n+1-k}[j, t \# 1]$.

(d2.2.2). otherwise. On account of $n+1-j < k$ we get that $\Omega_{n+1-j} + g_j t$ is not of the form $\Omega_k \# l_m$ for some m, so $g_{n+1-k^*}[j, t] = h_{k^*}(\Omega_{n+1-j} + g_j t) = h_k(\Omega_{n+1-j} + g_j t) = g_{n+1-k}[j, t]$.

(e). Follows from lemma 3.9(g).
(f). By def. 3.8 we would have under the given hypothesis that $h_{n+1-i}(\Omega_{n+1-s} + g_s y) = h_{n+1-j}(\Omega_{n+1-s} + g_s y)$.
(g). By lemma 3.9(h) $h_{n+1-i}(\Omega_{n+1-s} + g_s x) \leqslant h_{n+1-j}(\Omega_{n+1-s} + g_s x)$.

DEFINITION 4.4. We define the projection functions R and Q as follows: $R(x, y) = x$ and $Q(x, y) = y$.

LEMMA 4.5. *Assume* $0 \leqslant k \leqslant n+1$ *and* x^* *is a component of* x, *then*:
(a). *If* $1 \leqslant j \leqslant k-1$, *then* $u \in K_{n+1-k} Rg_k[j, x^*]$ *implies that* $u \in K_{n+1-k} Rg_k[j, x]$.
(b). *If* $1 \leqslant j \leqslant n+1$, *then* $g_k[j, x^*] \leqslant g_k[j, x]$.

PROOF.

(a). The trick is to show more generally that for $1 \leqslant t \leqslant k-j$, $u \in K_{n+1-k} Rg_{j+t}[j, x^*]$ implies $u \in K_{n+1-k} Rg_{j+t}[j, x]$. This can easily be done by induction on t. One considers cases $t = 1$, $t = 2$, and $t > 2$. The induction hypothesis is only used in the latter case.
(b). This is done by induction on k making use of part (a) of this lemma and lemma 3.10. The cases to be considered are $j \geqslant k$, $j = k-1$, and $j < k-1$.

The induction hypothesis is used only for the latter case.

LEMMA 4.6. *Suppose* $0 \leqslant k \leqslant n+1$, *then*:
(a). $g_k[t, z] < h_{n+1-k}(g_k[t, z])$ *provided* $1 \leqslant t < k$.
(b) $g_k x < h_{n+1-k}(\Omega_{n+1-k} + g_k x)$.

PROOF.
(a). From $t < k$ we get by lemma 4.3(a) that $Sg_k[t, z] = n+1-k$. From $t < k$ we also get using def. 4.2 that $g_k[t, z]$ has the form (u, v) where $u \neq 0$. So by def. 3.8 $h_{n+1-k}(g_k[t, z]) = (0, g_k[t, z])$.
(b). $h_{n+1-k}(\Omega_{n+1-k} + g_k x)$ is connected and by lemma 3.9(a) $h_{n+1-k}(\Omega_{n+1-k} + g_k x^*) \leqslant h_{n+1-k}(\Omega_{n+1-k} + g_k x)$ whenever x^* is a component of x, so it suffices to show that $g_k x^* < h_{n+1-k}(\Omega_{n+1-k} + g_k x^*)$ for each component x^* of x.
(b1). $g_k x^* < \Omega_{n+1-k} + g_k x^*$. Then using lemma 3.9(d) $g_k x^* < \Omega_{n+1-k} + g_k x^* \leqslant h_{n+1-k}(\Omega_{n+1-k} + g_k x^*)$.
(b2). $g_k x^* = \Omega_{n+1-k} + g_k x^*$. Then it suffices to show $g_k x^* < h_{n+1-k}(g_k x^*)$.
Noting that $Sg_k x^* \geqslant n+1-k$ we see from def. 3.8 that $(0, g_k x^*) = h_{n+1-k}(g_k x^*)$

LEMMA 4.7. *If* $1 \leqslant k \leqslant n+1$, *then*:
(a). $1 <_k y \wedge y = [i, x] \wedge i \geqslant k$ *implies* $1 <_k F_k y$.
(b). $1 <_k y$ *and* y *connected implies* $1 < g_k y$.
(c). $g_k F_k y = l_t$ *for some* $t \geqslant 0$ *implies that* $y = z \# l_t$ *where each non-zero component of* z *has index less than* k.

PROOF.
(a). Immediate from def. 2.12.
(b). Immediate from def. 4.2.
(c). Suppose not, then we obtain a contradiction by using (a) and (b).

LEMMA 4.8. *Assume* $1 \leqslant k \leqslant n+1$, *then*:
(a). $g_k F_k x \leqslant g_k x$.
(b). $g_k x \leqslant g_k F_k[k, x]$.

PROOF.
(a). It suffices to consider the case where x is connected:
(a1.). $x = 0$. Then trivial.
(a2). $x = [s, y]$ for some s and some y:
(a2.1). $F_k x = x$. Then $g_k F_k x = g_k x$.
(a2.2). $F_k x = y$. Then by def. 2.12 we see that $s = k$ and $y \neq 0$, so by lemma 4.5(b) $g_k F_k x = g_k y < h_{n+1-k}(\Omega_{n+1-k} + g_k y) = g_k[k, y] = g_k x$.

(a2.3). $F_k x = [k, v]$ where $v \# 1 = y$. Then by def. 2.12 we see that $s = k$ and $g_k F_k x = g_k[k, v] = h_{n+1-k}(\Omega_{n+1-k} + g_k v) < h_{n+1-k}(\Omega_{n+1-k} + g_k(v \# 1)) = g_k[k, y] = g_k x$.

(b).

(b1). $F_k[k, x] = [k, x]$. Then if $x = 0$ our result is trivial, while if $x \neq 0$ we get by lemma 4.6(b) $g_k x < h_{n+1-k}(\Omega_{n+1-k} + g_k x) = g_k[k, x] = g_k F_k[k, x]$.

(b2). $F_k[k, x] = x$. Then $g_k x = g_k F_k[k, x]$.

(b3). $F_k[k, x] = [k, v]$ where $v \# 1 = x$. By def. 2.12 we see that $v \neq 0$, so $g_k x = g_k v \# 1 < h_{n+1-k}(\Omega_{n+1-k} + g_k v) = g_k[k, v] = g_k F_k[k, x]$.

LEMMA 4.9.

(a). *If* $1 \leqslant j \leqslant k-1 \leqslant n$ *and* $1 \leqslant i = k-1$, *then* $1 < Rg_k[j, [i, y]]$. *If in addition* $y \neq 0$, *then* $Rg_k[j, [i, y]]$ *is connected.*

(b). *If* $1 \leqslant j < k-1 \leqslant n$, *then* $g_{j+t}[k, y] \in K_{n+1-k} Rg_k[j, [k, y]]$ *provided that* $2 \leqslant t \leqslant k-j$.

(c). *If* $1 \leqslant j < k-1 \leqslant n$, *then* $g_k[k, y] < g_k[j, [k, y]]$.

PROOF.

(a). Immediate from def. 4.2.

(b). We first note that under the given hypothesis $g_{j+1}F_{j+1}[k, y] = g_{j+1}[k, y]$. So it suffices to show that $g_{j+1}F_{j+1}[k, y] \in K_{n+1-k} Rg_{j+t}[j, [k, y]]$. We show this by induction on t:

(b1). $t = 2$. Then $Rg_{j+t}[j, [k, y]] = g_{j+1}[j, [k, y]] = (1, \Omega_{n+1-(j+1)} + (B_{j+1}[k, y] \# g_{j+1}F_{j+1}[k, y]))$. Since $Sg_{j+1}F_{j+1}[k, y] = n+1-k$ we get $g_{j+1}F_{j+1}[k, y] \in K_{n+1-k} g_{j+1}F_{j+1}[k, y]$. This with $n+1-(j+1) > n+1-k$ gives $g_{j+1}F_{j+1}[k, y] \in K_{n+1-k} Rg_{j+t}[j, [k, y]]$.

(b2). $t = r+1$ for some $r \geqslant 2$. By induction hypothesis $g_{j+1}F_{j+1}[k, y] \in K_{n+1-k} Rg_{j+r}[j, [k, y]]$. But $Sg_{j+r}[j, [k, y]] = n+1 + -(j+r) > n+1-k$, so $g_{j+1}F_{j+1}[k, y] \in K_{n+1-k} g_{j+r}[j, [k, y]]$. It remains only to note that $g_{j+r}[j, [k, y]] = Rg_{j+t}[j, [k, y]]$.

(c). $g_k[k, y] \in K_{n+1-k} Rg_k[j, [k, y]]$ by virtue of part (b) of this lemma. But $Sg_k[j, [k, y] = n+1-k$, so $g_k[k, y] < g_k[j, [k, y]]$ by lemma 3.10.

LEMMA 4.10.

(a). *If* $1 \leqslant i < k-1$, $i < s \leqslant n+1$, $0 \leqslant p \leqslant n+1-k$, *and* $u \neq 1$, *then* $u \in K_p g_{i+1} F_{i+1}[s, y]$ *if and only if* $u \in K_p g_i[s, y]$.

(b). *If* $1 \leqslant j < i \leqslant n+1$, $0 \leqslant p < n+1-i$, *and* $u \neq 1$, *then* $u \in K_p g_i x$ *implies* $u \in K_p g_{j+1} F_{j+1}[i, x]$.

PROOF.

(a).

(a1). $i+1 < s$. Then $F_{i+1}[s, y] = [s, y]$, so $g_{i+1}F_{i+1}[s, y] = g_{i+1}[s, y]$. But $g_{i+1}[s, y] = g_i[s, y]$ by lemma 4.3(f).

(a2). $i+1 = s$. Then $n+1-s = n+1-(i+1) > n+1-k \geqslant p$:

(a2.1). y is *not* of the form $[t, w] \# l_m$ where $t < i+1$ and $m \geqslant 0$. Then $F_{i+1}[s, y] = [s, y]$ so $g_{i+1}F_{i+1}[s, y] = g_{i+1}[s, y] = h_{n+1-(i+1)}(\Omega_{n+1-s} + g_s y)$. Therefore since $u \neq 1$ we get using lemma 3.9(f) that $u \in K_p g_{i+1} F_{i+1}[s, y]$ if and only if $u \in K_p g_s y$, and $u \in K_p g_s y$ if and only if $u \in K_p h_{n+1-i}(\Omega_{n+1-s} + g_s y)$. It remains only to note that $h_{n+1-i}(\Omega_{n+1-s} + g_s y) = g_i[s, y]$.

(a2.2). y is of the form $[t, w] \# l_m$ where $t < i+1$ and $m \geqslant 0$;

(a2.2.1). $m = 0$. Then $F_{i+1}[s, y] = y$ so $g_{i+1}F_{i+1}[s, y] = g_{i+1}y$. Now since $i+1 = s$, $g_i[s, y] = h_{n+1-i}(\Omega_{n+1-s} + g_s y) = h_{n+1-i}(\Omega_{n+1-(i+1)} + g_{i+1}y)$. From this it follows using $u \neq 1$ and lemma 3.9(f) that $u \in K_p g_{i+1} y$ if and only if $u \in K_p g_i[s, y]$.

(a2.2.2). $m > 0$. Then $F_{i+1}[s, y] = [s, v]$ where $v \# 1 = y$. Thus $g_{i+1}F_{i+1}[s, y] = g_{i+1}[s, v] = h_{n+1-(i+1)}(\Omega_{n+1-(i+1)} + g_{i+1}v)$. On the other hand $g_i[s, v] = h_{n+1-i}(\Omega_{n+1-(i+1)} + g_{i+1}v)$, so since $u \neq 1$, $u \in K_p g_{i+1}[s, v]$ if and only if $u \in K_p g_{i+1} v$, and $u \in K_p g_{i+1} v$ if and only if $u \in K_p g_{i+1} y$, and $u \in K_p g_{i+1} y$ if and only if $u \in K_p g_i[s, y]$.

(b).

(b1). $F_{j+1}[i, x] = [i, x]$. Then $g_{j+1}F_{j+1}[i, x] = g_{j+1}[i, x] = h_{n+1-(j+1)}(\Omega_{n+1-i} + g_i x)$, thus since $u \neq 1$ we have by lemma 3.9(f) that $u \in K_p g_i x$ implies $u \in K_p g_{j+1} F_{j+1}[i, x]$.

(b2). $F_{j+1}[i, x] = x$. For this to happen $i = j+1$, but then $g_{j+1}F_{j+1}[i, x] = g_i x$.

(b3). $F_{j+1}[i, x] = [i, v]$ where $v \# 1 = x$. For this to happen $i = j+1$ so $g_{j+1}F_{j+1}[i, x] = g_{j+1}[i, v] = h_{n+1-(j+1)}(\Omega_{n+1-i} + g_i v)$. Now since $u \neq 1$ we get $u \in K_p g_i x$ implies $u \in K_p g_i v$, but then we are finished by lemma 3.9(f).

LEMMA 4.11.

(a). *If* $1 \leqslant j < i \leqslant n+1$, *then* $g_i x \leqslant g_{j+1} F_{j+1}[i, x]$.

(b). *If* $1 \leqslant j < i \leqslant n+1$ *and* $n+1-i \leqslant p$, *then* $u \in K_p g_i x$ *implies* $u \leqslant g_{j+1} F_{j+1}[i, x]$.

(c). *If* $1 \leqslant j < i \leqslant n+1$ *and* $n+1-i \leqslant p$, *then* $Sg_{j+1}F_{j+1}[i, x] \leqslant p$.

PROOF.

(a).

(a1). $F_{j+1}[i, x] = [i, x]$. Then $g_{j+1}F_{j+1}[i, x] = h_{n+1-(j+1)}(\Omega_{n+1-i} + g_i x)$

and the desired result follows from lemma 4.6(b).

(a2). $F_{j+1}[i, x] = x$. For this to happen it must be the case (cf. def. 2.12) that $i = j+1$ so $g_{j+1}F_{j+1}x = g_i x$.

(a3). $F_{j+1}[i, x] = [i, v]$ where $x = v \# 1$. For this to happen it must be the case that $i = j+1$, so $g_{j+1}F_{j+1}[i, x] = g_i[i, v] = h_{n+1-i}(\Omega_{n+1-i}+g_i v)$. If $v = 0$ then $x = 1$ so the desired result would be trivial. If $v \neq 0$ then $g_i v < h_{n+1-i}(\Omega_{n+1-i}+g_i v)$ by lemma 4.6(b), so $g_i x = g_i v \# 1 < < h_{n+1-i}(\Omega_{n+1-i}+g_i v)$.

(b). We first note by lemma 4.3(a) that $Sg_i x \leqslant n+1-i \leqslant p$, so $u = g_i x^*$ where x^* is a component of x. So using part (a) of this lemma $u = g_i x^* \leqslant \leqslant g_i x \leqslant g_{j+1}F_{j+1}[i, x]$.

(c).

(c1). $F_{j+1}[i, x] = [i, z]$ for some z. Then by lemma 4.3(a) we have $Sg_{j+1}[i, x] = n+1-i \leqslant p$.

(c2). $F_{j+1}[i, x] = x$. For this to happen $i = j+1$ and $x = [s, z]$ for some z and some $s < i$. Then by lemma 4.3(a) $Sg_{j+1}[s, y] = n+1-i \leqslant p$.

LEMMA 4.12. *If* $1 \leqslant i \leqslant k-1 \leqslant n$, $0 \leqslant p \leqslant n+1-k$, *then* $1 \neq u \in K_p Rg_k[i, x]$ *implies that* $u \leqslant v \in K_p g_i x$ *for some* v *or that* $u = h_s w$ *for some* s *and some* w *such that* $Sw \leqslant p$ *and for which* $z \in K_p w$ *implies* $z \in K_p g_i x$.

PROOF. By induction on $k-i$:

(1). $k-i = 1$. Then $Rg_k[i, x] = 1+H_k x$, since $u \neq 1$ we can assert that $u \in K_p H_k x$. From this it follows that $u \in K_p H_k x^*$ where x^* is a component of x. If $x^* = 0$ or $x^* = [s, y]$ for $s \geqslant k$ then $H_k x^* = 0$ and our desired result would be trivial, so we can assume $x^* = [s, y]$ where $s \leqslant k-1$.

(1.1). $s < k-1$. Then $H_k[s, y] = g_{k-1}[s, y] = g_i[s, y]$ thus $u \in K_p g_i x^*$, so $u \in K_p g_i x$.

(1.2). $s = k-1$. Then $H_k[s, y] = h_{n+1-(k-1)}(g_{k-1}y)$:

(1.2.1). $Sh_{n+1-(k-1)}(g_{k-1}y) > p$. Then $u \in K_p g_{k-1}y$. But from $i = k-1 = s$ it follows that $g_i[s, y] = h_{n+1-(k-1)}(\Omega_{n+1-(k-1)}+g_{k-1}y)$, then using lemma 3.9(f) together with the fact that $u \neq 1$ we get $u \in K_p g_i[s, y]$.

(1.2.2). $Sh_{n+1-(k-1)}(g_{k-1}y) \leqslant p$. Then $u = h_{n+1-(k-1)}(g_{k-1}y)$. We see then that $g_{k-1}y$ plays the role of w mentioned in the statement of this lemma, for $z \in K_p g_{k-1}y$ implies $z \in K_p h_{n+1-(k-1)}(\Omega_{n+1-(k-1)} + g_{k-1}y)$ while $h_{n+1-(k-1)}(\Omega_{n+1-(k-1)}+g_{k-1}y) = g_{k-1}[k-1, y] = g_i[s, y] = g_i x^*$.

(2). $k-i = 2$. Then $Rg_k[i, x] = g_{k-1}[i, x] = (1+H_{k-1}x, \Omega_{n+1-(k-1)}+ +(B_{k-1}x \# g_{k-1}F_{k-1}x))$ so $u \in K_p H_{k-1}x$ or $u \in K_p g_{k-1}F_{k-1}x$:

(2.1). $u \in K_p g_{k-1} F_{k-1} x$. Then $u \in K_p g_{k-1} F_{k-1} x^*$ where x^* is a connected component of x. If $x^* = 0$ then $u = 0$ and our result is trivial, so we can assume that x^* is of the form $[s, y]$ where $s \geqslant k-1$ (if $s < k-1$, $g_{k-1} F_{k-1} x^* = 0$). Recalling that $k-1 = i+1$ and $u \neq 1$ we have by lemma 4.10(a) that $u \in K_p g_i x^*$.

(2.2). $u \in K_p H_{k-1} x$. In this case we can proceed in the same way as in case 1, except that we replace all occurrences of $k-1$ by $k-2$.

(3). $i < k-2$. Then $Rg_k[i, k] = g_{k-1}[i, x] = (g_{k-2}[i, x], \Omega_{n+1-(k-1)})$. Since $n+1-(k-1) > n+1-k \geqslant p$ we see that $u \in K_p Rg_k[i, x]$ implies $u \in K_p Rg_{k-1}[i, x]$ so we have the right to employ our induction hypothesis.

LEMMA 4.13. *If* $1 \leqslant i \leqslant k-1 \leqslant n$, $1 \leqslant j \leqslant m-1 \leqslant k-1$, $0 \leqslant p \leqslant n+1-k$, *and* $u \neq 1$, *then* $u \in K_p g_i x$ *implies* $u \leqslant v \in (K_p Rg_m[j, [i, x]] \cup K_p Qg_m[j, [i, x]])$ *for some* v.

PROOF. We argue by induction on $m-j$. $u \in K_p g_i x^*$ for some component x^* and we can assume that $x^* \neq 0$, so $x^* = [s, y]$ for some s and some y:

(1). $m-j = 1$:

(1.1). $i = j$. Then $g_m[j, [i, x]] = g_{i+1}[i, [i, x]] = (h_{n+1-i} g_i x, \Omega_{n+1-m})$:

(1.1.1). $Sg_i x > p$. Then since by hypothesis $u \neq 1$, we get by lemma 3.9(f) $u \in K_p h_{n+1-i} g_i x$.

(1.1.2). $Sg_i x \leqslant p$. Then $u = g_i x^* \leqslant g_i x = h_{n+1-i} g_i x \in K_p Rg_m[j, [i, x]]$.

(1.2). $i < j$. Then $g_m[j, [i, x]] = g_{j+1}[j, [i, x]] = (g_j[i, x], \Omega_{n+1-m} \# 1)$. It suffices to show that $u \leqslant v \in K_p g_{i+t}[i, x]$ for all t such that $j-i \geqslant t \geqslant 1$. We do this by an 'inner induction' on t:

(1.2.1). $t = 1$. $g_{i+t}[i, x] = g_{i+1}[i, x] = (1 + H_{i+1} x, \Omega_{n+1-(i+1)} + (B_{i+1} x \# g_{i+1} F_{i+1} x)$. In view of the fact that $p \leqslant n+1-(j+1) < n+1-(i+1)$, it would suffice to show that $u \leqslant v \in K_p H_{i+1} x^*$ for some v or that $u \leqslant v \in K_p g_{i+1} F_{i+1} x^*$ for some v:

(1.2.1.1). $s < i$. Then $H_{i+1} x^* = g_i x^*$.

(1.2.1.2). $s = i$. Then $g_i x^* = h_{n+1-i}(\Omega_{n+1-i} + g_i y)$. But then from $n+1+-i > p$ we see that $u \in K_p g_i x^*$ implies $u \in K_p g_i y$. Furthermore $H_{i+1} x^* = h_{n+1-i} g_i y$, so we need only show that $u \leqslant v \in K_p h_{n+1-i} g_i y$ for some v:

(1.2.1.2.1). $Sg_i y > p$. Then since $u \neq 1$, we have by lemma 3.9(f) that $u \in K_p h_{n+1-i} g_i y$.

(1.2.1.2.2). $Sg_i y \leqslant p$. Then $u \leqslant g_i y \leqslant h_{n+1-i} g_i y$. But $h_{n+1-i} g_i y \in K_p h_{n+1-i} g_i y$.

(1.2.1.3). $s > i$. Recalling that $i < j \leqslant m-1 \leqslant k-1$ we see using $u \neq 1$ together with lemma 4.10(a) that $u \in K_p g_{i+1} F_{i+1} [s, y]$.

(1.2.2). $t > 1$. So we write $t = r+1$ for some $r > 0$. Now $g_{i+t}[i, x] = g_{i+r+1}[i, x] = (g_{i+r}[i, x], \ \Omega_{n+1-(i+t)})$. By the inner induction hypothesis $u \in K_p g_{i+r}[i, x]$. This with $p < n+1-(i+t)$ gives $u \in K_p g_{i+t}[i, x]$.

(1.3). $j < i$. Now $g_m[j, [i, x]] = (1, \Omega_{n+1-(j+1)} + (B_{j+1}[i, x] \# \# (g_{j+1} F_{j+1}[i, x])))$:

(1.3.1). $n+1-i > p$. Then by lemma 4.10(b) we get $u \in K_p g_{j+1} F_{j+1}[i, x]$. That is, $u \in K_p Q g_m[j, [i, x]]$.

(1.3.2). $n+1-i \leqslant p$. Then by lemma 4.11(b) $u \leqslant g_{j+1} F_{j+1}[i, x]$. By lemma 4.11(c) $S g_{j+1} F_{j+1}[i, x] \leqslant p$ so $g_{j+1} F_{j+1}[i, x] \in K_p g_{j+1} F_{j+1}[i, x]$, that is, $g_{j+1} F_{j+1}[i, x] \in K_p Q g_m[j, [i, x]]$.

(2). $m-j > 1$. Then $g_m[j, [i, x]] = (g_{m-1}[j, [i, x]], \ \Omega_{n+1-m})$. By induction hypothesis $u \leqslant v \in (K_p R g_{m-1}[j, [i, x]] \cup K_p Q g_{m-1}[j, [i, x]])$ for some v. But $S g_{m-1}[j, [i, x]] = n+1-(m-1) > n+1-k \geqslant p$, so $v \in K_p g_{m-1}[j, [i, x]]$. Thus $v \in K_p R g_m[j, [i, x]]$.

LEMMA 4.14. *If* $1 \leqslant i \leqslant k-1 \leqslant n$ *and* $1 \leqslant j \leqslant k-1$, *then* $u \in K_{n+1-k} R g_k[i, x]$ *implies* $u < g_k[j, [i, x]]$.

PROOF.

(1). $u \leqslant 1$. Then $u < g_k[j, [i, x]]$ by defs. 4.2 and 3.5.

(2). $u > 1$. By lemma 4.12 $u \leqslant v \in K_{n+1-k} g_i x$ for some v, or $u = h_s w$ for some s and some w such that $Sw \leqslant n+1-k$ and for which $z \in K_{n+1-k} w$ implies $z \in K_{n+1-k} g_i x$:

(2.1). $u \leqslant v \in K_{n+1-k} g_i x$ for some v. By lemma 4.13

$$v \leqslant w \in (K_{n+1-k} R g_k[j, [i, x]] \cup K_{n+1-k} Q g_k[j, [i, x]])$$

for some w, but $w < g_k[j, [i, x]]$ by lemma 3.10.

(2.2). $u = h_s w$ for some s and some w such that $Sw \leqslant n+1-k$ and for which $z \in K_{n+1-k} w$ implies $z \in K_{n+1-k} \, g_i x$:

(2.2.1). $h_s w = w$. Then $w \in K_{n+1-k} w$ so $w \in K_{n+1-k} g_i x$. Then we have only to use lemma 4.13 followed by lemma 3.10 to get $w < g_k[j, [i, x]]$.

(2.2.2). $h_s w = (0, w)$ or $h_s w = (0, t)$ where $w = t \# 1$. Then $R g_k h_s w = 0 < R g_k[j, [i, x]]$. Moreover $z \in K_{n+1-k} Q h_s w$ implies $z \in K_{n+1-k} g_i x$, so by lemma 4.13 followed by lemma 3.10 we get $z < g_k[j, [i, x]]$, thus $h_s w < g_k[j, [i, x]]$.

LEMMA 4.15. *If* $1 \leqslant j \leqslant k \leqslant n+1$, *then* $g_k x < g_k[j, x]$.

PROOF. By induction on k. Our induction hypothesis is that if $k' < k$, then for every j and every $x, j \leqslant k'$ implies $g_{k'} x < g_{k'}[j, x]$. Let j, x be given where $j \leqslant k$. Since $g_k[j, x]$ is connected it suffices to show that $g_k x^* < g_k[j, x]$ for every component x^* if x. Moreover if $x^* = 0$ our result is trivial, so we can assume x^* is of the form $[i, y]$ for some i, y. By lemma 4.5(b) it would, in fact, suffice to show $g_k[i, y] < g_k[j, [i, y]]$.

(1). $j = k$. Then using lemma 4.6(b) $g_k[i,y] < h_{n+1-k}(\Omega_{n+1-k}+g_k[i, y]) = g_k[j, [i, y]]$.

(2). $j < k$:

(2.1). $i > k$. Then $Sg_k[i, y] = n+1-i < n+1-k = Sg_k[j, [i, y]]$ so finished by def. 3.5.

(2.2). $i = k$:

(2.2.1). $j = k-1$. Using lemma 4.8(b) and lemma 3.10 we get

$$\Omega_{n+1-k}+g_k y \leqslant \Omega_{n+1-k}+(B_k[i, y] \# g_k F_k[i, y]) < (1, \Omega_{n+1-k} + (B_k[i, y] \# g_k F_k[i, y])) = g_k[j, [i, y]].$$

(2.2.2). $j < k-1$. Then by lemma 4.9(c) $g_k[i, y] < g_k[j, [i, y]]$.

(2.3). $i < k$:

(2.3.1). $i < k-1 \wedge j = k-1$. Then $Rg_k[i, y] = g_{k-1}[i, y] = Rg_k[j, [i, y]]$ and $Qg_k[i, y] = \Omega_{n+1-k} < \Omega_{n+1-k} \# 1 = Qg_k[j, [i, y]]$ so by def. 3.5 $g_k[i, y] < g_k[j, [i, y]]$.

(2.3.2). $i < k-1 \wedge j < k-1$ or $i = k-1 \wedge j \leqslant k-1$. We now assert and will show that $Rg_k[i, y] < Rg_k[j, [i, y]]$. We prefix by 2.3.2.A the various cases which arise in showing this assertion:

(2.3.2.A.1). $i < k-1 \wedge j < k-1$. Using induction hypothesis we see that $Rg_k[i, y] = g_{k-1}[i, y] < g_{k-1}[j, [i, y]] = Rg_k[j, [i, y]]$.

(2.3.2.A.2). $i = k-1 \wedge j \leqslant k-1$. Then $Rg_k[i, y] = 1+H_k y$:

(2.3.2.A.2.1). $y = 0$. Then $1+H_k y < Rg_k[j, [i, y]]$ by lemma 4.9(a).

(2.3.2.A.2.2). $y \neq 0$. Now by lemma 4.9(a) $Rg_k[j, [i, y]] > 1$ and is connected, so it suffices to show that $H_k y^* < Rg_k[j, [i, y]]$ for every non-zero component y^* of y. Let $y^* = [s, v]$ be such a component:

(2.3.2.A.2.2.1). $s > k-1$. Then $H_k y^* = 0$ so trivial.

(2.3.2.A.2.2.2). $s \leqslant k-1$. By two successive applications of the induction hypothesis we get $g_{k-1}v < g_{k-1}[s, v] < g_{k-1}[i, [s, v]]$:

(2.3.2.A.2.2.2.1). $j = k-1$. Then $Rg_k[j, [i, y]] = 1+H_k[i, y] = 1+h_{n+1-(k-1)}(g_{k-1}[i, y]) = h_{n+1-(k-1)}(g_{k-1}[i, y])$:

(2.3.2.A.2.2.2.1.1). $s = k-1$. Then by lemmas 3.9(a) and lemma 4.5(b)

$$H_k y^* = H_k[s, v] = h_{n+1-(k-1)}(g_{k-1}v) < h_{n+1-(k-1)}(g_{k-1}[s, v]) < h_{n+1-(k-1)}(g_{k-1}[i, [s, v]]) \leqslant h_{n+1-(k-1)}(g_{k-1}[i, y^*]) \leqslant h_{n+1-(k-1)}(g_{k-1}[i, y]).$$

(2.3.2.A.2.2.2.1.2). $s < k-1$. Then $H_k y^* = H_k[s, v] = g_{k-1}[s, v] = g_{k-1}y^* \leqslant g_{k-1}y$. By induction hypothesis $g_{k-1}y < g_{k-1}[i, y]$. On the other hand recalling that $y \neq 0$ we see that $g_{k-1}[i, y] \neq \Omega_{n+1-(k-1)}$ which together with the fact that $Sg_{k-1}[i, y] = n+1-(k-1)$ gives us by lemma 3.9(d) $g_{k-1}[i, y] < h_{n+1-(k-1)}g_{k-1}[i, y]$.

(2.3.2.A.2.2.2.2). $j < k-1$. Then $Rg_k[j, [i, y]] = g_{k-1}[j, [i, y]]$. We now assert that $H_k[s, v] \leqslant g_{k-1}[s, v]$, for if $s < k-1$, then $H_k[s, v] = g_{k-1}[s, v]$, while if $s = k-1$ we get $H_k[s, v] = h_{n+1-(k-1)}(g_{k-1}v) \leqslant \leqslant h_{n+1-(k-1)}(\Omega_{n+1-(k-1)}+g_{k-1}v) = g_{k-1}[k-1, v] = g_{k-1}[s, v]$. Next we get by two successive applications of the induction hypothesis: $g_{k-1}[s, v] \leqslant \leqslant g_{k-1}y < g_{k-1}[i, y] < g_{k-1}[j, [i, y]]$.

This concludes the proof of our original assertion made at the outset of case 2.3.2 that $Rg_k[i, y] < Rg_k[j, [i, y]]$. To complete the proof of our lemma it suffices to show that $u \in (K_{n+1-k}Rg_k[i, y] \cup K_{n+1-k}Qg_k[i, y])$ implies $u < g_k[j, [i, y]]$. We prefix the various cases in the proof of this by 2.3.2.B:

(2.3.2.B.1). $u \leqslant \Omega_{n+1-k}$. Then since $Sg_k[j, [i, y]] = n+1-k$ we have by defs. 4.2 and 3.5 $\Omega_{n+1-k} < g_k[j, [i, y]]$.

(2.3.2.B.2). $u > \Omega_{n+1-k}$.

(2.3.2.B.2.1). $u \in K_{n+1-k}Qg_k[i, y]$. Then $i = k-1$ (otherwise $u = \Omega_{n+1-k}$) so then $Qg_k[i, v] = \Omega_{n+1-k}+(B_k y \# g_k F_k y)$ so $u \in K_{n+1-k}g_k F_k y^*$ where y^* is a component of y of the form $[s, v]$ where $s \geqslant k$ (if $s < k$ then $g_k F_k[s, v] = 0$). Now $Sg_k F_k[s, v] \leqslant n+1-k$, so $u = g_k F_k[s, v]$. Using lemmas 4.8(a) and 4.3(e) we see that $g_k F_k[s, v] \leqslant g_k[s, v] \leqslant (0, g_i[s, v])$. By lemma 4.3(a) together with the fact that $u > \Omega_{n+1-k}$ we see $S(0, g_i[s, v]) = = n+1-k$. Furthermore $R(0, g_i[s, v]) < Rg_k[j, [i, y]]$ so it would suffice to show that $z \in K_{n+1-k}g_i[s, v]$ implies $z < g_k[j, [i, y]]$. If $z = 1$ this would be trivial, if $z \neq 1$ then recalling that $[s, v]$ is a component of y we see that $z \in K_{n+1-k}g_i y$ so we can invoke lemma 4.13 and then lemma 3.10.

(2.3.2.B.2.2). $u \in K_{n+1-k}Rg_k[i, y]$. Then by lemma 4.14 $u < g_k[j, [i, y]]$.

LEMMA 4.16. *If* $2 \leqslant k \leqslant n+1$, $1 \leqslant i < k$, *and* $1 \leqslant s < k$, *then* $1 < z \in K_{n+1-k}g_s[i, x]$ *implies* $z \leqslant g_k y$ *where* $y <_k [i, x]$ *and* $Ly < L[i, x]$.

PROOF. By induction on $\omega \cdot (L[i, x])+s$. Our induction hypothesis is that $\omega \cdot (L[i', x'])+s' < \omega \cdot (L[i, x])+s$ implies that $z \in K_{n+1-k}g_{s'}[i', x']$ implies $z \leqslant g_k y$ where $y <_k [i', x']$ and $Ly < L[i', x']$ provided that $1 \leqslant \leqslant i' < k$ and $1 \leqslant s' < k$:

(1). $i < s-1$. Then $g_s[i, x] = (g_{s-1}[i, x], \Omega_{n+1-s})$. $n+1-s > n+1-k$ so $z \in K_{n+1-s}g_s[i, x]$ implies $z \in K_{n+1-k}g_{s-1}[i, x]$. It remains only to apply the induction hypothesis.

(2). $i = s-1$. Then $g_s[i, x] = (1+H_s x, \Omega_{n+1-s}+(B_s x \# g_s F_s x)$. Thus since by hypothesis $z > 1$, we get $z \in K_{n+1-k} g_s[i, x]$ implies $z \in K_{n+1-k} H_s x$ or $z \in K_{n+1-k} g_s F_s x$:

(2.1). $z \in K_{n+1-k} H_s x$. Then $z \in K_{n+1-k} H_s x^*$ where x^* is a component of x of the form $[j, w]$ where $j \leqslant s-1$. By lemmas 2.7 and 2.9(a) $[j, w] <_k <_k [j, [j, w]] \leqslant_k [i, x]$ and, of course, $L[j, w] < L[i, x]$ so it would suffice to show that $z \leqslant g_k y$ where $y \leqslant_k [j, w]$ and $Ly \leqslant L[j, w]$;

2.1.1. $j < s-1$. Then $H_s x^* = g_s[j, w]$, since $j < s-1 < k$, we get by induction hypothesis $z \leqslant g_k y$ where $y <_k [j, w]$ and $Ly < L[j, w]$.

(2.1.2). $j = s-1$. Then $H_s x^* = h_{n+1-(s-1)}(g_{s-1} w)$:

(2.1.2.1). $SH_s x^* \leqslant n+1-k$. Then $z = h_{n+1-(s-1)}(g_{s-1} w)$. Since by hypothesis $z > 1$, we see that $w \neq 0$ and by lemma 4.3(a) we see that each non-zero component of w has index equal or greater than k. That is, $w = [a_1, u_1] \# \dots \# [a_t, u_t]$ where $t \geqslant 1$ and $a_r \geqslant k$ for $1 \leqslant r \leqslant t$. By lemma 4.3(g) $g_{s-1}[a_r, u_r] \leqslant g_k[a_r, u_r]$ for $1 \leqslant r \leqslant t$. So $z = h_{n+1-(s-1)}(g_{s-1} w) \leqslant \leqslant h_{n+1-(s-1)}(g_k w)$ and by lemma 3.9(h) $h_{n+1-(s-1)}(g_k w) \leqslant \leqslant h_{n+1-k}(g_k w) \leqslant h_{n+1-k}(\Omega_{n+1-k} + g_k w) = g_k[k, w]$. Thus $[k, w]$ plays the role of the y called for in the statement of this lemma, for by lemma 2.9(b) and lemma 2.7 we get $[k, w] <_k [s-1, w] = [j, w]$ and $L[k, w] \leqslant L[j, w]$.

(2.1.2.2). $SH_s x^* > n+1-k$. Then $z \in K_{n+1-k} g_{s-1} w^*$ where w^* is a component of w. Since $z > 1$, w^* has the form $[a, u]$:

(2.1.2.2.1). $a \geqslant k$. Then $z = g_{s-1}[a, u]$ and by lemma 4.3(g) $g_{s-1}[a, u] \leqslant \leqslant g_k[a, u] = g_k w^*$. Let $y = w^*$ and note that $w^* <_k [j, w^*] \leqslant_k [j, w]$ and $Lw^* < L[j, w]$.

(2.1.2.2.2). $a < k$. Then by induction hypothesis $z \leqslant g_k y$ where $y <_k [a, u] = w^* <_k [j, w]$ and $Ly < L[a, u] = Lw^* < L[j, w]$.

(2.2). $z \in K_{n+1-k} g_s F_s x$. Then $z \in K_{n+1-k} g_s F_s x^*$ where x^* is a component of x of the form $[j, w]$ where $j \geqslant s$ (if $j < s$, $F_s x^* = 0$). Since $x^* <_k [i, x^*] <_k [i, x]$, and $Lx^* < L[i, x]$, it would suffice to show that $z \leqslant g_k y$ where $y \leqslant_k x^*$ and $Ly \leqslant Lx^*$:

(2.2.1). $F_s[j, w] = [j, w]$. So $g_s F_s[j, w] = g_s[j, w]$:

(2.2.1.1). $j \geqslant k$. Then $Sg_s[j, w] \leqslant n+1-k$ so $z = g_s[j, w]$. By lemma 4.3(g) $g_s[j, w] \leqslant g_k[j, w]$ so let $y = [j, w] = x^*$.

(2.2.1.2). $j < k$. Then by induction hypothesis there exists y such that $z \leqslant g_k y$ where $y <_k [j, w] = x^*$ and $Ly < L[j, w]$.

(2.2.2). $F_s[j, w] = w$. For this to happen $j = s$ and $w = [t, u]$ where $t < s$. So $z \in K_{n+1-k} g_s[t, u]$ and by induction hypothesis there exists y such that $z \leqslant g_k y$, $y <_k [t, u]$, and $Ly < L[t, u]$. But $[t, u] <_k [j, [t, u]] = [j, w]$ by lemma 2.7 and of course $L[t, u] < L[j, w]$.

(2.2.3). $F_s[j, w] = [s, v]$ where $v \# 1 = w$. For this to happen $s = j$. By induction hypothesis there exists y such that $z \leqslant g_k y$ and $y <_k [s, v]$ and $Ly < L[s, v]$. But $[s, v] = [j, v] <_k [j, w]$ and $L[s, v] < L[j, w]$.

(3). $i > s-1$. So $g_s[i, x] = h_{n+1-s}(\Omega_{n+1-i}+g_i x)$. From $n+1-i > n+1-k$ and $z > 1$ follows $z \in K_{n+1-k} g_i x^*$ where x^* is a component of x of the form $[j, w]$. Since $[j, w] <_k [i, x]$ and $L[j, w] < L[i, x]$ it suffices to show that $z \leqslant g_k y$ where $y \leqslant_k [j, w]$ and $Ly \leqslant L[j, w]$:

(3.1). $j < k$. From $z \in K_{n+1-k} g_i[j, w]$ the existence of the desired y follows by the induction hypothesis.

(3.2). $j \geqslant k$. Then $z = g_i[j, w]$ and by lemma 4.3(g) $g_i[j, w] \leqslant g_k[j, w]$ so let $y = [j, w]$.

LEMMA 4.17. *If* $2 \leqslant k \leqslant n+1$, *then* $1 < z \in K_{n+1-k} h_{n+1-(k-1)}(g_{k-1} w)$ *implies that* $z \leqslant g_k y$ *where* $y \leqslant_k [k-1, w]$ *and* $Ly \leqslant L[k-1, w]$.

PROOF.

(1). $Sh_{n+1-(k-1)}(g_{k-1} w) > n+1-k$. Then $z \in K_{n+1-k} g_{k-1} w^*$ where w^* is a component of w of the form $[t, u]$. Since $[t, u] = w^* \leqslant_k [k-1, w]$ and $L[t, u] \leqslant L[k-1, w]$ it would suffice to show that there exists y such that $z \leqslant_k g_k y$ where $y \leqslant_k [t, u]$ and $Ly \leqslant L[t, u]$:

(1.1). $t \geqslant k$. Then $z = g_{k-1}[t, u]$. By lemma 4.3(g) $g_{k-1}[t, u] \leqslant g_k[t, u]$ so let $y = [t, u]$.

(1.2). $t < k$. Then since $z \in K_{n+1-k} g_{k-1}[t, u]$ we have the existence of the desired y guaranteed to us by lemma 4.16.

(2). $Sh_{n+1-(k-1)}(g_{k-1} w) \leqslant n+1-k$. Then $z = h_{n+1-(k-1)}(g_{k-1} w)$. Then the same argument which is used in case 2.1.2.1 of lemma 4.16 can be employed word for word (writing k for the s used there) to show that $z \leqslant g_k[k, w]$. So let $y = [k, w]$ and note that $[k, w] <_k [k-1, w]$ and $L[k, w] \leqslant L[k-1, w]$.

THEOREM 4.18 (Order preservation). *If* $0 \leqslant k \leqslant n+1$, *then* $u <_k v$ *in* $P^*(n+1)$ *implies* $g_k u < g_k v$ *in* $\Sigma^*(n)$.

PROOF. Our proof is by induction on $\omega \cdot (Lw+Lv)+k$. If u or v has more than one non-zero component we can apply induction hypothesis immediately, while if $u = 0$ our conclusion is trivial. So we need only consider the case that u has the form $[i, x]$ and v has the form $[j, y]$.

(1). $k \leqslant i = j$. Then by lemma 2.9(a) $x <_i y$, so by induction hypothesis $g_i x < g_i y$. Thus using lemma 3.9(a) $g_k[i, x] = h_{n+1-k}(\Omega_{n+1-i}+g_i x) < h_{n+1-k}(\Omega_{n+1-i}+g_i y) = g_k[j, y]$.

(2). $i \neq j \vee i < k$. By lemma 2.8 we have three cases to consider:

(2.1). $k = 0 \wedge (j < i \vee (j = i \wedge x <_i y))$. By virtue of the basic assumption of case 2 we see that $k = 0 \wedge j < i$, but then $Sg_0[i, x] = n+1-i < n+ +1-j = Sg_0[j, y]$ by lemma 4.3(a), so $g_0[i, x] < g_0[j, y]$ by definition 3.5.

(2.2). $k > 0 \wedge j \leqslant k \wedge [i, x] \leqslant_k y$. Then by induction hypothesis $g_k[i, x] \leqslant \leqslant g_k y$ while $g_k y < g_k[j, y]$ by lemma 4.15.

(2.3). $k > 0 \wedge ([i, x] <_{k-1} [j, y]) \wedge (i > k \vee (i \leqslant k \wedge x <_k [j, y]))$. By the induction hypothesis $g_{k-1}[i, x] < g_{k-1}[j, y]$:

(2.3.1). $i > k$. Then by virtue of the basic assumption of case 2 we get $i \neq j$, while from lemma 2.9(b) we see that $j > i$ is impossible. Thus $j < i$, but then using lemma 4.3(a) we see that $Sg_k[i, x] = n+1-i < < n+1-\max\{k, j\} = Sg_k[j, y]$, so $g_k[i, x] < g_k[j, y]$ by def. 3.5.

(2.3.2). $i \leqslant k \wedge x <_k [j, y]$. From lemma 2.9(b) we see that it cannot be the case that $i \leqslant k < j$, thus $i \leqslant k \wedge j \leqslant k$. On the other hand $i = k \wedge j = k$ is impossible by virtue of the basic assumption of case 2. Furthermore using lemma 2.9(b) together with the previous assumption that $[i, x] <_{k-1} [j, y]$ we see also that $i < k \wedge j = k$ is also impossible. Thus we have only to consider the two cases $i = k \wedge j < k$ and $i < k \wedge j < k$:

(2.3.2.1). $i = k \wedge j < k$. Then $g_k[i, x] = h_{n+1-k}(\Omega_{n+1-k} + g_k x)$. From $x <_k [j, y]$ we get by induction hypothesis that $g_k x < g_k[j, y]$. Furthermore, from def. 4.2 we see that $g_k[j, y] = (z, \Omega_{n+1-k} + w)$ for some $z \geqslant 1$ and some $w \geqslant 0$. Thus using lemma 3.10 we see that $\Omega_{n+1-k} + g_k x < g_k[j, y]$ and then using lemma 3.9(d) we see that $h_{n+1-k}(\Omega_{n+1-k} + g_k x) < g_k[j, y]$.

(2.3.2.2). $i < k \wedge j < k$. We now assert and will show that $z \in K_{n+1-k} R g_k[i, x]$ implies $z < g_k[j, y]$. We prefix the various cases which arise in the proof of this assertion by 2.3.2.2.A. We can assume $z > 1$ for otherwise our assertion would be trivial:

(2.3.2.2.A.1). $i < k-1$. Then $Rg_k[i, x] = g_{k-1}[i, x]$. By lemma 4.16 $z \in K_{n+1-k} g_{k-1}[i, x]$ implies $z \leqslant g_k w$ for some $w <_k [i, x]$ where $Lw < < L[i, x]$. Now by induction hypothesis $g_k w < g_k[j, y]$, so $z < g_k[j, y]$.

(2.3.2.2.A.2). $i = k-1$. Then $Rg_k[i, x] = 1 + H_k x$ so $z \in K_{n+1-k} H_k x^*$ where x^* is a component of x. If $H_k x^* = 0$ our assertion would be trivial, so we can assume that $x^* = [t, p]$ for $t < k$ and p some ordinal diagram:

(2.3.2.2.A.2.1). $t < k-1$. Then $H_k x^* = g_{k-1}[t, p]$ so we need only apply lemma 4.16 and induction hypothesis as we did in case 2.3.2.2.A.1.

(2.3.2.2.A.2.2). $t = k-1$. Then $H_k x^* = h_{n+1-(k-1)}(g_{k-1} p)$. By lemma 4.17 $z \leqslant g_k w$ where $w \leqslant_k [k-1, p]$ and $Lw \leqslant L[k-1, p]$. But $[k-1, p] = = x^* <_k [k-1, x^*] \leqslant_k [i, x]$ and $L[k-1, p] < L[i, x]$ so by induction hypothesis $g_k w < g_k[j, y]$, thus $z < g_k[j, y]$.

This completes the proof of the assertion made at the outset of case 2.3.2.2. It remains to show that $Rg_k[i, x] < Rg_k[j, y] \wedge Qg_k[i, x] < g_k[j, y]$ or $Rg_k[i, x] = Rg_k[j, y] \wedge Qg_k[i, x] < Qg_k[j, y]$. We prefix the cases which arise in showing this by 2.3.2.2.B:

(2.3.2.2.B.1). $i = k-1$. Then $Qg_k[i, x] = \Omega_{n+1-k}+(B_k x \# g_k F_k x)$. We first note by lemma 4.8(a) that $g_k F_k x \leqslant g_k x$, but $x <_k [i, x]$ by lemma 2.7 so $g_k x < g_k[j, y]$ by induction hypothesis. Using lemma 3.10 we see that $\Omega_{n+1-k} < g_k[j, y]$. Noting further that $B_k x \leqslant 1$ we get $\Omega_{n+1-k}+(B_k x \# \# g_k F_k x) < g_k[j, y]$:

(2.3.2.2.B.1.1). $j < k-1$. Then $Rg_k[j, y] = g_{k-1}[j, y]$. Now each component of $Rg_k[i, x]$ is of the form $H_k x^*$ where x^* is a connected component of x. If $H_k x^* = 0$ then trivially $H_k x^* < Rg_k[j, y]$ so we can assume that $x^* = [t, z]$ where $t < k$ and z is some ordinal diagram:

(2.3.2.2.B.1.1.1). $t = k-1$. Then $H_k x^* = h_{n+1-(k-1)}(g_{k-1} z)$. Now $z <_{k-1} [t, z] = x^* \leqslant_{k-1} x <_{k-1} [i, x] <_{k-1} [j, y]$ so by induction hypothesis $g_{k-1} z < g_{k-1}[j, y]$ and by lemma 3.9(d) $h_{n+1-(k-1)}(g_{k-1} z) < g_{k-1}[j, y]$.

(2.3.2.2.B.1.1.2). $t < k-1$. Then $H_k x^* = g_{k-1}[t, z]$. Now $[t, z] <_{k-1} [i, x] <_{k-1} [j, y]$ so by induction hypothesis $g_{k-1}[t, z] < g_{k-1}[j, y]$.

(2.3.2.2.B.1.2). $j = k-1$. From $[i, x] <_{k-1} [j, y]$ follows $x <_{k-1} y$ by lemma 2.9(a). Write $x = x_1 \# x_2$ where each non-zero component of x_1 has index equal or greater than k an each non-zero component of x_2 has index less than k. In a similar fashion write $y = y_1 \# y_2$. Now $x <_{k-1} y$ implies $(x_2 = y_2 \wedge x_1 <_{k-1} y_1) \vee (x_2 <_{k-1} y_2)$:

(2.3.2.2.B.1.2.1). $x_2 = y_2 \wedge x_1 <_{k-1} y_1$. Then by def. 4.2 $Rg_k[i, x] = = 1+H_k x = 1+H_k x_2 = 1+H_k y_2 = 1+H_k y = Rg_k[j, y]$. We now show that $Qg_k[i, x] < Qg_k[j, y]$. From lemma 2.13(c) and def. 2.12 we see that $F_k x = F_k x_1 <_k F_k y_1 = F_k y$. Thus by induction hypothesis $g_k F_k x < g_k F_k y$. Now recalling that B_k has for its range the values 0 and 1 we assert and will show that $B_k x \# g_k F_k x < B_k y \# g_k F_k y$; from this $Qg_k[i, x] < Qg_k[j, y]$ would readily follow:

(2.3.2.2.B.1.2.1.1). $(B_k x = 1 \wedge B_k y = 1) \vee (B_k x = 0)$. Then trivial.

(2.3.2.2.B.1.2.1.2.) $B_k x = 1 \wedge B_k y = 0$. If our assertion did not hold we would have $B_k x \# g_k F_k x = B_k y \# g_k F_k y$. But then by def. 4.1 x would be of the form $[s, z] \# l_t$ for some $s < k-1$, some z, and some $t \geqslant 0$. This would mean that $g_k F_k y = l_{t+1}$. Using the fact that $x_2 = y_2$ together with lemma 4.7(c) we would have that $y = [s, z] \# l_{t+1}$. But then by def. 4.1 $B_k y = 1$ which is contrary to our assumption.

(2.3.2.2.B.1.2.2). $x_2 <_{k-1} y_2$. We now assert and will show that $H_k x_2 <$

$< H_k y_2$ from this would follow $Rg_k[i, x] = 1 + H_k x = 1 + H_k x_2 < 1 + H_k y_2 = = Rg_k[j, y]$. It is sufficient to consider the case where x_2 and y_2 are connected:

(2.3.2.2.B.1.2.2.1). $x_2 = [k-1, z]$ and $y_2 = [k-1, w]$ for some z and some w. Now $z <_{k-1} w$ so $g_{k-1} z < g_{k-1} w$ by induction hypothesis. Using def. 4.2 and lemma 3.9(a) we get $H_k x_2 = h_{n+1-(k-1)}(g_{k-1} z) < < h_{n+1-(k-1)}(g_{k-1} w) = H_k y_2$.

(2.3.2.2.B.1.2.2.2). $x_2 = [k-1, z]$ and $y_2 = [t, w]$ for some z, some w, and some $t < k-1$. Then from $z \leqslant_{k-1} [k-1, z] <_{k-1} [t, w]$ it follows by the induction hypothesis that $g_{k-1} z < g_{k-1}[t, w]$, so using lemma 3.9(d) with def. 4.2 we see that $H_k x_2 = h_{n+1-(k-1)}(g_{k-1} z) < g_{k-1}[t, w] = H_k y_2$.

(2.3.2.2.B.1.2.2.3). $x_2 = [t, z]$ and $y_2 = [s, w]$ for some z, w and some $t, s < k-1$. Then using induction hypothesis we have that $H_k x_2 = = g_{k-1}[t, z] < g_{k-1}[s, w] = H_k y_2$.

(2.3.2.2.B.1.2.2.4). $x_2 = [t, z]$ and $y_2 = [k-1, w]$ for some z, w and some $t < k-1$. From $t < k-1$ follows $y_2 <_{k-2} x_2$, so by lemma 2.8 we see that $x_2 \leqslant_{k-1} w$. If $x_2 <_{k-1} w$ then by induction hypothesis $g_{k-1} x_2 < g_{k-1} w$, so we have, using lemma 3.9(d), that $H_k x_2 = g_{k-1} x_2 < g_{k-1} w \leqslant \leqslant h_{n+1-(k-1)}(g_{k-1} w) = H_k y_2$. On the other hand if $x_2 = w$ then using the fact that $t < k-1$ along with lemma 4.6(a) we get $H_k x_2 = g_{k-1}[t, z] < < h_{n+1-(k-1)}(g_{k-1}[t, z]) = h_{n+1-(k-1)}(g_{k-1} w) = H_k[k-1, w] = H_k y_2$.

(2.3.2.2.B.2). $i < k-1$. Then $Qg_k[i, x] = \Omega_{n+1-k} < g_k[j, y]$ by lemma 3.10. Furthermore $Rg_k[i, x] = g_{k-1}[i, x]$:

(2.3.2.2.B.2.1). $j < k-1$. Then from $[i, x] <_{k-1} [j, y]$ it follows by induction that $g_{k-1}[i, x] < g_{k-1}[j, y] = Rg_k[j, y]$.

(2.3.2.2.B.2.2). $j = k-1$. From $i < k-1$ follows $[j, y] <_{k-2} [i, x]$ so by lemma 2.8 $[i, x] <_{k-1} [j, y]$ can only happen by virtue of having $[i, x] \leqslant_{k-1} y$:

(2.3.2.2.B.2.2.1). $[i, x] = y$. Then $B_k y = 1$, so $g_k[i, x] = = (1 + g_{k-1}[i, x], \Omega_{n+1-k})$ while $g_k[j, y] = (1 + g_{k-1}[i, x], \Omega_{n+1-k} \# 1)$.

(2.3.2.2.B.2.2.2). $[i, x] <_{k-1} y$:

(2.3.2.2.B.2.2.2.1). $y = [i, x] \# z$ where $z \neq 0$. Then $g_k[i, x] = = (1 + g_{k-1}[i, x], \Omega_{n+1-k})$ while $g_k[j, y] = (1 + g_{k-1}[i, x] \# \# H_k z, \Omega_{n+1-k} + (B_k([i, x] \# z) \# g_k F_k z))$. But $H_k z \neq 0$ or $g_k F_k z \neq 0$, in either case we are finished.

(2.3.2.2.B.2.2.2.2). $[i, x] <_{k-1} y^*$ where y^* is a component of y. Then y^* must have index less than k:

(2.3.2.2.B.2.2.2.2.1). y^* has index less than $k-1$. By induction hypothesis $g_{k-1}[i, x] < g_{k-1} y^*$, so $g_{k-1}[i, x] < g_{k-1} y^* = H_k y^* \leqslant 1 + H_k y = Rg_k[j, y]$.

(2.3.2.2.B.2.2.2.2.2). $y^* = [k-1, z]$ some z. Now $i < k-1$ means that $[k-1, z] <_{k-2} [i, x]$ so to have $[i, x] <_{k-1} y^*$ we must have $[i, x] \leqslant_{k-1} z$. If $[i, x] <_{k-1} z$ then by induction $g_{k-1}[i, x] < g_{k-1}z$ so by lemma 3.9(e) $g_{k-1}[i, x] < g_{k-1}z \leqslant h_{n+1-(k-1)}(g_{k-1}z) = H_k[k-1, z] = H_k y^* \leqslant \leqslant 1+H_k y = Rg_k[j, y]$. While if $[i, x] = z$ we have using lemma 4.6(a) $g_{k-1}[i, x] < h_{n+1-(k-1)}(g_{k-1}[i, x]) = h_{n+1-(k-1)}(g_{k-1}z) = H_k[k-1, z] = = H_k y^* \leqslant 1+H_k y = Rg_k[j, y]$.

DEFINITION 4.19. We define $D(n:k)$ for $0 \leqslant k \leqslant n$ as follows:

$$D(n\colon k) = \begin{cases} (1, \Omega_k) & \text{if } k = n, \\ (D(n\colon k+1), \Omega_k) & \text{if } 0 \leqslant k < n. \end{cases}$$

It is easy to see that $SD(n\colon k) = k$ from which it follows that $i < j$ implies $D(n\colon i) < D(n\colon j)$.

THEOREM 4.20. (Closure). *If* $0 \leqslant k \leqslant n+1$, *then* $g_k x < D(n\colon Sg_k x)$.

PROOF. By induction on $\omega \cdot Lx+k$. Our induction hypothesis is that $g_{k'}x' < D(n\colon Sg_{k'}x')$ whenever $\omega \cdot Lx'+k' < \omega \cdot Lx+k$. We must show under this assumption that $g_k x < D(n\colon Sg_k x)$:

(1). $x = 0$. Then trivial.

(2). x has more than one non-zero component. Let these components be $x_1, x_2, \ldots, x_t$ for $t \geqslant 2$. By induction hypothesis $g_k x_i < D(n\colon Sg_k x_i) \leqslant \leqslant \max_i D(n\colon Sg_k x_i) = D(n\colon \max_i Sg_k x_i) = D(n\colon Sg_k x)$.

(3). x has exactly one non-zero component. Then x has the form $[i, y]$ for some y:

(3.1). $i \geqslant k$. Then $g_k x = g_k[i, y] = h_{n+1-k}(\Omega_{n+1-i}+g_i y)$. Using lemma 4.3(a) we see that $\Omega_{n+1-i} < D(n\colon n+1-i) = D(n\colon Sg_k x)$. Furthermore by induction hypothesis along with lemma 4.3(a) we get $g_i y < D(n\colon Sg_i y) \leqslant \leqslant D(n\colon n+1-i)$. Thus $\Omega_{n+1-i}+g_i y < D(n\colon n+1-i)$ and by lemma 3.9(d) so is $h_{n+1-k}(\Omega_{n+1-i}+g_i y)$.

(3.2). $i < k-1$. Then $g_k[i, x] = (g_{k-1}[i, x], \Omega_{n+1-k})$. By induction hypothesis $g_{k-1}[i, x] < D(n\colon Sg_{k-1}[i, y]) = D(n\colon n+1-(k-1)) = RD(n\colon Sg_k[i, y])$. Thus $Rg_k[i, y] < RD(n\colon Sg_k[i, y])$. Also, $Qg_k[i, y] = = \Omega_{n+1-k} < D(n\colon Sg_k[i, y])$. It remains only to show that $z \in K_{n+1-k} Rg_k[i, y]$ implies $z < D(n\colon Sg_k[i, x])$. Let such a z be given then $z \in K_{n+1-k} g_{k-1}[i, y]$. But then by lemma 4.16 $z \leqslant g_k w$ where $Lw < L[i, y]$. By induction hypothesis $g_k w < D(n\colon Sg_k w) \leqslant D(n\colon n+1-k) = D(n\colon Sg_k[i, y])$, so $z < < D(n\colon Sg_k[i, y])$.

(3.3). $i = k-1$ then $g_k[i, y] = (1+H_k y, \Omega_{n+1-k}+(B_k y \# g_k F_k y))$. We first note that $LF_k y \leqslant Ly < L[i, y]$ so by induction $g_k F_k y < D(n: Sg_k F_k y) \leqslant \leqslant D(n: n+1-k) = D(n: Sg_k[i, y])$. From this it easily follows that $Qg_k[i, y] < D(n: Sg_k[i, y])$. Using lemmas 4.16, 4.17, and induction hypothesis we show in a fashion similar to case 3.2 that $z \in K_{n+1-k} Rg_k[i, y]$ implies $z < D(n: Sg_k[i, y])$. It remains to show that $Rg_k[i, y] < < RD(n: Sg_k[i, y])$, but this is also handled in a fashion similar to case 3.2.

COROLLARY 4.21 (Closure). $g_{n+1}x < D(n: 0)$.

LEMMA 4.22. $(x, y) < D(n: k) \wedge y \geqslant \Omega_k$ *implies* $x < RD(n: k)$.

PROOF.

(1). $x = 0$. Then trivial since $RD(n: k)$ is never zero.

(2). $x \neq 0$. Suppose to the contrary that $RD(n: k) \leqslant x$:

(2.1). $RD(n: k) = x$. Then since $QD(n: k) = \Omega_k \leqslant y$ it would follow that $D(n: k) \leqslant (x, y)$, contradiction.

(2.2). $RD(n: k) < x$. It is easy to show that $z \in K_k RD(n: k)$ implies $z \leqslant 1$. But $1 < (x, y)$ since $x \neq 0$. Moreover $\Omega_k \leqslant y < (x, y)$. Thus $D(n: k) < (x, y)$, contradiction.

DEFINITION 4.23. To each term u of $\Sigma(n)$ we define recursively the notion of *subterm* of u and the notion of *depth* of a subterm of u in u. Au will denote the set of subterms of u.

(1). If u is Ω_j then $Au = \{0, u\}$. These subterms will have depth 0 in u.

(2). If u is (x, y) then $Au = \{u\} \cup Ax \cup Ay$. u will have depth 0 in u. While if z has depth i in x or y, then z has depth $i+1$ in u.

(3). If u has components $u_1, u_2, \ldots, u_r$ $(r \geqslant 2)$ then $Au = \bigcup_{i=1}^{r} Au_i$, if z has depth i in u_j, then z has depth i in u.

Note that $u = v$ implies $Au = Av$.

THEOREM 4.24. *If* $v < D(n: Sv)$ *whenever* v *is a subterm of* u, *then there exists a* w *such that* $u = g_{n+1-Su}(w)$.

PROOF. By induction on Lu. Denote Su by k:

(1). $u = 0$. Then trivial.

(2). u has more than one non-zero component. Let u^* be such a component and denote Su^* by k^*, so $k^* \leqslant k$. By induction hypothesis $u^* = g_{n+1-k^*}(x^*)$ for some x^*. By lemma 4.3(d) $u^* = g_{n+1-k} z^*$ for some z^*. Thus $u = g_{n+1-k} z$ for some z.

(3). u has exactly one non-zero component:

(3.1). $u = \Omega_j$ for some $j \neq 0$. Then $u = g_{n+1-j}[n+1-j, 0]$.

(3.2). $u = (x, y)$ for some x and some y. Since $Sy = k$ we can write

$y = \Omega_k + t$ for some t. Moreover every subterm of t is a subterm of u, so by induction hypothesis we can write $t = g_{n+1-k}v$ for some v:

(3.2.1). $x = 0$. Then $u = (0, y) = (0, \Omega_k + g_{n+1-k}v)$. Using lemma 3.9(b) two cases arise:

(3.2.1.1). $(0, \Omega_k + g_{n+1-k}v) = h_k(\Omega_k + g_{n+1-k}v)$. Then $u = = g_{n+1-k}[n+1-k, v]$.

(3.2.1.2). $(0, \Omega_k + g_{n+1-k}v) = h_k(\Omega_k + g_{n+1-k}(v) \# 1)$. Then $u = = g_{n+1-k}[n+1-k, v \# 1]$.

(3.2.2). $x \neq 0$:

(3.2.2.1). $x = (p, q)$ where $p \neq 0$ and $Sx = k+1$. Then by induction hypothesis $x = g_{n+1-(k+1)}(w)$ for some w, and we see by lemma 4.3 that $w = = [i, z]$ for some z where $i < n+1-(k+1)$:

(3.2.2.1.1). $t = 0$. Then $u = g_{n+1-k}[i, z]$.

(3.2.2.1.2). $t = l_{m+1}$ for some $m \geqslant 0$. Then $u = g_{n+1-k}[n-k, l_m \# [i, z]]$.

(3.2.2.1.3). otherwise. As seen previously $t = g_{n+1-k}v$ for some v, but by lemma 2.13(a) $v = F_{n+1-k}(f_{n+1-k}v)$. Therefore $t = g_{n+1-k}(F_{n+1-k}(f_{n+1-k}v))$, thus $u = g_{n+1-k}[n-k, f_{n+1-k}v \# [i, z]]$.

(3.2.2.2). $x = 1$. Then $u = g_{n+1-k}[n-k, f_{n+1-k}v]$.

(3.2.2.3). otherwise. So $x = 1+r$ for some r. Since $u = (x, y)$ is a subterm of u by hypothesis, we have that $(x, y) < D(n{:}\ S(x, y)) = D(n{:}\ Sy) = = D(n{:}k)$. Using $y \geqslant \Omega_{Sy} = \Omega_k$ we see from lemma 4.22 that $x < RD(n{:}\ k)$. Now $k \neq n$ for otherwise $RD(n{:}\ k) = 1$ and $x = 0$ contrary to the basic assumption of case 3.2.2. Since $k \neq n$, $RD(n{:}\ k) = D(n{:}\ k+1)$, so $x < < D(n{:}\ k+1)$ from which it follows that $Sx \leqslant k+1$. Now by lemma 3.9(c) we see that it is possible to write $r = p \# q$ where each non-zero component q_i of q can be written in the form $q_i = (a_i, b_i)$ for some $a_i \neq 0$ and some b_i such that $Sq_i = k+1$, and each non-zero component p_i of p can be written $p_i = h_{k+1}z_i$ for some z_i:

(3.2.2.3.1). $p = 0$. Then q has more than one non-zero component (otherwise we would contradict the basic assumption of case 3.2.2.3.) call them $q_1, q_2, \ldots, q_c$ $(c \geqslant 2)$. By induction hypothesis we have that for $1 \leqslant i \leqslant c$, $q_i = g_{n-k}w_i$ for some w_i, and by lemma 4.3(c) $w_i = [j_i, s_i]$ for some s_i and some $j_i < n-k$. Thus $u = g_{n+1-k}[n-k, f_{n+1-k}v \# [j_i, s_i] \# \ldots \# [j_c, s_c]]$.

(3.2.2.3.2). $p \neq 0$ and $q \neq 0$. Then p has components $p_1, p_2, \ldots, p_d$ $(d \geqslant 1)$ and q has components $q_1, q_2, \ldots, q_c$ $(c \geqslant 1)$. As in the previous case $q_i = = g_{n-k}w_i$ for $1 \leqslant i \leqslant c$ where $w_i = [j_i, s_i]$ with $j_i < n-k$. As previously noted $p_i = h_{k+1}z_i$ for $1 \leqslant i \leqslant d$. By induction hypothesis $z_i = g_{n+1-Sz_i}(e_i)$ for some e_i. But as we have already seen $Sx \leqslant k+1$ so $Sz_i = Sp_i \leqslant Sx \leqslant$

$\leqslant k+1$. This gives us the right to employ lemma 4.3(d) getting $z_i = g_{n-k}(e'_i)$ for some e'_i. Thus

$u = [n-k,$

$f_{n+1-k}v \# [n-k, e'_1] \# \ldots \# [n-k, e'_d] \# [j_1, s_1] \# \ldots \# [j_c, s_c]]$.

(3.2.2.3.3). $p \neq 0$ and $q = 0$. Then p has components $p_1, p_2, \ldots, p_d$ ($d \geqslant 1$) and as in the previous case we see $p_i = h_{k+1}g_{n-k}e'_i$ for some e'_i so

$$u = [n-k, f_{n+1-k}v \# [n-k, e'_1] \# \ldots \# [n-k, e'_d]].$$

LEMMA 4.25. *Let $\{a_s\}$ be a sequence of non-negative integers such that $a_0 = 0$ and for some j, $a_{j+1} < a_j$, and $a_{s+1} \leqslant a_s+1$ for all s such that $0 \leqslant s \leqslant j$, then there exists an i where $0 \leqslant i < j$ such that $a_{j+1} = a_i$ and $a_{j+1} < a_s$ for all s such that $i < s \leqslant j$.*

PROOF. We first note that $j > 0$, otherwise $0 = a_0 = a_j > a_{j+1}$ which violates the assumption that all terms of the sequence are non-negative. Let $N = \{t \mid 0 \leqslant t < j \wedge a_t \leqslant a_{j+1}\}$. From $0 \leqslant 0 < j$ and $a_0 = 0 \leqslant a_{j+1}$ it follows that $0 \in N$ so N is non-empty. Let i be the greatest member of N. We now show that i has the properties ascribed to it in the statement of this lemma. From $i < j$ we get $i+1 \leqslant j$:

(1). $i+1 = j$. Then $a_{j+1} < a_j = a_{i+1} \leqslant a_i+1$, so $a_{j+1} \leqslant a_i$. On the other hand from the definition of N we see that $a_i \leqslant a_{j+1}$, so $a_i = a_{j+1}$. Furthermore $i < s \leqslant j = i+1$ implies that $s = j$ so $a_s = a_j > a_{j+1}$.

(2). $i+1 < j$. We now assert that $a_i = a_{j+1}$, for if $a_i < a_{j+1}$ it would follow that $a_{i+1} \leqslant a_i+1 \leqslant a_{j+1}$, but then $(i+1) \in N$, and this would contradict the fact that i is the greatest member of N. It remains only to show that $i < s \leqslant j$ implies $a_s > a_{j+1}$:

(2.1). $s = j$. Then $a_s = a_j > a_{j+1}$.

(2.2). $i < s < j$. Then if $a_s \leqslant a_{j+1}$ we would have $s \in N$ which contradicts the fact that i is the greatest member of N.

LEMMA 4.26. *If $u < D(n{:}\, 0)$, then for every subterm u^* of u:*

(a). *$u^* < D(n{:}\, Su^*)$.*

(b). *$u^* = (x, y)$ implies $Sx, Sy \leqslant Su^*+1$.*

PROOF. We prove the conjunction of (a) and (b) by induction on the depth of u^* in u. We first note that (b) follows from (a) since first of all $Sy = Su^* \leqslant Su^*+1$, moreover from $(x, y) < D(n{:}\, Su^*)$ and $y \geqslant \Omega_{Sy} = \Omega_{Su^*}$ it follows from lemma 4.22 that $x < RD(n{:}\, Su^*)$, thus $Sx \leqslant SRD(n{:}\, Su^*) \leqslant Su^*+1$.

We now show that (a) holds under the assumption that (a) and (b) both hold for subterms of smaller depth:

(1). u^* has depth 0 in u. Then u^* is a component of u so $Su^* = 0$ and $u^* \leqslant u < D(n\colon 0) = D(n\colon Su^*)$.

(2). u^* has depth $k+1$ in u. Then there exists a subterm $z = (x, y)$ of depth k in u such that u^* is a component of x or u^* is a component of y:

(2.1). $Su^* = Sz$. Using lemma 3.10 we see that $u^* < z$. But by induction hypothesis $z < D(n\colon Sz) = D(n\colon Su^*)$.

(2.2). $Su^* > Sz$. Then u^* is a component of x, so $u^* \leqslant x$. Since by induction hypothesis $(x, y) < D(n\colon Sz)$ we see using lemma 4.22 together with the fact that $y \geqslant \Omega_{Sy} = \Omega_{Sz}$ that $x < RD(n\colon Sz)$:

(2.2.1). $Sz = n$. Then $RD(n\colon Sz) = 1 < D(n\colon Su^*)$.

(2.2.2). $Sz < n$. Then $RD(n\colon Sz) = D(n\colon Sz+1) \leqslant D(n\colon Su^*)$.

(2.3). $Su^* < Sz$. Since u^* has depth $k+1$ in u, we can find a sequence $u_0, u_1, \ldots, u_{k+1}$ of subterms of u such that u_0 is a component of u, $u_k = z$, $u_{k+1} = u^*$, and for each s such that $0 \leqslant s \leqslant k$ the depth of u_{s+1} in u equals the depth of u_s in u plus one. By the induction hypothesis $Su_t \leqslant Su_t+1$ for $0 \leqslant t \leqslant k$, so by lemma 4.25 there exists an i such that $0 \leqslant i < k$ and such that $Su_i = Su_{k+1}$ and such that $Su_{k+1} < Su_t$ whenever $i < t \leqslant k$. Thus $u_{k+1} \in (K_{Su_i} Ru_i \cup K_{Su_i} Qu_i)$ thus it follows by lemma 3.10 that $u^* = u_{k+1} < < u_i$. But by induction hypothesis $u_i < D(n\colon Su_i) = D(n\colon Su_{k+1}) = = D(n\colon Su^*)$.

Remark. The above lemma does *not* generalize by replacing the 0 by an arbitrary positive integer. To see this note that in the system $\Sigma^*(2)$ we get $(\Omega_2, 0) < D(2\colon 1)$ but it is *not* true that $(\Omega_2, 0) < D(2\colon 0)$.

THEOREM 4.27 (Onto-ness). *If* $u < D(n\colon 0)$, *then* $u = g_{n+1} w$ *for some* w.

PROOF. Immediate consequence of lemma 4.26 and theorem 4.24.

Remark. The obvious generalization of the above theorem would be that $u < D(n\colon k)$ implies $u = g_{n+1-k}(w)$ for some w. This proves to be false as can be seen by the following considerations: in the system $\Sigma^*(2)$ if we let $u = (\Omega_2, 0)$, then $u < D(2 : 1)$. On the other hand we see from def. 3.5 and lemma 4.3(a) that if (x, y) is an image under some g_i, then $Sx \leqslant Sy+1$.

THEOREM 4.28. $\|\langle P^*(n+1), <_{n+1}\rangle\| = \|D(n\colon 0) \in \Sigma^*(n)\|$.

PROOF. By corollary 4.21 g_{n+1} is a mapping from $P^*(n+1)$ into $\{x | x \in \Sigma^*(n) \wedge x < D(n\colon 0)\}$. By theorem 4.18 it is order preserving. By theorem 4.27 it is onto.

Remark. If $n > 1$, then the set of images under g_i does not form an initial segment when $0 \leqslant i < n+1$. To see this note that $\Omega_{n+1-i} = g_i[i, 0]$ is an image, $(\Omega_{n+2-i}, 0) < \Omega_{n+1-i}$, but $(\Omega_{n+2-i}, 0)$ is not an image since $S\Omega_{n+2-i} > S0+1$.

5. The main conclusions. In the previous section we showed an order preserving mapping from $\langle P^*(n+1), <_{n+1}\rangle$ onto an initial segment of $\langle \Sigma^*(n), <\rangle$. We now show that $\langle O(n+1), <_{n+1}\rangle$ can be mapped onto an initial segment of $\langle \Sigma(n), <\rangle$. To do this we first remind the reader of the author's result (cf. § 2) that $||\langle O^*(n+1), <_{n+1}\rangle|| = ||[1, [1, 1]] \in \langle P^*(n+2), <_{n+2}\rangle||$. Moreover it is only a matter of calculation to see that under the order preserving mapping g_{n+2} from $\langle P^*(n+2), <_{n+2}\rangle$ onto an initial segment of $\langle \Sigma^*(n+1), <\rangle$ the ordinal diagram $[1, [1, 1]]$ is carried onto the term $u_n = ((\ldots(((0, 1), \Omega_n), \Omega_{n-1}), \ldots), \Omega_0)$. Now in the order preserving mapping from $\langle \Sigma^*(n+1), <\rangle$ onto $\langle \Sigma(n+1), <\rangle$ (cf. § 3) u_n is mapped onto the term $v_n = ((\ldots(((1, 1), \Omega_n), \Omega_{n-1}), \ldots), 1)$. So recalling (§ 2) that $||\langle O(n+1), <_{n+1}\rangle|| = ||\langle O^*(n+1, <_{n+1}\rangle||$ we have that $||\langle O(n+1), <_{n+1}\rangle|| = ||v_n \in \langle \Sigma\ (n+1), <\rangle||$. Again it is only a matter of calculation to see that $v_n < \Omega[n+1, 0]$†. According to ([**11**], theorem 6), $v_n \in \Sigma(n)$ and $||v_n \in \langle \Sigma(n+1), <\rangle|| = ||v_n \in \langle \Sigma(n), <\rangle||$. This concludes our argument that $\langle O(n+1), <_{n+1}\rangle$ is order isomorphic to an initial segment of $\langle \Sigma(n), <\rangle$.

By calculation one can see that $\Omega[n, 0] < v_n$ and we have already seen that $v_n < \Omega[n+1, 0]$, so

$$\lim_{m<\omega} ||\langle O(m), <_m\rangle|| = \lim_{m<\omega} ||v_m \in \langle \Sigma(m), <\rangle|| = \lim_{m<\omega} ||\Omega[m, 0] \in \langle \Sigma(m), <\rangle||.$$

This latter limit was shown ([**11**], theorem 9) to be the order type of the largest well ordered initial segment of $\bigcup_{m<\omega} \Sigma(m)$.

REFERENCES

[1] H. Bachmann, Die Normalfunktionen und das Problem der ausgezeichneten Folgen von Ordnungszahlen, *Vierteljahrschr. Naturf. Ges. Zürich* **95** (1950) 115–147.

[2] H. Gerber, An extension of Schütte's Klammer symbols, *Math. Ann.* **174** (1967) 203–216.

[3] D. Isles, Regular ordinals and normal forms, these proceedings, 339–361.

[4] A. Kino, On ordinal diagrams, *J. Math. Soc. Japan* **13** (1961) 346–356.

† The notation $\Omega[n+1, 0]$ is defined in [**11**] to be the term

$$((\ldots((\Omega_{n+1}, \Omega_n), \Omega_{n-1}), \ldots), 1).$$

[5] H. LEVITZ, *On the ordinal notations of Schütte and the ordinal diagrams of Takeuti*, Ph. D. thesis, Pennsylvania State Univ. (1965).
[6] H. LEVITZ, On a simplification of Takeuti's ordinal diagrams of finite order, *Zeitschr. Math. Logik u. Grundl. Math.*, to appear.
[7] H. PFEIFFER, *Ausgezeichnete Folge für gewisse Abschnitte der zweiten und weiteren Zahlklassen*, Dissertation, Technische Hochschule, Hannover (1964).
[8] H. PFEIFFER, Zur Kennzeichnung von Ordinalzahlen (abstract), *J. Symb. Logic* **32** (1967) 565.
[9] K. SCHÜTTE, Kennzeichnung von Ordnungszahlen durch rekursiv erklärte Funktionen, *Math. Ann.* **127** (1954) 15–32.
[10] K. SCHÜTTE, Predicative well-orderings, in *Formal systems and recursive functions*, eds. F. N. Crossly and M. A. E. Dummet, North-Holland, Amsterdam (1965).
[11] K. SCHÜTTE, Ein konstruktives System von Ordnungszahlen, *Archiv Math. Logik u. Grundlagenforschung*, to appear.
[12] G. TAKEUTI, Ordinal diagrams, *J. Math. Soc. Japan* **9** (1957) 386–394.
[13] G. TAKEUTI, On the fundamental conjecture of GLC, V, *J. Math. Soc. Japan* **10** (1958) 121–134.
[14] G. TAKEUTI, Ordinal diagrams, II, *J. Math. Soc. Japan* **12** (1960) 385–391.
[15] G. TAKEUTI, On the fundamental conjecture of GLC, VI, *Proc. Japan Acad.* **37** (1961) 440–443.
[16] G. TAKEUTI, Consistency proofs of subsystems of classical analysis, *Ann. Math.* **86** (1967) 299–348.
[17] O. VEBLEN, Continuous increasing functions of finite and transfinite ordinals, *Trans. Am. Math. Soc.* **9** (1908) 280–292.

SECTION F

PROOF THEORY

ON THE ORIGINAL GENTZEN CONSISTENCY PROOF FOR NUMBER THEORY [+]

PAUL BERNAYS

The first published Gentzen consistency proof for the formal system of first order number theory, including standard logic, the Peano axioms and recursive definitions, was given in Gentzen's paper 'Die Widerspruchsfreiheit der reinen Zahlentheorie' (*Math. Ann.* **112** (1936)). It was however not his original proof but a revised version of it. The revision was motivated by a criticism, in which I myself for some time concurred of the original proof on the grounds that it implicitly included an application of the fan theorem. Gentzen did not expressly oppose this opinion; he took care of the criticism by modifying his consistency proof before it was published. Fortunately the text of the original proof is preserved in galley proof*.

On rereading the original text, I came to doubt the mentioned opinion[†]. It seems worth while reconsidering the original proof, because

1. it is certainly easier to follow than the first published proof and at least as easy to follow as the second Gentzen consistency proof,

2. it does not require the generalized form of induction (ordinal induction up to ε_0).

I shall give in this paper a description of Gentzen's original proof in a way sufficiently detailed to make apparent the kind of constructive methods here used. At the same time I shall make a slight simplification in this proof, making use of some remarks in Gentzen's Annalen proof.

I begin by describing the formal system to be considered. The logical calculus used is the calculus of sequents[‡] $\Gamma \rightarrow A$ where Γ, the antecedent, is a finite (possibly empty) list of formulas separated by commas, and

[+] Since Prof. Bernays was unfortunately unable to be present, this paper was read by William Howard. — *Eds.*

* An English translation of it will soon appear in an edition of Gentzen's works in English by Manfred Szabo.

[†] Georg Kreisel had previously stated in conversation that he dissented from this opinion.

[‡] 'Sequent' as a technical term should be distinguished from 'sequence' in its usual sense.

where A, the succedent, is a single formula. The logical symbols $\vee$ (or), $\exists$ (existence) and $\supset$ (implication) are eliminated, and only & (and), $\neg$ (not), $\forall$ (universality) are used.

As Gentzen admits arithmetical function symbols (with the restriction that for numerical arguments the value of the function must be computable), there is no loss of generality in assuming that all prime formulas are equations between terms. (Terms are built up in the usual way from free number variables*, numerals and function symbols.)

The rules of the calculus, after the mentioned elimination, are the following:

Initial sequents are:

(1). Logical initial sequents, i.e. sequents of one of the forms

$$A \& B \to A, \qquad A \& B \to B, \qquad A, B \to A \& B,$$
$$A, \neg A \to 1 = 2, \qquad \neg\neg A \to A,$$
$$(\forall x)F(x) \to F(t),$$

where x is a bound variable, and t a term.

(2). Arithmetic initial sequents, i.e. sequents whose formulas are equations and which have the property that by replacing each free variable by a numeral (of course equal variables by equal numerals) and by computing the function values, either the succedent formula gets the truth value 'true' or one of the antecedent formulas gets the truth value 'false', according to the usual valuation of numerical equations.

The *rules of inference* are:

(a). Rules of structural change in a sequent, permitting one

(a_1). to interchange the order of the formulas of the antecedent,

(a_2). to add an arbitrary formula to the antecedent,

(a_3). to delete a repetition of a formula in the antecedent,

(a_4). to change a bound variable of a universal quantifier, everywhere in its scope, into another bound variable.

(b). Logical inference schemata

$$\frac{\Gamma \to A \quad A, \Delta \to B}{\Gamma, \Delta \to B} \qquad (\text{cut})^{\dagger}$$

* Gentzen makes a notational distinction between free and bound variables.

† This schema does not occur in the original text as a fundamental schema, but it is derivable from the schemata for negation there stated, which Gentzen later changed in § 14 of the Annalen paper.

$$\frac{\Gamma, A \rightarrow 1 = 2}{\Gamma \rightarrow \neg A}$$ (negation introduction)

$$\frac{\Gamma \rightarrow F(a)}{\Gamma \rightarrow (\forall x)F(x)}$$ (where a is a free variable not occurring in any formula of Γ nor in F(x), and where **x** is a bound variable) (universality introduction)

(c). Induction

$$\frac{\Gamma \rightarrow F(1) \quad F(a), \Delta \rightarrow F(a+1)}{\Gamma, \Delta \rightarrow F(t)}$$

where t is a term and a a free variable not occurring in Γ, Δ, F(1) or F(t).

In this calculus from any two formulas A, $\neg$ A we can derive, using the initial sequent A, $\neg$ A → 1 = 2 and cut, the sequent → 1 = 2; hence, in order to prove consistency of the considered formal system, it is sufficient to show that the sequent → 1 = 2 is not derivable.

A concept of '*reduction*' of a sequent is introduced. The following are the possible '*reduction steps*' on a sequent:

(α_1). Replacing a free variable, wherever it occurs in the sequent, by the the same numeral, which can be *arbitrarily chosen.*

(α_2). Replacing a function symbol all of whose arguments are constants by its value.

(β_1). When the succedent has the form (∀x)F(x), replacing it by F(k), where k is an *arbitrarily chosen* numeral.

(β_2). When the succedent has the form A & B, replacing it by A or by B, according to an arbitrary choice.

(β_3). When the sequent has the form Γ → $\neg$ A, replacing it by A, Γ → 1 = 2.

(γ). When the succedent is a false numerical equation:

(γ_1). Replacing an antecedent formula (∀x)F(x) by F(k), or adding F(k) to it in the antecedent, where k is a numeral.

(γ_2). Replacing an antecedent formula A & B by one of the formulas A, B or adding one of these in the antecedent.

(γ_3). If an antecedent formula $\neg$ A occurs, replacing the succedent formula by A and possibly cancelling the formula $\neg$ A in the antecedent.

The description of these reduction steps must be completed by the following *rule of preference*: The step (α_1) has preference over all other reduction steps, and (α_1), (α_2) have preference over the other reduction steps. That means: the steps (α_2) are admitted only for a sequent which contains no free variable, and the steps (β_1), (β_2), (β_3), (γ_1), (γ_2), (γ_3) are admitted only for sequents which contain neither a free variable nor a term which is not a numeral.

Related to the concept of a reduction step is that of a '*reduction process*'. (Reduziervorschrift). By a reduction process for a sequent is meant a procedure consisting of a terminating sequence of successive reduction steps by which the sequent is brought into a 'final form' (Endform), i.e. to a sequent satisfying at least one of the two conditions: (1) that the succedent is a true numerical equation, or (2) that some antecedent formula is a false numerical equation. This defining property of a reduction process is to be understood in the strong sense that, whenever reduction steps of the kinds (α_1), (β_1), (β_2) occur in the procedure, the final form will be attained for *every decision on the arbitrary choices*, by *suitably* making choices in connection with steps of the kind (γ_1), (γ_2), (γ_3).

A consequence of the rule of preference is that whenever for a sequent S there is a reduction process, there is a reduction process for any sequent resulting from S by replacing some or all of the free variables of S by numerals.

As an illustration of a reduction process may serve the sequents of the form $A \rightarrow A$.

First, by applications of (α_1) the free variables are removed. In the resulting sequent $A^* \rightarrow A^*$, by applications of (β_1), (β_2) and (α_2) the succedent is brought into either the form of an equation $r = s$ where r and s are numerals, or into the form $\neg C$, each term in C being a numeral.

In the first case the equation $r = s$ is a numerical equation. If this equation is true (i.e. of the form $m = m$) then a final form has been reached. Otherwise we have a sequent $A^* \rightarrow m = n$ with $m = n$ false. Now we can apply the reduction steps (α_2), (γ_1), (γ_2) to the antecedent A^*; and this can be done in an exactly parallel fashion to the reduction steps (α_2), (β_1), (β_2) previously applied to the succedent A^*. In this way the antecedent turns into an equation $m = n$, so that we get a false numerical equation in the antecedent, and so the sequent is again brought into a final form.

In the second case, where we have, after the first reduction steps, the sequent $A^* \rightarrow \neg C$, we get, by applying (β_3), the sequent $C, A^* \rightarrow 1 = 2$.

Applying here again to the antecedent formula A* the reduction steps (γ_1), (γ_2), (α_2) in an exactly parallel fashion to the steps (β_1), (β_2), (α_2) previously applied to the succedent A*, we obtain the sequent C, $\neg$ C $\rightarrow$ 1 = 2, then by applying (γ_3) we obtain C $\rightarrow$ C. Here the formula C contains at least one logical symbol less than A*. Proceeding with the sequent C $\rightarrow$ C in the same way as we did before with A* $\rightarrow$ A*, we either obtain a final form or we get a sequent D $\rightarrow$ D, where D contains fewer logical symbols than C. Thus, continuing in the same way, we come, if we have not already obtained a final form, to a sequent Q $\rightarrow$ Q, where Q is a numerical equation m = n. The sequent m = n $\rightarrow$ m = n has in any case a final form.

It is to be observed that the course of the reduction following the given process depends on the choices to be made at the reduction steps (α_1), (β_1), (β_2), which are arbitrary. The succession of these choices constitutes a *free choice sequence* in Brouwer's sense*. And the given reduction process consists in assigning to any such free choice sequence and to any sequent A $\rightarrow$ A a succession of sequents, which in a finitist way can be seen to end with a sequent in final form.

Using the method of the reduction process for sequents A $\rightarrow$ A, and also that process itself, reduction processes can be given for each of the logical initial sequents. The arithmetical initial sequents can be brought into final form by reduction steps (α_1), (α_2).

If it can be shown that for every derivable sequent there exists a reduction process, then it follows that the formal system under consideration is consistent. For there is no reduction process for the sequent $\rightarrow$ 1 = 2. Hence, in order to prove consistency, it is sufficient to show for each of the inference rules, that if we have a reduction process for the premise, or in the many-premise case for each of the premises, we get a reduction process for the conclusion. Let us try to state this for the various rules of inference.

For the rules (a_1), (a_2), (a_4) the statement is trivial. For (a_3) the statement follows from the fact that in the reduction steps (γ_1), (γ_2), (γ_3) one is allowed to leave unchanged the antecedent formula to which the step applies.

For the schemata of negation and universality introduction the statement is obvious.

* The choice of a member of a conjunction A & B at a step (β_2) can be transformed to the choice of a number, by agreeing that the first or the second conjunction member will be chosen, according as the number is odd or even.

In the schema of induction the conclusion $\Gamma, \Delta \rightarrow F(t)$, by the use of steps (α_1), (α_2) can be turned into a sequent $\Gamma^*, \Delta^* \rightarrow F^*(n)$ where n is a numeral. By applying (α_1), (α_2) *with the same replacements of the variables of* Γ, Δ, $F(1)$ to the premises, these will be turned into the sequents $\Gamma^* \rightarrow F^*(1)$ and $F^*(k), \Delta^* \rightarrow F^*(k+1)$, where k is an arbitrary numeral. (Possibly not yet all permitted applications of (α_2) are made here.) From the assumption that a reduction process exists for the sequents $\Gamma \rightarrow F(1)$ and $F(a), \Delta \rightarrow F(a+1)$, it follows that we have also reduction processes for $\Gamma^* \rightarrow F^*(1)$ and also for $F^*(k), \Delta^* \rightarrow F^*(k+1)$, where k is any numeral. (It is assumed that the variable a does not occur in Γ, Δ, $F(1)$, $F(t)$.)

If now n is 1, then the sequent $\Gamma^*, \Delta^* \rightarrow F(n)$ is either identical with $\Gamma^* \rightarrow F(1)$ or obtainable from it by rule (a_2). If n is the successor of m, then $\Gamma^*, \Delta^* \rightarrow F^*(n)$ is obtainable from $\Gamma^* \rightarrow F^*(1)$ and the m sequents $F^*(k), \Delta^* \rightarrow F^*(k+1)$, wherein k is successively 1, 2, . . ., m by applications of cut, together with rule (a_3).

Thus the only thing still to be shown is that also cut has the property that if for both premises $\Gamma \rightarrow A$ and $A, \Delta \rightarrow B$ we have a reduction process, we can get from them a reduction process for the conclusion $\Gamma, \Delta \rightarrow B$.

To show this, we begin with a remark about free variables. A reduction of the sequent $\Gamma, \Delta \rightarrow B$ must begin by replacing the free variables by numerals. By such replacements (arbitrarily chosen) Γ, Δ, B becomes $\tilde{\Gamma}$, $\tilde{\Delta}$, $\tilde{B}$, and by making these replacements for those free variables in A which occur in the sequent $\Gamma, \Delta \rightarrow B$, and adding replacements for the other free variables (if any) in A, the formula A becomes $\tilde{A}$. Since by assumption we have reduction processes for the sequents $\Gamma \rightarrow A$ and $A, \Delta \rightarrow B$, we also have such processes for the sequents $\tilde{\Gamma} \rightarrow \tilde{A}$ and $\tilde{A}, \tilde{\Delta} \rightarrow \tilde{B}$ resulting from the former by reduction steps (α_1). The proof will be complete if from these reduction processes we can obtain a process for the sequent $\tilde{\Gamma}, \tilde{\Delta} \rightarrow \tilde{B}$.

There is no loss of generality in assuming from the beginning that the sequents $\Gamma \rightarrow A$ and $A, \Delta \rightarrow B$ (therefore also $\Gamma, \Delta \rightarrow B$) contain no free variables. Likewise there is no loss of generality in assuming that all terms in the sequents are computed so that no other terms occur than numerals.

First consider the case in which the formula A contains no logical symbols and hence is a numerical equation. Notice two things:

1. From a reduction process for a sequent S we can immediately obtain a reduction process for any sequent obtained from S by adding other formulas to the antecedent.

2. From a reduction process for a sequent S which has a *true* numerical

equation Q in the antecedent, we can immediately get a reduction process for the sequent obtained from S by deleting the formula Q from the antecedent.

If now in the sequent $A, \Delta \to B$ for which we have a reduction process, A is a true numerical equation, it follows from the second remark that we can also obtain a process for the sequent $\Delta \to B$, and, by the first remark, also for the sequent $\Gamma, \Delta \to B$. If A is a false numerical equation, then by applying reduction steps (β_1), (β_2), (β_3) to the sequent $\Gamma, \Delta \to B$ we come either to a final form; or to a sequent $\Gamma, \Delta \to Q$, where Q is a false numerical equation; or to a sequent $C, \Gamma, \Delta \to 1 = 2$. By hypothesis we have a reduction process for $\Gamma \to A$; and by the first remark above also for $\Gamma, \Delta \to A$ and $C, \Gamma, \Delta \to A$. But since Q and $1 = 2$, like A, are false numerical equations, the process for $\Gamma, \Delta \to A$ is also a process for $\Gamma, \Delta \to Q$, and the process for $C, \Gamma, \Delta \to A$ is also a process for $C, \Gamma, \Delta \to 1 = 2$.

Hence, if A is a numerical equation, we can get from reduction processes for the sequents $\Gamma \to A$, $A, \Delta \to B$ a reduction process for $\Gamma, \Delta \to B$. In order to prove the same thing for a cut with an arbitrary A (supposing only that in the sequents of the cut all terms are numerals), we proceed by reducing successively the number of logical symbols in the formula A, which Gentzen calls the mix-formula (Mischformel) of the cut. So we have to show that we have a method for getting from reduction processes for the premises of a cut schema (with no other terms than numerals) a reduction process for the conclusion, *provided* that we know already how to do this for any cut schema whose mix-formula has fewer logical symbols than the one of the cut schema under consideration. This proviso we shall refer as to 'the inductive hypothesis'.

We begin by paralleling the reduction of the sequent $A, \Delta \to B$. As long as the reduction steps do not involve the antecedent formula A, each such step can likewise be applied to the sequent $\Gamma, \Delta \to B$. If by these steps the sequent $A, \Delta \to B$ is reduced to a final form, the same holds for $\Gamma, \Delta \to B$. Otherwise there is in the reduction of $A, \Delta \to B$ a first step which involves the mix-formula A. This step must be of one of the kinds (γ_1), (γ_2), (γ_3), and the sequent to which it applies has the form $A, \Delta^* \to Q$, where Q is a false numerical equation. The mix-formula A has one of the forms $(\forall x)F(x)$, $C \,\&\, D$, $\neg C$.

In case A is a formula $(\forall x)F(x)$, the reduction step under consideration is of the kind (γ_1) and it yields either a sequent $F(k), \Delta^* \to Q$, where k is a numeral, or a sequent $A, F(k), \Delta^* \to Q$. If the numeral k in F(k) occurs as a part of a term which contains a function symbol, we have to apply one or more steps (α_2), by which F(k) becomes a formula F_1, all terms of which are numerals. Hence in the reduction of $A, \Delta \rightarrow B$ we come either to $F_1, \Delta^* \rightarrow Q$ (Case 1) or to $A, F_1, \Delta^* \rightarrow Q$ (Case 2), whereas in the reduction of $\Gamma, \Delta \rightarrow B$ we have at this stage arrived at $\Gamma, \Delta^* \rightarrow Q$.

In case 1 we are almost at our goal. For in the reduction of the sequent $\Gamma \rightarrow A$ the first steps can be chosen so as to turn it into $\Gamma \rightarrow F_1$. And the reduction process for $\Gamma \rightarrow A$ gives a process for $\Gamma \rightarrow F_1$. Likewise the process for $A, \Delta \rightarrow B$ contains a process for $F_1, \Delta^* \rightarrow Q$. And since in the formula F_1 the number of logical symbols is smaller than in A, we can apply the inductive hypothesis according to which we know already how to obtain from the reduction process for $\Gamma \rightarrow F_1$ and $F_1, \Delta^* \rightarrow Q$ a reduction process for $\Gamma, \Delta^* \rightarrow Q$ which, combined with the reduction steps already used to get from $\Gamma, \Delta \rightarrow B$ to $\Gamma, \Delta^* \rightarrow Q$, yields a reduction process for the sequent $\Gamma, \Delta \rightarrow B$.

In case 2 we have a reduction process for the sequent $A, F_1, \Delta^* \rightarrow Q$, and the reduction of $\Gamma, \Delta \rightarrow B$ has again arrived at the sequent $\Gamma, \Delta^* \rightarrow Q$, Let us now *provisionally* assume that from the reduction process for $\Gamma \rightarrow A$ and $A, F_1, \Delta^* \rightarrow Q$ we have obtained a process for the sequent $\Gamma, F_1, \Delta^* \rightarrow Q$ which results from the two of them by cut: then we have likewise a process for $F_1, \Gamma, \Delta^* \rightarrow Q$; and from this together with the process for $\Gamma \rightarrow F_1$ (already used in case 1) we obtain according to the inductive hypothesis a process for $\Gamma, \Gamma, \Delta^* \rightarrow Q$, and hence also for $\Gamma, \Delta^* \rightarrow Q$. which again together with the performed reduction of $\Gamma, \Delta \rightarrow B$ to $\Gamma, \Delta^* \rightarrow Q$ yields a reduction process for $\Gamma, \Delta \rightarrow B$. So in case 2 our goal is attained upon the provisional assumption.

Before discussing this assumption, let us consider the other two possible forms of the mix-formula A. If A is a conjunction C & D, almost nothing is changed, except the formula F_1 is replaced by one of the conjunction members. When A is a formula $\neg$ C, the reduction step to be applied to $A, \Delta^* \rightarrow Q$ makes this sequence either into $\Delta^* \rightarrow C$ (case 1) or into $A, \Delta^* \rightarrow C$ (case 2). And in the reduction of the sequent $\Gamma \rightarrow A$ the first step makes it into $C, \Gamma \rightarrow 1 = 2$.

Now in the first case, since C has fewer logical symbols than A, from the reduction process for the sequents $\Delta^* \rightarrow C$ and $C, \Gamma \rightarrow 1 = 2$ we obtain by the inductive hypothesis a process for the sequent $\Delta^*, \Gamma \rightarrow 1 = 2$, and hence also a process for $\Gamma, \Delta^* \rightarrow Q$, which, together with the reduction steps leading from $\Gamma, \Delta \rightarrow B$ to $\Gamma, \Delta^* \rightarrow Q$ yields a process for $\Gamma, \Delta \rightarrow B$.

In case 2 the provisional assumption is that from the reduction processes for $\Gamma \to A$ and $A, \Delta^* \to C$ we get a process for the sequent $\Gamma, \Delta^* \to C$ (which results from the two of them by the cut schema). This process together with the one for $C, \Gamma \to 1 = 2$, yields, according to the inductive hypothesis, a process for $\Gamma, \Delta^*, \Gamma \to 1 = 2$, and hence for $\Gamma, \Delta^* \to Q$, and so again for $\Gamma, \Delta \to B$.

Now it remains to consider the provisional assumption which, for all forms of the mix-formula syas that from the reduction processes we have for $\Gamma \to A$ and for a sequent $A, \Delta_1 \to B_1$, we can get a process for $\Gamma, \Delta_1 \to B_1$. It might first seem that nothing has been gained by replacing, in the assertion to be proved, the sequent $A, \Delta \to B$ by $A, \Delta_1 \to B_1$. But the last sequent occurs in the reduction of $A, \Delta \to B$, and its reduction is the part of the reduction of $A, \Delta \to B$ which follows the steps leading from $A, \Delta \to B$ to $A, \Delta_1 \to B_1$. Thus the replacement means progressing in the reduction of $A, \Delta \to B$, and therefore it can take place only a limited number of times. This argument concludes the consistency proof.

Concerning this proof of Gentzen's one might ask in what respect it transgresses the methods formalizable in the formal system under consideration, as must be the case by the Gödel incompleteness theorem. Gentzen himself gave the answer by stating that it is in the concept of a reduction process that the transgression comes about. Indeed this concept involves universal quantification over free choice sequences, and this quantification occurs not only in assertions, but also in hypotheses.

The concept of a reduction process is also introduced in Gentzen's Annalen paper, but there it is not properly used; it is rather replaced by the more elementary concept of a reduction step applied to a derivation ('Reduktionsschritt an einer Herleitung'). Whereas in the concept of a reduction process the requirement of terminating after finitely many steps is involved, in the Annalen paper the ending of the procedure is proved, as you know, by assigning ordinals below ε_0 to the derivations, next showing that every reduction step on a deiivation lowers its ordinal, and finally proving ordinal induction up to ε_0.

HERBRAND-STYLE CONSISTENCY PROOFS

BURTON DREBEN AND JOHN DENTON

Introduction. In this paper we outline an approach for studying consistency stemming from ideas of Herbrand. This approach 'finitistically' exploits the oldest and most naive idea in proof theory: a set of axioms is consistent if it has a model. Hence it is to be contrasted with that approach initiated by Gentzen in 1938 [7] and continued by Schütte [**18**, **19**, **20**] in which proofs, that is, formal derivations, are subject to various purely syntactic manipulations, and questions of interpretation play little role. Indeed, the Herbrand approach is perhaps best viewed as a reformulation of Hilbert's evaluation method, a reformulation that frees that method from its customary (and in our opinion obfuscating) dependence on the ε-calculus [**2**, **12**, **13**].

The basic result on which we depend is the fundamental theorem of Herbrand, the finitistic correlate of the Löwenheim–Skolem Theorem [**10**]. The fundamental theorem says, roughly, that a set of axioms is consistent (in any standard formulation of the predicate calculus) if and only if there exist arbitrarily large 'finite approximations' to models. (A precise statement of the theorem is given below.) There are several preliminary comments worth making. First, the proof of the fundamental theorem is constructive, in the sense that given a proof of a contradiction from the axioms, we can effectively show a point beyond which the construction of the 'finite approximations' to models becomes impossible, and conversely. Second, because of the natural model theoretic interpretations of the systems studied, under this approach we can often use our intuition of what a model of a given set of axioms 'should be' to suggest ways of showing the consistency of the axioms. Third, the methods used to prove consistency generally give as immediate corollaries properties such as the recursive satisfaction of AE-formulas and the Kreisel no-counterexample interpretation, properties for which an additional argument is necessary under the Gentzen-Schütte approach. On the one hand, this means that in the case of theories which have been shown consistent but for which a no-counterexample interpretation is not known, it is presumably more difficult to prove consistency by this approach than by the pure syntactic approach; on the other hand, if we do succeed in proving consistency by this approach, we are likely to obtain considerable additional information.

The main body of this paper is divided into three parts. In the first, we give a precise formulation of the fundamental theorem of Herbrand. In the second part, we sketch how the method can be used to give a consistency proof for elementary number theory, and how the recursive satisfaction of AE-formulas and the no-counterexample interpretation follow immediately from the proof. Finally, in the third section we list some additional results and open questions.

1. Statement of the fundamental theorem. We follow to a large extent the notations and terminology of Shoenfield **[21]**. We have a first order language with symbols $\neg$, $\vee$, and $\exists$, *variables*, and for each n, n-ary *function* and *predicate symbols*. In particular, we suppose that for each n, the language contains infinitely many n-ary function symbols. We use x, y, z, w as syntactical variables for formal variables; f, g, for function symbols; p, q, for predicate symbols; and e for constants (0-ary function symbols). *Terms* are built up from variables and constants using function symbols; we use a, b, c, d as syntactical variables for terms. An *atomic formula* is an expression of the form $pa_1 \ldots a_n$, where p is n-ary; *formulas* are built up from the atomic formulas using $\neg$, $\vee$, and $\exists$. *Free* and *bound* occurrences of a variable in a formula are defined in the usual way. We write $b_x[a]$ for the expression obtained from b by replacing all occurrences of x in b by a, and $A_x[a]$ for the expression obtained from A by replacing all free occurrences of x by a, provided that for each variable y occurring in a, no part of A of the form $\exists yB$ contains an occurrence of x which is free in A. The abbreviations $(A \rightarrow B)$, $(A \,\&\, B)$, $(A \leftrightarrow B)$, $\forall xA$ have their usual meanings; we follow Shoenfield's conventions for omitting and inserting parentheses. (Cf. **[21]**, pp. 14–18.)

We depart slightly from Shoenfield in our definition of the logical axioms. For us, a *logical axiom* is a formula of one of the forms $\neg A \vee A$ or $A_x[a] \rightarrow \exists xA$. (Thus, we take identity and equality axioms, where needed, as nonlogical axioms.) We adopt as rules of inference the *expansion rule* (infer $B \vee A$ from A), the *contraction rule* (infer A from $A \vee A$), the *associative rule* (infer $(A \vee B) \vee C$ from $A \vee (B \vee C)$), the *cut rule* (infer $B \vee C$ from $A \vee B$ and $\neg A \vee C$), and the $\exists$-*introduction rule* (if x is not free in B, infer $\exists xA \to B$ from $A \to B$). *The theorems* of a theory are the formulas obtained starting from the logical and nonlogical axioms of the theory using the above five rules of inference; and a theorem is *logical* if it has a logical proof, that is, if it can be thus obtained without nonlogical axioms. A theory **T** is *consistent* if not every formula in (the language of) **T** is a theorem.(Cf. [**21**], pp. 4, 20–22.)

We now introduce some notions not occurring in Shoenfield. An occurrence of an (existential) quantifier in a formula is *restricted* if and only if it lies within the scopes of an even (possibly zero) number of negation symbols; an occurrence that is not restricted is *general*. (In languages taking the universal quantifier as a basic symbol, occurrences of universal quantifiers are *restricted* or *general* according as they lie within the scopes of an odd or even number of negation symbols; for formulas in prenex form, the existential quantifiers are restricted and the universal quantifiers are general.) We obtain a *validity functional form* of a formula by the following steps:

(i). replace the free variables of the formula by new and distinct constants, and rewrite the bound variables so that no two occurrences of quantifiers contain the same variable;

(ii). delete each general quantifier of the resulting formula, and replace the occurrences of the variable quantified by it with occurrences of the term $fx_1 \ldots x_n$, where $x_1, \ldots, x_n$ are the variables quantified by restricted quantifiers within whose scopes the general quantifier lies, and f is an n-ary function symbol not previously used. We obtain a *satisfiability functional form* similarly, except that the restricted quantifiers are deleted instead of the general quantifiers, and the argument places of the new function symbols are filled by the variables quantified by general quantifiers within whose scopes the corresponding restricted quantifier lies. Thus, if A is a quantifier-free formula with free variables x, y, z, w, then a validity functional form of $\exists x \forall y \exists z A$ would have the form $\exists x \exists z A_{w,y}[e_1, f_1 x]$, while a satisfiability functional form of $\exists x \forall y \exists z A$ would have the form $\forall y A_{w,x,z}[e_1, e_2, f_2 y]$. The new function symbols introduced into a validity or satisfiability functional form are called *indicial* function symbols.

We also need the notion of the expansion of a formula over a domain. A *domain* is a finite nonempty set of variable-free terms; and the *height* of a domain is the maximum height represented in it, where the height of a constant is 0 and the height of a term $fa_1 \ldots a_n$ is $1 +$ the maximum of the heights of the terms $a_1, \ldots, a_n$. The *expansion of a formula A over a domain D*, written $\mathscr{E}(A, D)$, is defined by induction as follows:

(1). if A is an atomic formula, then $\mathscr{E}(A, D)$ is A;
(2). if A is $\neg B$, then $\mathscr{E}(A, D)$ is $\neg \mathscr{E}(B, D)$;
(3). if A is $B \vee C$, then $\mathscr{E}(A, D)$ is $\mathscr{E}(B, D) \vee \mathscr{E}(C, D)$;
(4). if A is $\exists xB$, and $\mathscr{E}(B, D)$ is C, then $\mathscr{E}(A, D)$ is $C_x[a_1] \vee C_x[a_2] \vee \ldots \vee C_x[a_n]$, where $a_1, \ldots, a_n$ are all the elements of D in some order.

It is easy to see that for any formula A and any domain D, $\mathscr{E}(A, D)$ is a quantifier-free formula whose free variables are exactly the free variables of A. Moreover, if all of the quantifiers of A are restricted (in particular, if A is a validity functional form of some formula), then $\mathscr{E}(A, D)$ is truth-functionally equivalent to the disjunction of the formulas obtained by deleting the quantifiers of A and replacing variables quantified by them with members of D in all possible ways. (The dual of the above statement also holds, in which 'restricted', 'validity', 'disjunction', are replaced by 'general', 'satisfiability', 'conjunction' respectively.) We will refer to an expansion of a validity functional form of a formula A as a *validity expansion* of A, and an expansion of a satisfiability functional form of A as a *satisfiability expansion* of A. It should be noted that none of the above definitions or assertions are limited to formulas in prenex form. (The formulas A_H and A_S defined by Shoenfield on pages 53 and 56 are validity and satisfiability functional forms respectively of closed prenex formulas A.)

We can now state the fundamental theorem of Herbrand **[10]**:

(a). *There is a uniform way to find (primitive recursively) a tautologous validity expansion for any logical theorem A from any logical proof of A.*
(b). *There is a uniform way to find (primitive recursively) a logical proof for a formula A from any tautologous validity expansion of A.*

As an immediate corollary we have the Herbrand consistency theorem:

A theory all of whose nonlogical axioms are closed (i.e., contain no free variables) is consistent if and only if every satisfiability expansion of each (finite) conjunction of its nonlogical axioms is truth-functionally satisfiable.

For expository convenience, both the fundamental and the consistency theorem have been stated in terms of Shoenfield's formulation of the predicate calculus. But, of course, strictly analogous theorems can be stated for every (standard) formulation of the predicate calculus. And with respect to several of these formulations, the fundamental theorem can be thought of as a more general version (more general because the constituent formulas in the end sequent need not be prenex) of Gentzen's *verschärfter Hauptsatz* **[6]**.

Interestingly enough, though, part of the contrast between what we have called the Herbrand and the Gentzen approaches to proof theory can already be seen in the quite different kinds of argument that Herbrand and Gentzen give for this Herbrand–Gentzen theorem. Herbrand's argument does not turn on syntactic manipulations, and hence is readily applicable to practically all formulations of the predicate calculus. Herbrand's primary concern is to establish part (a) of the fundamental theorem. Thus, in terms of Shoenfield's system, the core of the argument is the construction of an *analyzing function* for the cut rule, that is, a five-place primitive recursive function $\varphi(i, j, k, p, q)$ with the property that, for all $i, j, k, p, q \geqslant 1$, if formulas A, B, C, contain i, j, and k occurrences of quantifiers respectively, and if the formulas $A \vee B$ and $\neg A \vee C$ have tautologous validity expansions over domains of heights p and q respectively, then the formula $B \vee C$ has a tautologous validity expansion over a domain of height $\varphi(i, j, k, p, q)$. The rest of the argument for part (a) is simple. Indeed, for each of Shoenfield's other four rules of inference the identity function can serve as an *analyzing function*, that is, if A is any formula having a tautologous validity expansion over a domain of height p and the formula B comes from A by one application of the expansion, contraction, associative, or $\exists$-introduction rule, then B also has a tautologous validity expansion over a domain of height p. Finally, for each $j \geqslant 1$ and each term a of height $h \geqslant 0$, if a formula A contains j occurrences of quantifiers, then the formula $A \vee \neg A$ has a tautologous validity expansion over a domain of height j, and the formula $A_x[a] \rightarrow \exists x A$ has a tautologous validity expansion over a domain of height $j+h$.

A detailed proof of the fundamental theorem as well as a discussion of its relation to the *verschärfter Hauptsatz* and the Hilbert-Bernays ε-theorems will appear in our forthcoming monograph with Scanlon [**4**]. (The proofs Shoenfield gives in pages 41–55 of what he calls the consistency theorem and Herbrand's theorem are adapted from the proofs in Hilbert-Bernays [**13**] of the ε-theorems. It is important to realize, as Hilbert and Bernays do, that these proofs are of a piece with the Gentzen approach but *not* with the Hilbert evaluation approach.)

To see the way in which the fundamental theorem (more precisely, its corollary the consistency theorem) reduces the problem of consistency to the construction of 'finite approximations' to models, let us consider the case of a theory whose nonlogical axioms A_i are closed and of the form $\forall x_1 \ldots \forall x_n \exists y A_i'$, where A_i' is quantifier-free. The satisfiability functional forms $A_i^{(s)}$ of such formulas are of the form $\forall x_1 \ldots \forall x_n A_{iy}'[f_i x_1 \ldots x_n]$, and a satisfiability expansion of a conjunction of such formulas will be a conjunction of formulas of the form

$$A'_{ix_1,\ldots,x_n,y}[a_1,\ldots,a_n, f_i a_1 \ldots a_n]. \tag{1}$$

The fundamental theorem tells us that the theory will be consistent if and only if every *finite* conjunction of the formulas (1) is satisfiable.

From a nonconstructive point of view, of course, the assertion that every finite conjunction of formulas (1) is truth-functionally satisfiable is equivalent to the assertion that the theory has a model, i.e., that there is a structure in which all formulas (1) (for every i and any terms $a_1, \ldots, a_n$ of the theory) and hence all the axioms of the theory are satisfied. (The connection is made via the 'infinity lemma' or the 'law of infinite conjunction'.) But there are theories (e.g. elementary number theory) for which one cannot provide a model in any constructive way (i.e., a way which would enable us to determine effectively the truth values of formulas of the theory in that model), but for which one *can* provide a general method which enables one, given any finite conjunction of formulas (1), to construct a truth assignment under which these formulas are all true. The various truth assignments provided by this general method give us information about the theory (and its theorems) which is not provided by a model presented in a nonconstructive way.

As an example of such additional information, suppose that a closed formula of the form $\forall z \exists w B$, B quantifier-free, is a theorem of a theory whose nonlogical axioms A_i are as above. Then, by the deduction theorem, a formula of the form

$$(A_1 \mathbin{\&} A_2 \mathbin{\&} \ldots \mathbin{\&} A_n) \rightarrow \forall z \exists w B \tag{2}$$

is a theorem of a theory with no nonlogical axioms. Now a validity functional form of (2) will be of the form

$$(A_1^{(s)} \mathbin{\&} \ldots \mathbin{\&} A_n^{(s)}) \rightarrow \exists w B_z[e],$$

where $A_i^{(s)}$ is a satisfiability functional form of A_i. (Note that an occurrence of a quantifier is restricted in A_i if and only if the correspondingly placed occurrence of the quantifier is general in (2)). A validity expansion of (2) will then have the form

$$(\mathscr{E}(A_1^{(s)}, D) \mathbin{\&} \ldots \mathbin{\&} \mathscr{E}(A_n^{(s)}, D)) \rightarrow \mathscr{E}(\exists w B_z[e], D). \tag{3}$$

It can easily be shown that if a formula has a validity expansion which is a tautology, then it has such an expansion over a domain whose terms are built up from the constants and function symbols occurring in its validity functional form (provided that at least one constant occurs in the functional form). Thus, in the present case, we may suppose that the domain D consists of terms built up from the constant e using contants and function symbols occurring in the axioms A_i, together with the indicial function symbols f_i. If we have a model $\mathscr{A}$ for the functional forms $A_i^{(s)}$, and we assign e any value in the universe of $\mathscr{A}$, then we can compute relative to the model the values of the terms in D. Since the expansions $\mathscr{E}(A_i^{(s)}, D)$ all hold in $\mathscr{A}$, and (3) is a tautology, it must be that for some a in D, $B_{z,w}[e, a]$ holds in $\mathscr{A}$. Thus, for each element $e_{\mathscr{A}}$ of the universe of $\mathscr{A}$, we can effectively find an element $a_{\mathscr{A}}$ such that $B_{z,w}[e, a]$ holds in $\mathscr{A}$, where $e_{\mathscr{A}}$ and $a_{\mathscr{A}}$ are the elements denoted by e and a respectively. In the case of number theory, this gives us essentially the recursive satisfaction of AE-formulas.

2. The consistency of elementary number theory. As one might expect, the Herbrand approach to problems of consistency is most easily applicable to those theories for which we have a fairly clear idea of what a model should be. An extremely simple example of this is afforded by Shoenfield's theory N on pages 22 and 51 of **[21]**, or by any other formalization of (elementary) number theory without induction in which no indicial function symbols occur in the functional forms of the axioms. Here the elements of the model will be the natural numbers. Hence, to specify a suitable structure $\mathscr{A}$ (see **[21]**, p. 18), we need only assign in the obvious way numbers, computable functions, and decidable relations to whatever functions and relation symbols occur in the axioms. For example, to 0, S, $+$, $\cdot$, $=$, and $<$, the primitive symbols of N, are assigned respectively the number $0_{\mathscr{A}}$, the successor function $S_{\mathscr{A}}$, the sum $+_{\mathscr{A}}$, the product $\cdot_{\mathscr{A}}$, the identity relation $=_{\mathscr{A}}$, and the less than relation $<_{\mathscr{A}}$. Clearly, $\mathscr{A}$ is an (effective) model for the axioms, and in particular for the satisfiability expansion of any conjunction of closures of the non-logical axioms over any domain D that consists just of terms built up from the constants and function symbols occurring in the functional forms of the axioms. (It follows from the remark in the last paragraph of section 1 that only such domains need be considered; henceforth we shall tacitly restrict our attention to them.) By the consistency theorem, elementary number theory without induction is consistent.

Now let us extend N, or any analogous theory, by adding induction. First, consider an induction axiom of the form

$$\forall z((A_x[0] \;\&\; \forall x(A \to A_x[Sx])) \to \forall x A), \tag{1}$$

where A is a quantifier-free formula whose free variables are z and x. A satisfiability functional form of the closure of this formula will be of the form

$$\forall z((A_x[0] \mathbin{\&} (A_x[fz] \rightarrow A_x[Sfz])) \rightarrow \forall xA), \tag{2}$$

where f is the indicial function symbol corresponding to the restricted quantifier $\forall x$ appearing in the antecedent of the conditional. Intuitively, we want f to stand for a number theoretic function with the property that if for some number k, $\forall xA_z[k]$ is false and $A_{z,x}[k, 0]$ is true, then $A_{z,x}[k, fk]$ is true and $A_{z,x}[k, Sfk]$ is false (for example, by letting fk be the least number n such that $A_{z,x}[k, Sn]$ is false). But there is no way in general of deciding effectively whether $\forall xA_z[k]$ is (number theoretically) false. So we cannot proceed as we did in the case of the system without induction. It is at this point that the full power of the fundamental theorem comes into play. Namely, to show the consistency of the induction axiom (1) with the other axioms of number theory, it suffices to show that for each domain D there is a structure $\mathscr{A}(D)$ in which the satisfiability expansion $\mathscr{E}((2), D)$ (and the expansions of the other axioms) is true. In this structure $\mathscr{A}(D)$, we do not have to insure that $A[k, fk]$ is true and $A[k, Sfk]$ false unless, for some term a belonging to D, $A[k, a]$ is false in $\mathscr{A}(D)$ (and $A[k, 0]$ is true). That is, if the least number n such that $A[k, Sn]$ is false is 'too large' in relation to D, then we do not have to take it into consideration. (Here and frequently below, we simplify the substitution notation by omitting subscripts.)

Now for each D, an (effective) structure $\mathscr{A}(D)$ that satisfies the expansions over D of all the other axioms is obtainable from the structure $\mathscr{A}$ merely by assigning *any* computable function α to the function symbol f. Of course, distinct α's will normally be picked for distinct D's. Our whole task is to find for a given D an α such that $\mathscr{A}(D)$ satisfies $\mathscr{E}((2), D)$ as well. More precisely, for each domain D and function α, let m be a mapping of the terms of D into the numbers such that

$$\begin{aligned} m(0) &= 0_{\mathscr{A}} & m(a \cdot b) &= m(a) \cdot_{\mathscr{A}} m(b) \\ m(Sa) &= S_{\mathscr{A}} m(a) & m(fa) &= \alpha(m(a)) \\ m(a+b) &= m(a) +_{\mathscr{A}} m(b) \end{aligned} \tag{3}$$

Each such mapping will be said to *induce* a structure $\mathscr{A}(D)$. To induce a model for $\mathscr{E}((2), D)$, we proceed by successive approximation.

We begin by trying the function α_0 such that $\alpha_0(k) = 0_{\mathscr{A}}$ for all numbers k.

Assuming that α_i has been defined for some i, we define m_i by conditions (3), using α_i in place of α. We then let $\mathscr{A}_i$ be the structure induced by m_i. If the expansion $\mathscr{E}((2), D)$ is true in $\mathscr{A}_i$, then clearly we are done; if $\mathscr{E}((2), D)$ is false in $\mathscr{A}_i$, then it is because for some term a belonging to D, $A[\text{a}, 0]$ and $A[a, fa] \rightarrow A[a, Sfa]$ are true in $\mathscr{A}_i$, but for some b in D, $A[a, b]$ is false in $\mathscr{A}_i$. Now we have $m_i(b) \neq 0_{\mathscr{A}}$, since if $m_i(b) = 0_{\mathscr{A}}$, then $A[a, 0]$ and $A[a, b]$ would have the same truth-value in $\mathscr{A}_i$. Thus, our difficulty comes from the fact that we have not chosen $m_i(fa) = \alpha_i(m(a))$ in such a way that $A[a, fa]$ is true in $\mathscr{A}_i$ but $A[a, Sfa]$ is false in $\mathscr{A}_i$. However, the remedy is clear: Since $A[m_i(a), 0_{\mathscr{A}}]$ is true (over the numbers) but $A[m_i(a), m_i(b)]$ is false, we can find a number $n < m_i(b)$ such that $A[m_i(a), n]$ is true but $A[m_i(a), S_{\mathscr{A}}n]$ is false. Hence, we define the function α_{i+1} as follows: $\alpha_{i+1}(k) = \alpha_i(k)$ for all numbers k except $k = m_i(a)$, where a is as above, in which case we define $\alpha_{i+1}(k) = n$, where n is as above. We define m_{i+1} by conditions (3), replacing α by α_{i+1}, and we let $\mathscr{A}_{i+1}$ be the induced structure.

Clearly, α_{i+1} is a better approximation to the desired function than is α_1; our problem now is to show that by repeating the above procedure sufficiently many times, we will eventually find a structure in which $\mathscr{E}((2), D)$ is true. The first observation to be made is that for all i, non-zero values of α_i are 'correct', more precisely, if $\alpha_i(k) \neq 0_{\mathscr{A}}$, then $A[k, \alpha_i(k)]$ is true and $A[k, S_{\mathscr{A}}\alpha_i(k)]$ is false. This implies that we can measure progress towards our goal by counting the number of terms a belonging to D such that $m_i(fa) = 0_{\mathscr{A}}$; the fewer of these there are, roughly speaking, the closer we are to our goal. In calculating this measure, however, we have to give priority to terms of low height. The reason for this is that in going from α_i to α_{i+1} we may have changed the value of $m_i(fa)$, where the height of a is relatively low, and in so doing we may change the value of $m_i(fb)$, when a occurs in b, in unpredictable ways. An appropriate way to measure progress is the following: We let $h(i, p)$ be the number of terms a in D of height p such that $m_i(fa) = 0_{\mathscr{A}}$, and we let *index* (i) be the p_0+1-tuple $(h(i, 0), \ldots, h(i, p_0))$, where p_0 is the height of D; we write *index* $(i_1) \prec$ *index*(i_2) if and only if, for some p $(0 \leqslant p \leqslant p_0)$, we have $h(i_1, 0) = h(i_2, 0) = \ldots = h(i_1, p-1) = h(i_2, p-1)$, and $h(i_1, p) < h(i_2, p)$. It is easy to show that if $\mathscr{E}((2), D)$ is false in $\mathscr{A}_i$, then *index*$(i+1) \prec$ *index*(i). Since the relation $\prec$ is a linear ordering, and since the numbers $h(i, p)$ are bounded by q, where q is the number of terms in D, it follows that for some $i \leqslant (1+q)^{p_0}$, the satisfiability expansion $\mathscr{E}((2), D)$ must be true in $\mathscr{A}_i$. The expansions of the other axioms of elementary number theory are true in every $\mathscr{A}_i$, as we have seen, so we have that for every domain D there exists a structure $\mathscr{A}(D)$ in which the satisfiability expansions of all of the nonlogical axioms of our theory are true. Hence, by the fundamental theorem the theory is consistent. (This theory can be shown consistent by simpler arguments, and Herbrand and Gentzen have both done so; see **[9]**, **[6]**, and also **[15]**. But such arguments cannot be extended to full number theory. Moreover, the argument just sketched for constructing $\mathscr{A}_i$ is essentially the one used for constructing an analyzing function for the cut rule; see **[3]**, **[22]**, and **[4]**.)

In the proof of the consistency of systems such as N, we were able to use the same structure as a model of the satisfiability expansion of all the axioms over a domain D, independent of D. When we added induction axioms for quantifier-free formulas we could no longer do this, but we were still able to construct our successive approximations to models without back-tracking, in the sense that once we had found a 'correct' value for $\alpha_i(k)$, we never needed to change that value at a later stage in our construction. However, in order to prove the consistency of elementary number theory with an unrestricted axiom schema for induction, we must abandon this characteristic of our construction in order to preserve the principle that 'non-zero values are correct'. Necessarily, this means that we must use more delicate means to measure progress towards our goal. It is in establishing that these measures do in fact show that we reach our goal after a finite number of iterations that we use methods not formalizable in the theory being shown consistent, and thus escape the limitations imposed by Gödel's theorem on consistency proofs. Nevertheless, the basic strategy of our construction remains unchanged: we map terms occurring in satisfiability expansions into elements of an intuitive model so as induce an appropriate structure.

To illustrate how this is done, consider the case of an induction axiom (1), in which we now suppose A to be of the form $\exists yB$, where B is quantifier-free and has free variables z, x, y. Then (1) becomes

$$\forall z((\exists yB[0, y] \& \forall x(\exists yB[x, y] \rightarrow \exists yB[Sx, y])) \rightarrow \forall x \exists yB[x, y]), \qquad (4)$$

where $B[a, b]$ denotes $B_{x,y}[a, b]$. Now if we were carrying out the details we would see that it is convenient to adjoin a new axiom

$$\forall z \forall x(\exists yB[x, y] \rightarrow B[x, gzx]), \qquad (5)$$

where g is a new binary function symbol. Clearly the consistency of the system obtained by adjoining this axiom implies the consistency of the original system; on the other hand, formula (5) is a satisfiability functional form of $\forall z \forall x(\exists y B \rightarrow \exists y B)$, and hence its adjunction cannot destroy consistency. (This has nothing to do with the axiom of choice.) In the presence of (5), (4) is provably equivalent to

$$\forall z((B[0, gz0] \;\&\; \forall x(B[x, gzx] \rightarrow B[Sx, gzSx])) \rightarrow \forall x B[x, gzx]), \qquad (6)$$

which in turn has as a satisfiability function form

$$\forall z((B[0, gz0] \;\&\; (B[fz, gzfz] \rightarrow B[Sfz, gzSfz])) \rightarrow \forall x B[x, gzx]). \qquad (7)$$

Thus, our problem is to show that any satisfiability expansion of the conjunction of (5) and (7) (and the other axioms of number theory) is satisfiable. As before, our method is to find a mapping m sending the terms occurring in the expansion into numbers in such a way that the expansions are true in the induced structure. This mapping m is to satisfy the conditions (3), and the additional condition $m(gab) = \beta(m(a), m(b))$, where β is a binary function to be determined by successive approximation. We start by taking $\alpha_0(k) = \beta_0(k, n) = 0_{\mathscr{A}}$ for all numbers k and n. Given α_i and β_i, we define m_i by conditions like those just stated for m, replacing α and β with α_i and β_i.

For a given domain D, if the induced structure $\mathscr{A}_i$ is such that the expansions $\mathscr{E}((5), D)$ and $\mathscr{E}((7), D)$ are true, then of course we have reached our goal. Otherwise, there are two alternatives. Either there exist terms a, b, c in D making $B[a, b, c]$ true in $\mathscr{A}_i$ and $B[a, b, gab]$ false in $\mathscr{A}_i$, or there exist terms a, b in D such that $B[a, 0, ga0]$ and $B[a, fa, gafa] \rightarrow B[a, Sfa, gaSfa]$ are true in $\mathscr{A}_i$ but $B[a, b, gab]$ is false in $\mathscr{A}_i$. (Here $B[a, b, c]$ denotes $B_{z,x,y}[a, b, c]$.)

In the first case, the difficulty is clearly that $m_i(gab) = \beta_i(m_i(a), m_i(b))$ has an 'incorrect' value which we can change to a 'correct' value $m_i(c)$. But in order to preserve the principle that non-zero values are correct for α_i, we must make sure not to pass on a non-zero value of α_i which has become 'incorrect' by virtue of this change in β_i. We take care of this by a seemingly brutal procedure: If we go from β_i to β_{i+1} by correcting an 'incorrect' value, then we define $\alpha_{i+1}(n)$ to be zero for all numbers n, thus, so to speak, erasing *all* non-zero values of α_i. Although this might appear to be a step in the wrong direction, it will turn out that if we think in terms of sequences of maps, we can still devise a measure of progress with the right properties. We turn now to the second of the alternatives.

If the satisfiability expansion $\mathscr{E}((7), D)$ is false, then it is because $m_i(fa)$

$= \alpha_i(m_i(a))$ has an 'incorrect' value. Hence we define $\alpha_{i+1}(k) = \alpha_i(k)$, except when $k = m_i(a)$; for this k, we take $\alpha_{i+1}(k)$ to be the least number n such that $B[m_i(a), n, \beta_i(m_i(a), n)]$ is true and $B[m_i(a), S_{\mathscr{A}}n, \beta_i(m_i(a), S_{\mathscr{A}}n)]$ is false; such a number exists and is smaller than $m_i(b)$. We also set $\beta_{i+1}(k, n) = \beta_i(k, n)$ for all k, n. We have not violated the principle 'non-zero values are correct' in so doing, since the function symbol f does not occur in $B[z, x, y] \rightarrow B[z, x, gzx]$, the formula serving as the criterion for the 'correctness' of values of β_i.

The method by which we devise measures of progress in order to conclude that the above procedure eventually gives us a model for the expansions $\mathscr{E}((5), D)$ and $\mathscr{E}((7), D)$ is essentially that of Ackermann's 1940 consistency proof [**1**] (see also Wang [**23**], pp. 362–375) adapted to Herbrand's language. The formulas (5) and (7) correspond to critical formulas of the first and second kinds respectively. The use in our approach of function symbols instead of ε-terms makes it easier to see what is going on. Briefly, what happens is that when we 'erase' all non-zero values of α_i, we eventually replace them with at least as many new 'correct' values (correct according to the new definition of β_i), and in this way we eventually define a mapping m_i inducing a structure in which $\mathscr{E}((5), D)$ and $\mathscr{E}((7), D)$ are true. Ordinal numbers are assigned to the pairs of functions (α_i, β_i), finite sequences of such pairs, finite sequences of finite sequences of such pairs, etc, (Note that these functions, sequences, etc., have values different from zero for only finitely many sets of arguments, and hence can be coded into numbers.) The construction sketched above leads to decreasing sequences of ordinals until a model for the expansion is reached; since a decreasing sequence of ordinals must terminate after finitely many terms, we have our desired conclusion. The ordinals employed are constructive, and the bounds on the size of the ordinals involved are essentially the same as those found in the Gentzen-style proofs. Although the bounds increase as a function of the number of quantifiers occurring in the formulas appearing in the induction axioms, the conceptual difficulties do not increase; only the bookkeeping gets more complicated.

As we mentioned in the introduction, the recursive satisfaction of AE-formulas and the no-counterexample interpretation result quickly from our consistency proof. The remarks at the end of section 1 should suffice to indicate how recursive satisfaction is obtained; we turn now to the Kreisel no-counterexample interpretation. Let us consider a theorem of elementary number theory of the form $\forall x \exists y \forall z B[x, y, z]$, where $B[x, y, z]$ is quantifier-free and has only the indicated free variables. By the deduction theorem, we have a logical theorem of the form

$$A_1 \mathbin{\&} \ldots \mathbin{\&} A_r \rightarrow \forall x \exists y \forall z B[x, y, z],$$

where the formulas A_i are closures of axioms of number theory. A validity functional form of this formula will be of the form

$$A_1^{(s)} \mathbin{\&} \ldots \mathbin{\&} A_r^{(s)} \rightarrow \exists y B[e, y, fy], \tag{8}$$

and by the fundamental theorem we can find a domain D such that $\mathscr{E}((8), D)$ is a tautology. Thus, if we have a structure in which each of the $\mathscr{E}(A_i^{(s)}, D)$ is true, then for some a in D, $B[e, a, fa]$ must also be true, since $\mathscr{E}((\exists y B[e, y, fy]), D)$ is a disjunction. Now suppose someone comes to us and says: 'I have a number n and a function φ such that for all numbers k, $B[n, k, \varphi(k)]$ is false.' Using the procedure described above, we can find a mapping m which maps the terms occurring in $\mathscr{E}((8), D)$ into numbers, maps e to n, maps fa to $\varphi(m(a))$ for all terms a, and is such that the mapping m induces a structure in which $\mathscr{E}(A_i^{(s)}, D)$ is true for $i = 1, \ldots, r$. In this structure, $B(e, a, fa]$ is true for some a in D, and hence $B[n, m(a), \varphi(m(a))]$ must be true. Thus we have been able to defeat the proposed counterexample to the truth of $\forall x \exists y \forall z B[x, y, z]$. It is easy to make this argument completely general; it will apply to any consistency proof in which we map the terms occurring in a satisfiability expansion of the axioms so as to induce a structure in which the expansion is true.

3. Further results and prospects. The fundamental theorem in conjunction with mapping techniques which induce suitable structures has proved useful for investigating solvable cases of the decision problem (e.g., see [**5**]), as well as for clarifying Kreisel's primitive recursive solution to Hilbert's seventeenth problem [**14**].

In addition, Scanlon has extended the argument sketched in section 2 to provide a proof of the ω-consistency of elementary number theory [**4**]. This proof is of the no-counterexample kind discussed by Kreisel in [**16**]. It is shown that given a proof of a formula $\exists x B$ and a number theoretic function ψ, we can find a natural number n such that if D is a domain of height $\psi(n)$, then the validity expansion over D of the formula $A_1 \mathbin{\&} \ldots \mathbin{\&} A_k \rightarrow \neg B_x[S^{(n)}0]$, where the axioms A_i have at most $\psi(n)$ quantifiers, is not a tautology. This is the sense in which ω-consistency must be taken in order for the notion to have constructive content, as Kreisel has remarked. (There is an interesting contrast between ω-consistency and simple consistency. Kreisel shows in **[16]** that the ω-consistency of number theory without induction immediately implies the simple consistency of full number theory. But Parsons has pointed out that the (arithmetical correlate of the) converse is not provable in full number theory).

Candidates for further extensions of the Herbrand approach are the various subsystems of analysis and type theory which have already been shown consistent by other methods. An obvious candidate is the so-called ramified analysis in which there are different levels of sets, and the comprehension axioms for the sets of each level contain only quantifiers for sets of lower levels. It seems clear that a consistency proof along the lines of section 2 will involve great combinatorial complexities, for any such proof will afford much insight into ramified analysis. But the finding of such a proof should perhaps be taken as a touchstone for the likelihood of further useful results from the Herbrand approach to consistency, especially since Parsons establishes in **[17]** the ω-consistency of ramified analysis, and Kreisel states that Gödel's consistency proof for number theory **[8, 21]** can be extended to give a no-counterexample interpretation for ramified analysis.

Acknowledgements. We are grateful to Warren D. Goldfarb, W. V. Quine, and Thomas N. Scanlon for much helpful advice.

REFERENCES

[1] W. Ackermann, Zur Widerspruchsfreiheit der Zahlentheorie, *Math. Ann.* **117** (1940).

[2] P. Bernays, Zusatz zu Hilberts Vortrag 'Über die Grundlagen der Mathematik', *Abhandl. math. Seminar Hamburgischen Univ.* **6** (1927). Translation in **[22]** 485–489.

[3] B. Dreben and J. Denton, A supplement to Herbrand, *J. Symb. Logic* **31** (1966).

[4] B. Dreben, J. Denton and T. M. Scanlon, *The Herbrand theorem and the consistency of number theory* (forthcoming).

[5] B. Dreben, A. S. Kahr and H. Wang, Classification of *AEA* formulas by letter atoms, *Bull. Amer. Math. Soc.* **68** (1962).

[6] G. Gentzen, Untersuchungen über das logische Schliessen, *Math. Z.* **39** (1934).

[7] G. Gentzen, Neue Fassung des Widerspruchsfreiheitsbeweises für die reine Zahlentheorie, *Forsch. Logik u. Grundl. exakten Wiss.* N.S. **4** (1938).

[8] K. Gödel, Über eine bisher noch nicht benutzte Erweiterung des finiten Standpunktes, *Dialectica* **12** (1958).

[9] J. Herbrand, Sur la non-contradiction de l'arithmétique, *J. reine u. angew. Math.* **166** (1931). Reprinted in **[11]** 221–232. Translation in **[22]** 618–628.

[10] J. Herbrand, *Recherches sur la théorie de la démonstration, Prace Towarzystwa Naukowego Warszawskiego, Wydzial* III **33**. Reprinted in **[11]** 35–153. Translation of ch. 5 in **[22]** 525–581.

[11] J. HERBRAND, *Écrits logiques*, ed. J. van Heijenoort, Paris (1968).
[12] D. HILBERT, Neubegründung der Mathematik (erste Mitteilung), *Abhandl. math. Seminar Hamburgischen Univ.* **1** (1922).
Die Grundlagen der Mathematik, *ibid.* **6** (1928). Translation of the latter in **[22]** 464–479.
[13] D. HILBERT and P. BERNAYS, *Grundl. Math.* **1** (1934), **2** (1939).
[14] D. ISAACSON, *A constructive solution of Hilbert's seventeenth problem by use of the fundamental theorem of Herbrand*, senior thesis, Department of Mathematics, Harvard College (1967).
[15] S. C. KLEENE, *Introduction to metamathematics*, New York (1952).
[16] G. KREISEL, Models, translations and interpretations, in *Mathematical interpretation of formal systems*, Amsterdam (1955).
[17] C. PARSONS, The ω-consistency of ramified analysis, *Arch. math. Logik u. Grundlagenforschung* **6** (1962).
[18] K. SCHÜTTE, Beweistheoretische Erfassung der unendlichen Induktion in der Zahlentheorie, *Math. Ann.* **122** (1951).
[19] K. SCHÜTTE, Beweistheoretische Untersuchung der verzweigten Analysis, *Math. Ann.* **124** (1952).
[20] K. SCHÜTTE, *Beweistheorie*, Berlin (1960).
[21] J. R. SHOENFIELD, *Mathematical logic*, Reading, Mass., (1967).
[22] J. VAN HEIJENOORT, ed., *From Frege to Gödel: a sourcebook in mathematical logic 1879–1931*, Cambridge, Mass. (1967).
[23] H. WANG, *A survey of mathematical logic*, Peking (1962).

ITERATED INDUCTIVE DEFINITIONS AND Σ_2^1–AC*

HARVEY FRIEDMAN

In this paper, we discuss the relations between Σ_{k+1}^1–AC and Π_k^1–CA, $k \geqslant 0$. After that, we discuss Σ_k^1–DC and iterated generalized inductive definitions. Π_k^1–CA, for $k > 0$, is just the comprehension axiom (schema) applied to Π_k^1 formulae, together with EA. A Π_k^1 formula is one which has a block of k function quantifiers, starting with a universal one, followed by only number quantifiers and propositional combinations of atomic formulae.† EA is composed of first-order arithmetic together with the schema of ordinary induction on all second-order formulae. A Π_0^1 formula is a Π_1^0 formula, for the purposes of this paper. Σ_k^1–AC is the schema $(\forall n)(\exists f)P(n, f) \to (\exists g)(\forall n)P(n, g_{(n)})$, where $g_{(n)}(m) = g(2^{n+1} \cdot 3^{m+1})$, and P is Π_{k-1}^1, together with EA, if $k > 1$. If $k = 1$, then take P to be arithmetical.

It is well known that Σ_{k+1}^1–AC is much stronger than Π_k^1–CA, in the sense that Σ_{k+1}^1–AC can prove the existence of an ω-model of Π_k^1–CA. This actually follows from our theorem. An ω-model is one in which the integers are standard. Instead, if we consider a natural process of iteration of Π_k^1–CA described below, and we do this process ε_0 times, we get a theory which we call $(\Pi_k^1\text{–CA})^{<\varepsilon_0}$, and we have the

THEOREM. *Σ_{k+1}^1–AC is a conservative extension of $(\Pi_k^1\text{–CA})^{<\varepsilon_0}$ for Π_4^1 sentences if $k > 1$. If $k = 0$, then it is a conservative extension for Π_2^1 sentences. For $k = 1$, we have Π_3^1 sentences.*

(A theory $\boldsymbol{T}$ is said to be a conservative extension of $\boldsymbol{S}$ with respect to Π_p^1 sentences if and only if every Π_p^1 sentence provable in $\boldsymbol{S}$ is provable in $\boldsymbol{T}$ and $\boldsymbol{T}$ contains $\boldsymbol{S}$.)

The case where $k=0$ was treated in the author's doctoral dissertation [**3**].

* This research was partially supported by NSF G.P. 8764.

† We use this particular definition of Π_k^1 so that we do not need extra axioms to prove the existence of a complete Π_k^1 predicate; one only needs Π_0^1–CA.

The other cases of the theorem, as one can see from this paper, are proved by adaptation of the argument for the case $k = 0$.

Now we define $(\Pi^1_k\text{–CA})^{<\varepsilon_0}$. There is a standard complete Π^1_k predicate $P_k(n, f, g)$ of the free variables shown, for each $k > 0$. We define, for a recursive linear ordering indexed by e (the field may not be all of ω), the predicate $H^g_k(f, e)$, k fixed $\geqslant 0$, as

$(\forall p)$(if p is the least point in the ordering e, then $f_{(p)} = g$) &

$(\forall p)$(if p is not in the field of e then $f_{(p)}$ is everywhere 0)&

$(\forall p)(\forall q)$(if q is the successor of p in the ordering e then

$$(\forall n)(f_{(q)}(n) = 0 \leftrightarrow P_k(n, f_{(p)}, g)\ \&\ f_{(q)}(n) = 1 \leftrightarrow \sim P(n, f_{(p)}, g))\ \&$$

$(\forall p)$(if p is a limit then

$$(\forall n)(f_{(p)}(n) = 0 \leftrightarrow [n = \langle k, q\rangle\ \&\ q \text{ is below } p \text{ in } e\ \&\ f_{(q)}(k) = 0]\ \&$$
$$[f_{(p)}(n) = 1 \leftrightarrow \sim f_{(p)}(n) = 0])).$$

Thus, when $k = 0$, and e is a well-ordering, we are describing the hyperarithmetic hierarchy (relative to g).

Now consider the standard recursive well-ordering of type ε_0. The field is ω. For each n, $\varepsilon_0(n)$ is defined as the natural index of the initial segment of the standard ordering, ε_0, up to (but not including) n. $\varepsilon_0(n)$ is a primitive recursive function.

Finally, $(\Pi^1_k\text{–CA})^{<\varepsilon_0}$ is Π^1_0–CA together with the schema $(\forall g)(\exists f)(H^g_k(f, \varepsilon_0(\mathbf{n})))$, where n varies through ω.

This theorem has special significance in the cases $k = 0$ and 1. For $k = 0$, Σ^1_1–AC is, on the face of it, impredicative, further corroborated by the theorem of Kreisel that the minimum ω-model of Σ^1_1–AC is the collection of all hyperarithmetic functions (sets). But this theorem shows that the Π^1_2 statements provable in Σ^1_1–AC can be predicatively proved. Furthermore, the proof of this metatheorem can be easily made strictly finitary.

In the case of $k = 1$, there is a completely straightforward direct translation (which we refer to later) of $(\Pi^1_k\text{–CA})^{<\varepsilon_0}$ into (and onto) the theory of iterated inductive definitions, where the iteration is carried through ε_0 times. This system $\mathrm{ID}^{<\varepsilon_0}$ will be described later. Our theorem for $k = 1$ gives (a finitary proof) that Σ^1_2–AC and $\mathrm{ID}^{<\varepsilon_0}$ have the same Π^1_1 theorems. This will be made more precise later. Of course, finitary relative consistency proofs are immediately obvious from the finitary proofs of conservative extension results.

Rather than first give the most complicated argument that produces the most refined results (namely the whole of the theorem), we successively give sketches of more and more sharpened versions.

We define $(\Pi_k^1\text{-CA})^{\varepsilon_0}$ as $(\forall n)(\forall g)(\exists f)(H_k^g(f, \varepsilon_0(n)))+\Pi_0^1$-CA. Note that this addition to Π_0^1-CA is *not* a schema.

We first prove

THEOREM 1. *Any* Σ_1^1 *sentence provable in* Σ_1^1-AC *is provable in* $T=(\Pi_0^1\text{-CA})^{\varepsilon_0}$ + *all instances of transfinite induction on our standard ordering*, ε_0, *for formulae of complexity* < 29.

Our proof uses a basic lemma from proof theory, due to G. Kreisel [**4**] that follows from Gentzen's work.

LEMMA 1. *Let A be any consistent axiom system in the language of 2nd order arithmetic that contains* EA *and such that the set of all axioms in A minus the axioms in* EA *form a set of sentences of bounded complexity. Then there is an instance of transfinite induction on our natural ordering of* ε_0 *which is not provable in A. In fact, the predicate which the unprovable (in A) transfinite induction is applied to can be taken to have only one free variable, the number variable on which the transfinite induction is being carried out. Moreover, this is best possible, in the sense that for each predicate Fn, (with possibly more free variables) and each m, we have that* $\mathrm{TI}(\varepsilon_0(\overline{m}), Fn)$ *is provable in* EA.

Unless explicitly stated otherwise, the only facts we shall use about the ordering ε_0 are 1) that the ordering is given by some recursive index e, 2) that, using e, lemma 1 holds. Hence, the theorem will hold for any ordering R, indexed by some e satisfying these conditions, in place of ε_0. Any R satisfying these conditions must be a well-ordering of type $\leqslant \varepsilon_0$.

Proof of theorem 1. We will suppose that we have a Π_1^1 sentence P, which is consistent with T. We write $T+P$ for $T+\{P\}$. We have to show that Σ_1^1-AC $+P$ is consistent. We do this by constructing a *model* of Σ_1^1-AC$+P$, assuming Con$(T+P)$.

We first note that since $T+P$ is consistent, by lemma 1 we get a particular instance of transfinite induction on ε_0, $\mathrm{TI}(\varepsilon_0; Fn)$, which is not provable in $T+P$. The induction is thought of as being performed on n as an element of the domain of the ordering ε_0. F will not have other free variables. Now consider $T+P+\sim TI(\varepsilon_0; Fn)$. We know it is consistent, and so it has a model, M. We are adding the *negation* of an instance of transfinite induction on ε_0. We are therefore considering a model of a false theory of analysis.

The reader should note that this model M has, *necessarily*, non-standard integers. We do not make use of this fact. We, instead, form a submodel N of M, in the sense that N will have the *same* 'integers' as M, but less 2nd order objects (functions). It this sense, we are using an inner model construction, and we are interpreting Σ_1^1–AC+P in $\boldsymbol{T}$+P+ $\sim$TI(ε_0; Fn).

Now let Gn be $(\forall k)$(if k is below n in ε_0 then Fk). We now come to the crucial step in the construction. We have $\sim TI(\varepsilon_0, Gn)$ holding in M. We will now form a simple *submodel* of M which we shall see satisfies Σ_1^1–AC+P. We take the submodel N to have the same integers as M. The functions in N will be the collection of all functions g in M such that M satisfies

$$(\exists n)(Gn \;\&\; (\exists h)(H_0(h, \varepsilon_0(n)) \;\&\; g \text{ is recursive in } h)).$$

At this point, we advise the reader to draw a vertical line representing the ordinals $< \varepsilon_0$ *according to* M. Then to note that the n with Gn do not have a l.u.b. in M. The reader should draw a wavy horizontal line through where the l.u.b. ought to have been. P is satisfied in N since N is a submodel of M and P is satisfied in M. N must satisfy EA since N is an inner model of M definable by a formula and EA is satisfied in M. To see that N satisfies Π_0^1–CA, use that M satisfies that every point in the ordering ε_0 has an (immediate) successor. This makes use of the transfinite induction on ε_0 that is part of $\boldsymbol{T}$.

We shall now show that N satisfies Σ_1^1–AC. Let $(\forall n)(\exists g)A(n, g, h)$, A arithmetical, h fixed in N, hold in N. A has no other free variables.

Now consider the predicate

$$\begin{aligned} Qm \leftrightarrow (\exists n)\{(\exists \alpha)(\exists g)(H_0(\alpha, \varepsilon_0(m)) \;\&\; g \text{ is recursive in } \alpha \;\&\; A(n, g, h)) \;\&\\ (\forall \alpha)(\forall g)(\forall r)\,((H_0(\alpha, \varepsilon_0(r)) \;\&\; g \text{ is recursive in } \alpha \;\&\; A(n, g, h))\\ \rightarrow r \text{ above } m \text{ or } r = m \text{ in } \varepsilon_0)\}. \end{aligned}$$

It is easily seen that M satisfies

$$\begin{aligned} (\exists! s)(\forall t)(((t \text{ above } s \text{ or } t = s \text{ in } \varepsilon_0) \rightarrow \sim Qt) \;\&\\ (t \text{ below } s \text{ in } \varepsilon_0 \rightarrow (\exists m)\; ((m \text{ above } t \text{ or } m = t) \;\&\; Qm))), \end{aligned}$$

since M satisfies TI on ε_0 for sufficiently complicated formulae, and the absoluteness of arithmetic properties. From the definition of N, it is clear that M satisfies

$$(\forall n)(n \text{ below the unique } s \rightarrow Gn),$$

again by absoluteness. But then M satisfies Gs. Now choose t as the first limit point in ε_0, $\geqslant s$ in ε_0. We can do this in M, by the transfinite induction on ε_0 available in $\boldsymbol{T}$. Then M will satisfy Gt. There is a $Z \in N$ such that N satisfies $H_0(Z, \varepsilon_0(t))$. Then N satisfies

$$(\forall n)(\exists g)(A(n, g, h) \;\&\; g \text{ is recursive in the pair } \langle Z, h\rangle).$$

So, by Π_0^1–CA, N satisfies $(\exists Y)(\forall n)A(n, (Y)_n, h)$, and we are done.

We now use the following refinement of lemma 1.

LEMMA 2. *Let A be any consistent axiom system in the language of 2nd order arithmetic, containing 1st order arithmetic. Furthermore suppose that all axioms of A which are instances of ordinary induction, are instances of induction applied to formulae of a certain bounded complexity, k. Also suppose that the axioms in A minus the axioms in* EA *have bounded complexity p as in lemma* 1. *Then one can find an instance of transfinite induction on $\varepsilon_0(G(k))$ applied to a predicate of complexity $F(p)$, which cannot be proved in A. G and F are primitive recursive functions on natural numbers. As in lemma* 1, *we can restrict the free variables to one in the transfinite induction.*

With this, we can obtain

THEOREM 2. *Any Σ_1^1 sentence provable in Σ_1^1–*AC *is already provable in* $(\Pi_0^1$–CA$)^{<\varepsilon_0}$.

An important point here is that the complexity of the induction is $F(p)$, so it depends only on p, not k. The proof of theorem 2 is the same as of theorem 1, except that the two systems are broken up into subsystems: Let $(\Sigma_1^1\text{–AC})_k$ be the same as Σ_1^1–AC, except that in EA, the induction is only applied to formulae of complexity k. Let T_n be the theory $(\Pi_0^1\text{–CA})^{\varepsilon_0(\boldsymbol{n})}$ + all instances of transfinite induction on $\varepsilon_0(\boldsymbol{n})$, for formulae of complexity < 29, *minus* ordinary induction. Let p be the complexity of $\bigcup_n T_n$ minus EA. (Π_0^1–AC can be axiomatized so that there is this bound $\bar{p}$). Then, in the same way as theorem 1 was proved from lemma 1, we can prove that every Σ_1^1 sentence provable in $(\Sigma_1^1\text{–AC})_k$ is provable in $T_{G(k \times F(p))}$ + ordinary induction applied to formulae of complexity $k \times F(p)$, using lemma 2. Now using condition (2) on the ordering ε_0, we see that each T_n is a subsystem of $(\Pi_0^1\text{–CA})^{<\varepsilon_0}$, and we have theorem 2. The addition of ordinary induction applied to formulae of complexity $k \times F(p)$ comes in when trying to show that the submodel satisfies ordinary induction applied to formulae of complexity k.

At the crucial point in the proof of theorem 1 we took the submodel N of M as the functions $g \in M$ such that M satisfies

$$(\exists n)(Gn \;\&\; (\exists h)(H_0(h, \varepsilon_0(n)) \;\&\; g \text{ recursive in } h)).$$

We can choose an $\alpha \in M$ and relativize this construction to the $g \in M$ such that M satisfies

$$(\exists n)(Gn \;\&\; (\exists h)(H_0^\alpha(h, \varepsilon_0(n)) \;\&\; g \text{ recursive in } h)).$$

In this way, we immediately obtain

THEOREM 3. *Any Π^1_2 sentence provable in Σ^1_1–AC is provable in $(\Pi^1_0\text{–CA})^{<\varepsilon_0}$.*

We now prove the analogue of theorem 1 for $k = 2$.

THEOREM 4. *Any Σ^1_1 sentence provable in Σ^1_2–AC is provable in $(\Pi^1_1\text{–CA})^{\varepsilon_0}+$ transfinite induction on ε_0 applied to all formulae of complexity < 29. Again call this theory* ***T***.

PROOF. Keeping the same notation as in the proof of theorem 1, we come to the assumption that N satisfies $(\forall n)(\exists g)A(n, g, h)$, $h \in N$, where A is now Π^1_1. The absoluteness assumption in the proof of theorem 1 was that for each $g \in N$, $A(n, g, h)$ holds in N if and only if it holds in M, and that for any $f \in N$, M satisfies $H_0(f, \varepsilon_0(n))$ if and only if N satisfies it. In this case, we have this too. The first is guaranteed by the Kleene basis theorem, which must hold in M since it is provable in Σ^1_2–AC. For Kleene's theorem says that the functions recursive in the complete Π^1_1 set in g satisfy the same Π^1_1 formulae with parameter g as do all the functions. Hence, any Σ^1_2 formula with parameters in N that holds in N will hold in M, because for any $g \in N$, the complete Π^1_1 set in g, *according to M*, is in N. We can, of course, take formulae that have number quantifiers to the left of the function quantifiers $\exists$, $\forall$, and this will still be true. Now, the predicate $H_1(f, \varepsilon_0(n))$ is indeed of this form. Now, for any $g \in N$, we have that the complete Π^1_1 set in g *according to M* is in N, and is also the complete Π^1_1 *set according to N*; also, if $H_1(f, \varepsilon_0, (n))$ holds in N for some particular $f \in N$, then it holds in M, and vice versa.

It is an easy matter, using this lifting of Σ^1_2 formulae from N to M and splitting into subsystems and lemma 2, to get

THEOREM 5. *Any Π^1_3 sentence provable in Σ^1_2–AC is provable in $(\Pi^1_1\text{–CA})^{<\varepsilon_0}$.*

We mention a result of *R.* Mansfield:

THEOREM 6. Δ^1_2–CA, Σ^1_2–AC, Σ^1_2–DC (*dependent choice*) *all have the same theorems.*

In the author's doctoral dissertation, we have

THEOREM 7. Δ^1_1–CA, Σ^1_1–AC, Σ^1_1–DC *have the same Π^1_2 theorems, and, incidentally, the same theorems about hyperarithmetic functions.*

LEMMA 3. *We can prove in Π^1_2–CA that every Π^1_2 formula with one free variable g which holds when the quantifiers are restricted to the functions recursive in the complete Π^1_2 set in g must hold when interpreted over all functions. In fact, we may weaken the hypothesis to insist only that we take the functions Δ^1_2 in g.*

This follows from a result of R. Mansfield that the Kondo uniformization theorem is provable in Δ_2^1–CA (and hence in Π_2^1–CA).

So we obtain

THEOREM 8. *Every* Π_4^1 *sentence provable in* Σ_3^1–AC *is provable in* $(\Pi_2^1\text{–CA})^{<\varepsilon_0}$.

We let $f \in L^g$ be an abbreviation for the natural formalization of 'f is constructible from g' in 2nd order arithmetic. Then there is a predicate $P(h, J, g)$, provably Δ_2^1 in Π_3^1–CA, such that we can prove $(\forall f)(f \in L^g) \rightarrow P(h, J, g)$ defines a well-ordering on all funtions, as a relation on h and J, in Π_3^1–CA. We obtain

LEMMA 4. *We can prove in* $\Pi_k^1\text{–CA} + (\exists g)(\forall f)(f \in L^g)$, $k > 2$, *that* $(\exists g)$ *(every* Σ_k^1 *formula with free variable h which holds, holds when the quantifiers are restricted to functions* Δ_k^1 *in the pair* $\langle h, g\rangle$*).*

From this, we obtain

LEMMA 5. *Every* Π_{k+2}^1 *sentence provable in* Σ_{k+1}^1–AC *is provable in* $(\Pi_k^1\text{–CA})^{<\varepsilon_0} + (\exists g)(\forall f)(f \in L^g)$, *for* $k > 2$.

In a paper in preparation, *The 2nd order comprehension axioms*, we will prove (among other things)

LEMMA 6. *Every* Π_4^1 *sentence provable in* $(\Pi_k^1\text{–CA})^{<\varepsilon_0} + (\exists g)(\forall f)(f \in L^g)$ *is provable in* $(\Pi_k^1\text{–CA})^{<\varepsilon_0}$, $k > 2$.

So we have

THEOREM 9. *Every* Π_4^1 *sentence provable in* Σ_{k+1}^1–AC *is provable in* $(\Pi_k^1\text{–CA})^{<\varepsilon_0}$, $k > 2$.

In the paper in preparation, we will also prove

LEMMA 7. *Every* Π_4^1 *sentence provable in* Σ_k^1–DC *is provable in* Δ_k^1–CA, $k > 2$.

To finish the THEOREM, we need

THEOREM 10. *Each* $(\Pi_k^1\text{–CA})^{<\varepsilon_0}$ *is a subsystem of* Σ_{k+1}^1–AC.

PROOF. We argue in Σ_{k+1}^1–AC. We let Qn be $(\forall g)(\exists f)(H_k^g(f, \varepsilon_0(n)))$. We wish to show that for each n, $Q\bar{n}$ is provable in Σ_{k+1}^1–AC. Fix an n. Choose an r above n in ε_0. Then r is, provably in Σ_{k+1}^1–AC, above n in ε_0, since ε_0 is recursively described. By lemma 1, transfinite induction on $\varepsilon_0(\boldsymbol{r})$ for any formula is provable in Σ_{k+1}^1–AC. Hence we can prove, in Σ_{k+1}^1–AC that n has an (immediate) successor. Let this successor be m. By using lemma 1, it suffices to prove in Σ^1_{k+1}–AC that $(\forall q)(q$ below p in $\varepsilon_0 \to Qq) \to Qp$, where p is below m. Arguing in Σ^1_{k+1}–AC, if p is the least point in ε_0, then Qp. If p has an (immediate) predecessor, q, then clearly $Qq \to Qp$, using Π^1_k–CA. If p is a limit, we assume $(\forall q)(q$ below $p \to Qq)$, and we define $X(n, g)$ as $n = \langle b, q\rangle$ & q is below p in ε_0 & $(\exists f)(H^g_k(f, \varepsilon_0(q))$ & $f(b) = 0)$. Let $Y(n, g)$ be $n = \langle b, q\rangle$ & q below p in ε_0 & $(\forall f)(H^g_k(f, \varepsilon_0(q)) \to f(b) = 0)$. Since p is below m, we can use transfinite induction on $\varepsilon_0(\boldsymbol{m})$ in Σ^1_{k+1}–AC to prove, in Σ^1_{k+1}–AC, that $X(n, g) \leftrightarrow Y(n, g)$. We can also find predicates $X^1(n, g)$, $Y^1(n, g)$, where X^1 is Σ^1_{k+1}, Y^1 is Π^1_{k+1}, and $X \leftrightarrow X^1$, $Y \leftrightarrow Y^1$ are provable in Σ^1_{k+1}–AC. Since Δ^1_{k+1}–CA $\subset \Sigma^1_{k+1}$–AC, we have, in Σ^1_{k+1}–AC, that $(\exists x)(\forall n)(n \in x \leftrightarrow X(n, g))$. Hence we have, in Σ^1_{k+1}–AC, that $(\exists f)(\forall n)$ $((f(n) = 0 \leftrightarrow X(n, g))$ & $(f(n) = 1 \leftrightarrow \sim X(n, g)))$. Hence we have Qp.

In Feferman's contribution [**1**] on the theories ID^ν, we have a formulation of the theory ID^e, where e is the recursive index of an ordering.

If we take the union of the systems $\mathrm{ID}^{\varepsilon_0(n)}$, we obtain the system $\mathrm{ID}^{<\varepsilon_0}$.

Now each P_A in $\mathrm{ID}^{<\varepsilon_0}$ has a standard interpretation as a function recursive in the unique f with $H_1(f, \varepsilon_0(\bar{n}))$, for some n. In this way, we can easily obtain

LEMMA 8. *Let A_0 be the usual positive predicate used in the standard inductive definition of O. Let n be such that $P_{A_0}(\boldsymbol{n})$ is provable in* $\mathrm{ID}^{<\varepsilon_0}$. *Then $\boldsymbol{n} \in O$ is provable in* $(\Pi^1_1\text{–CA})^{<\varepsilon_0}$.

By using the completeness of hyperjump among Π^1_1 predicates, a straightforward argument can be given, which is sketched in Feferman's contribution,

THEOREM 11. *For any n,* $\mathrm{ID}^{<\varepsilon_0}$ *proves $P_{A_0}(\boldsymbol{n})$ if and only if* $(\Pi^1_1\text{–CA})^{<\varepsilon_0}$ *proves $\boldsymbol{n} \in O$.*

This theorem 11, combined with theorems 5 and 6 give relationships between Σ^1_2–DC and $\mathrm{ID}^{<\varepsilon_0}$; in particular, that these theories have the same 'provable ordinals'.

When the ω-rule is added to the theories Σ^1_k–AC, analogous results may be obtained. In the theorem, the theories $(\Pi^1_k\text{–CA})^{<\omega_1}$ play the role of $(\Pi^1_k\text{–CA})^{<\varepsilon_0}$, where ω_1 is the first nonrecursive ordinal.

REFERENCES

[**1**] S. FEFERMAN, Formal theories for transfinite iterations of generalized inductive definitions and some subsystems of analysis, these proceedings, 303–326.

[**2**] H. FRIEDMAN, The 2nd order comprehension axioms, in preparation.

[**3**] H. FRIEDMAN, *Subsystems of set theory and analysis*, dissertation, Massachusetts Inst. Technology (August, 1967).

[**4**] G. KREISEL, A survey of proof theory, *J. Symb. Logic* **33** (1968) 321–388.

ASSIGNMENT OF ORDINALS TO TERMS FOR PRIMITIVE RECURSIVE FUNCTIONALS OF FINITE TYPE *

W. A. HOWARD

Introduction. Gentzen [**2**] showed that the consistency of first order (classical or intuitionistic) arithmetic can be proved by methods which are finitistic except for the use of the descending chain principle for the ordinals less than ε_0. On the other hand, Gödel [**4**] gave an interpretation of first order intuitionistic arithmetic $\mathscr{H}$ in a quantifier-free theory $\mathscr{T}$ of primitive recursive functionals of finite type, thereby reducing the consistency of $\mathscr{H}$ to that of $\mathscr{T}$.

In the following, the terms of $\mathscr{T}$ will be given in the λ-calculus provided with a finite type structure. We establish a direct connection between $\mathscr{T}$ and ε_0 by giving an assignment of ordinals less than ε_0 to the terms of $\mathscr{T}$ with the property that the reduction of a term (in the sense of λ-conversion) lowers the corresponding ordinal. Unfortunately we have been able to do this only for *restricted* reductions; i.e., reductions arising essentially from the contraction of closed subterms (§ 1). However, in § 4 we extend our result to the case of arbitrary reductions by the use of non-unique assignments of ordinals to terms. This allows us to assign to every reduction sequence of terms

$$A_1 \text{ red } A_2 \text{ red} \ldots \text{red } A_n \text{ red} \ldots$$

a corresponding descending sequence of ordinals

$$a_1 > a_2 > \ldots > a_n > \ldots.$$

If the ordinals less than ε_0 and the terms of $\mathscr{T}$ are enumerated in a natural way, our discussion can be formalized in Skolem (free variable, first order, primitive recursive) arithmetic. Thus the 'computability' of the

* Mention should be made of the paper of L. E. Sanchis, Functionals defined by recursion, *Notre Dame J. Formal Logic* **8** (1967) 161–174.

terms of $\mathscr{T}$ in the sense of Tait [5], namely the reducibility of each term of $\mathscr{T}$ to normal form, follows from the descending chain principle for the ordinals less than ε_0. Tait uses combinator-terms rather than λ-terms but it is easy to model combinators in the system of λ-terms.

Our treatment is developed in a rather general form because we intend in the future to extend our results to certain extensions of $\mathscr{T}$: in particular to type-zero-bar-recursive functionals. For extensions of $\mathscr{T}$, the ordinals less than ε_0 may no longer be adequate. Indeed, we shall show in the future that for the analysis of the extension of $\mathscr{T}$ just mentioned, the appropriate ordinals are those less than Bachmann's ordinal $\varphi_c(0)$, $c = \varepsilon_{\Omega+1}$ (as developed in H. Gerber's paper [3]).

1. Terms. The terms of $\mathscr{T}$ are obtained from the *prime terms* of $\mathscr{T}$ by applying the following operations finitely often.

(i). Application: from terms A and B get AB, with the restriction on the pair A, B given in clause (a) under ***Type levels*** below. The *interpretation* of AB is the value of the functional A when applied to the argument B.

(ii). λ-abstraction: from any variable X and term A get $\lambda X.A$.

Type levels. The general situation to which the method of the present paper applies is: one has a system of terms, generated as just described, in which it is possible to assign to each term A a non-negative integer level(A) in such a way that whenever AB is well-formed, level(A) > level(B) and level(A) $\geqslant$ level(AB). In the case of $\mathscr{T}$ this assignment is obtained by first assigning to each term A a *type symbol*, called the type of A, as follows. Type symbols are generated from a prime type symbol 0 by means of the operation: from type symbols σ and τ get the type symbol $(\sigma)\tau$. After type symbols are assigned to the prime terms of $\mathscr{T}$ (see ***Prime terms*** below) the assignment of type symbols to the remaining terms of $\mathscr{T}$ is determined by the following two clauses:

(a). If A has type $(\sigma)\tau$ and B has type σ, then AB is well-formed and has type τ.

(b). If the variable X has type σ and A has type τ, then $\lambda X.A$ is well-formed and has type $(\sigma)\tau$.

The *level* of a type symbol is defined inductively by the following two clauses:

(i). The level of the type symbol 0 is zero.

(ii). The level of $(\sigma)\tau$ is the maximum of $1+\text{level}(\sigma)$ and level(τ).

It is easily seen that every type symbol σ other than 0 has the form $(\sigma_1)\ldots(\sigma_n)0$ and that the level of σ is the maximum of

$$1+\text{level}(\sigma_1), \ldots, 1+\text{level}(\sigma_n).$$

The level of a term A is defined to be the level of the type symbol assigned to A.

The *length* of a term is defined by the following clauses:

(i). Prime terms have length 1.

(ii). The length of AB is length(A)+length(B).

(iii). The length of $\lambda X.A$ is $1+$length(A).

Prime terms. The prime terms of $\mathscr{T}$ are as follows:

(i). Variables of every type.

(ii). A numeral $\boldsymbol{n}$ of type 0 corresponding to each non-negative integer n.

(iii). A constant $\mathfrak{S}$ of type (0)0 for the successor function.

(iv). For each type symbol σ, a constant R of type $(0)((0)(\sigma)\sigma)(\sigma)\sigma$ for a 'primitive recursion functional'.

(v). For each type symbol σ and non-negative integer n, a constant $R^{\boldsymbol{n}}$ of type $((0)(\sigma)\sigma)(\sigma)\sigma$ for a 'restricted primitive recursion functional'.

Free and bound variables. In the generation of terms by the two processes of application and λ-abstraction, the (possibly vacuous) occurrences of a variable X in a term are said to be *free* until the stage is reached where the operation λX is applied; thus the free occurrences of X in a term A become bound occurrences in $\lambda X.A$. A term is said to be *closed* if it has no non-vacuous occurrences of a free variable.

Subform and subterm. In order to define the notion of subform, let $|B|$ denote the set of subforms of a term B. Then

(i). $|B| = \{B\}$ if B is prime.

(ii). $|AB| = |A| \cup |B| \cup \{AB\}$.

(iii). $|\lambda X.A| = |A| \cup \{\lambda X.A\}$.

The notion of *subterm* is defined similarly except that clause (iii) (where $|A|$ now stands for the set of subterms of A) is replaced by the clause

(iii)*. $|\lambda X.A| = (|A| \cup \{\lambda X.A\}) - \mathfrak{X}$,

where $\mathfrak{X}$ denotes the set of all those subterms of A which contain a (non-vacuous) free occurrence of X.

Notation. For terms A, B and C, ABC denotes $(AB)C$. More generally, $A_1A_2A_3 \ldots A_k$ denotes $(\ldots(A_1A_2)A_3\ldots)A_k$. The result of substituting a term B for all free occurrences of a variable X in A is denoted by $[B/X]A$.

Contractions. In the following schemata, A contr B means: A contracts into B.

(i). λ-contraction: $(\lambda X.A)B$ contr $[B/X]A$ so long as no free occurrence of a variable in B becomes bound in $[B/X]A$.

(ii). $\mathfrak{S}\boldsymbol{n}$ contr $\boldsymbol{n}+1$.

(iii). $R\boldsymbol{n}$ contr $R^{\boldsymbol{n}}$.

(iva). R^0HG contr G.

(ivb). $R^{\boldsymbol{n}+1}HG$ contr $H\boldsymbol{n}(R^{\boldsymbol{n}}HG)$.

Restricted reductions. A red B if B arises from A by contracting one occurrence of a sub*term* of A.

General reductions. A red B if B arises from A by contracting one occurrence of a sub*form* of A.

Motivation for our formulation. In case our formulation of the terms of $\mathscr{T}$ appears peculiar, the following motivation should be borne in mind. As mentioned in the introduction, the results of the present paper, together with the descending chain principle for the ordinals less than ε_0, yield the computability of the terms of $\mathscr{T}$; i.e., the reducibility of each term A to an irreducible term: the so-called normal form of A. Thus in the present paper we are concerned with an analysis of the *terms* of $\mathscr{T}$, whereas $\mathscr{T}$ as a *formal system* contains equations between terms and propositional combinations of such equations. Once the computability of the closed terms of $\mathscr{T}$ has been established, *then* intensional equality can be introduced: two terms are said to be intensionally equal if they have normal forms which are congruent (i.e., the same except for changes of bound variables). For this purpose it is necessary to be assured that two normal forms of the same term are congruent. Tait [5] achieves this by imposing a rule which uniquely determines for each term A the subterm of A that is allowed to be contracted in reducing A. For more general reduction procedures, the uniqueness (up to congruence) of the normal form of a term is assured by a well-known theorem of Church and Rosser.

The notion of intensional equality, just described, provides a truth valuation for the closed formulae of $\mathscr{T}$ (i.e. propositional combinations of equations between closed terms). Thus one gets a proof-theoretic analysis of the system $\mathscr{T}^c$ obtained by restricting $\mathscr{T}$ to closed formulae. Finally one gets a proof-theoretic analysis of $\mathscr{T}$ itself from the observation that a proof in $\mathscr{T}$ can be transformed into a proof in $\mathscr{T}^c$ by replacing all free variables by suitable constants, starting from the end of the proof and working back, the induction rule in $\mathscr{T}$ being eliminated by the calculation of numerical constants.

In the discussion of $\mathscr{T}$ (and its extensions), we permit any methods formalizable in Skolem (free variable, first order, primitive recursive) arithmetic. Hence sets of axioms of the form A contr B are permissible so long as the number of B (in a natural enumeration of terms) is a primitive recursive function of the number of A.

In view of the motivation just described, the contractions given above for the constants R and R^n are sufficient; i.e., it is not necessary to require the stronger contraction $\lambda x.R(\mathfrak{S}x)HG$ contr $\lambda x.Hx(RxHG)$.

2. A theory $\mathscr{E}$ of expressions

Introduction. In the present section we introduce a theory $\mathscr{E}$ whose objects are *expressions*. Expressions are generated from constants and from variables x_j^r by two operations: from expressions f and g obtain $f+g$ and (f, g). By a *vector of level n* is meant an $n+1$-tuple $\boldsymbol{h} = \langle h_0, \ldots, h_n \rangle$ of expressions h_i. We introduce operations $\square$ and δ^r which produce vectors $\boldsymbol{f} \square \boldsymbol{g}$ and $\delta^r \boldsymbol{f}$ from vectors $\boldsymbol{f}$, $\boldsymbol{g}$.

The motivation of the present section is as follows. In § 3 we shall define a mapping from the terms of $\mathscr{T}$ into vectors which assigns to each term of type level n a vector of the same level. In particular, to the variable X^r of type level n is assigned the vector $\boldsymbol{x}^r = \langle x_0^r, \ldots, x_n^r \rangle$, it being assumed that the variables of $\mathscr{T}$ have been enumerated: $X^0, X^1, \ldots, X^r, \ldots$. More generally, the presence of a free variable X^r in a term H is reflected by the presence of the variables $x_0^r, \ldots, x_n^r$ in some of the components h_i of the vector $\boldsymbol{h}$ assigned to H. It is crucial, however, that x_j^r is not contained in h_k for $k > j$ (i.e. $\boldsymbol{h}$ belongs to the class $\boldsymbol{C}$ defined in the present section). If $\boldsymbol{f}$ and $\boldsymbol{g}$ are assigned to F and G, respectively, then to FG is assigned the vector $\boldsymbol{h}$, of the proper level, whose components are equal to the corresponding components of $\boldsymbol{f} \square \boldsymbol{g}$. If $\boldsymbol{h}$ is assigned to H, then $\delta^r \boldsymbol{h}$ is assigned to $\lambda X^r.H$. Thus δ^r is a kind of 'abstraction' operator which maps a vector $\boldsymbol{h}$ which contains the variables x_j^r into another vector $\delta^r \boldsymbol{h}$ which does not contain the variables x_j^r.

As will be mentioned in the present section, the theory $\mathscr{E}$ of expressions has *interpretations* in which the constants are ordinals and the variables range over a set of ordinals (or ordinal notations). In such interpretations an expression is interpreted as a function (more precisely: intensional function) of the variables that it contains.

In § 3 by the expression assigned to H is meant the initial component h_0 of the vector $\boldsymbol{h}$ assigned to H. When expressions are interpreted by means of ordinals the expression h_0 becomes an ordinal if H is closed, and this is taken to be the ordinal assigned to H.

The theory $\mathscr{E}$. We construct expressions from: constants, variables x_j^r, the symbol $+$, and the symbol $(\cdot, \cdot)$ as follows:

(i). A constant is an expression.

(ii). A variable x_j^r is an expression.

(iii). If f and g are expressions, so are $f+g$ and (f, g).

It is assumed that among the constants of $\mathscr{E}$ there are three constants denoted by 0, 1 and ω.

The theory $\mathscr{E}$ is an axiomatic theory of a relation $\prec$ between expressions. Equality between expressions is treated axiomatically: it is assumed to be reflexive and to obey the replacement axiom. $f \succ g$ means $g \prec f$. $f \preccurlyeq g$ means: $f \prec g$ or $f = g$.

Axioms for $\mathscr{E}$

2.1. If $f \prec g$ and $g \prec h$, then $f \prec h$.

2.2. If $f \prec g$, then $f \neq g$.

2.3. $f+g = g+f$; $f+(g+h) = (f+g)+h$.

2.4. If $f \prec g$, then $f+h \prec g+h$.

2.5. $f+g = f$ if and only if $g = 0$.

2.6. $0 \preccurlyeq f$; $0 \prec 1 \prec \omega$.

2.7. If $f \prec \omega$ and $g \prec \omega$, then $f+g \prec \omega$.

2.8. $(f, g+h) = (f, g)+(f, h)$.

2.9. If $g \prec c$ and $h \prec c$, then $(g,f)+(h,f) \preccurlyeq (c,f)$.

2.10. If $f \prec g$, then $(h,f) \prec (h, g)$.

2.11. If $f \prec g$ and $h \neq 0$, then $(f, h) \prec (g, h)$.

2.12. $(0,f) = f$.

2.13. $(f, (g, h)) = (f+g, h)$.

From 2.5 and 2.8 it is easy to prove: $(f, 0) = 0$. From 2.4, 2.5 and 2.9 it is easy to prove

2.14. If $g \succ 0$ and $h \succ 0$, then $(g,f)+(h,f) \preccurlyeq (g+h,f)$.

Interpretation of $\mathscr{E}$. For the analysis of primitive recursive functionals in § 3, the following interpretation of $\mathscr{E}$ is used. The variables range over ordinals (or ordinal notations) less than ε_0; expressions are interpreted as functions, of the variables contained in them, in a manner to be described presently; $a \prec b$ is interpreted as meaning: $a < b$ (the ordinary ordering of the ordinals) for all values of the variables. $a+b$ is interpreted as the natural (i.e. Hessenberg) sum $a \# b$ which is defined as follows (Bachmann **[1]**):

Represent a and b in Cantor normal form $a = \omega^{a_1} + \ldots + \omega^{a_n}$ and $b = \omega^{b_1} + \ldots + \omega^{b_m}$, where $a_1 \geqslant \ldots \geqslant a_n$ and $b_1 \geqslant \ldots \geqslant b_m$; then

$$a \# b = \omega^{c_1} + \ldots + \omega^{c_{n+m}},$$

where the sequence $c_1 \geqslant \ldots \geqslant c_{n+m}$ is a rearrangement of the sequence $a_1, \ldots, a_n, b_1, \ldots, b_m$.

To define (a, b) in the case $b \neq 0$, represent b in Cantor normal form to the base 2: $b = 2^{b_1} + \ldots + 2^{b_n}$, where $b_1 > \ldots > b_n$. Then take (a, b) to be $2^{c_1} + \ldots 2^{c_n}$, where $c_i = a \# b_i$ $(1 \leqslant i \leqslant n)$. Finally take $(a, 0)$ to be 0.

It is easy to see that this interpretation satisfies the axioms 2.1–2.13.

Expression vectors. If $f_0, \ldots, f_n$ are expressions, the $n+1$-tuple $\boldsymbol{f} = \langle f_0, \ldots, f_n \rangle$ is called a *vector of level n*; and for $0 \leqslant i \leqslant n$ the expression f_i is called the ith *component* of $\boldsymbol{f}$. We also use $(\boldsymbol{f})_i$ to denote the ith component of $\boldsymbol{f}$. If $i >$ level$(\boldsymbol{f})$ then $(\boldsymbol{f})_i$ is defined to be 0. We shall often write f_i for $(\boldsymbol{f})_i$. We define $\boldsymbol{f}+\boldsymbol{g}$ to be the vector $\boldsymbol{h}$ of level max {level($\boldsymbol{f}$), level($\boldsymbol{g}$)} such that $h_i = f_i + g_i$ $(0 \leqslant i \leqslant \text{level}(\boldsymbol{h}))$.

The operation $\boldsymbol{f} \,\square\, \boldsymbol{g}$. Let n denote max {level($\boldsymbol{f}$), level($\boldsymbol{g}$)}. Then $\boldsymbol{f} \,\square\, \boldsymbol{g}$ is defined to be the vector $\boldsymbol{h} = \langle h_0, \ldots, h_n \rangle$ such that

$$h_n = f_n + g_n,$$

$$h_i = (h_{i+1}, f_i + g_i) \quad \text{for } 0 \leqslant i \leqslant n.$$

Clearly $\boldsymbol{f} \,\square\, \boldsymbol{g} = \boldsymbol{g} \,\square\, \boldsymbol{f}$, by axiom 2.3.

The following four lemmas are easy to prove from axioms 2.1–2.13 by downward induction on i.

LEMMA 2.1. *If $f_i \succ 0$ for all $i \leqslant n$, then $(\boldsymbol{f} \,\square\, \boldsymbol{g})_i \succ 0$ for all $i \leqslant n$.*

LEMMA 2.2. *$(\boldsymbol{f} \,\square\, \boldsymbol{g})_i \succcurlyeq f_i$ for all i.*

LEMMA 2.3. *Assume* level($\boldsymbol{f}$) = level($\boldsymbol{g}$) = n, *and* $f_i \succcurlyeq g_i$ *for* $0 \leqslant i \leqslant n$. *Then* $(\boldsymbol{f} \,\square\, \boldsymbol{h})_i \succcurlyeq (\boldsymbol{g} \,\square\, \boldsymbol{h})_i$ *for all* i.

LEMMA 2.4. *Under the assumption of lemma* 2.3 *and the additional assumption* $f_i \succ g_i$ *for* $0 \leqslant i \leqslant k$, *some* $k \leqslant n$, *we have*: $(\boldsymbol{f} \,\square\, \boldsymbol{h})_i \succ (\boldsymbol{g} \,\square\, \boldsymbol{h})_i$ *for* $0 \leqslant i \leqslant k$.

We now prove:

LEMMA 2.5. *Assume* level($\boldsymbol{f}$) = level($\boldsymbol{g}$) = $n+1$ > level($\boldsymbol{h}$) *and* $f_i \succ 0$, $g_i \succ 0$ *for* $0 \leqslant i \leqslant n+1$. *Then*

$$(\boldsymbol{f} \,\square\, \boldsymbol{h})_i + (\boldsymbol{g} \,\square\, \boldsymbol{h})_i \preccurlyeq ((\boldsymbol{f}+\boldsymbol{g}) \,\square\, \boldsymbol{h})_i \quad \textit{for } 0 \leqslant i \leqslant n+1.$$

PROOF. The proof is by downward induction on i. The lemma is clearly true for $i = n+1$. To obtain the induction step, let $\boldsymbol{a}$, $\boldsymbol{b}$ and c_i denote $\boldsymbol{f} \,\square\, \boldsymbol{h}$, $\boldsymbol{g} \,\square\, \boldsymbol{h}$ and $f_i + g_i + h_i$, respectively. Observe that by lemma 2.1 $a_{i+1} \succ 0$ and $b_{i+1} \succ 0$ for all $i < n+1$. Hence by 2.14

$$(a_{i+1}, c_i) + (b_{i+1}, c_i) \preccurlyeq (a_{i+1} + b_{i+1}, c_i).$$

It is easy to see that

$$(\boldsymbol{f} \,\square\, \boldsymbol{h})_i + (\boldsymbol{g} \,\square\, \boldsymbol{h})_i \prec (a_{i+1}, c_i) + (b_{i+1}, c_i),$$

whereas by induction hypothesis

$$a_{i+1} + b_{i+1} \preccurlyeq ((\boldsymbol{f}+\boldsymbol{g}) \,\square\, \boldsymbol{h})_{i+1},$$

so

$$(a_{i+1} + b_{i+1}, c_i) \preccurlyeq ((\boldsymbol{f}+\boldsymbol{g}) \,\square\, \boldsymbol{h})_i.$$

Notation. kf denotes $f + \ldots + f$ (k summands).

LEMMA 2.6. *Let the assumptions be as in lemma* 2.5. *Let* $\boldsymbol{d}$ *be a vector such that* $2f_{n+1} + 2g_{n+1} \prec d_{n+1}$ *and* $f_i + g_i \preccurlyeq d_i$ *for all* $i \leqslant n$. *Then*

$$2((\boldsymbol{f} \,\square\, \boldsymbol{h}) \,\square\, (\boldsymbol{g} \,\square\, \boldsymbol{h}))_i \prec (\boldsymbol{d} \,\square\, \boldsymbol{h})_i \quad \textit{for all } i \leqslant n+1.$$

PROOF. Let $\boldsymbol{a}$, $\boldsymbol{b}$ and c_i denote $\boldsymbol{f} \,\square\, \boldsymbol{h}$, $\boldsymbol{g} \,\square\, \boldsymbol{h}$ and $f_i + g_i + h_i$, respectively. Let $\boldsymbol{e}$ denote $\boldsymbol{a} \,\square\, \boldsymbol{b}$. The induction hypothesis is $2e_{i+1} \prec (\boldsymbol{d} \,\square\, \boldsymbol{h})_{i+1}$ for a given $i < n+1$. We must prove $2e_i \prec (\boldsymbol{d} \,\square\, \boldsymbol{h})_i$. Observe that

$$a_i + b_i = (a_{i+1}, f_i + h_i) + (b_{i+1}, g_i + h_i).$$

Hence

$$a_i + b_i \prec (a_{i+1}, c_i) + (b_{i+1}, c_i).$$

But $e_i = (e_{i+1}, a_i+b_i)$. Hence by use of the axioms 2.10, 2.8 and 2.13 we conclude

$$e_i \prec (e_{i+1}+a_{i+1}, c_i)+(e_{i+1}+b_{i+1}, c_i).$$

By lemma 2.1 $b_{i+1} \succ 0$. Also $e_{i+1} \succcurlyeq a_{i+1}+b_{i+1}$. Hence $e_{i+1} \succ a_{i+1}$. Similarly $e_{i+1} \succ b_{i+1}$. Hence $e_i \prec (2e_{i+1}, c_i)$ by axiom 2.9. Hence $2e_i \prec ((\boldsymbol{d} \,\square\, \boldsymbol{h})_{i+1}, c_i)$ by the induction hypothesis and axiom 2.9. The desired result $2e_i \prec (\boldsymbol{d} \,\square\, \boldsymbol{h})_i$ now follows from $c_i \preccurlyeq d_i+h_i$.

The classes C_i and C. Recall that the variables occurring in *expressions* are taken from a list of variables x_i^r. We now define the classes C_i of expressions by four clauses.

Starting clauses:

(i). If the expression h contains no variables, then h is in C_i.

(ii). For every r, the variable x_i^r is in C_i.

Inductive clauses:

(iii). If f and g are in C_i, then so is $f+g$.

(iv). If f is in C_{i+1} and g is in C_i, then (f, g) is in C_i.

A crucial property of expressions in C_i is given by the following lemma.

LEMMA 2.7. *If h is in C_i then h contains no variable x_j^r such that $j < i$.*

PROOF. By induction on the number of applications of clauses (iii) and (iv) in the definition of the classes C_i.

The class $\boldsymbol{C}$ is defined to consist of all vectors $\boldsymbol{h}$ such that $(\boldsymbol{h})_i$ is in C_i $(0 \leqslant i \leqslant \text{level}(\boldsymbol{h}))$.

LEMMA 2.8. *If $\boldsymbol{f}$ and $\boldsymbol{g}$ are in $\boldsymbol{C}$, then so is $\boldsymbol{f} \,\square\, \boldsymbol{g}$.*

PROOF. Immediate from clauses (iii) and (iv) in the definition of the classes C_i.

Notation. $[e/x_j^r]h$ denotes the result of substituting e for all occurrences of x_j^r in the expression h.

LEMMA 2.9. *Suppose e is in C_j. Then the operation of substituting e for x_j^r transforms each class C_i into itself $(i = 0, 1, 2, \ldots)$.*

PROOF. We must prove the assertion: for all i and all h, if h is in C_i then $[e/x_j^r]h$ is in C_i. It is easy to verify this assertion if h is as in clauses (i) or (ii), and then prove the assertion by induction on the number of applications of clauses (iii) and (iv) in the formation of h.

The operation δ^r. It will now be assumed that by means of a function $n(r)$ we have obtained a list of vector variables $\boldsymbol{x}^r = \langle x_0^r, \ldots, x_{n(r)}^r \rangle$ $(r = 0, 1, 2, \ldots)$. To each h in $\bigcup C_i$ we associate a vector $\delta^r h$ in $\boldsymbol{C}$, such that $\delta^r h$ has level $n(r)+1$ and does not contain any component of $\boldsymbol{x}^r$, as follows. In order to avoid ambiguity in clause (a), below, we shall regard h in C_i as being completely given only when the particular C_i, to which h belongs, is specified.

Starting clauses:

(a). If h is in C_i and contains no component of $\boldsymbol{x}^r$, then $\delta^r h$ is the vector of level $n(r)$ such that $(\delta^r h)_i = h+1$ and $(\delta^r h)_j = 1$ when $j \neq i$, $0 \leqslant j \leqslant n(r)+1$.

(b). If h is x_i^r, then $(\delta^r h)_j = 1$ $(0 \leqslant j \leqslant n(r)+1)$.

Inductive clauses:

(c). If h contains a component of $\boldsymbol{x}^r$ and $h = f+g$, where f and g are in C_i, then $\delta^r h = \delta^r f + \delta^r g$.

(d). If h contains a component of $\boldsymbol{x}^r$ and $h = (f, g)$, where f is in C_{i+1} and g is in C_i, then

$$(\delta^r h)_j = (\delta^r f)_j + (\delta^r g)_j \quad \text{if } 0 \leqslant j \leqslant n(r),$$

and

$$(\delta^r h)_j = 2(\delta^r f)_j + 2(\delta^r g)_j + 1 \quad \text{if } j = n(r)+1.$$

We also define δ^r as acting on *vectors* $\boldsymbol{h} = \langle h_0, \ldots, h_p \rangle$ in $\boldsymbol{C}$ as follows:

$$(\delta^r \boldsymbol{h})_j = (\delta^r h_0)_j + \ldots + (\delta^r h_p)_j \quad \text{if } 0 \leqslant j \leqslant n(r)+1,$$

and

$$(\delta^r \boldsymbol{h})_j = h_j + 1 \quad \text{if } n(r)+1 < j \leqslant p.$$

By lemma 2.7 $\delta^r h$ contains no component of $\boldsymbol{x}^r$.

LEMMA 2.10. *Suppose e is in* C_j *and contains no component of* $\boldsymbol{x}^r$. *Suppose* $s \neq r$. *Then for any h in* $\bigcup C_i$

$$\delta^r [e/x_j^s] h = [e/x_j^s] \delta^r h.$$

PROOF. By induction on the number of applications of clauses (iii) and (iv) in the definition of δ^r.

COROLLARY. *Suppose* $\boldsymbol{e}$ *is in* $\boldsymbol{C}$ *and contains no component of* $\boldsymbol{x}^r$. *Suppose* $s \neq r$. *Then for any* $\boldsymbol{h}$ *in* $\boldsymbol{C}$

$$\delta^r [\boldsymbol{e}/\boldsymbol{x}^s] \boldsymbol{h} = [\boldsymbol{e}/\boldsymbol{x}^s] \delta^r \boldsymbol{h}.$$

(We assume level$(\boldsymbol{x}^s)$ = level$(\boldsymbol{e})$.)

LEMMA 2.11. *Let* $\boldsymbol{e}$ *be a vector of level* $n(r)$ *and assume* h *is in* C_i. *Then* $((\delta^r h) \square \boldsymbol{e})_i \succ [\boldsymbol{e}/\boldsymbol{x}^r]h$.

PROOF. By induction on the number of applications of clauses (iii) and (iv) in the definition of δ^r. Clause (iii) is handled by lemma 2.5. Clause (iv) is handled by lemma 2.6. Namely, suppose $h = (f, g)$, where f is in C_{i+1} and g is in C_i. Denote $(\delta^r f) \square \boldsymbol{e}$ and $(\delta^r g) \square \boldsymbol{e}$ by $\boldsymbol{u}$ and $\boldsymbol{v}$, respectively. Then $((\delta^r h) \square \boldsymbol{e})_i \succcurlyeq (\boldsymbol{u} \square \boldsymbol{v})_i$ by lemma 2.6. But $(\boldsymbol{u} \square \boldsymbol{v})_i \succcurlyeq (u_{i+1}, v_i) \succ (f, g)$, since $u_{i+1} \succ f$ and $v_i \succ g$ by induction hypothesis.

COROLLARY. *If* $\boldsymbol{h}$ *is in* $\boldsymbol{C}$ *and* $\boldsymbol{e}$ *has level* $n(r)$, *then* $((\delta^r \boldsymbol{h}) \square \boldsymbol{e})_i \succ ([\boldsymbol{e}/\boldsymbol{x}^r]\boldsymbol{h})_i$ *for all* $i \leqslant$ *level*$(\boldsymbol{h})$.

LEMMA 2.12. *Let* a, b *and* h *be expressions. Suppose* $a \succ b$. *Then* $[a/x_i^r]h \succcurlyeq [b/x_i^r]h$.

PROOF. By induction on the number of times the operations (iii) under ***Expressions*** above are used in building up h.

LEMMA 2.13. *Let* a, b *and* h *be expressions. Suppose* $a \succ b$. *Suppose further that* h *is in* C_0 *and that* x_0^r *is contained in* h *non-vacuously. Then* $[a/x_0^r]h \succ [b/x_0^r]h$.

PROOF. By induction on the number of times the operations (iii) and (iv) under ***The classes*** C_i ***and*** C above are used in building up h. In particular, when h is (f, g), where $f \in C_1$ and $g \in C_0$, we know by lemma 2.7 that x_0^r is contained non-vacuously in g; so axiom 2.10 can be applied.

3. Assignment to terms of $\mathscr{T}$. The main discussion in this and the following section applies not only to $\mathscr{T}$ but to any extension $\mathscr{U}$ of $\mathscr{T}$. Of course we treat only the contractions given in § 1; i.e. λ-contractions and the contractions peculiar to $\mathscr{T}$. It is assumed that the terms of $\mathscr{U}$ have been provided with type levels satisfying the conditions given in § 1; namely, whenever FG is well-formed, then level$(F) >$ level(G) and level$(F) \geqslant$ $\geqslant$ level(FG). Indeed, more generally, we need make no restriction on the formation of terms FG so long as we allow the contraction of FG only when the above conditions on the type levels are satisfied.

If a term H of $\mathscr{U}$ is not of the form FG or $\lambda X.F$, then H is said to be prime. In the present section we shall make assignments of vectors to the prime terms of $\mathscr{T}$ and shall give prescriptions for passing from the assignment of vectors to F and G to the assignment of vectors to FG and $\lambda X.F$. Hence for our assignment to be complete it is necessary to have, in addition, a prescription for assigning vectors to the prime terms of $\mathscr{U}$ which are not prime terms of $\mathscr{T}$. For the purpose of this and the following section we need only assume that such a prescription exists and satisfies the condition that if $\boldsymbol{h}$ is assigned to the prime term H of level n, then $h_i \succ 0$ for all $i \leqslant n$.

It is assumed that the variables of $\mathscr{U}$ have been enumerated: $X^0, X^1, \ldots, X^r, \ldots$, and that the vector variables $\boldsymbol{x}^r$ of § 2 have been listed in such a way that $\boldsymbol{x}^r$ has the same level as X^r. We shall assign to each term F in $\mathscr{U}$ a vector $\boldsymbol{f}$ in $\boldsymbol{C}$ such that level$(\boldsymbol{f})$ = level(F). By the *expression* assigned to F is meant the initial component f_0 of the vector $\boldsymbol{f}$ assigned to F.

Assignment to prime terms of $\mathscr{T}$

(i). To the variable X^r is assigned $\boldsymbol{x}^r$.

(ii). To the numeral $\boldsymbol{n}$ is assigned $\langle 1 \rangle$.

(iii). To the constant $\mathfrak{S}$ for the successor function is assigned $\langle 1, 1 \rangle$.

(iv). To the primitive recursion constant R of type level n is assigned the vector $\langle 1, \ldots, 1, \omega \rangle$ of level n.

(v). To the 'restricted primitive recursion' constant R^k of type level n is assigned the vector $\langle 1, \ldots, 1, 2(k+1) \rangle$ of level n.

Terms formed by application. Suppose $\boldsymbol{f}$ and $\boldsymbol{g}$ have been assigned to terms F and G, respectively; and that FG is well-formed and has type level n. Then to FG is assigned the vector $\boldsymbol{h}$ such that $(\boldsymbol{h})_i = (\boldsymbol{f} \,\square\, \boldsymbol{g})_i$ $(0 \leqslant i \leqslant n)$.

Terms formed by λ-abstraction. Suppose $\boldsymbol{h}$ has been assigned to the term H. Then to $\lambda X^r.H$ is assigned the vector $\delta^r \boldsymbol{h}$, where δ^r is the operator defined in § 2.

LEMMA 3.1. *Let X^s be a free variable of H. Let F be a term of the same type as X^s and assume no free variable of F becomes bound in $[F/X^s]H$. Suppose $\boldsymbol{f}$ and $\boldsymbol{h}$ are vectors assigned to F and H, respectively. Then $[\boldsymbol{f}/\boldsymbol{x}^s]\boldsymbol{h}$ is a vector assigned to $[F/X^s]H$.*

PROOF. By induction on the number of times the operations of application and λ-abstraction are used in building up H from prime terms. To handle λ-abstraction, suppose H is $\lambda X^r.G$, where $r \neq s$. Then $\delta^r \boldsymbol{g}$ is assigned to H, where $\boldsymbol{g}$ is the vector assigned to G. By induction hypothesis $[\boldsymbol{f}/\boldsymbol{x}^s]\boldsymbol{g}$ is assigned to $[F/X^s]G$. Hence from the fact that $\lambda X^r.[F/X^s]G$ is $[F/X^s]H$ we conclude that $\delta^r[\boldsymbol{f}/\boldsymbol{x}^s]\boldsymbol{g}$ is assigned to the latter term. But by lemma 2.10 and corollary $\delta^r[\boldsymbol{f}/\boldsymbol{x}^s]\boldsymbol{g} = [\boldsymbol{f}/\boldsymbol{x}^s]\delta^r \boldsymbol{g}$.

Addition of constants R^v ***to*** $\mathscr{T}$. Besides the constants $R^{\boldsymbol{n}}$, let us introduce a constant R^v, of the same type, for each expression v. To R^v assign the vector $\langle 1, \ldots, 1, 2(v+1)\rangle$ of the appropriate level.

LEMMA 3.2. *Let* $\boldsymbol{e}$ *and* $\boldsymbol{f}$ *be the vectors assigned to* $H0(R^vHG)$ *and* $R^{v+1}HG$, *respectively. Then* $e_i \prec f_i$ *for* $0 \leqslant i \leqslant$ *level*$(\boldsymbol{e})$.

PROOF. Let n denote level$(\boldsymbol{e})$; so G, H and R^v have levels n, $n+1$ and $n+2$, respectively. Let $\boldsymbol{a}$ be the vector of level $n+1$ defined as follows: $a_{n+1} = 1+h_{n+1}$ and $a_i = (a_{i+1}, 1+h_{i+1})$ for $0 \leqslant i \leqslant n$. Let $\boldsymbol{b}$, $\boldsymbol{c}$ and $\boldsymbol{t}$ be the vectors assigned to R^vH, G and R^vHG, respectively. Then for $i \leqslant n$

$$e_i \preccurlyeq (\boldsymbol{a} \,\square\, \boldsymbol{t})_i \preccurlyeq (\boldsymbol{a} \,\square\, (\boldsymbol{b} \,\square\, \boldsymbol{c}))_i.$$

Clearly $a_i \preccurlyeq (\boldsymbol{a} \,\square\, \boldsymbol{c})_i$ for all $i \leqslant$ level$(\boldsymbol{a})$. Hence $e_i \preccurlyeq ((\boldsymbol{a} \,\square\, \boldsymbol{c}) \,\square\, (\boldsymbol{b} \,\square\, \boldsymbol{c}))_i$ for all $i \leqslant n$. Hence it is sufficient to prove $((\boldsymbol{a} \,\square\, \boldsymbol{c}) \,\square\, (\boldsymbol{b} \,\square\, \boldsymbol{c}))_i \prec (\boldsymbol{d} \,\square\, \boldsymbol{c})_i$ for all $i \leqslant n+1$, where $\boldsymbol{d}$ is the vector assigned to $R^{v+1}H$. By lemma 2.1 $b_i \succ 0$ for $i \leqslant n+1$. Clearly $a_i \succ 0$ for $i \leqslant n+1$. Hence by lemma 2.6 it is sufficient to prove

$$2a_{n+1} + 2b_{n+1} \prec d_{n+1}, \tag{3.1}$$

$$a_i + b_i \preccurlyeq d_i \quad \text{for } i \leqslant n+1. \tag{3.2}$$

To prove (3.1) observe $2a_{n+1} = 2(0, 1+h_{n+1}) \preccurlyeq (1, 1+h_{n+1})$ by axiom 2.9; and $2b_{n+1} \preccurlyeq (2v+3, 1+h_{n+1})$ by axiom 2.9. Hence $2a_{n+1}+2b_{n+1} \prec 2(2v+3, 1+h_{n+1}) \preccurlyeq d_{n+1}$ by axiom 2.9. To prove (3.2) by downward induction on i, observe that for $i \leqslant n$, a_i+b_i is equal to

$$(a_{i+1}, 1+h_i)+(b_{i+1}, 1+h_i).$$

Hence $a_i+b_i \preccurlyeq (a_{i+1}+b_{i+1}, 1+h_i)$ by 2.14. Hence, by induction hypothesis, $a_i+b_i \preccurlyeq (d_{i+1}, 1+h_i) = d_i$.

Remark. In lemma 3.2 it would be desirable to replace R^{v+1} by R^w such that $w \succ v$. The difficulty would then arise, in the present proof, of establishing (3.1). This difficulty vanishes if we assume that $\mathscr{E}$ has the property $4(x, y) \preccurlyeq (z, y)$ whenever $x \prec z$. This property holds for the interpretation of $\mathscr{E}$ given in § 2 if, in the definition of (a, b), one uses the Cantor normal form to a base greater than or equal to 4 instead of 2.

THEOREM 3.1. *Suppose A contr B, and let* $\boldsymbol{a}$ *and* $\boldsymbol{b}$ *be the vectors assigned to A and B, respectively. Then* $a_i \succ b_i$ *for all* $i \leqslant$ *level*$(\boldsymbol{a})$.

PROOF. It is easy to verify theorem 3.1 for the contractions $\mathfrak{S}\boldsymbol{n}$ contr $\boldsymbol{n}+1$

and $\boldsymbol{Rn}$ contr $\boldsymbol{R^n}$. The verification of theorem 3.1 for the contractions R^0HG contr G and $R^{n+1}HG$ contr $Hn(R^nHG)$ is provided by lemmas 2.1 and 3.2, respectively. It remains to examine the contraction $(\lambda X^s H)F$ contr $[F/X^s]H$. Let $\boldsymbol{f}$ and $\boldsymbol{h}$ be the vectors assigned to F and H, respectively. Then $[\boldsymbol{f}/\boldsymbol{x}^s]\boldsymbol{h}$ is the vector assigned to $[F/X^s]H$ by lemma 3.1. But for all $i \leqslant \text{level}(\boldsymbol{h})$ the ith component of the vector assigned to $(\lambda X^s \cdot H)F$ is $((\delta^s\boldsymbol{h}) \square \boldsymbol{f})_i$.

The desired result now follows from the corollary to lemma 2.11.

THEOREM 3.2. *Suppose F reduces to G by contraction of one occurrence of a subterm A of F (restricted reduction of F). Let* $\boldsymbol{f}$ *and* $\boldsymbol{g}$ *be the vectors assigned to F and G, respectively. Then* $f_i \succcurlyeq g_i$ *for* $1 \leqslant i \leqslant$ *level*$(\boldsymbol{f})$, *and* $f_0 \succ g_0$.

PROOF. It is easy to see that since A is a subterm of F, there is a term H such that F is $[A/X^r]H$, where X^r has one free occurrence in H. Suppose A contracts to B. Then G is $[B/X^r]H$. Let $\boldsymbol{a}$, $\boldsymbol{b}$ and $\boldsymbol{h}$ be the vectors assigned to A, B and H, respectively. By lemma 3.1, $\boldsymbol{f}$ and $\boldsymbol{g}$ are $[\boldsymbol{a}/\boldsymbol{x}^r]\boldsymbol{h}$ and $[\boldsymbol{b}/\boldsymbol{x}^r]\boldsymbol{h}$, respectively. It is easy to see that the non-vacuous free occurrence of X^r in H implies the non-vacuous occurrence of x_0^r in h_0. Theorem 3.2 now follows from theorem 3.1 together with lemmas 2.12 and 2.13.

Assignment of ordinals to terms. To obtain an assignment of ordinals less than ε_0 to the terms of $\mathscr{T}$ proceed as follows. First assign expressions f_0 to terms F in the manner described in the present section. Next apply the interpretation of expressions given in § 2 under ***Interpretation of*** $\mathscr{E}$. This results in the assignment of a function to F; so apply this function to a suitable constant (say 0), in all argument places, to get an ordinal: this is the ordinal assigned to F. By theorem 3.2 reduction of F lowers the ordinal assigned to F.

4. General reductions. At first sight it might appear that the assignment given in § 3 is valid for *general* reductions; i.e. that theorem 3.2 is true even when A is a subform. Namely, one might try to prove this generalization of theorem 3.2 by induction on the length of F. This attempt fails when F is of the form $\lambda X^r.H$ for the following reason. Suppose $\lambda X^r.H$ is reduced to $\lambda X^r.G$ by contracting a subform of H, and let $\boldsymbol{h}$ and $\boldsymbol{g}$ be the vectors assigned to H and G, respectively. Then H red G, so by induction hypothesis $h_i \succcurlyeq g_i$ for all $i \leqslant \text{level}(\boldsymbol{h})$, and $h_0 \succ g_0$. Unfortunately this does not imply $(\delta^r\boldsymbol{h})_i \succcurlyeq (\delta^r\boldsymbol{g})_i$ for all $i \leqslant \text{level}(\delta^r\boldsymbol{h})$, and $(\delta^r\boldsymbol{h})_0 \succ (\delta^r\boldsymbol{g})_0$ (at least I can not prove that it does).

The above difficulty can be surmounted, if non-unique assignments are allowed, as follows. To $\lambda X^r.H$ we allow the assignment of $\delta^r \boldsymbol{d} + [\boldsymbol{e}/\boldsymbol{x}^r]\boldsymbol{h}$, where $\boldsymbol{e}$ is the vector $\langle 1, 1, \ldots, 1\rangle$ of the same level as $\boldsymbol{x}^r$, $\boldsymbol{h}$ is any vector assigned to H, and $\boldsymbol{d}$ is any vector assigned to a term D such that D reduces to H in a finite number of steps: $D = D_0$ red D_1 red . . . red $D_k = H$.

The following integer $t(F)$, associated with F and the manner in which a vector is assigned to F, is useful for the proof of the remaining results of this section: $t(F) = 1$ if F is prime;

$$t(AB) = t(A)+t(B);$$

$$t(\lambda X^r.H) = 1+t(D_0)+ \ldots +t(D_k)$$

where $D_0, \ldots, D_k$ are described above.

Lemma 3.1 holds for the new method of assignment: with the help of the proof in § 3 it is easy to get a proof for the new assignments by induction on $t(H)$.

Theorem 4.1 below will be proved under the assumption of the following axiom for expressions b, f and g:

4.1. If $f \succcurlyeq g$, then $[b/x_i^r]f \succcurlyeq [b/x_i^r]g$.

Axiom 4.1 clearly holds under the interpretations of the system $\mathscr{E}$ used in the present paper.

THEOREM 4.1. *Suppose F reduces to G by contraction of a subform (general reduction). Let* $\boldsymbol{f}$ *be a vector assigned to F. Then there exists a vector* $\boldsymbol{g}$ *assigned to G such that* $f_i \succcurlyeq g_i$ *for* $1 \leqslant i \leqslant$ *level*$(\boldsymbol{f})$, *and* $f_0 \succ g_0$.

PROOF. By induction on $t(F)$. We handle λ-contractions as follows. Suppose $F = (\lambda X^r.H)B$ red $[B/X^r]H$, where $\delta^r \boldsymbol{d} + [\boldsymbol{e}/\boldsymbol{x}^r]\boldsymbol{h}$ and $\boldsymbol{b}$ are assigned to $\lambda X^r \cdot H$ and B, respectively. By induction assumption there exists an assignment $\boldsymbol{d}^k$ to the term D_k described above such that $d_i \succcurlyeq d_i^k$ for $1 \leqslant i \leqslant$ level$(\boldsymbol{d})$, and $d_0 \succ d_0^k$. Hence by axiom 4.1 $([\boldsymbol{b}/\boldsymbol{x}^r]\boldsymbol{d})_i \succcurlyeq$ $\succcurlyeq ([\boldsymbol{b}/\boldsymbol{x}^r]\boldsymbol{d}^k)_i$ for $1 \leqslant i \leqslant$ level$(\boldsymbol{d})$, and $([\boldsymbol{b}/\boldsymbol{x}^r]\boldsymbol{d})_0 \succ ([\boldsymbol{b}/\boldsymbol{x}^r]\boldsymbol{d}^k)_0$. But D_k is H. Hence by lemma 3.1 $[\boldsymbol{b}/\boldsymbol{x}^r]\boldsymbol{d}^k$ is an assignment to $[B/X^r]H$. It now follows from the corollary to lemma 2.11 that this assignment has the required properties.

The case in which F is AB, and G arises from F by contraction of a subform of A or B, is handled by lemma 2.4. The case in which F is $\lambda X^r.H$ is handled by the induction hypothesis and (4.1).

5. More efficient assignment. Let $\omega_1 = \omega$ and $\omega_{k+1} = \omega^{\omega_k}$ $(k = 1, 2, \ldots)$. Let $\mathscr{T}_k$ denote the set of terms of $\mathscr{T}$ which contain primitive recursion constants R and R^n of level at most k. It is easy to see that the assignment of § 3, in assigning ordinals to terms of $\mathscr{T}_k$, makes use of the ordinals less than ω_{k+1}. However the work of Tait **[6]**, and independent work of C. Parsons (private communication to the author), suggests that it is the ordinals less than ω_k rather than ω_{k+1} that should be assigned to the terms of $\mathscr{T}_k$. The purpose of this section is to provide such an assignment which works so long as the following restrictions are made: if G has type level zero, the contractions $(\lambda X.F)G$ contr $[G/X]F$, R^0HG contr G, and $R^{n+1}HG$ contr $Hn(R^nHG)$ are allowed only when G is a numeral.

We shall modify the assignment, described in § 3, of vectors to terms so that to a term F will be assigned a vector $\boldsymbol{f}$ of level $\max\{1, \text{level}(F)\}$. This assignment will have the property that if F red G (restricted reduction) and if $\boldsymbol{g}$ is assigned to G, then $f_1 \succ g_1$. The expression f_1 will be assigned to F. When expressions are interpreted by ordinals as in § 3, this will yield an assignment to the terms of $\mathscr{T}_k$ by ordinals less than ω_k.

The modifications are as follows. When r is such that X^r has type level zero, the corresponding $\boldsymbol{x}^r$ is taken to be $\langle x_0^r, x_1^r\rangle$ rather than $\langle x_0^r\rangle$ (cf. § 2, ***The operation*** δ^r).

To numerals assign the vector $\langle 1, 0\rangle$. If X^r has type level zero, and $\boldsymbol{h}$ is assigned to H, then to $\lambda X^r.H$ assign the vector $\delta^r[0/x_1^r]\boldsymbol{h}$. If $\boldsymbol{f}$ and $\boldsymbol{g}$ have been assigned to F and G, respectively, then to FG assign the vector $\boldsymbol{h}$ such that $\text{level}(\boldsymbol{h}) = \max\{1, \text{level}(FG)\}$ and $h_i = (\boldsymbol{f} \mathbin{\square} \boldsymbol{g})_i$ for $0 \leqslant i \leqslant \text{level}(\boldsymbol{h})$.

Using the method of § 3 and the fact that, for all $\boldsymbol{b}$, $(\boldsymbol{b} \mathbin{\square} \langle 1, 0\rangle)_i = (\boldsymbol{b} \mathbin{\square} \langle 1\rangle)_i$ for all i, it is easy to verify that the modified assignment has the required properties.

University of Illinois at Chicago circle.

REFERENCES

[1] H. Bachmann, *Transfinite Zahlen*, Springer, Berlin (1955).

[2] G. Gentzen, Neue Fassung des Widerspruchsfreiheitsbeweises für die reine Zahlentheorie, *Forsch. Logik u. Grundl. exakten Wissenschaften* N.S. **4**, Hirzel, Leipzig (1938) 19–44.

[3] H. Gerber, An extension of Schütte's Klammersymbols, *Math. Ann.* **174** (1967) 203–216.

[4] K. Gödel, Über eine bisher noch nicht benützte Erweiterung des finiten Standpunktes, *Dialectica* **12** (1958) 280–287.

[5] W. Tait, Intensional interpretations of functionals of finite type, *J. Symb. Logic* **32** (1967) 198–212.

[6] W. Tait, Constructive reasoning, to appear.

ON A NUMBER THEORETIC CHOICE SCHEMA AND ITS RELATION TO INDUCTION

CHARLES PARSONS

The usual first order number theory Z can be viewed in a number of ways as the union of an infinite sequence of subtheories whose axioms and rules are of ascending complexity. In this paper we introduce and discuss the elementary relations of several hierarchies of subsystems based either on restricted induction principles or on others of a set theoretic character. The main result is an independence theorem for 'finite axioms of choice' which implies that for every $n > 0$, the axiom schema of induction with $\leqslant n$ nested quantifiers is stronger than the rule of induction with $\leqslant n$ nested quantifiers. This latter theorem is announced in [**8**] (and for $n = 1$ in [**6**]) on the basis of a different proof.

The paper is in the context of a larger proof theoretic investigation of subsystems of number theory, begun in [**5**], of which results are reported in [**6**], [**7**], and [**8**]. A paper in preparation will develop the work of [**8**] and give information about these subsystems based on Gödel's interpretation.

1. Basic notions. We consider systems whose formulae are in the notation of elementary number theory. We use $x, y, z, \ldots$ for bound variables, $a, b, c, \ldots$ for free variables, $f, g, h, \ldots$ for function symbols. Terms are built from 0, S (successor), variables, and certain function symbols in the usual way. We use $r, s, t, \ldots$ for terms. Formulae are composed from equations $s = t$ by the connectives $\neg, \wedge, \vee, \supset$ and the quantifiers $\forall x$ and $\exists x$.

Let Z_0 be a system which has for each definition of a function φ *elementary* in the Kalmar sense ([**3**], p. 285) symbols for the functions involved with the recursion equations as axioms. Z_0 has also the usual axioms for equality and successor and the rule of induction applied to *quantifier free* formulae. Z_0 has the deductive apparatus of classical first order logic.

By well-known arguments we can operate in Z_0 on formulae with only bounded quantifiers as if they were quantifier free formulae; hence if A is any such formula, by the rule of induction the formula

IA $$A0 \wedge \forall x < a \ (Ax \supset A(Sx)) \, . \supset Aa$$

is provable in Z_0. IA implies the usual axiom of induction on A.

In addition to IA and the rule of induction

IR $$\frac{A0 \quad Aa \supset A(Sa)}{Aa}$$

we consider some other schemata suggested by the fact that elementary number theory can be derived in the theory of finite sets:

FAC $$\forall x \leqslant a \ \exists y Axy \supset \exists y \forall x \leqslant a \ A[x, (y)_x]$$

AS $$\exists y \forall x \leqslant a \ [(y)_x = 0 \wedge Ax \, . \vee . \, (y)_x = 1 \wedge \neg Ax]$$

M $$\forall x \leqslant a \ \exists y Axy \supset \exists w \forall x \leqslant a \ \exists y \leqslant w \ Axy$$

($(y)_x$ is the xth exponent of y; **[3]**, p. 230.) FAC is a sort of choice axiom; AS is a version of the Aussonderungsaxiom; M (for maximum) is related to the axiom of replacement.

If S is one of our schemata, let S_n be S restricted to formulae A with $\leqslant n$ nested quantifiers; let S'_n be S restricted to A with $\leqslant n$ nested unbounded quantifiers. $S_n^\Sigma(S_n^\Pi)$ is S restricted to A which are $\Sigma_n^0(\Pi_n^0)$. (Hereafter we omit the superscript ^{0}). $S(B)$ is the instance of S with B in place of A.

The notation for a schema will be used for the system obtained by adding it as an axiom or rule to Z_0.S $\rightarrow$ S$'$ means that every theorem of S$'$ is a theorem of S.

We now state some simple facts about the relations of these schemata.

LEMMA 1. *In* FAC_{n+1}^Σ, *every formula with* $\leqslant n$ *nested unbounded quantifiers is equivalent to a* Σ_{n+1} *formula.*

PROOF. FAC_{n+1}^Σ implies, for any A with $\leqslant n$ nested quantifiers, the formulae

$$\forall x \leqslant a \ \exists y Axy \equiv \exists y \forall x \leqslant a \ A[x, (y)_x] \tag{1}$$

$$\exists x \geqslant a \ \forall y Axy \equiv \forall y \exists x \leqslant a \ A[x, (y)_x]. \tag{2}$$

If B has $\leqslant n$ nested unbounded quantifiers, it is equivalent to a prenex formula which, except for bounded quantifiers, is Σ_{n+1}. Starting from inside, these bounded quantifiers can be transposed inward by (1) and (2); when one reaches those outside the outermost unbounded quantifier, one is operating on a Σ_{n+1} formula.

LEMMA 2. (a). $FAC_n^{\Pi} \leftrightarrow FAC_{n+1}^{\Sigma} \leftrightarrow FAC_n'$

(b). $FAC_n^{\Pi} \rightarrow AS_n^{\Pi} \leftrightarrow AS_n' \leftrightarrow IA_n'$

(c). $IA_n' \rightarrow IA_n \rightarrow IR_n$

(d). $IR_n' \leftrightarrow IA_n'$

(e). $IA_{n+1}^{\Sigma} \rightarrow FAC_n^{\Pi}$

(f). $IR_{n+1} \rightarrow AS_n^{\Pi}$

PROOF. (a). The right-left arrows are obvious. If $\forall x \leqslant a\ \exists y \exists z\ Bxyz$ where B is Π_n then, if v is a pairing function with inverses v^1, v^2, we infer $\forall x \leqslant a\, \exists y\, B(x, v^1 y, v^2 y)$; by FAC_n^{Π} there is a y such that

$$\forall x \leqslant a\ \ B(x, v^1(y)_x, v^2(y)_x).$$

Then clearly if $y' = \prod_{i \leqslant a} p_i^{v^1(y)_i}$

$$\forall x \leqslant a\ \exists z\ \ B(x, (y')_x, z).$$

$FAC_{n+1}^{\Sigma} \rightarrow FAC_n'$ is immediate from lemma 1.

(*b*). $AS(A)$ can be proved by applying FAC to

$$y = 0 \wedge Ax\,.\ \vee\,.\, y = 1 \wedge \neg\, Ax;$$

by (a), if A is Π_n this can be done in FAC_n^{Π}.

We postpone proving $AS_n^{\Pi} \rightarrow AS_n'$. Sinse $AS(A)$ can be proved by IA on

$$\exists y \leqslant \prod_{i \leqslant a} p_i\ \forall x \leqslant a\ \ [(y)_x = 0 \wedge Ax\,.\wedge.\,(y)_x = 1 \wedge \neg\, Ax]$$

$IA_n' \rightarrow AS_n'$ is evident. Conversely if

$$\forall x \leqslant a\ \ [(y)_x = 0 \wedge Ax\,.\ \vee\ .\,(y)_x = 1 \wedge \neg\, Ax] \tag{3}$$

then the induction axiom (provable in Z_0)

$$(y)_0 = 0 \wedge \forall x < a\ \ [(y)_x = 0 \supset (y)_{Sx} = 0]\,.\supset (y)_a = 0$$

implies $IA(A)$, and since by the substitution restriction in AS Aa cannot contain free y, the existential quantification of (3) by y implies $IA(A)$.

(c). Trivial.

(d). $IA_n' \rightarrow IR_n'$ follows from the standard reduction of IR to IA; $IR_n' \rightarrow IA_n'$ by the proof given above for the case $n = 0$.

(e). $FAC(A)$ can be proved with the induction axiom

$$\exists y \forall x \leqslant 0\ \ A[x, (y)_x] \wedge \forall z < a\ \ \{\exists y \forall x \leqslant z\ \ A[x, (y)_x] \supset \exists y \forall x \leqslant Sz\ \ A[x, (y)_x]\}\,.\supset \exists y \forall x \leqslant a\ \ A[x, (y)_x].$$

We now prove $AS_n^\Pi \to AS_n'$. $AS_n^\Pi \to AS_n^\Sigma$ is obvious. Hence we have

$$AS_n^\Pi \to AS_n^\Sigma \to IA_n^\Sigma \to FAC_{n-1}^\Pi .$$

If Aa has $\leqslant n$ nested unbounded quantifiers, it is composed by propositional connectives and bounded quantification from formulae $\exists wBxw$ and $\forall wCaw$, where Baw and Caw have $\leqslant n-1$ unbounded quantifiers. By (a) and lemma 1 A is equivalent to a formula A' composed by connectives and bounded quantifiers from Π_n formulae. But by the formulae

$$\exists y \forall x \leqslant a \;\; [(y)_x = 0 \;\equiv\; (b)_x \neq 0]$$
$$\exists y \forall x \leqslant a \;\; [(y)_x = 0 \;\equiv\; (b)_x = 0 \wedge (c)_x = 0]$$
$$\exists y \forall x \leqslant a \;\; [(y)_x = 0 \;\equiv\; \forall z \leqslant t \;\; ((b)_{\nu(x,z)} = 0)]$$

the A for which $AS(A)$ is provable in AS_n^Π are closed under logical connectives and bounded quantifiers.

(f). If Aa is $\forall wBaw$ where Baw is Σ_{n-1}, we can prove AS_n^Π by the induction rule on the formula

$$\exists z \exists y \forall x \leqslant a \;\; \forall w[(y)_x = 0 \wedge Bxw \,.\vee.\, (y)_x = 1 \wedge \neg\, B(x, (z)_x)]$$

which is equivalent to a Σ_{n+1} formula. This proves (f).

LEMMA 3. (a) $\vdash_{z_0} FAC(A) \supset M(A)$

(b). $\vdash_{z_0} M(A) \wedge \forall a \;\; AS(A[\nu^1 a, \nu^2 a]\,.) \supset FAC(A)$

PROOF. (a). If the antecedent of $M(A)$ holds, by $FAC(A)$, for some y, $\forall x \leqslant a\, A(x, (y)_x)$. Then $w = \max_{x \leqslant a} (y)_x$ satisfies the consequent of $M(A)$.

(b). Assume $M(A)$ and $\forall x \leqslant a \;\exists y \; Axy$. Then for some w

$$\forall x \leqslant a \;\exists y \leqslant w \;\; Axy,$$

and by logic

$$\forall a \;\; AS(A[\nu^1 a, \nu^2 a]) \supset \exists y \forall x \leqslant \max_{\substack{x \leqslant a \\ y \leqslant w}} \nu(x, y)$$
$$[(y)_x = 0 \wedge A(\nu^1 x, \nu^2 x) \,.\vee.\, (y)_x = 1 \wedge \neg\, A(\nu^1 x, \nu^2 x)]$$

If y satisfies the consequent of this, $y' = \prod_{i \leqq a} p_i \exp \mu z \leqslant w \;\; ((y)_{\nu(i,z)} = 0)$ satisfies $\forall i \leqslant a \;\; A[i, (y')_i]$.

From lemma 3 we have $FAC_n \leftrightarrow AS_n + M_n$. Hence the relations of the systems can be diagrammed as follows:

$$\begin{array}{ccccc}
\mathrm{IA}_{n+1} & \longrightarrow \mathrm{IA}^{\Sigma}_{n+1} \longrightarrow & \mathrm{FAC}^{\Pi}_{n} & \leftrightarrow \mathrm{FAC}'_{n} \leftrightarrow \mathrm{FAC}^{\Sigma}_{n+1} \leftrightarrow \mathrm{AS}_{n} + \mathrm{M}_{n} \\
\downarrow & & \downarrow & \\
\mathrm{IR}_{n+1} & \longrightarrow & \mathrm{AS}^{\Pi}_{n} & \leftrightarrow \mathrm{AS}'_{n} \leftrightarrow \mathrm{IA}'_{n} \leftrightarrow \mathrm{IR}'_{n} \\
& \searrow & \swarrow & \\
& & \mathrm{IA}_{n} &
\end{array}$$

It is natural to ask whether any of the relations in the hexagonal part of the diagram holds in the reverse direction, and what the relation is between FAC^{Π}_{n} and IR_{n+1}. The main result below is that FAC^{Π}_{n} is not derivable even in IR^{Π}_{n+2}. It follows that $\mathrm{IR}_{n+1} \rightarrow \mathrm{IA}^{\Sigma}_{n+1}$ is false and that $\mathrm{AS}^{\Pi}_{n} \rightarrow \mathrm{FAC}^{\Pi}_{n}$ is false. $\mathrm{IA}_{n} \nrightarrow \mathrm{IR}_{n+1}$ follows from the fact that IR_{n+1} suffices to prove the consistency of IA_{n} (cf. [**8**]). It is easy to see that $\mathrm{FAC}^{\Pi}_{0} \nrightarrow \mathrm{IA}^{\Sigma}_{1}$; we conjecture that the same holds for higher n.

2. Independence results for FAC^{Π}_{n}**.** Since FAC^{Π}_{n} implies IA_{n}, it is clear that FAC^{Π}_{n} cannot be derived in IR_{n}. We strengthen this observation by showing that it is not derivable in IR^{Π}_{n+2}.

THEOREM 1. *For every n there is an instance of* FAC^{Π}_{n} *which is not derivable in Z_0 from true Π_{n+2} sentences.*

PROOF. By lemma 2 it suffices to show that there is such an instance of M with A Σ_{n+1}.

Let $\exists y Axy$ be a complete Σ_n predicate. Let $T_2^{*A}eaxy$ be a formula which expresses the following:

> y is the number of the least derivation (say in Kleene's formalism of recursive functions ([**3**], ch. XI)) from the equations with number e and equations of the form $g(\bar{k}) = \bar{l}$, of an equation $f(\bar{z}, \bar{x}) = \bar{p}$ (for some $p \leqslant y$), and $\exists u \forall z \forall w \leqslant y \, \forall k \leqslant y \, \forall l \leqslant y$, if w is a line of the derivation of the form $g(\bar{k}) = \bar{l}$, then

$$l = 0 \wedge A[k, (u)_w] \,.\vee.\, l = 1 \wedge \neg A[k, z].$$

It is clear that the predicate preceding the quantifiers is elementary and is expressed in Z_0 by a quantifier-free formula, and the predicate inside brackets is an $(n-1)$-quantifier predicate. Hence $T_2^{*A}eaxy$ can be chosen a Σ_{n+1} formula. Intuitively, it expresses the Kleene T-predicate relative to $\exists y Axy$. If $n = 0$ we omit A and use Kleene's predicate T_2 ([**3**], p. 291).

Now we consider the formula

$$\forall x \leqslant a \ \exists y \ T_2^{*A}eaxy \supset \exists w \forall x \leqslant a \ \exists y \leqslant w \ T_2^{*A}eaxy. \qquad (4)$$

Suppose (4) is derivable in Z_0 from Π_{n+2} sentences $B_1 \ldots B_r$. Let B_i be the formula

$$\forall x_1 \exists y_1 \ldots \forall x_l \exists y_l B_i'(x_1, \ldots, x_l, y_1, \ldots, y_l) \qquad (5)$$

(assuming $n+2 = 2l$). Expand the formalism to include symbols for the Skolem functions for $B_1 \ldots B_r$; then (4) is derivable from the formulae

$$B_i'[x_1, \ldots, x_l, f_1^i(x_1), \ldots, f_l^i(x_1, \ldots, x_l)]. \qquad (6)$$

By Herbrand's theorem we can derive from (6) and axioms of Z_0, by substitution, propositional logic, and quantifier-free induction (in fact the induction formula will not contain the f_j^i) an alternation of the form

$$\varphi_0 ea \leqslant a \wedge \neg T_2^{*A}(e, a, \varphi_0 ea, c_0) . \vee \neg(b_0 \leqslant a) \vee \exists y \leqslant \psi_0 ea \ T_2^{*A}(e, a, b_0, y) \vee \ldots \vee .$$

$$\varphi_m(e, a, c_0, \ldots, c_{m-1}, b_0, \ldots, b_{m-1}) \leqslant a \wedge \neg T_2^{*A}[e, a, \varphi_m(e, a, c_0, \ldots, c_{m-1}, b_0, \ldots, b_{m-1}), c_m] . \vee \neg(b_m \leqslant a) \vee \exists y \leqslant \psi_m(e, a, c_0, \ldots, c_{m-1}, b_0, \ldots, b_{m-1}) \ T_2^{*A}(e, a, b_m, y) \qquad (7)$$

where the terms $\varphi_i(e, a, \ldots)$ and $\psi_i(e, a, \ldots)$ are composed from the variables by the symbols f_j^i and the function symbols of Z_0. Hence they express functions which are recursive in the Skolem functions. The Skolem functions satisfy

$$f_j^i(x_1, \ldots, x_j) = y \equiv y = \mu y_j \forall x_{j+1} \exists y_{j+1} \ldots \forall x_l \exists y_l \ B_i'[x_1, \ldots, x_l, f_1^i(x_1), \ldots, f_{j-1}^i(x_1, \ldots, x_{j-1}), y_j, \ldots, y_l]$$

which, since $n+2 = 2l$, is a Σ_n predicate. Hence the functions f_j^i are recursive in $\exists y \ Axy$. Hence so are the functions φ_i and ψ_i.

We set

$$\tilde{c}_j = \mu y T_2^{*A}[e, a, \varphi_j(e, a, \tilde{c}_0, \ldots, \tilde{c}_{j-1}, \tilde{b}_0, \ldots, \tilde{b}_{j-1}), y]$$
$$\tilde{b}_j = \mu z \leqslant a \ \neg \exists y \leqslant \psi_j(e, a, \tilde{c}_0, \ldots, \tilde{c}_{j-1}, \tilde{b}_0, \ldots, \tilde{b}_{j-1}) \ T_2^{*A}(e, a, z, y)$$

Then we define

$$\varphi(e, a, i) = \psi_0(e, a)+1 \quad \text{if} \quad i = i_0 = \varphi_0(e, a)$$
$$= \psi_{j+1}(e, a, \tilde{c}_0, \ldots, \tilde{c}_j, \tilde{b}_0, \ldots, \tilde{b}_j)+1 \quad \text{if} \quad i = i_{j+1},$$

where

$$i_{j+1} = \varphi_{j+1}(e, a, \tilde{c}_0, \ldots, \tilde{c}_j, \tilde{b}_0, \ldots, \tilde{b}_j)$$
$$\text{if } \varphi_{j+1}(e, a, \tilde{c}_0, \ldots, \tilde{c}_j, \tilde{b}_0, \ldots, \tilde{b}_j) \neq i_0, \ldots, i_j;$$
$$i_{j+1} = \mu k\ (k \neq i_0 \ldots i_j) \quad \text{otherwise.}$$

By the recursion theorem there is an e which defines $\lambda ea\varphi(e, a, i)$ recursively from $\hat{x}\exists yAxy$.

Then certainly $e(a, i)$ is defined for $i = i_0$; hence there is a y satisfying $T_2^{*A}(e, a, \varphi_0 ea, y)$; hence $\tilde{c}_0$ is defined. If $\tilde{c}_0, \ldots, \tilde{c}_j$ are defined and $j < m$, then $e(a, i_{j+1})$ is defined (since $i_{j+1} \neq i_0, \ldots, i_j$, the stipulations do not conflict), and therefore $\tilde{c}_{j+1}$ is defined. By induction, $\tilde{c}_0, \ldots, \tilde{c}_m$ are all defined.

If we substitute our given e and $\tilde{c}_0 \ldots \tilde{c}_m, \tilde{b}_0 \ldots \tilde{b}_m$ in (7), the result is false for all $a > m$.

Suppose $\varphi_0 ea \leqslant a$. Since $U(\mu y\ T_2^{*A}(e, a, \varphi_0 ea, y)) = \psi_0 ea+1$,

$$\neg\, \exists y \leqslant \psi_0 ea\ T_2^{*A}(e, a, \varphi_0 ea, y)$$

holds; hence $\tilde{b}_0 \leqslant a$; moreover $T_2^{*A}(e, a, \varphi_0 ea, \tilde{c}_0)$ is true.

Suppose the first j alternands false and $\varphi_{j+1}(e, a, \tilde{c}_0, \ldots, \tilde{c}_j, \tilde{b}_0, \ldots, \tilde{b}_j) \leqslant a$. Since $\tilde{c}_{j+1}$ is defined, $T_2^{*A}[e, a, \varphi_j(e, a, \tilde{c}_0, \ldots, \tilde{c}_j, \tilde{b}_0, \ldots, \tilde{b}_j), \tilde{c}_{j+1}]$ is true, but

$$\varphi(e, a, i_{j+1}) > \psi_{j+1}(e, a, \tilde{c}_0, \ldots, \tilde{c}_j, \tilde{b}_0, \ldots, \tilde{b}_j);$$

hence $\tilde{b}_{j+1} \leqslant a$ and

$$\neg\, \exists y \leqslant \psi_{j+1}(e, a, \tilde{c}_0, \ldots, \tilde{c}_j, \tilde{b}_0, \ldots, \tilde{b}_j)\ T_2^{*A}(e, a, \tilde{b}_{j+1}, y).$$

($\tilde{b}_{j+1} \leqslant a$ depends on the fact that $a > m$, for by hypothesis of induction $\tilde{b}_k = i_k \leqslant a$ for every $k \leqslant j$; if $i_{j+1} = \varphi_{j+1}(e, a, \ldots)$ we know $\tilde{b}_{j+1} \leqslant a$; otherwise since $a > m$ there is $m' \leqslant a$, $m' \neq i_0, \ldots, i_j$, and the least such m' is i_{j+1}.) Hence the $(j+1)$st alternand is false.

From this refutation we can find an instance of one of the formulae (6) which is false. I.e. for some i and suitable terms $t_1, \ldots, t_l$,

$$B_i'[t_1, \ldots, t_l, f_1^i(t_1), \ldots, f_l^i(t_1, \ldots, t_l)]$$

is false. Hence B_i is false, i.e. not all of $B_1, \ldots, B_m$ are true, q.e.d.

Looked at constructively, the argument shows that if (4) is derivable from Π_{n+2} sentences (5), we can effectively find a no-counter-example interpretation of $\neg\, B_1 \vee \ldots \vee \neg\, B_m$.

COROLLARY. FAC_n^Π *is not derivable in* IR_{n+2}^Π; *hence for every* n *there is a formula, namely* (4) *with* A *a complete* Σ_n *predicate, which is derivable in* IA_{n+1}^Σ, *but not in* IR_{n+1} *or even in* IR_{n+2}^Π.

PROOF. Suppose (4) is provable in IR_{n+2}^Π. Then it follows in Z_0 from the conclusions $B_1, \ldots, B_m$ of the last applications of induction in the proof; their closures are Π_{n+2} sentences. By the theorem, we can effectively find a no-counter-example interpretation of $\neg B_1 \vee \ldots \vee \neg B_m$, which contradicts the uniform 1-consistency of IR_{n+2}^Π.

Remark. In [**4**] Kreisel gave an example of a 'non-Herbrand interpretable' theorem of Z. Our argument for $n = 0$ amounts to showing (4) to be non-Herbrand interpretable. A formula is Herbrand interpretable if it has a no-counter-example interpretation by functionals explicitly defined from function arguments and recursive functions.

Kreisel's example is more elementary than it appears since the only axiom needed in the proof which goes beyond Z_0 is a Σ_1 induction axiom. It is natural to expect such an axiom to be non-Herbrand interpretable (if the induction predicate is not recursive), because the Gödel interpretation [**2**] of such an axiom involves the universal recursion functional with values of type 0:

$$R0af = a \qquad R(Sx)af = f[x, Rxaf],$$

which depends on a variable number of values of its function arguments.

Our example is more elementary since its interpretation involves only elementary functions and the course-of-values functional $\prod_{i\leqslant a} p_i^{f(i)}$; but a glance at the functional form of (4) (in the sense of [**1**])

$$\forall x \leqslant a \;\; T_2(e, a, x, fx) \supset \exists w \exists y \leqslant w \;\; [gw \leqslant a \supset T_2(e, a, gw, y)]$$

indicates that the functional for w ought to depend on a values of f.

The Gödel translation of the negative version of an instance of FAC_0 is

$$\exists W \forall f \forall a \{\forall x \leqslant a \;\; A(x, fx) \supset \forall x \leqslant a \;\; A[x, (Wfa)_x]\}$$

which is obviously satisfied by taking $Wfa = \prod_{i\leqslant a} p_i^{f(i)}$. Then $Z_0 + \mathrm{FAC}_0$ can obviously be interpreted in a subsystem T_0' of T in which recursions are restricted to values of type 0, and the only recursion with a parameter of type > 0 is that for W. (This system is intermediate between T_0^* and T_0 of [**8**].) In fact this extends to $\mathrm{IR}_2^\Pi + \mathrm{FAC}_0$, and we have

THEOREM 2. (a). *Let* PR *be free variable primitive recursive arithmetic. Then if* $\forall x \exists y \, Aaxy$ (*A quantifier-free*) *is the conclusion of an induction in* $\mathrm{IR}_2^\Pi + \mathrm{FAC}_0$, *there is a constant* φ *of* PR *such that*

$$A(a, x, \varphi ax)$$

is provable in PR (*strengthens theorem* 1 of **[6]**).

(b). *If* B *is provable in* $\mathrm{IR}_2^{\Pi}+\mathrm{FAC}_0$, *then it is provable in* $\mathrm{IR}_1^{\Sigma}+\mathrm{FAC}_0$. *If* B *is provable in* IR_2^{Π} *it is provable in* IR_1^{Σ}.

(c). $\mathrm{IR}_2^{\Pi}+\mathrm{FAC}_0$ *is a proper subtheory of* IA_1^{Σ}.

PROOF. (a). Let T_0' be as above. We suppose it formulated in the extensional fashion of **[10]**. Types are 0 and $(\sigma)\tau$ for types σ, τ. Let $(0)^0 0 = 0$, $(0)^{m+1}\, 0 = (0)(0)^m 0$. ($(0)^m 0$ is the type of number-theoretic functions of m arguments.) Terms of T_0' are composed from variables and constants (including 0 and S by application; 0 and S are given constants; further constants are introduced by the schema

ED $$\varphi c_1 \ldots c_n = t$$

where t is a term whose free variables are among $c_1, \ldots, c_n$. (Note that if s and t are not of type 0, $s = t$ is an abbreviation for $sa_1 \ldots a_n = ta_1 \ldots a_n$, where $a_1 \ldots a_n$ are new variables and $sa_1 \ldots a_n$ is of type 0.) If t is a term with free variables $c_1, \ldots, c_n$ and perhaps a, λat is represented by the term $\theta c_1 \ldots c_n$, where θ is defined by

$$\theta c_1 \ldots c_n a = t.$$

Constants are also introduced by primitive recursion

PR $$\varphi 0 a_1 \ldots a_n = \psi a_1 \ldots a_n \quad \varphi(Sx)a_1 \ldots a_n = \chi(\varphi x a_1 \ldots a_n)x a_1 \ldots a_n$$

where $a_1, \ldots, a_n, x, \varphi x a_1 \ldots a_n$ are all of type 0, and by the recursion

$$W0f = 2^{f0} \qquad W(Sx)f = Wxf \cdot p_{Sx}^{f(Sx)}.\ *$$

Let A^- be the negative version of a number theoretic formula A and let A' be the Gödel translation of A into a formula $\exists F \forall g\, A_1(F, g)$, where $A_1(F, g)$ is a formula of the free variable system T. Then if A is a theorem of $\mathrm{IR}_2^{\Pi}+\mathrm{FAC}_0$ and $(A^-)'$ is $\exists F \forall g\, A_1(F, g)$ then for some term s of T_0', not containing g, $A_1(s, g)$ is provable in T_0'.

* Evidently $T_0{}'$ is closed under elementary recursions with parameters of arbitrary type. For example if t is a term of type (0)0, $\Pi_{i \leqq a}\, ti$ is expressed by $sa(Wat)$, where, $sax = \Pi_{i \leqq a}\, (x)_i$.

This is clear for the axioms, and it is well-known that the interpretation of logical inferences does not involve recursion (except for a few elementary functions to handle definition by cases). Hence it suffices to consider induction. Let

$$\frac{\forall x \exists y\, B0xy \qquad \forall x \exists y\, Baxy \supset \forall x \exists y\, B(Sa, x, y)}{\forall x \exists y\, Baxy}$$

be an instance of induction. By hypothesis of induction there are constants φ_0, ψ, χ such that

$$B(0, x, \varphi_0 x) \qquad B[a, \psi fax, f(\psi fax)] \supset B[Sa, x, \chi fax] \tag{8}$$

are provable in T_0'. It suffices to find φ, θ such that

$$\begin{aligned} \varphi 0x &= \varphi_0 x \\ \varphi(Sa)x &= \chi(\varphi a)ax \end{aligned} \tag{9}$$

$$\begin{aligned} \theta 0ax &= x \\ \theta(Sb)ax &= \psi[\varphi(a \dot{-} Sb), a \dot{-} Sb, \theta bax] \end{aligned} \tag{10}$$

are provable in T_0'. For then we can derive by induction

$$b \leqslant a \supset B[b, \theta(a \dot{-} b)ax, \varphi b(\theta(a \dot{-} b)ax)]$$

which for $a = b$ yields $B[a, x, \varphi ax]$.

(10) is an ordinary primitive recursion and will be satisfiable if (9) is. That (9) will be satisfiable is apparent if we observe that φ and χ are explicitly definable from primitive recursive functions and the functional W. Therefore χf is uniformly elementary in f and finitely many primitive recursive functions. This suggests

Lemma 4. *T_0' is closed under recursions of the form* (9) (a, x, φax *of type* 0).

Proof. The terms $\varphi_0 x$ and χfax have 'λ-normal forms' from which explicitly defined constants have been eliminated as far as possible. Consider a term t whose constants are among 0, S, W, $\psi_1, \ldots, \psi_n$ introduced by primitive recursion, and others explicitly defined from these. If t contains no free variables of type $\neq 0$ except f, then the normal form of t belongs to the set U inductively defined by

(U1). If t is 0 or a variable of type 0, then $t \in U$.

(U2). If t is St_1 or ft_1 or $\psi_i t_1 \ldots t_{n_i}$ (ψ_i of type $(0)^{n_i}0$) and $t_1 \ldots t_{n_i} \in U$, then $t \in U$.

(U3). If b is of type 0, t is $Wr(\lambda bs)$ and $r, s \in U$, then $t \in U$.
The heart of the proof of lemma 4 is finding an evaluation function for the terms in U which do not contain f. Let $a_0, a_1 \dots$ be all the variables of type 0. For a suitable Gödel numbering we find a constant $\bar{V}$ of T_0' such that

$$\bar{V}(p_{\bar{i}_1}^{a_{i_1}} \cdot \dots \cdot p_{\bar{i}_n}^{a_{i_n}}, \bar{k}) = t, \tag{11}$$

if $k = gn(t)$ and $a_{i_1} \dots a_{i_n}$ include all the free variables of t.

To let $\bar{V}$ depend on a parameter f and to allow t in (11) to contain f requires more powerful recursions than are available in T_0'. For a fixed variable x we can define a function σcd such that if $d = gn(t(f))$ and $c = gn(s)$, $s, t(f) \in U$, then σcd is the g.n. of the normal form of $t(\lambda xs)$, and we do have

$$\vdash \tau c = 0 \supset \bar{V}(p_{\bar{i}_1}^{a_{i_1}} \cdot \dots \cdot p_{\bar{i}_n}^{a_{i_n}}, \sigma c\bar{k} = t[\lambda x \bar{V}(p_{\bar{i}_1}^{a_{i_1}} \cdot \dots \cdot p_{\bar{i}_n}^{a_{i_n}} \cdot p_{\bar{k}}^{x}, c)] \tag{12}$$

where $\tau c = 0$ expresses 'c is the g.n. of a term in U without f', x is a_k, and in the right-hand product the factor $p_{\bar{i}_j}^{a_{i_j}}$ is ommitted if $i_j = k$.

Clearly for any n, $\lambda x\varphi nx$ is expressed by the nth term in the sequence

$$\varphi_0 x, \ \chi\varphi_0 0x, \ \chi(\chi\varphi_0 0)1x, \dots .$$

Let $u_0, u_1, u_2, \dots$ be the normal forms of these terms. Then we have a primitive recursive φ' such that $\varphi' 0 = gn(u_0)$, $\varphi(Sa) = \sigma(\varphi' a, \chi' a)$, where $\chi' n$ is the g.n. of the normal form $v(f, \bar{n})$ of $\chi f\bar{n}x$. Then $\varphi' a = gn(u_a)$. If we set

$$\varphi ax = \bar{V}(p_{\bar{i}}^{a} \cdot p_{\bar{k}}^{x}, \varphi' a)$$

(where a_i is a), then φ intuitively satisfies (9). In fact, from (11) we have immediately $\vdash \varphi 0x = u_0 = \varphi_0 x$, and from (12) we obtain

$$\vdash \varphi(Sa)x = v(\lambda x\varphi ax, a) = \chi(\varphi a)ax.$$

Thus the equations (9) are provable.

To define $\bar{V}$, with each term $t \in U$ not containing f we associate a term $\tilde{t}$ with a sole free variable a, which expresses a course-of-values function of the function expressed by t in that it will have the property

$$p_{\bar{i}_1}^{a_{i_1}} \cdot \dots \cdot p_{\bar{i}_n}^{a_{i_n}} \leqslant a \ \supset t = (\tilde{t}) \text{ sub } p_{\bar{i}_1}^{a_{i_1}} \cdot \dots \cdot p_{\bar{i}_n}^{a_{i_n}} \tag{13}$$

if $a_{i_1} \dots a_{i_n}$ include all the free variables of t.

$\tilde{t}$ will be explicitly definable from a fixed finite set of functions (cf. [**9**]). For example, if with r, s we associate $\tilde{r}, \tilde{s}(a)$ respectively, then with $Wr(\lambda a_k s)$

we associate $\omega[\bar{k}, a, \tilde{r}, \tilde{s}(M(\bar{k}, a, \tilde{r}))]$, where

$$N^0(r, k, j, l) = (j)_r \quad \text{if} \quad r \neq k,$$
$$= l \quad \text{if} \quad r = k$$

$$N(k, j, l, a) = \prod_{r \leqslant a} p_r \exp N^0(r, k, j, l)$$

$$M(k, a, c) = \max_{\substack{j \leqslant a \\ l \leqslant c}} N(k, j, l, a)$$

$$\omega(k, a, c, d) = \prod_{\substack{j \leqslant a \\ l \leqslant s}} p_j \exp \prod p_k \exp (d)_{N(k, j, l, a)}$$

Then we can easily define a function V which has the property analogous to (12) for terms composed from the functions used for the $\tilde{t}$, plus $\lambda xy\, x^y$, $\lambda xy(x \cdot y)$, yxp_x, $\lambda y(x)_y$, and then $\bar{V}$ is defined in terms of V, and (13) will imply that it satisfies (11) and, with a little more work, (12).

This proves (a) with PR replaced by T_0'. ((a) then follows from the fact that T_0' is a conservative extension of PR in the following sense:

Lemma 5. *Let T_0 be the extension of T_0' in which the parameters of* PR *can be of arbitrary type (the value must still be of type* 0). *Let φ be a constant of T_0 of type* $(0)^m 0$, $m \geqslant 0$. *With φ we can associate a constant φ of* PR *such that if A is a formula of T_0 contaning only such constants and variables only of type* 0, *and A' is the result of replacing each φ in A by φ', then A is provable in T_0 if and only if A' is provable in* PR. *If φ is a constant of* PR *then $\varphi = \varphi'$.*

Proof. We can take PR as T_0 with the notation so restricted that only variables of type 0 are admitted. In both we suppose the axioms and rules to be as in **[10]**, pp. 11–12 (with ED in place of PR 1–5; the rule G6 of extensionality is redundant in PR).

Given a constant ψ of T_0, we can replace it by an equivalent constant ψ_1 by replacing those recursions PR in its definition tree which involve parameters of type $\neq 0$ by explicit definitions with the functional R satisfying

$$R0af = a \qquad R(Sx)af = f(Rxaf)x$$

(f of type (0)(0)0); i.e. if φ is defined by PR, φ_1 is introduced by

$$\varphi_1 xa_1 \ldots a_n = Rx(\psi a_1 \ldots a_n)(\lambda yx\chi yxa_1 \ldots a_n)$$

$\psi = \psi_1$ if ψ is a constant of PR. Clearly if $\vdash A$ in T_0, then $\vdash A_1$ (the result of replacing each φ in A by φ_1) by a proof involving no recursion axioms except those for R and those with parameters of type 0.

Let t be a term of T_0 thus restricted, of type 0 and with free variables only of type 0. Then the normal form of t is in the set U inductively defined by (U1), (U2) without ft_1, and

(U3′). If t is $Rsu(\lambda xyv)$ and s, u, $v \in U$, then $t \in U$ where, as before, $\psi_1 \ldots \psi_n$ are introduced by PR with parameters of type 0.

If φ is defined by PR, then φ' is defined by the same recursion from ψ' and χ'. Thus if we assume as hypothesis of induction that φ' is defined for every φ whose definition involves fewer applications of PR than the maximum for $\psi_1 \ldots \psi_n$, it follows that $\psi'_1 \ldots \psi'_n$ are all defined. $0' = 0$ and $S' = S$. In case (U1) $t' = t$, in case (U2) t' is St_1 or $\psi'_i t'_1 \ldots t'_{n_i}$; in case (U3′), if $c_1 \ldots c_n$ are the free variables of t, we set

$$\psi_t c_1 \ldots c_n = u',$$

$$\chi_t xyc_1 \ldots c_n = v',$$

$$\varphi_t 0c_1 \ldots c_n = \psi_t c_1 \ldots c_n,$$

$$\varphi_t(Sy)c_1 \ldots c_n = \chi_t(\varphi_t yc_1 \ldots c_n)yc_1 \ldots c_n;$$

let t' be $\varphi_t s' c_1 \ldots c_n$.

Then if φ (of type $(0)^m 0$) is defined by ED and t is in normal form, define φ' in PR by $\varphi' c_1 \ldots c_m = t'$.

Next we note that if A has no free variables of type $\neq 0$ then a proof of A in T_0 can be transformed into one which does not use the extensionality rule ([**10**], p. 8)

$$\frac{P \rightarrow ua_1 \ldots a_n = va_1 \ldots a_n}{P \rightarrow t(u) = t(v)} \tag{G6}$$

($ua_1 \ldots a_n$ of type 0, $a_1 \ldots a_n$ not in P, u, v). For in any proof in T_0 we can eliminate all applications of G6 except those where $t(u)$ is of the form $at_1 \ldots t_n$, a a variable. (Call a constant φ *extensional* if, where $\varphi a_1 \ldots a_n$ is of type 0, for any P we can derive $P \rightarrow \varphi a_1 \ldots a_n = \varphi b_1 \ldots b_n$ from $P \rightarrow a_i = b_i$, $i = 1 \ldots n$, by G6 thus restricted. By induction on the definition of φ we can show every φ extensional and thus derive the unrestricted G6.)

If A has no free variables not of type 0, we can substitute zero functionals for all variables not of type 0 in the proof below the premisses of the last G6, but then these inferences can be eliminated, and by a sequence of such steps we can eliminate all applications of G6.

Given a proof of A in T_0 without G6, we can by pushing substitutions back to the axioms obtain a 'proof' in which no free variables not of type 0 occur.

For each line B, B' is defined; the rules go over into the corresponding rules of PR, and it is trivial that if B is a substitution-case of an axiom, B' is provable in PR. Hence A' is provable in PR, q.e.d.

(b). Let Z_0^* be the extension of Z_0 obtained by allowing introduction of constants by arbitrary primitive recursion. From (a) it is obvious that $IR_2^\Pi + FAC_0$ is a subsystem of $Z_0^* + FAC_0$ and that IR_2^Π is a subsystem of Z_0^*. To prove (b), it suffices to show that $Z_0^* + FAC_0$ is a conservative extension of $IR_1^\Sigma + FAC_0$ and Z_0^* a conservative extension of IR_1^Σ. This is easy to see, using the fact that if φ is primitive recursive, $\varphi(a_1 \ldots a_n) = b$ can be expressed in Z_0 by

$$(\exists y)[T_n(\bar{e}, a_1 \ldots a_n, y) \wedge U(y) = b]$$

(e is a p.r. Gödel number of φ), and the recursion equations can be proved by Σ_1-induction. We omit the details.

(c). $IA_1^\Sigma \to IR_2^\Pi + FAC_0$ is obvious from (b). If Pa expresses in Z_0 'a is the Gödel number of a p.r. definition' then inspection of the representation of primitive recursive functions in IR_1^Σ shows that in IA_1^Σ we can prove

$$\forall x \leqslant a\ [Px \supset \forall y \exists z\ T_1 xyz] \supset \forall x \leqslant Sa\ [Px \supset \forall y \exists y\ T_1 xyz].$$

Suppose every induction axiom in this proof were provable in $IR_1^\Sigma + FAC_0$. Then (since $P0 \supset \forall y \exists z T_1 0yz$ is certainly provable) by the closure of $IR_1^\Sigma +$ FAC_0 under Π_2 induction $\forall x[Px \supset \forall y \exists z\ T_1 xyz]$ would be a theorem of it. But then it would be satisfiable by a primitive recursive function, which is impossible.

THEOREM 3. *If A is Π_2, and A is provable in* IA_1, *then A is provable in* IR_1^Σ.

PROOF. Let A be $\forall x \exists y\ Bxy$. By theorem 2 of [**8**] there is a constant φ of T_0 such that $B(x, \varphi x)$ is provable in T_0. By lemma 5, $B(x, \varphi' x)$ is provable in PR. But then A is provable in Z_0^* and by the argument of (b) above it is provable in IR_1^Σ.

REFERENCES

[1] B. DREBEN and J. DENTON, Herbrand style consistency proofs, these proceedings, 419–433.

[2] K. GÖDEL, Über eine bisher noch nicht benützte Erweiterung des finiten Standpunktes, *Dialectica* **12** (1958) 280–287.

[3] S. C. KLEENE, *Introdution to metamathematics*, New York, Toronto, Amsterdam and Groningen (1952).

[4] G. KREISEL, On the concepts of completeness and interpretation of formal systems, *Fund. Math.* **39** (1952) 103–127.

[5] CH. PARSONS, *On constructive interpretation of predicative mathematics*, thesis, Harvard University (1961).

[6] CH. PARSONS, Reduction of inductions to quantifier-free induction, abstract in *Notices Amer. Math. Soc.* **13** (1966) 740.

[7] CH. PARSONS, Ordinal recursion in partial systems of number theory, abstract in *Ibid.* 857–858.

[8] CH. PARSONS, Proof-theoretic analysis of restricted induction schemata, abstract in *J. Symb. Logic*, to appear.

[9] D. RÖDDING, Über die Eliminierbarkeit von Definitionschemata in der Theorie der rekursiven Funktionen, *Z. math. Logik u. Grundl. Math.* **10** (1964) 315–330.

[10] C. SPECTOR, Provably recursive functionals of analysis: A consistency proof of analysis by an extension of principles formulated in current intuitionistic mathematics, *Proc. Symposia Pure Math.* **5** (1962) 1–27.

APPLICATIONS OF THE CUT ELIMINATION THEOREM TO SOME SUBSYSTEMS OF CLASSICAL ANALYSIS

W. W. TAIT

The principal result of this paper is a constructive consistency proof for the system (Σ_2^1-ADC) of second order number theory with the Σ_2^1 axiom of dependent choice. The proof will proceed by showing that every derivation in this system of an arithmetic formula $\mathfrak{A}$ can be translated into a *normal* (i.e. cut-free) derivation of $\mathfrak{A}$ in infinitary logic. The crux of the proof is the introduction of (constructively) uncountable formulae and derivations, using the constructive conception of uncountable well founded trees which is discussed in Tait [7]. In preparation for the main result, I will summarize some proof theory concerning (Σ_1^1-ADC) and its subsystems. This involves only countably infinite logic, and it yields sharper results than mere consistency. Namely it gives bounds on the provable ordinals of the systems considered (i.e. the ordinals of decidable well-orderings for which induction is derivable). This is possible because of the existence of suitable decidable systems of ordinal notations with which the provable ordinals can be measured. Takeuti [**8**] has been able to use his ordinal diagrams to measure the provable ordinals of (Π_1^1-CA), i.e. second order number theory with the Π_1^1-comprehension axiom; but so far no measure has been found for the stronger systems which I will consider. It seems quite possible that some of the systems of notations, including higher order ordinal diagrams, which have already been developed would suffice; but I have not yet learned how to use them. What remarks I do have on further refinements of my results, and, more generally, of proof theory, will be saved for the end of the paper. Mainly, I will be concerned with the problem of constructive consistency proofs, which is, in any case, of a different character than the (non-constructively meaningful) problem of provable ordinals. On the other hand, I will give independent consistency proofs for certain subsystems of (Σ_2^1-ADC). For, with the discovery of suitable ordinal measures, this would lead to lower bounds on the provable ordinals for these systems.

1. Second order number theory. I will use a, b, $a_1, \ldots$ and x, y, z, $x_1, \ldots$ to denote free and bound numerical variables, resp., and P, Q, $P_1, \ldots$ and X, Y, Z, $X_1, \ldots$ to denote free and bound set variables. The *terms* are built up from free numerical variables, **0**, the successor operation $'$, and computable function constants. For convenience, I will assume that the latter include a constant for each primitive recursive definition. The *-*predicates* are built up from free set variables and constants $\mathscr{P}$, $\mathscr{P}_1, \ldots$ for set valued functions of 0 or more sets. The *atomic *-formulae* are the expressions $\mathfrak{s} = \mathfrak{t}$, $\boldsymbol{F}\mathfrak{s}$, and their negations $\neg\, \mathfrak{s} = \mathfrak{t}$, $\neg\, \boldsymbol{F}\mathfrak{s}$, where $\mathfrak{s}$ and $\mathfrak{t}$ are terms and $\boldsymbol{F}$ a *-predicate. The **-formulae* are built up from the atomic *-formulae by means of the operations $\mathfrak{A} \vee \mathfrak{B}$, $\mathfrak{A} \wedge \mathfrak{B}$, $\bigvee x\mathfrak{A}(x)$, $\bigwedge x\mathfrak{A}(x)$, $\bigvee X\mathfrak{A}(X)$ and $\bigwedge X\mathfrak{A}(X)$. Here $\mathfrak{A}(x)$ ($\mathfrak{A}(X)$) is obtained by replacing b by x (P by X) in a *-formula $\mathfrak{A}(b)$ ($\mathfrak{A}(P)$) which does not contain x (X). The negation $\neg\, \mathfrak{A}$ of a non-atomic *-formula $\mathfrak{A}$ is defined in the obvious way via De Morgan's laws and the law of double negation. The logical axioms and rules of inference are the usual ones for classical two-sorted predicate logic. The non-logical axioms include the equality axioms for numbers, the axioms for **0** and $'$, the defining axioms for the function constants, and the schema $\mathfrak{A}(\mathbf{0}) \wedge \bigwedge x(\mathfrak{A}(x) \to \mathfrak{A}(x')) \to \bigwedge x\mathfrak{A}(x)$ of mathematical induction. These non-logical axioms will be called the *first order axioms.*

Among the additional axioms which we will consider will be certain restricted cases of the axiom schemata of *comprehension*, *choice* and *dependent choice*. The comprehension schema is

CA $$\bigvee Z \bigwedge x(Zx \leftrightarrow \mathfrak{A}(x)).$$

Here, and elsewhere unless it is otherwise specified, $\mathfrak{A}(b)$ may contain free variables other than b, and the same is true for expressions

$$\mathfrak{A}(P_1, \ldots, P_m, b_1, \ldots, b_n).$$

Let $\langle a, b\rangle$ denote a primitive recursive pairing function with inverse $c = ((c)_0, (c)_1)$, where the components $(c)_i$ are primitive recursive. $\boldsymbol{F}^{\mathfrak{s}}\mathfrak{t}$ will be an abbreviation for $\boldsymbol{F}\langle \mathfrak{s}, \mathfrak{t}\rangle$. The choice and dependent choice schemata are

AC $$\bigwedge x \bigvee Z\mathfrak{A}(x, Z) \to \bigvee Z \bigwedge x\mathfrak{A}(x, Z^x).$$

ADC $$\bigwedge X \bigvee Z\mathfrak{A}(X, Z) \to \bigvee Z(Z^0 = P \wedge \bigwedge x\mathfrak{A}(Z^x, Z^{x'})).$$

$P = Q$ is an abbreviation for $\bigwedge x(Px \leftrightarrow Qx)$. If M denotes a class of formulae, then M-CA denotes CA with $\mathfrak{A}(b)$ restricted to M; and similarly for the other schemata.

We will use the terms *formula* and *predicate* for *-formulae and *-predicates which do not contain any set function constants $\mathscr{P}$, $\mathscr{P}_1$, etc. *At and $*\Sigma^0$ denote the sets of atomic and arithmetic (i.e. without set quantifiers) *-formulae, resp. $*\Sigma_1^1$ is the set of *-formulae without universal set quantifiers, and $*\Sigma_2^1$ is the set of *-formulae all of whose existential set quantifiers precede all of its universal set quantifiers. Dropping * all around, we obtain the classes At, Σ^0, Σ_1^1 and Σ_2^1 of formulae. For $k = 1$ and 2, we will also discuss the $*\Delta_k^1$*-comprehension rule*

$$*\Delta_k^1\text{-CR} \qquad \frac{\bigwedge x(\mathfrak{A}(x) \leftrightarrow \neg\, \mathfrak{B}(x))}{\bigvee Z \bigwedge x(Zx \leftrightarrow \mathfrak{A}(x))}$$

if $\mathfrak{A}(b)$ and $\mathfrak{B}(b)$ are $*\Sigma_k^1$, and the $*\Delta_k^1$*-comprehension axiom*

$$*\Delta_k^1\text{-CA} \qquad \bigwedge x(\mathfrak{A}(x) \leftrightarrow \neg\, \mathfrak{B}(x)) \rightarrow \bigvee Z \bigwedge x(Zx \leftrightarrow \mathfrak{A}(x))$$

if $\mathfrak{A}(b)$ and $\mathfrak{B}(b)$ are $*\Sigma_k^1$. Dropping * we obtain Δ_k^1-CR and Δ_k^1-CA. Finally we will consider axioms for *inductively defined sets* of numbers. Let $\mathfrak{A}(P, \vec{Q}, b)$ be a Σ^0-formula which contains only P, $\vec{Q}$ and b as its free variables and does not contain $\neg\, P$. $\vec{Q}$ denotes a list of 0 or more set variables. Then $\mathfrak{A}$ is called an *inductive condition* on P. For each such inductive condition $\mathfrak{A}$, we introduce a set function constant $\mathscr{P}_{\mathfrak{A}}$. The axioms for $\mathscr{P}_{\mathfrak{A}}$ are

$$\text{Ind 1} \qquad \bigwedge x(\mathfrak{A}(\mathscr{P}_{\mathfrak{A}}(\vec{Q}), \vec{Q}, x) \rightarrow \mathscr{P}_{\mathfrak{A}}(\vec{Q})x),$$

$$\text{Ind 2} \qquad \bigwedge x(\mathfrak{A}(\mathfrak{B}, \vec{Q}, x) \rightarrow \mathfrak{B}(x)) \rightarrow \bigwedge x(\mathscr{P}_{\mathfrak{A}}(\vec{Q})x \rightarrow \mathfrak{B}(x)),$$

for arbitrary *-formulae $\mathfrak{B}(b)$. These schemata are collectively denoted by Ind. It is important to notice that inductive conditions are Σ^0; they contain neither set function constants nor set quantifiers.

Besides the first-order axioms, all of the systems which we consider contain *At-CA. If the remaining axioms are all instances of the schema S, the system will be denoted by (S). Since (S) contains At-CA and $\neg\, Pb$ is atomic, (S) will always contain CA for $\neg\, \mathfrak{A}(b)$ when it contains it for $\mathfrak{A}(b)$. $*\Pi_k^1$ is the class of formulae whose negations are $*\Sigma_k^1$. Thus $(*\Pi_k^1\text{-CA}) = (*\Sigma_k^1\text{-CA})$.

It is evident that (*At-CA) $\subseteq$ (*Σ^0-CA) $\equiv$ (*Δ^1_1-CR) $\subseteq$ (*Σ^1_1-AC) $\subseteq$ (*Σ^1_1-ADC). Also, using *Σ^0-AC, every *Σ^1_1 formula can be put in the form $\bigvee Z\mathfrak{A}(Z)$, where $\mathfrak{A}(P)$ is *Σ^0. This will be called the *Σ^1_1-*normal form*: *Σ^1_1NF. From this, it easily follows that (*Σ^1_1-AC) = (*Σ^0-AC) and (*Σ^1_1-ADC) = (*Σ^0-ADC). These remarks also hold without *; but in this case, we get a better normal form. Quantification $\bigvee f$ and $\bigwedge f$ over numerical functions can be introduced in the usual way as relativizations of $\bigvee Z$ and $\bigwedge Z$. Using Σ^0-AC every Σ^1_1 formula can be put in the form $\bigvee f \bigwedge x\mathfrak{A}(\mathbf{f}(x))$, where $\mathfrak{A}(b)$ is Σ^0 and $\mathbf{f}(k)$ is the sequence number of the sequence $(f(0), \ldots, f(k-1))$. This is called Σ^1_1-*normal form*: Σ^1_1-NF. Π^1_1-NF is its negation.

Ind′ is like Ind, except that the inductive conditions $\mathfrak{A}(P, \vec{Q}, b)$ are restricted to the form $\mathfrak{A}_0(\vec{Q}, b) \vee \bigwedge xP\varphi(b, x)$, and Ind′2 is restricted to $\mathfrak{B}(b)$ which are in Π^1_1NF. In (*At-CA, and so in all of the systems we consider every instance of Ind′ can be put in Π^1_2NF (i.e. Σ^1_1NF preceded by universal set quantifiers).

$$(\Sigma^1_1\text{-CA}) = (\text{Ind}').$$

That (Ind′) $\subseteq$ (Σ^1_1-CA) is easy, since we can define $\mathscr{P}_{\mathfrak{A}}(\vec{Q})x \leftrightarrow \bigwedge Z(\bigwedge x(\mathfrak{A}(Z, \vec{O}, x) \rightarrow Zb)$ using Π^1_1-CA; and this definition satisfies Ind′ in (Π^1_1-CA). We will prove the other inclusion:

If k and m are the numbers of $(k_0, \ldots, k_{p-1})$ and $(m_0, \ldots, m_{q-1})$ resp., then $k{*}m$ is the number of $(k_0, \ldots, k_{p-1}, m_0, \ldots, m_{q-1})$ and $k^\frown n$ is the number of $(k_0, \ldots, k_{p-1}, n)$. Let $\mathfrak{A}(\vec{Q}, b)$ be Σ^0 and contain only $\vec{Q}$ and b free. Let $\mathfrak{B}(P, \vec{Q}, b) = \mathfrak{A}(\vec{Q}, b) \vee \bigwedge xPb^\frown x$. Then $\mathfrak{B}$ is an inductive condition. Let $\varphi(a)$ be the least c such that $\neg\, \mathscr{P}_{\mathfrak{B}}(\vec{Q})\varphi(a)^\frown c$, or 0 if no such c exists. φ is arithmetic in $\mathscr{P}_{\mathfrak{B}}(\vec{Q})$ and so it exists in (Ind′). (This uses the fact that Σ^0-CA is contained in (Ind′).) Also $\vdash \bigvee x\mathfrak{A}(\vec{Q}, \boldsymbol{\varphi}(x)) \rightarrow \mathscr{P}_{\mathfrak{B}}(\vec{Q})\mathbf{1}$ in (Ind′), where 1 is the number of the empty sequence, and so $\vdash \bigwedge f \bigvee x\mathfrak{A}(\vec{Q}, \mathbf{f}(x)) \rightarrow \mathscr{P}_{\mathfrak{B}}(\vec{Q})\mathbf{1}$. Conversely, let $\mathfrak{C}(b) = \bigwedge f \bigvee x\mathfrak{A}(\vec{Q}, b{*}\mathbf{f}(x))$. $\mathfrak{C}(b)$ is in Π^1_1NF and clearly $\vdash \bigwedge x(\mathfrak{B}(\mathfrak{C}, \vec{Q}, z) \rightarrow \mathfrak{C}(z))$, so by Ind′2 $\vdash \mathscr{P}_{\mathfrak{B}}(\vec{Q})\mathbf{1} \rightarrow \mathfrak{C}(\mathbf{1})$. But $\mathfrak{C}(\mathbf{1})$ is equivalent to $\bigwedge f \bigvee x\mathfrak{A}(\vec{Q}, \mathbf{f}(x))$ in (Ind′). So we have $\vdash \mathscr{P}_{\mathfrak{B}}(\vec{Q})\mathbf{1} \leftrightarrow \bigwedge f \bigvee x\mathfrak{A}(\vec{Q}, \mathbf{f}(x))$ in (Ind′). Now let $\mathfrak{A}_0(b)$ be in Π^1_1NF. Then $\mathfrak{A}_0(b)$ can be put in the form $\bigwedge f \bigvee x\mathfrak{A}(\vec{Q}, (b), \mathbf{f}(x))$; so $\vdash \bigwedge z(\mathscr{P}_{\mathfrak{B}}(\vec{Q}, \{z\})\mathbf{1} \leftrightarrow \mathfrak{A}_0(z))$ in (Ind′). Hence (by *At-CA) $\vdash \bigvee Z \bigwedge x(Zx \leftrightarrow$

$\mathfrak{A}_0(x)$), i.e. Σ_1^1NF-CA is contained in (Ind′). But using this schema we can derive Σ^0-AC and using the latter, every Σ_1^1 formula can be put in normal form. This completes the proof that (Ind′) = (Σ_1^1-CA).

It also follows from the above that every Σ_2^1-formula can be put in $*\Sigma_1^1$ form in (Ind′). Thus (Δ_2^1-CR) $\subseteq$ (Δ_1^1-CR+Ind′) and (Σ_2^1-ADC) $\subseteq$ ($*\Sigma_1^1$-ADC+Ind′). The proof that (Σ_1^1-CA) $\subseteq$ (Ind′) also shows that (Ind) contains the axiom schema of *bar induction* BI:

$$\bigwedge f \bigvee x \mathfrak{A}(\vec{Q}, \mathbf{f}(x)) \wedge \bigwedge x(\mathfrak{A}(\vec{Q}, x) \to \mathfrak{C}(x)) \wedge \bigwedge x(\bigwedge y \mathfrak{C}(x^\frown y) \to \mathfrak{C}(x)) \to \mathfrak{C}(\mathbf{1}).$$

For define the inductive condition $\mathfrak{B}(P, \vec{Q}, b)$ as above; we saw that the first conjunct in the antecedent of BI implies $\mathscr{P}_{\mathfrak{B}}(\vec{Q})\mathbf{1}$, while the second and third imply $\mathscr{P}_{\mathfrak{B}}(\vec{Q})\mathbf{1} \to C(\mathbf{1})$ by Ind 2.

§ 2. **Countable logic.** The *countable *-formulae* and **-predicates* are built up as follows: T and $\neg$ T are *-formulae. The *-formulae are closed under set quantification, denumerable disjunction $\bigvee_n \mathfrak{A}_n$ and denumerable conjunction $\bigwedge_n \mathfrak{A}_n$. Each free set variable is a *-predicate. If $\mathscr{P}$ has n argument places and $\boldsymbol{F}_1, \ldots, \boldsymbol{F}_n$ are *-predicates, then so is $\mathscr{P}(\boldsymbol{F}_1, \ldots, \boldsymbol{F}_n)$. If $\mathfrak{A}_0, \mathfrak{A}_1, \ldots$ are *-formulae which contain no quantifiers, then $\lambda x \mathfrak{A}_x$ is a *-predicate. If $\boldsymbol{F}$ is a *-predicate, then $\boldsymbol{F}\mathbf{n}$ and $\neg \boldsymbol{F}\mathbf{n}$ are *-formulae for each n. We will identify $\lambda x \mathfrak{A}_x \mathbf{n}$ with $\mathfrak{A}_n$ and $\neg \lambda x \mathfrak{A}_x \mathbf{n}$ with $\neg \mathfrak{A}_n$. The *countable formulae* and *predicates* are the *-formulae and *-predicates which contain no set function constants. The atomic (*-)formulae are those of the forms T, $P\mathbf{n}$, $\mathscr{P}(\vec{\boldsymbol{F}})\mathbf{n}$, and their negations.

From now on I will drop the term countable and refer to the (*-)predicates and (*-)formulae of § 1 as *finitary*. But we will only consider finitary (*-)formulae which contain no free numerical variables. Finitary (*-)predicates and (*-)formulae form a subclass of the (countable) (*-)predicates and (*-)formulae, if we make the following identifications: $\bigvee x \mathfrak{A}(x) = \bigvee_n \mathfrak{A}(\mathbf{n})$; $\bigwedge x \mathfrak{A}(x) = \bigwedge_n \mathfrak{A}(\mathbf{n})$; if $\mathfrak{s}$ has the value n, we identify it with the numeral $\mathbf{n}$; $\mathbf{n} = \mathbf{n}$ is identified with T; and for $m \neq n$, $\mathbf{m} = \mathbf{n}$ is identified with $\neg$ T.

The rules of inference for countable logic are most conveniently stated for finite sets Γ, Δ, Γ_1, etc., of *-formulae. These should be regarded as expressing disjunctions of all their members. $\Gamma + \Delta$ denotes the union of Γ and Δ. The axioms are T (i.e. (T)), $P\mathbf{n} + \neg P\mathbf{n}$ and $\mathscr{P}(\vec{\boldsymbol{F}})\mathbf{n} + \neg \mathscr{P}(\vec{\boldsymbol{F}})\mathbf{n}$, for all P, $\mathscr{P}$, $\mathbf{n}$ and lists of *-predicates $\overleftarrow{\boldsymbol{F}}$. The *normal* rules of inference are

$$\mathbf{A} \qquad \Gamma + \Delta \text{ (if } \Delta \text{ is an axiom)}$$

$$\bigvee \quad \frac{\Gamma + \mathfrak{A}_k}{\Gamma + \bigvee_n \mathfrak{A}_n} \text{ (some } k) \qquad \bigwedge \quad \frac{\Gamma + \mathfrak{A}_k}{\Gamma + \bigwedge_n \mathfrak{A}_n} \text{ (all } k)$$

$$\exists \quad \frac{\Gamma + \mathfrak{A}(\boldsymbol{F})}{\Gamma + \bigvee \mathrm{Z}\mathfrak{A}(\mathrm{Z})} \qquad \forall \quad \frac{\Gamma + \mathfrak{A}(P)}{\Gamma + \bigwedge \mathrm{Z}\mathfrak{A}(\mathrm{Z})}$$

In $\forall$, P does not occur in any member of Γ. In $\exists$, $\boldsymbol{F}$ is a *-predicate, called the *predicate of quantification.* Besides the normal rules, we have the *cut rule*

$$\mathbf{C} \quad \frac{\Gamma + \mathfrak{A} \qquad \Gamma + \neg\, \mathfrak{A}}{\Gamma}$$

$\mathfrak{A}$ and $\neg\,\mathfrak{A}$ are called the *cut formulae.* (Since $\neg\neg\,\mathfrak{A} = \mathfrak{A}$, this rule is symmetric.)

Let $\mathscr{F} = (\mathfrak{F}_0, \mathfrak{F}_1, \ldots)$ be a set of *-predicates. $\mathscr{F}$ is *closed* if it contains the atomic predicates and if whenever $\mathfrak{F}_k = \mathfrak{G}(P)$, then for every n, $\mathfrak{G}(\mathfrak{F}_n)$ is in it. Note that $\mathscr{F}$ need not contain any atomic *-predicates. For example At = the set of $\lambda x\mathfrak{A}(x)$ and Σ^0 = the set of $\lambda x\mathfrak{B}(x)$, where $\mathfrak{A}(\mathbf{0})$ is finitary atomic and $\mathfrak{B}(\mathbf{0})$ is finitary Σ^0, are closed. If $\mathscr{F}$ is closed, and we will assume always that it is, unless specified otherwise, $(\mathscr{F})$ will refer to the system with the predicates of quantification restricted to $\mathscr{F}$.

To measure the length of derivations and the complexity of cut formula, we introduce a decidable linear system of ordinal notations. These will be denoted by u, v, x, y, z, u_1, etc., and the ordering relation by $<$. This is to be decidable; and, moreover, the system is to be closed under the function $\chi^{\mathrm{z}}(\mathrm{u})$, where $\chi^0(\mathrm{u}) = 2^{\mathrm{u}}$ and for $\mathrm{z} > 0$, $\chi^{\mathrm{z}}(\mathrm{u})$ is the $(\mathrm{u}+1)$st fixed point of all the χ^{x} with $\mathrm{x} < \mathrm{z}$. χ is of course to be computable on the notations. Such systems of notations are well-known. Let $\subset$ denote a well-founded partial ordering of $\alpha, \beta, \gamma, \ldots$. $\beta \leqslant \mathrm{z}$ (β is of *rank* $\leqslant \mathrm{z}$) is inductively defined to mean that, for each $\alpha \subset \beta$ there is an $\mathrm{x} < \mathrm{z}$ with $\alpha \preccurlyeq \mathrm{x}$. $\beta \prec \mathrm{z}$ means that $\beta \preccurlyeq \mathrm{x}$ for some $\mathrm{x} < \mathrm{z}$. The class of *-formulae and the class of derivations can be regarded as wellfounded partial orderings, built up from the atomic *-formula and from the instances of $\mathbf{A}$, resp.. So the rank relation makes sense for both of these classes. Note that atomic

*-formulae are of rank 0 (i.e. $\leqslant 0$), even in the case $\mathscr{P}(\vec{F})\mathbf{n}$, where $\vec{F}$ may consist of very complex predicates. We say that a derivation is of *cut degree* $\leqslant$ v if every cut formula in it is of rank < v. $\vdash \Delta[\mathrm{u}, \mathrm{v}]$ means that there is a derivation of Δ of rank < u (not $\leqslant$ u, as in Tait **[6]**) and cut degree $\leqslant$ v. $\vdash \Delta[\mathrm{u}]$ means that there is a normal derivation of Δ of rank < u. I.e. $[\mathrm{u}] = [\mathrm{u}, 0]$.

I. *If* $\vdash \mathfrak{A}$ *in* (*At-CA) (*in* *Σ^0-CA), *then* $\vdash \mathfrak{A}[\omega^2, \mathrm{k}]$ *in* (*At) (*in* (*Σ^0)) *for some* k < ω. *Similarly without* *.

This is essentially proved by Schütte **[5]**. There are two other results which form the basis for the present paper. $\mathscr{F} \preccurlyeq \mathrm{z}$ means $\mathfrak{F}_k \prec \mathrm{z}$ for each k.

II. *If* $\vdash \Delta[\mathrm{u}, \mathrm{v}]$ *in* ($\mathscr{F}$), *where* $\mathscr{F} \preccurlyeq \mathrm{z}$ *and* $\mathrm{z}+\mathrm{v} \leqslant \omega^{\mathrm{x}_1} + \ldots + \omega^{\mathrm{x}_n}$ *then* $\vdash \Delta[\chi^{\mathrm{x}_1}(\ldots \chi^{\mathrm{x}_n}(2\mathrm{z}+\mathrm{u}) \ldots)]$ *in* ($\mathscr{F}$).

Let $\subset$ be a decidable well-ordering, and let

$$J(\subset) = \bigwedge \mathrm{x}(\bigwedge \mathrm{y}(\mathrm{y} \subset \mathrm{x} \rightarrow P\mathrm{y}) \rightarrow P\mathrm{x}) \rightarrow \bigwedge \mathrm{x} P\mathrm{x}.$$

So $J(\subset)$ expresses well-foundedness. Let $|\subset| \leqslant \mathrm{z}$ mean that $\subset$ is well-founded and each n is of rank $\leqslant$ z in the ordering $\subset$.

III. *If* $\vdash J(\subset)[\chi^1(\mathrm{x})]$ *in* ($\mathscr{F}$), *then* $|\subset| < \chi^1(\mathrm{x})$.

The proofs of II and III are in Tait **[6]**.

THEOREM 1. ε_0 *is the ordinal* (*i.e. least bound on the provable ordinals*) *of* (*At-CA), *and* $\varepsilon_{\varepsilon_0}$ *is the ordinal of* (*Σ^0-CA).

As usual, $\varepsilon_{\mathrm{z}} = \chi^1(1+\mathrm{z})$. That ε_0 and $\varepsilon_{\varepsilon_0}$ are bounds on the provable ordinals of these systems follows from I–III, since *At $\preccurlyeq 1$ and *$\Sigma \preccurlyeq \omega$. The two parts of the theorem are due to Gentzen [3] and Schütte [5] resp. (Note that (Σ^0-CA) is simply the lowest level of ramified analysis.) In the following sections we consider some further applications of I–III.

3. Some subsystems of (*Σ_1^1-ADC). $\mathfrak{A}(\mathscr{F})$ is the result of replacing each part $\bigvee Z\mathfrak{B}(Z)$ and $\bigwedge Z\mathfrak{B}(Z)$ of $\mathfrak{A}$ by $\bigvee_k \mathfrak{B}(\boldsymbol{F}_k)$ and $\bigwedge_k \mathfrak{B}(\boldsymbol{F}_k)$ resp., having first made these substitutions in $\mathfrak{B}(P)$.

$\mathfrak{A}(\mathscr{F}) \preccurlyeq \mathrm{z}+\mathrm{u}$ if $\mathscr{F} \preccurlyeq \mathrm{z}$ (i.e. $\boldsymbol{F}_k \prec \mathrm{z}$ for each k) and $\mathfrak{A} \preccurlyeq \mathrm{u}$. Let $*\mathscr{F}_0 = *\mathrm{At}$. For limits z, let $*\mathscr{F}^{\mathrm{z}}$ enumerate $\bigcup_{\mathrm{x}<\mathrm{z}} *\mathscr{F}_{\mathrm{x}}$. Let $*\mathscr{F}_{\mathrm{z}+1}$ enumerate the least closed class including $*\mathscr{F}_{\mathrm{z}}$ and containing $\lambda \mathrm{x}\mathfrak{A}(*\mathscr{F}_{\mathrm{z}})(\mathrm{x})$ for each finitary *Σ_1^1 formula $\mathfrak{A}(b)$. It is easy to show that $*\mathscr{F}_{\mathrm{z}} \preccurlyeq \omega^{\mathrm{z}}$. Dropping * we obtain the sets $\mathscr{F}_{\mathrm{z}} \preccurlyeq \omega^{\mathrm{z}}$.

LEMMA 1. *If* $\vdash \mathfrak{A}$ *in* ($*\Delta^1_1$-CR), *then* $\vdash \mathfrak{A}[\chi^\omega(\mathbf{0})]$ *in some* ($*\mathscr{F}_k$). *Similarly without* *.

The *-less proof is in Tait [6]. The proof with * is just the same. So

THEOREM 2. *The ordinal of* ($*\Delta^1_1$-CR) *is* $\chi^\omega(0)$.

The fact that $\chi^\omega(0)$ is the *least* bound on the provable ordinals follows easily from (6.19) of Feferman [1].

THEOREM 3. *The ordinal of* ($*\Sigma^1_1$-AC), ($*\Sigma^1_1$-ADC) *and* ($*\Delta^1_1$-CA) *is* $\chi^{\varepsilon_0}(0)$.

That this is a bound on the provable ordinals was first proved by Friedman. That it is the least bound for (Σ^1_1-AC) follows easily from (6.19) of Feferman [1]. That it is the least bound for (Δ^1_1-CA) follows from Friedman's [2] result that (Σ^1_1-ADC) is a conservative extension of (Δ^1_1-CA) for Π^1_2 formulae. In Tait [6] I obtained $\chi^{\varepsilon_0}(0)$ as a bound for (Σ^1_1-AC) by showing that every proof in this system of a Σ^1_1-formula preceded by universal set quantifiers can be translated into a normal derivation of rank $< \chi^{\varepsilon_0}(0)$ in some suitable ($\mathscr{F}$) with $\mathscr{F} \prec \varepsilon_0$. The proof for ($*\Sigma^1_1$-ADC) is essentially the same; but I will give it without the ordinal bounds.

Let $\mathfrak{A}(P, Q)$ be finitary $*\Sigma^0$ and $\mathscr{F} = \mathscr{F}(P)$ a set of *-predicates $\boldsymbol{F}_k = \boldsymbol{F}_k(P)$, $k \geqslant 0$. Set

$$H = H(\mathscr{F}(P), P) = \lambda x \bigvee_n (\mathfrak{A}_n(P\boldsymbol{F}_n) \wedge \bigwedge_{k<n} \neg \mathfrak{A}(P, \boldsymbol{F}_k) \wedge \boldsymbol{F}_n x).$$

Then

$$\vdash \bigvee_n \mathfrak{A}(P, \boldsymbol{F}_n) \rightarrow \mathfrak{A}(P, H).$$

Let $\boldsymbol{F}$ be *At. Set $\boldsymbol{G}_0 = \boldsymbol{F}$ and $\boldsymbol{G}_{n+1} = H(\mathscr{F}(\boldsymbol{G}_n), \boldsymbol{G}_n)$. The *-predicate $\boldsymbol{G} = \lambda x \boldsymbol{G}_{(x)_0}(x)_1$ is called the *dependent choice predicate for* $\mathfrak{A}(P, Q)$ *and* $\boldsymbol{F}$ *relative to* $\mathscr{F}$. Substituting $\boldsymbol{G}^n$ for P in the above derivation, we have

$$\vdash \bigvee_k \mathfrak{A}(\boldsymbol{G}^n, \boldsymbol{F}_k(\boldsymbol{G}^n)) \rightarrow \mathfrak{A}(\boldsymbol{G}^n, \boldsymbol{G}^{n+1}) \tag{1}$$

for all n. Let $*\mathscr{F}^{\mathrm{z}}$ be defined like $*\mathscr{F}_{\mathrm{z}}$ above, except that $*\mathscr{F}^{\mathrm{z}+1}$ enumerates the least closed class which includes $*\mathscr{F}^{\mathrm{z}}$ and contains the dependent choice predicate relative to $*\mathscr{F}^{\mathrm{z}}$ for each $*\Sigma^0$ formula $\mathfrak{A}(P, Q)$ and each $\boldsymbol{F}$ in *At. $\mathfrak{A}^{\mathrm{u}}$ and $\mathfrak{A}^{\mathrm{u}}_{(n)}$ will always denote *-formulae of the form $\bigvee_k \mathfrak{A}(\mathscr{F}_k)$, where the $\mathscr{F}_k$ are (not necessarily closed) lists of *-predicates in $*\mathscr{F}^{\mathrm{u}}$ containing all the predicates which occur in $\mathfrak{A}$. If $\mathfrak{A}$ is $*\Sigma^1_1$, then $\vdash \mathfrak{A}^{\mathrm{u}} \rightarrow \mathfrak{A}(*\mathscr{F}^{\mathrm{u}})$. Δ^{u} and $\Delta^{\mathrm{u}}_{(n)}$ denote sets consisting of *-formulae $\mathfrak{A}^{\mathrm{u}}$ where $\mathfrak{A}$ is in Δ. Note that each Δ^{u} is in Δ^{v} when $\mathrm{u} < \mathrm{v}$; and if $\vdash \Gamma_n + \Delta^{\mathrm{u}}_{(n)}$

for each n, then there is a single Δ^u with $\vdash \Gamma_n + \Delta^u$ for all n. Also, if $\vdash \mathfrak{A}(P_1, \ldots, P_n) + \Delta^u$, $P_1, \ldots, P_n$ are not in any formula of Δ, and $G_1, \ldots, G_n$ are in $*\mathscr{F}^u$, then $\vdash \mathfrak{A}(G_1, \ldots, G_n) + \Delta^u_{(0)}$ for some $\Delta^u_{(0)}$ simply by substituting G_i for P_i throughout the derivation.

LEMMA 2. *Let Γ consist of *-formulae $\neg \mathfrak{B}$ where $\mathfrak{B}$ is an instance of* $*\Sigma^0$-ADC *preceded by* 0 *or more universal set quantifiers; and let Δ consist of formulae of the form $\bigvee X_1 \ldots X_m \bigwedge Y_1 \ldots Y_n \mathfrak{A}(X_1, \ldots, X_m, Y_1, \ldots, Y_n)$ where $\mathfrak{A}$ is $*\Sigma^1_1$. Then $\vdash \Gamma + \Delta[u]$ in* (*At) *implies $\vdash \Delta^u$ for some Δ^u.*

PROOF. The proof is by induction on u. The only case which does not follow immediately from the induction hypothesis is when the last step of the derivation is of the form

$$\frac{\Gamma' + \Delta + \bigwedge X \bigvee Y \mathfrak{A}(X, Y) \qquad \Gamma' + \Delta + \bigwedge Z(\neg Z^0 = F \vee \bigwedge_n \mathfrak{A}(Z^n, Z^{n'}))}{\Gamma + \Delta}$$

where $\Gamma = \Gamma' + \bigwedge X \bigvee Y \mathfrak{A}(X, Y) \rightarrow \bigvee Z(Z^0 - F \wedge \bigwedge_n \mathfrak{A}(Z^n, Z^{n'}))$.

There are normal derivations of the premises of rank $<$ v for some v $<$ u. By the reduction lemma of Tait [6] $\Gamma' + \Delta + \bigvee Y \mathfrak{A}(P, Y)[\mathrm{v}]$ and $\vdash \Gamma' + \Delta + \neg P^0 = F \vee \bigvee_n \neg \mathfrak{A}(P^n, P^{n'})[\mathrm{v}]$, where P is a new variable. By the induction hypothesis $\vdash \Delta + \bigvee_k \mathfrak{A}(P, F^{\mathrm{v}}_k)$, where the F^{v}_k are the elements of $*\mathscr{F}^{\mathrm{v}}$, and $\vdash \Delta^{\mathrm{v}} + \neg P^0 = F \vee \bigvee_n \neg \mathfrak{A}(P^n, P^{n'})$. Substituting the choice predicate G for A and F relative to $*\mathscr{F}^{\mathrm{v}}$ for P in these, and applying (1), $\vdash \Delta^u_{(n)} + \mathfrak{A}(G^n, G^{n'})$ for each n and $\vdash \Delta^u + \neg G^0 = F \vee \bigvee_n \neg \mathfrak{A}(G^n, G^{n'})$, since G is in $*\mathscr{F}^u$. We can assume $\Delta^u_{(n)} = \Delta^u$ for each n, and we have $\vdash G^0 = F$. So by two cuts $\vdash \Delta^u$.

It is not hard to see that $*\mathscr{F}^u \leqslant \omega^{2z}$ and to obtain the bound $\chi^u(0)$ on the derivation of Δ^u above. Note that the ($*\Sigma^1_1$-ADC) case of theorem 3 is an immediate consequence of the lemma (with the bounds). For $\vdash \mathfrak{A}$ in ($*\Sigma^1_1$-ADC) = ($*\Sigma^0$-ADC) means that $\vdash \bigwedge_{i=1}^{n} \mathfrak{B}_i \rightarrow \mathfrak{A}$ in At-ADC), where each $\mathfrak{B}_i$ is an instance of ($*\Sigma^0$-ADC) preceded by universal quantifiers. I.e. $\vdash \{\mathfrak{B}_1, \ldots, \neg \mathfrak{B}_n, \mathfrak{A}\}[\varepsilon_0]$ in (At). When $\mathfrak{A}$ is $*\Sigma^1_1$, we can apply the lemma to obtain $\vdash \mathfrak{A}[\chi^{\varepsilon_0}(0)]$ in ($*\mathscr{F}^u$) for some u, since $\vdash \mathfrak{A}^u$ implies $\vdash$ A in ($*\mathscr{F}^u$) when A is $*\Sigma^1_1$.

4. Uncountable logic; restricted upper bound principle. The species T_z of *well-founded trees of class* z are defined by recursion on z: T_0 is the set of natural numbers. For $z > 0$ T_z is inductively defined by: $\langle z, 0\rangle \in T_z$, and if $x < z$ and f is a constructive operation defined on T_x,

$$\forall_n \in T_x(fn \in T_z) \Rightarrow \langle z, x, f\rangle \in T_z .$$

See Tait [7] for a discussion of a constructive conception of such inductive definitions. Under Church's thesis, the well-founded trees can be coded by numbers; but of course T_z is uncountable (constructively) for $z > 0$. The T_z are closely related to the so called constructive higher number classes of Kreider–Rodgers [4], but are simpler because we do not require that the subtrees of a given tree be simply oıdered. $\boldsymbol{m}, \boldsymbol{n}, \boldsymbol{k}, \boldsymbol{m}_1$, etc., will range over well-founded trees from now on.

We extend infinitary logic to uncountable formulae and derivations by introducing disjunction $\bigvee^z_{\boldsymbol{n}}$ and conjunction $\bigwedge^z_{\boldsymbol{n}}$ over arbitrary T_z. Thus $\bigvee^0$ and $\bigwedge^0$ are the countable operations $\bigvee$ and $\bigwedge$ introduced above. The rules of inference are the same as above, with the obvious modification of V and $\mathsf{\Lambda}$. A formula is of $\bigvee$*-class* ($\bigwedge$*-class*) z if $x < z$ whenever $\bigvee^x$ ($\bigwedge^x$) occurs in it. It is of *class* z if it is both of $\bigvee$-class z and of $\bigwedge$-class z. $\boldsymbol{m} \in \boldsymbol{n}$ will mean that $\boldsymbol{n}$ is of the form $\langle z, x, f\rangle$ and $\boldsymbol{m} = f\boldsymbol{k}$ for some $\boldsymbol{k} \in T_x$. If $\boldsymbol{n} \in T_z$, then $\bigvee_{\boldsymbol{m}\in\boldsymbol{n}}$ and $\bigwedge_{\boldsymbol{m}\in\boldsymbol{n}}$ are of class z. Put

$$\bigvee_{\boldsymbol{k}}{}^{\boldsymbol{n}}\mathfrak{A}_{\boldsymbol{k}} = \bigvee_{\boldsymbol{m}\in\boldsymbol{n}}(\mathfrak{A}_{\boldsymbol{m}} \vee \bigvee{}^{\boldsymbol{m}}\mathfrak{A}_{\boldsymbol{k}})$$

and $\bigwedge_{\boldsymbol{k}}^{\boldsymbol{n}} = \neg \bigvee_{\boldsymbol{k}}^{\boldsymbol{n}} \neg$. If $\boldsymbol{n} \in T_z$, then $\bigvee^{\boldsymbol{n}}$ and $\bigwedge^{\boldsymbol{n}}$ are of class z.

The formulae and proofs which will interest us are too big to measure with countable ordinals (at least, in the present very general setting.) So we will measure them with well-founded trees instead. The rank relation is defined just as with ordinals.

IV. *If* $\vdash \Delta[\boldsymbol{m}, \boldsymbol{n}]$ *in* $(\mathscr{F})$, *then* $\vdash \Delta[\mathrm{p}]$ *in* $(\mathscr{F})$ *for some* p.

The proof is exactly the same as in the countable case and is well-known. It proceeds by induction on $\boldsymbol{n}$, and within that by induction on $\boldsymbol{m}$. In the present setting p is of no significance. This is because it is generally uncountable, whereas the ordinals of formal systems are $< \omega_1$. I will return to this point below.

For the remainder of this section, we will be considering only propositional logic i.e. the quantifiers $\bigvee_Z$ and $\bigwedge_Z$ aıe dropped.

Let $\Delta(\bigvee^{\boldsymbol{n}})$ denote the result of replacing some occurrences of $\bigvee^z$ in formulae of Δ by $\bigvee^{\boldsymbol{n}}$ (where $\boldsymbol{n} \in T_z$). As a consequence of IV, we have

LEMMA 3. *If* $\vdash \Delta$ *and* Δ *is of* $\bigwedge$*-class* z, *then* $\vdash \Delta(\bigvee^{\boldsymbol{n}})$ *for some* $\boldsymbol{n} \in \mathsf{T}_z$.

PROOF. This is easily proved by induction on the rank of a normal derivation of Δ, noting that each step of such a derivation is of $\bigwedge$-class z. If the last step is by $\bigvee$ applied to one of the designated $\bigvee^z$, then we can assume that it has the form $\Delta + \mathfrak{A}_k \Rightarrow \Delta$, where $\boldsymbol{k} \in \mathsf{T}_z$. By the induction hypothesis $\vdash \Delta(\bigvee^{\boldsymbol{p}}) + \mathfrak{A}_k(\bigvee^{\boldsymbol{p}})$ for some $\boldsymbol{p} \in \mathsf{T}_z$. The lemma follows by choosing $\boldsymbol{n}$ with $\boldsymbol{k}$ and $\boldsymbol{p} \in \boldsymbol{n}$, noting that $\vdash \Delta(\bigvee^{\boldsymbol{p}})$ implies $\vdash \Delta(\bigvee^{\boldsymbol{n}})$ when $\boldsymbol{p} \in \boldsymbol{n}$. The only other crucial case is when the last step is $\vdash \Gamma + \mathfrak{A}_k$ (all $\boldsymbol{k} \in \mathsf{T}_x$) $\Rightarrow \vdash \Gamma + \bigwedge_{\boldsymbol{k}}^{x} \mathfrak{A}_k = \Delta$. We have $\vdash \Gamma(\bigvee^{f\boldsymbol{k}}) + \mathfrak{A}_k(\bigvee^{f\boldsymbol{k}})$ for each $\boldsymbol{k} \in \mathsf{T}_x$, and since Δ is of $\bigwedge$-class z, x < z. So we can take $\boldsymbol{n} = \langle z, x, f \rangle$.

The main result we need concerns the *restricted upper bound principle*

$$\text{RUB} \qquad \bigwedge_{\boldsymbol{m}}^{x} \bigvee_{\boldsymbol{n}}^{z} \mathfrak{A}_{mn} \rightarrow \bigvee_{\boldsymbol{p}}^{z} \bigwedge_{\boldsymbol{m}}^{x} \bigvee_{\boldsymbol{n}}^{\boldsymbol{p}} \mathfrak{A}_{mn},$$

where x < z and each $\mathfrak{A}_{mn}$ is of class z. The corresponding rule (from the antecedent to infer the consequent) is valid for the normal rules by lemma 3. But RUB is not itself provable in our system, for it is non-constructively false. Let $\mathfrak{A}_{mn}$ mean that $\boldsymbol{n}$ is the $\boldsymbol{m}$th element in some non-constructive enumeration of T_1, x = 0 and z = 1. RUB^{v} denotes the restriction of RUB to z < v. Let $\mathfrak{B} = \bigvee_{\boldsymbol{k}}^{w} \mathfrak{B}_k$, where each $\mathfrak{B}_k \in \text{RUB}$. $\mathfrak{B}^{(\text{v})}$ denotes the disjunction of all the $\neg \mathfrak{B}_k$ with $\mathfrak{B}_k \in \text{RUB}^{\text{v}}$.

V. *If* $\vdash \mathfrak{B} + \Delta[\text{p}]$, *where* Δ *is of* $\bigwedge$*-class* u *and each* $\mathfrak{B}_k \in \text{RUB}^{\text{v}}$, *then* $\vdash \mathfrak{B}^{(\text{u})} + \Delta$.

We assume that this is true for all u, p and v where (i) v < v′ and p < p′, or (ii) v < v′; and we prove it for v = v′ and p = p′. The induction hypothesis (i) obviously takes care of all cases but when the last step in the derivation is $\mathfrak{B} + \neg \mathfrak{B}_k + \Delta \Rightarrow \mathfrak{B} + \Delta$, by $\bigvee$, where $\mathfrak{B}_k$ is $\text{RUB}^{\text{v}} - \text{RUB}^{\text{u}}$. I.e. $\mathfrak{B}_k = \bigwedge_{\boldsymbol{m}}^{x} \bigvee_{\boldsymbol{n}}^{z} \mathfrak{A}_{mn} \rightarrow \bigvee_{\boldsymbol{r}}^{z} \bigwedge_{\boldsymbol{m}}^{x} \bigvee_{\boldsymbol{n}}^{\boldsymbol{r}} \mathfrak{A}_{mn}$, where the premise has a normal proof of rank < q < p. Replacing $\neg \mathfrak{B}_k$ by its conjuncts, we get

$$(1) \qquad \vdash \mathfrak{B} + \Delta + \bigwedge_{\boldsymbol{m}}^{x} \bigvee_{\boldsymbol{n}}^{z} \mathfrak{A}_{mn}[\text{q}],$$

$$(2) \qquad \vdash \mathfrak{B} + \Delta + \bigvee_{\boldsymbol{m}}^{x} \bigwedge_{\boldsymbol{n}}^{\boldsymbol{r}} \mathfrak{A}_{mn}[\text{q}] \quad (\text{all } \boldsymbol{r} \in \mathsf{T}_z).$$

By (i) and (1) $\vdash \mathfrak{B}^{(\text{z})} + \Delta + \bigwedge_{\boldsymbol{m}}^{x} \bigvee_{\boldsymbol{n}}^{z} \mathfrak{A}_{mn}$, since $\Delta + \bigwedge_{\boldsymbol{m}}^{x} \bigvee_{\boldsymbol{n}}^{z} \mathfrak{A}_{mn}$ is of $\bigwedge$-class z. So by lemma 3 $\vdash \mathfrak{B}^{(\text{z})} + \Delta + \bigwedge_{\boldsymbol{m}}^{x} \bigvee_{\boldsymbol{n}}^{\boldsymbol{r}} \mathfrak{A}_{mn}$ for some $\boldsymbol{r} \in \mathsf{T}_z$. By (i) and (2) $\vdash \mathfrak{B}^{(\text{z})} + \Delta + \bigvee_{\boldsymbol{m}}^{x} \bigwedge_{\boldsymbol{n}}^{\boldsymbol{r}} \neg \mathfrak{A}_{mn}$: and so by a cut, $\vdash \mathfrak{B}^{(\text{z})} + \Delta$. Since $\mathfrak{B}_k$ is RUB^{z}

for the $\neg\,\mathfrak{B}_k$ which are disjuncts of $\mathfrak{B}^{(z)}$ and $z < v$, $\vdash \mathfrak{B}^{(u)} + \Delta$ follows by (ii).

Since RUB^1 is empty we have the following

COROLLARY. *If Δ is of $\bigwedge$-class* 1, *then* RUB $\vdash \Delta$ *implies* $\vdash \Delta$.

We will use RUB to study the theory of inductively defined sets. First we need

LEMMA 4. *Let $\mathfrak{B}(P)$ be of class* z *and not contain $\neg\, P$. Let $\mathfrak{A}_k(b)$ be of class* z *for each $\boldsymbol{k} \in \mathsf{T}_z$, and assume that for each such $\boldsymbol{k}$ and each $\boldsymbol{m} \in \boldsymbol{k}$, $\vdash \mathfrak{A}_m(\mathbf{n}) \rightarrow \mathrm{A}_k(\mathbf{n})$ for all $n \in \mathsf{T}_0$. Then* RUB $\vdash \mathfrak{B}(\bigvee_k{}^{z}\mathfrak{A}_k) \rightarrow \bigvee_k{}^{z}\mathfrak{B}(\mathfrak{A}_k)$.

PROOF. The proof is by induction on $\mathfrak{B}(P)$. If $\mathfrak{B}(P) = P_{\mathbf{n}}$, there is nothing to prove. Assume that it holds for $\mathfrak{B}_m(P)'$ for each $\boldsymbol{m} \in \mathsf{T}_x$ where $x < z$. Then it clearly holds for $\bigvee_m{}^{x}\mathfrak{B}_m(P)$. By RUB

$$\bigwedge_m{}^{x}\mathfrak{B}_m(\bigvee_k{}^{z}\mathfrak{A}_k) \rightarrow \bigwedge_m{}^{x}\bigvee_k{}^{z}\mathfrak{B}_m(\mathfrak{A}_k) \rightarrow \bigvee_k{}^{z}\bigwedge_m{}^{x}\mathfrak{B}_m(\mathfrak{A}_k),$$

since $\bigvee_i{}^{P}\mathfrak{B}_m(\mathfrak{A}_i) \rightarrow \mathfrak{B}_m(\mathfrak{A}_P)$.

In what follows $(\mathrm{PL})^z$ will denote the system of *propositional logic of class* z; i.e. which involves only formulae which contain no quantifiers and are of class z. It is obvious that each formula and derivation of (PL^z) can be coded by a tree in T_z.

5. Theory of inductively defined sets. Let $\mathfrak{A}(P, b)$ be of class z and not contain $\neg\, P$. Set

$$\mathscr{P}^k(b) = \bigvee_{m \in k} \mathfrak{A}(\mathscr{P}^m, b)$$

for each $\boldsymbol{k} \in \mathsf{T}_z$ so that $\mathscr{P}^k$ is of class z. Set

$$\mathscr{P}(b) = \bigvee_k{}^{z}\mathscr{P}^k(b).$$

Choose $\boldsymbol{m}$ with $\boldsymbol{k} \in \boldsymbol{m}$. Then $\vdash \mathfrak{A}(\mathscr{P}^k, b) \rightarrow \mathscr{P}^m(b)$, and so $\vdash \mathfrak{A}(\mathscr{P}^k, b) \rightarrow \mathscr{P}(b)$, for all $\boldsymbol{k} \in \mathsf{T}_z$. So by lemma 4

(a). RUB $\qquad \vdash \bigwedge_n{}^{0}((\mathfrak{A}\mathscr{P}, \mathbf{n}) \rightarrow \mathscr{P}(\mathbf{n}))$.

Also, using the fact that $\neg\, P$ does not occur in $\mathfrak{A}(P, b)$,

(b). $\qquad \vdash \bigwedge_n{}^{0}(\mathfrak{A}(\mathfrak{B}, \mathbf{n}) \rightarrow \mathfrak{B}(\mathbf{n})) \rightarrow \bigwedge_n{}^{0}(\mathscr{P}(\mathbf{n}) \rightarrow \mathfrak{B}(\mathbf{n}))$.

To each propositional *-formula $\mathfrak{B}$ we assign an interpretation $\widetilde{\mathfrak{B}}$ by replacing each part $\mathscr{P}_{\mathfrak{A}_0}(F)$ by the disjunction $\lambda x \bigvee_{k}^{z} \underset{\sim}{\mathscr{P}^k}(x)$, as defined above for $\mathfrak{A}(P, b) = \mathfrak{A}_0(P, F, b)$ of rank $\leqslant$ z. Note that $\widetilde{{}^*\mathrm{At}}$ is of class ω (i.e. each of its members is of finite class), and $^*\widetilde{\mathscr{F}}_z$ is of class ω^{2z}.

THEOREM 4. *If* $\mathfrak{C}$ *is* Σ^0, *then every derivation of* $\mathfrak{C}$ *in* (Ind) (*and so in* (Σ_1^1-CA)) *can be transformed into a derivation of* $\mathfrak{C}$ *in* (PL$^\omega$).

For $\vdash \mathfrak{C}$ in (Ind) means $\vdash \mathfrak{D} \rightarrow \mathfrak{C}$ in (*At-CA) where $\mathfrak{D}$ is a finite conjunction of universal quantifications of instances of Ind. So $\vdash \widetilde{\mathfrak{D}(^*\mathrm{At})} \rightarrow \mathfrak{C}$ in (PL$^\omega$). But $\widetilde{\mathfrak{D}(^*\mathrm{At})}$ is a conjunction of instances of (a) and (b).

THEOREM 5. *If* $\mathfrak{C}$ *is* Σ^0, *then every derivation of* $\mathfrak{C}$ *in* (Δ_2^1-CR) *transforms into a derivation of* $\mathfrak{C}$ *in* (PL$^{\omega^\omega}$). $\vdash \mathfrak{C}$ *in* (Δ_2^1-CR) *implies* $\vdash \mathfrak{D} \rightarrow \mathfrak{C}$ *in* ($^*\Delta_1^1$-CR), *where* $\mathfrak{D}$ *is as above.*

By lemma 1 $\vdash \mathfrak{D} \rightarrow \mathfrak{C}$ in some ($^*\mathscr{F}_k$), $k < \omega$. So $\vdash \widetilde{\mathfrak{D}(^*\mathscr{F}_k)} \rightarrow \mathfrak{C}$ in (PL$^{\omega^\omega}$).

THEOREM 6. *If* $\mathfrak{C}$ *is* Σ^0, *then every derivation of* $\mathfrak{C}$ *in* (Σ_2^1-ADC) *transforms into a derivation of* $\mathfrak{C}$ *in* (PL$^{\varepsilon_0}$).

$\vdash \mathfrak{C}$ *in* (Σ_2^1-ADC) *implies* $\vdash \bigwedge_{i=1}^{m} \mathfrak{D}_i \wedge \bigwedge_{i=1}^{n} \mathfrak{E}_i \rightarrow \mathfrak{C}$ *in* (*At-CA), *where* $\mathfrak{D}_i$ *and* $\mathfrak{E}_i$ *are universal quantifications of instances of* $^*\Sigma_1^1$-ADC *and* Ind′, *resp. So* $\vdash \neg \mathfrak{D}_1 + \ldots + \neg \mathfrak{D}_m + \bigwedge_{i=1}^{n} \mathfrak{E}_i \rightarrow \mathfrak{C}[\mathrm{u}]$ *in* (*At), *for some* $\mathrm{u} < \varepsilon_0$.

It is easy to see that each instance of Ind′ can be put in the form $\bigwedge X_1 \ldots X_p \bigvee Y_1 \ldots Y_q \mathfrak{A}(X_1, \ldots, X_p, Y_1, \ldots, Y_q)$ where $\mathfrak{A}$ is $^*\Sigma^0$. So each $\mathfrak{E}_i$ is of this form, and hence $\bigwedge_{i=1}^{n} \mathfrak{E}_i^{\mathrm{u}} \rightarrow \mathfrak{C}$ is the negation of this form. Applying lemma 2, $\vdash \underset{\sim}{\bigwedge_{i=1}^{n} \mathfrak{E}_i^{\mathrm{u}}} \rightarrow \mathfrak{C}$. But $\mathfrak{E}_i^{\mathrm{u}}$ is a conjunction of instances of (a) and (b) and is of class 2u. So $\vdash \mathfrak{C}$ in (PL$^{2\mathrm{u}}$).

6. Remark. The statements of theorems 4–6 suffer from the defect that, if a set of Σ^0 formulae is derivable in any PL(z), then it has a normal derivation in PL(1). What is really wanted for these theorems is a statement of exactly what constructive methods are used in transforming the formal derivation into a normal derivation in PL(1). The formulae and derivations in PL(z) can be coded in a natural way by elements of T_z; and all of our arguments can be recast as definitions of operations on T_z by recursion and free variable proofs by induction on T_z. I will not give the details here; but the constructive principles involved are discussed explicitly in Tait [7]. One consequence of giving such a complete description of the constructive principles involved is this: All of the operations on trees which we use are introduced by a finite set of definitional schemata. The constant terms built up using these schemata form a decidable model T_z^+ for the T_x ($x \leqslant z$) and the definitional schemata. Indeed this model arises by restricting $\langle x, y, f\rangle$ in T_x to the case in which f is obtained by these schemata. Thus the partial orderings given by the elements of T_z^+, and in particular the formulae and derivations of $PL(z)^+$, are recursive well-founded orderings. An investigation of the ranks of these orderings should lead us to bounds on the provable ordinals of the formal systems considered in theorems 4–6. For example, in view of Takeuti's result, we should expect that the ranks of elements of T_μ^+ are bounded by ordinal diagrams of order $\omega+1$.

REFERENCES

[1] S. Feferman, Systems of predicative analysis, *J. Symb. Logic* **29** (1964) 1–30.

[2] H. Friedman, *Subsystems of set theory and analysis*, thesis, M.I.T.

[3] G. Gentzen, Beweisbarkeit und Unbeweisbarkeit von Anfangsfällen der transfiniten Induktion in der reinen Zahlentheorie, *Math. Ann.* **119** (1943) 140–161.

[4] H. Kreider and H. Rodgers, Constructive versions of ordinal number classes, *Trans. Am. Math. Soc.* **100** (1967) 325–369.

[5] K. Schütte, Beweistheoretische Erfassung der unendlichen Induktion in der Zahlentheorie, *Math. Ann.* **122** (1955) 369–389.

[6] W. W. Tait, Normal derivability in classical logic, to appear.

[7] W. W. Tait, Constructive reasoning, to appear.

[8] G. Takeuti, Consistency proofs of subsystems of classical analysis, *Ann. Math.* **86** (1967) 299–348.

PRINCIPLES OF PROOF AND ORDINALS IMPLICIT IN GIVEN CONCEPTS

G. KREISEL*

This lecture concerns the principal[1] defect of existing proof theory stressed in the survey **[18]**, particularly p. 323 or p. 360, the *lack of a clear and convincing analysis of the choice of methods of proof*; more specifically, of the choice of formal systems to be studied and of the metamathematical methods to be used in this study. Many metamathematical problems such as the consistency problem depend on such a choice. The ultimate aim is nothing else but *the discovery of objective criteria for such a choice.*[2] As indicated in **[18]**, what one is after is a (phenomenological) description of certain kinds $\mathscr{P}$ of mathematical reasoning; the *objective question* is then simply this: whether the proofs represented or described by derivations of a given formal system $\mathscr{F}$ are in $\mathscr{P}$ (soundness of $\mathscr{F}$); whether all proofs in $\mathscr{P}$ are represented in $\mathscr{F}$ (completeness with respect to $\mathscr{P}$ or the weaker condition of completeness with respect to provability in $\mathscr{P}$).

The *particular* kinds of reasoning considered in the present lecture can be roughly described as follows:

> What principles of proof do we recognize as valid once we have understood (or, as one sometimes says, 'accepted') certain given concepts?

The process of recognizing the validity of such principles (including principles for *defining* new concepts, that is, formally, of extending a given language) is here conceived as a *process of reflection*; reflecting on the given concepts, reflecting on this process of reflection, and so forth. It is not assumed that *every* significant area of mathematics is properly analyzed in this manner; not even all those areas which may be described as: what is implicit in given concepts. For instance, if the basic concepts involve a very high degree of *self reflection.*

Granted that we have to do with an area $\mathscr{P}$ which lends itself to the kind

* Preparation of this paper was partially supported by Grant DA-ARO-31-124-G985

of analysis indicated, it is evident that *ordinals* play a basic role. They index the stages in the reflection process. A moment's thought (for people not totally ignorant of classical set theory) shows that some basic *distinctions* in the meaning of the notion of ordinal are needed corresponding to the concepts considered as given; distinctions parallel to the familiar 'classical' material summarized in technical note I.

The two principal sets of concepts considered are:

1. The concepts of ω-sequence and ω-iteration.

2. The concepts of set of natural numbers and numerical quantification.

Though related to earlier work on *autonomous progressions* ([**16**], pp. 168–173 for 'finitist' mathematics, [**4**] for 'predicative' mathematics) the present paper involves an *essential change* in that it *separates* two distinct questions which were previously treated simultaneously.

One question is, so to speak, the *theoretical* question: what is implicit in given concepts? perhaps to be compared with a question of the sort: what (physical or mathematical objects) can be built up by using given basic material as fully as possible? The other, so to speak, *empirical* question comes about as follows: There are objects which we have come to recognize under a certain name or by external properties of which we are more or less explicitly aware (say solids in physics, *algebraic* proof in mathematics etc.). Do these objects coincide with those generated by 'theoretical' or, perhaps better, more explicitly analyzed processes?

Evidently, the kind of separation here considered would be out of place at an early stage of the work except when one happens to deal with childishly simple situations. For instance, if the concepts needed to answer the theoretical question are already available or if some very familiar properties of the empirical material determine all its laws (subject only to very general assumptions; cf. the discovery of the science of geometry). In general, one has to be prepared for a detailed theoretical development before one can even *begin* to compare theory and experience precisely. Before that the choice of theoretical notions is, more or less, suggested by the empirical material, and modifications in the empirical notions are suggested by the shape of the theory.

But it seems to me that, in our subject, it is not unreasonable at the present time to attempt a comparison. In technical note II, I shall go over some of the evidence relating Hilbert's notion of finitist proof not with the area 1 described above, but with the principles formulated in primitive recursive arithmetic.

1. Introduction (not needed for understanding the proposals and results below which ultimately must be judged on their merits). Our first aim is to make the study of informal notions of proof *plausible*. Put differently, since the *raison d'être* of anything like existing proof theory seems to rest on such notions, the aim is nothing else but to make a case for proof theory; a subject which in point of fact is not popular. At least in my opinion no useful purpose is served by attributing this (sociological) fact to such fictions as a prejudiced logical 'establishment' or an 'apathetic' body of logical workers. At present a good number of proof theoretic *methods* are available (and thus a long list of both solved and open formal problems); as anybody familiar with the subject knows, some of these methods are ingenious. What is lacking is a good answer to the objection: why pursue proof theory now when we know that its original aim (Hilbert's program) was based on false assumptions about the nature of mathematical reasoning?

The first point to note is that the question of characterizing notions of proof has presented itself repeatedly in the history of mathematics (and is thus, literally, a natural question). The current distinction between, say, projective and affine *theorems*, in the sense of: valid statements about all models of the axioms of projective and affine geometry, corresponds to an earlier distinction between projective and metric *methods of proof*. It was a *discovery* that this distinction can be analyzed in terms of generality of the results; more technically, in terms of a restriction on axioms used (rather than, say, in terms of rules of inference); of course there is no reason to assume that *every* legitimate distinction between different methods of proof admits this kind of analysis.[3]

In number theory, serious workers spoke of a distinction between *elementary* and *analytic* proof, and, more specifically, between proofs using *real* or *complex* analysis; see, e.g., Ingham's monograph **[11]**. Their formulation was illiterate (if one remembers that complex numbers are, traditionally, regarded as pairs of real numbers): but this in no way means that it had no substance.

In **[13]**, p. 248 I proposed an analysis of this distinction roughly as follows. We consider quantifier-free theorems T and call a (quantifier-free) proof of T *elementary* if it contains only the function symbols occurring in T, their definitions (including thus the auxiliary functions used in these definitions, e.g. multiplication in the definition of factorials), and some basic minimal apparatus. The restriction to quantifier-free, that is logic-free, reasoning is clear: the set-theoretic operations involved in the meaning of quantified propositions are, roughly, what's *typical* of analytic proofs! Shepherdson **[26]** discovered several ***familiar*** theorems which, demonstrably, do not have elementary proofs in the sense above.

The defect of my formulation was, of course, not the mild ambiguity in what counts as 'basic minimal apparatus', but simply that it was too *formal*. Why restrict oneself only to the function symbols *actually* occurring in *T*, and not allow all that is *implicit* in the operations denoted by these symbols?[4] Though (or: because) subtler, the kind of notions of proof considered in the present lecture may permit a more significant formulation of the old distinction between elementary and analytic proof in number theory.

At the present time the legitimacy of this old distinction is not in doubt. Also Gödel's incompleteness theorem, with an absolute minimum of assumptions on the details of the distinction, shows the *existence* of theorems stated in elementary terms which do not have an elementary proof.[5] But a natural modification of the old question is open, namely:

> What can we say about the *kind*, say syntactic structure, of elementary theorems which may need analytic proofs? More generally, we should here replace 'analytic' (i.e., real variable proofs) by 'set theoretic' (i.e., proofs involving axioms of infinity).

Let it be noted that people currently working in number theory do not seem to analyze their proofs or conjectures in 'logical' terms such as those above. But they are very sensitive to the *kind* of considerations that may be essential to a particular problem.[6]

One last word of introduction. Perhaps the single most striking aspect of distinctions between notions of proof is a certain *finesse* (which, according to one's intellectual temperament, may be satisfying or frustrating). Logically, as is well known, the simple minded idea is that we want our proofs to be 'reliable'; (cf., e.g., **[18]**, p. 361(ii)) or quite explicitly (as Hilbert once said **[10]**, p. 157) that Zermelo's axiom of choice be ... reliable in the same sense ... as $2+2 = 4$. But though the degree of reliability may be the same (for instance: certainty) the kind is different in the two cases; c.f. **[18]**, p. 361(ii). Mathematically, the simple minded idea is that since (quite properly) our primary purpose is to find out what is true, we don't want to be bothered with distinctions between different kinds of proof. But this overlooks the following point which, at least for some, can be practically useful: if we have (mastered!) theoretical reasons, for instance abstract interpretations, *restricting* the kinds of proofs (or kinds of conjectures) that are liable to be successful, we have in fact a better chance of discovering the truth.

2. Ordinals. Quite naively (and also formally in set-theoretic foundations, cf. Note I) we distinguish between several more or less related notions (quite well illustrated by 'the' notion of finite ordinal):

The *process* of building up the integers by a *successor operation* say σ, with the property that σx is distinct from x and from all y built up before x. This process determines an *ordering* (= built up before) between the integers, and hence an *abstract order type* $<$.

A much used property of the order type $<$ is its *well-foundedness*, usually formulated either with *variables* X over subsets of our ordering or (monadic) *variables* f over *functions* from (canonically given) integers n into our ordering, where n^+ is the canonical successor of n.

$$\forall X\{\forall x[(\forall y < x)(y \in X) \rightarrow (x \in X)] \rightarrow \forall x(x \in X)\}^7 \quad \text{or} \quad \forall f \exists n \neg (fn^+ < fn).$$

Clearly, the meaning of these principles involves the meanings of

subset X and the *logical operations* $\forall$, $\rightarrow$
ω-*sequence*, and the *quantifier combination* $\forall f \exists n$

Trivially, so does the relation *between* the two principles, and the relation between the abstract order type and the building up process.

Illustration. There are primitive recursive ω-orderings (in the usual sense) for which well foundedness can be proved in the most elementary way, but we do not know the first element.[8]

More important, for a *classical* interpretation of the quantifiers: $\forall X$ and $\forall f$, the formulations of well-foundedness assume a well defined range even for the variables X and f.[9]

In contrast, in terms of the notion of *natural number* and specific ω-*sequences* we can express quite straightforwardly the *stronger*[10] assertion that some given ordering $<$ has been built up from an (explicitly given) x_0, by means of iterating an explicit σ finitely often. (In fact, for variable x over our ordering

$$\sigma x \neq x_0, \quad \sigma^{[\pi x]} x_0 = x, \quad \sigma x = \sigma y \leftrightarrow x = y$$

where $\sigma^{[n]}$ is the nth iterate of σ, and π is a numerical valued function defined on the ordering.) Put in more 'mathematical' terms, if we want to express the idea of an ordering built up by means of a process, we have to think of an *algebraic structure*, an ordering ***together*** with certain functions on it (and usually the latter are primary in that they alone may be enough to determine the ordering).

Now the notions used above in formulating the process of building up ω-orderings also allow the analysis of larger orderings. Our problem is to make the analysis sufficiently precise to establish *limits* to this process.

Some of the principal results take the form:

If an algebraic structure $\mathfrak{A}$ can be obtained by the process in question so can $\boldsymbol{F}(\mathfrak{A})$, where $\boldsymbol{F}$ is some (familiar) operation. Needless to say, 'corresponding' results for the different notions of ordinal at the beginning of this section may be incomparable. Specifically, compare orderings built up by some process and orderings seen to be well founded (in both cases, by methods implicit in given concepts). Even if a larger class of orderings may satisfy the second condition, the former may be closed under 'stronger' operations, simply because we know more about an ordering when it has been built up in a prescribed way.[11]

In terms of the distinctions above, it will be possible to deal quite quickly with the ordinals implicit in two important groups of concepts related to a constructive and a non-constructive use of the notion of natural number (or, more precisely, set of natural numbers).

3. Ordinals built up by ω-iteration starting with the notion of ω-sequence (and two distinct objects of course). The essential formal problem is to *express* properly the idea that some ordering has been built up by (iterating the process of) ω-iteration, starting with the natural ordering of the integers (the latter is determined uniquely up to isomorphism, as explained in the last section, an isomorphism built up from x_0, σ, π; x_0', σ', π' if the orderings $<$ and $<'$ satisfy the conditions given). *If an ordering has been seen to be built up in this way, proof by induction on it or definition by recursion are then evident consequences.*[12]

(a). *Multiplication by ω*: the basic step. Given an ordering (say of natural numbers) and an element ξ_1, it is perfectly clear what quantifier free information expresses that the ordering is built up from its initial segment (preceding ξ_1) by adding ω copies of itself:

a sequence $\xi_1, \xi_2, \ldots$, and a numerical valued mapping v defined on the ordering such that $\xi_{vy} \leqslant y < \xi_{(vy)+1}$; mappings $\sigma(n, x)$, $\pi(n, x)$ such that, for each $n = 1, 2, \ldots$ σ maps the segment ξ_1 onto $[\xi_n, \xi_{n+1})$ preserving order (where π is used to express 'onto', i.e.

$\pi(n, x)$ takes some conventional value if $x \notin [\xi_n, \xi_{n+1})$,
$\pi(n, \sigma(n, x)) = x$ for x preceding ξ_1).

Note that the definition is meaningful for any ordering (indeed any binary relation). It preserves the basic property of *uniqueness up to isomorphism* as follows:

Given two orderings $<$, $<'$, sequences ξ, ν, σ, π and ξ', ν', σ', π' satisfying the conditions above, and order preserving mappings μ, μ' between the segments $\{x: x < \xi_1\}$ and $\{x': x' <' \xi'_1\}$ then μ, μ' can be uniquely extended to mappings between the whole orderings.[13]

(b). *Iteration of the basic step.* The general idea is clear enough. We start with the ordinal ω; as always, 'ordinal' in the sense of an algebraic structure ***together*** with assertions expressing that the ordering has been built up in the way intended (here: ω-iteration of a successor operation). Suppose now α is an ordinal built up by ω-iteration; then we get (the ordinal, in the sense above) ω^α by iterating the basic step α times; in particular, since α was *seen* to have been built up as required, the usual definition of ω^α by recursion on α *expresses* that the ω-sequences (functions) are uniquely defined. Putting $\omega_1 = \omega$, $\omega_{n+1} = \omega^{\omega_n}$, we thus get to ω_n for each $n = 1, 2, \ldots$.[14] I shall set out elsewhere in full (and, I hope, agreeable) detail the *whole body of operations and assertions* about them *that constitute the ordinal* ω_n in our sense.

Now it is obvious that we do *not* get to ε_0 by the particular process of reflection just described; we'd have to recognize α_0 for which $\varepsilon_0 = \omega^{\alpha_0}$ as an ordinal before recognizing ε_0 as an ordinal; but $\alpha_0 = \varepsilon_0$ itself. So the open question is whether we can get to ε_0 at all by means of principles implicit in ω-sequence and ω-iteration. A really conclusive (negative) answer will be given in section 6 when enough machinery is developed. But (as so often) it is good to analyze what we can say about the matter at the present stage.

Note first that there is no doubt *which* ordering, if any, for ε_0 is to be considered; nor of the functions, say $x \oplus y$, $\exp_\omega$ on the ordering to represent addition and exponentiation to the base ω; that is, if $|x|$ is the order type of the segment preceding x,

$$|x \oplus y| = |x| + |y|, \quad |\exp_\omega x| = \omega^{|x|};$$

in particular, we have a sequence w_n, for which $|w_n| = \omega_n$. Any 'conceivable' set of recursion equations satisfied by our ordinal functions can be formally derived. Similarly our ordering can be seen to be the *limit* of the w_n since we easily get a numerical valued function λ such that x precedes $w_{\lambda x}$. What is missing is the recognition, *by means of principles implicit in the concepts considered,* ***that*** *our ordering is built up in the way intended.*[15]

The main issue can be put as follows: Let $\Omega(a)$ mean: $|a|$ is an ordering that can be built up by iterating the process of ω-iteration. We certainly do not dispute the *truth* of

$$(*) \qquad \forall n[\Omega(w_n) \rightarrow \Omega(w_{n+1})].$$

In fact, we admit $\forall n\Omega(w_n)$ (granted that Ω is meaningful). *Can we infer the truth of* $\Omega(\lim w_n)$? What stands in the way?

(i). Of course we should have $\Omega(\lim w_n)$ if (*) were *proved by means of the principles* considered.

But is there any stage, in our reflection on the notion of ω-iteration, where Ω is even *defined* for *all* w_n (on our understanding of the concepts used)? Let alone where (*) is so proved? It is precisely this matter which requires the close analysis below of the representation of proofs implicit in our concepts.[16]

(ii). Clearly, we should also have the truth of $\Omega(\lim w_n)$, granted the truth of $\forall n\Omega(w_n)$, if the *length* of the sequence w_n were significant. In other words if the truth of $\Omega(\lim x_\alpha)$, for $\alpha < \beta$, followed from the fact that β is a *small* ordinal.

Consider, in place of Ω, the set theoretic property Ω_ω: to be an infinite cardinal $< \aleph_\omega$. The sequence $\aleph_n$, $n = 0, 1, \ldots$ is short, and, for each n, $\Omega_\omega(\aleph_n)$. One would be ill advised to conclude $\Omega_\omega(\aleph_\omega)$.

I do not know if this comparison is a mere debating point. Be that as it may, we certainly have no evidence for the proposed inference (ii).

Digression. If one is interested in the kind of reason that can be given for (ii), we can, of course, look for the *application* we wish to make of our 'theoretical' notion of proof (in the sense of p. 491); I think we get an obviously negative answer to (ii) if our interest is that described in [**16**], pp. 169–173, namely to obtain limits to what we can *learn to visualize*, given the ability to visualize a sequence of ω-copies of a configuration which we can visualize. But there is also a more *theoretical* way of looking at the matter.

Even granted that ε_0 is not implicit in the concept of ω-iteration, we now ask ourselves: *what is implicit in the given concepts* ***together*** *with the concept of reflection on these concepts*? (reflection of the kind analyzed above).[17]

Certainly this is a natural question for anybody interested in getting at things from 'below'. Here it is to be remarked that the *mathematical* apparatus of [**3**] gets its most *natural interpretation* in terms of the question above. Feferman starts with the function $1+\alpha$, call it λ_0^0, and enumerates in λ_β^0 the critical points of λ_γ^0 for $\gamma < \beta$, that is

$$\lambda_\beta^0 \alpha = \omega^\beta + \alpha.$$

Defining $\lambda_0^1 \alpha = \lambda_\alpha^0 0$, we have $\lambda_0^1 \alpha = \omega^\alpha$, $\lambda_1^1 \alpha = \varepsilon_\alpha$ etc. Feferman *uses* only the stretch preceding the first critical number Γ_0 of λ_0^2, but, for the *mathematical process described*, this is by no means a natural stopping place; and one of his contributions to the present conference gives a far reaching extension (by use of higher types) which not only doesn't go beyond the *idea* of the process mentioned, but doesn't exhaust it.

We shall not pursue this idea here, but rather analyze a notion of proof for which Γ_0 *is* significant. This asymmetry between (i) the significance of the methods of proof (or: the natural context of the methods) and (ii) the results established is common enough; as somebody said one need only think of the *geometrical* significance of theorems in n-dimensional geometry for $n > 4$ say. In fact, it goes without saying (because it has been said often enough) that the *discovery* of elegant mathematical methods needed to deal with a subject matter, may use ideas not implicit in the latter. From the present point of view, Feferman's use of the process mentioned to deal with the 'small' segment $< \Gamma_0$, is a successful application of this truism within metamathematics itself; thereby avoiding one of the horrors of proof theory described in note 1 on p. 507.

4. Ordinals implicit in the classical logical operations on sets of natural numbers: boolean operations, cartesian products, permutations and identification, projection (= numerical quantification and, in particular, the set of all natural numbers[18]). The notion of proof here considered should be compared to what is called 'predicative' or 'predicative relative to the notion of natural numbers' in the recent literature; mainly of Feferman and Schütte following proposals in [**14**]. The principal points that seem to me to have been neglected, are these.

(i). The notion of set (of natural numbers) or, formally, the use of unramified *free* variables for sets, far from being a defect or a mere technical device, is an integral part of the notion considered. To use a hackneyed phrase: it's not the notion of set, but what you do with it that's problematic.

An immediate corollary is that *the notion of ordinal in the sense of a well founded relation can be expressed directly* (cf. note 9, p. 509). Similarly, we have *ordinal functions* in the sense of: preserving well foundedness.

Examples: To justify: $\alpha \to 2^\alpha$ we use, for any given set X, a suitable X_1, defined essentially just by projection, such that

[(Induction on α applied to X_1) $\to$ (Induction on 2^α applied to X)].

Plainly, since we assume numerical quantification to be understood, we can form X_ω defined from X by ω-iterations of our basic operations and justify: $\alpha \to \varepsilon_\alpha$.

(ii). Though of course a principal problem is the formulation of definition principles for our notions, one mustn't forget that *something*, more specifically, some set of natural numbers is being defined:[19]

The critical open *problem* now is this. Since we are considering ordinals in sense (i), iteration processes have to be justified, not directly, but *via* well foundedness; in particular, in connection with the ramified hierarchy, that is the transfinite iteration of our basic operations on sets, induction has to be applied to the property P:

> the (formal) definitions at a level of the hierarchy considered are understood if our basic concepts are understood.[20]

Though P may be thought of as a property of *numbers* (or, if preferred, Gödel numbers) there is no stage in our reflection on the concepts where we can assume P to be generally understood; cf. Ω in the preceding section. The obvious solution is this:

Recall that having proved at stage α that β is well-founded in sense (i) (formulated with *free* set variables, cf. note 9, p. 509), we use infinite trees of ordinal β as formal definitions (at stage β of the hierarchy). At each node is a formula, either infinite or its finite code (cf. note 20, p. 510). The build-up is 'locally correct', that is the formula at a node N is built up from the formulae at the immediate predecessors of N by means of the classical logical operations listed in the section heading. There are two questions:

(a). Is the final formula, say F, *qua* (infinite) syntactic object, determined?

(b). Is F a good definition?

As to (*a*), well-foundedness in sense (i) is (more than) enough; we need it only for a suitable specific arithmetic set (coding the sequence of subformulae of F) in place of the free variable X. As to (b) the *truth* of well-foundedness is certainly not involved (cf. last sentence of note 9, p. 509). Since we do not have an explicit definition for P to substitute for X, it seems reasonable to suppose that the *formal derivation of the well-foundedness of* β *is needed for* (b); specifically, we expect *to use the derivation as a* (naturally, infinite) *schema* which need be applied only to instances of P whose meaning *is* determined at stage α.[21] In other words the (infinite) formal derivation would be used analogously to a piece of quantifier free algebra for *strictly* finitist applications, that is as a schema for purely numerical substitutions (cf. [**13**], p. 242, 4).

5. Autonomous progressions. Having looked at the ordinals, we now turn to proofs, more precisely to *other* concepts and *principles* of deductions implicit in given concepts. A first step is to describe the latter by a (recursive or non recursive) hierarchy of systems made up of *finite* formulae and *finite derivations*. It is only a first step; or, if preferred, we have a finite *description* of infinite (extensional) configurations which *represent* more faithfully the objects under study, namely intuitive proofs.[22] I shall confine myself to a few examples of the *kinds* of results one has for the notions discussed in (a) section 3 and (b) section 4.

(a). *ω-iteration and ω-sequences.* Since our notions are 'logic free', the language used is quantifier-free; the essentials are therefore definitions principles. The most obvious use to be made of the ordinals is for *definition by recursion.* Let the system P_α express principles of definition by recursion on $\omega^{\omega\cdot\alpha}$.[23]

(i). Clearly, if P_α is justified, we have seen that each formal theorem of P_α is *valid* (on our principles). Formally, we should be able to prove the reflection principle for P_α, which requires a *valuation function* for P_α. This is in fact available in P_β for some $\beta > \alpha$. (The details are familiar.)

(ii). We have also a *converse* to (i), namely if we build up a hierarchy P'_α where $P'_{\alpha+1}$ is obtained by adding the canonical valuation function for P'_α,

$$\bigcup_{\alpha<\varepsilon_0} P_\alpha = \bigcup_{\alpha<\varepsilon_0} P'_\alpha;$$

see e.g. [**16**], p. 172. The converse is plausible in the sense that the 'most' one can expect of P'_α (or of any formal system!) is that all its formal theorems are valid.[24]

(iii). We may add *free variables f for ω-sequences,*[25] and corresponding definition principles for operations on them (functionals). The property of being well founded can now be expressed by

$$\neg f(\tau f+1) < f(\tau f)$$

for some functional constant τ. We then get the results stated in note 16, p. 510. For reference, call this progression P''_α.

(iv). In, so to speak, an opposite direction, we may use the same language for all systems considered, say E_α ('E' for existential), using only rudimentary functions and a *constructive existential quantifier* as in **[14]** p. 293[26]; $E_{\alpha+1}$ is obtained from E_α by adding (in place of the valuation function) the reflection principle for E_α by use of the *satisfaction relation* for E_α. This is possible since, as observed by Myhill **[20]**, the satisfaction relation for a purely existential language can be defined in the language itself.

$$\bigcup_{\alpha<\varepsilon_0} P_\alpha \quad \text{and} \quad \bigcup_{\alpha<\varepsilon_0} E_\alpha$$

are then equivalent in the obvious sense (in particular for any theorem $\exists x A(n, x)$ of the latter there is a function term f_A such that $A(n, f_A n)$ is proved in some P_α).

(v). In terms of (iv) we then get an easy comparison with (classical or intuitionistic) first order arithmetic. For each rudimentary A let A' be its canonical translation (unique up to provable isomorphism) in first order arithmetic Z_1. Then

$$\exists x A(n, x) \in \bigcup_{\alpha<\varepsilon_0} E_\alpha \text{ if and only if } \exists x A'(n, x) \in Z_1$$

(b). *Classical logical operations on sets of natural numbers.* The reader is referred to **[4]** for a survey of corresponding results. Ramified hierarchies with and without free set variables correspond to (iii) and (i) respectively. Hierarchies based on the Σ^1_1-rule of choice together with the reflection principle correspond (more or less) to (iv).[27]

Remark. 'Autonomous progression' means: progression using autonomous ordinals, since we first pick out the ordinals (by considerations proper to the concepts treated) and then build up the progression. It turns out as a *theorem* that these ordinals are equivalent to those which can be proved in the progression to be well founded; cf. (a) (iii) above. But, as stressed at length at the end of section 4, we cannot use *these* proofs directly to justify the iteration of the progression.[28]

6. Proofs: infinite representations and their finite descriptions. Recall the basic issue at the end of section 3 (in particular, note 15, p. 509): why can't we infer $\Omega(\lim w_n)$ from the truth of $\forall n \Omega(w_n)$? This issue has a perfect parallel for any of the progressions in the preceding section; using, say, P''_α of (a)(iii), we can define the proof predicates P''_{ω_n} or better P''_{w_n} (for variable n) in P''_0; and using $\boldsymbol{O}$ to express well foundedness (in the language of P'') we can explicitly give a function π in P''_0 and establish, for variable n:

$$P''_{w_n}(\pi n, \boldsymbol{O}_n),$$

where $\boldsymbol{O}_n$ is a term which gives the Gödel number of a formula expressing well foundedness of ω_{n+1}.[29] Hasn't this established $\forall n \Omega(w_n)$ *in* our progression?

The obvious answer is this. Though we have *described* the proof predicates P''_{w_n}, there is no stage (of our reflection process) where we know that they are *sound* for our notion of proof. The most we can say is that the formal derivations *appear to us* 'good'. More explicitly, let us recall the *long and tortuous process by which we convince ourselves that the formal derivations of each P_{w_n} provide proofs implicit in the notions treated*; a formal derivation in P_{w_n} in no way reflects this process which is, after all, the object under study.

To put this answer into more 'mathematical' (quantitative) form we simply require *more explicit representations* of the process in question, and propose to use infinite *proof figures*, cf. note 22, p. 511. Let us write $\mathscr{P}_\alpha$ for the corresponding progression.

Just *how explicit should the representation be*? Evidently, if we are to read the result 'straight off' the representation, we'd never get off the ground. More precisely, suppose the representation of the proof justifying P''_α, that is the definition principle by recursion on $\omega^{\omega \cdot \alpha}$, is so detailed that an enumeration of all $\omega^{\omega \cdot \alpha}$-recursive functions is, say, primitive recursive[30] in the (infinite figure representing the) given proof; then trivially the representation is no simpler than $\omega^{\omega \cdot \alpha}$-recursion. But let us remember our basic starting point: *ω-iteration is taken to be understood*, to be regarded as a *single* act; it follows that a representation will be explicit *enough* (for somebody capable of such acts) if it symbolizes a sequence of ω copies by a single element, and such a representation of a proof justiying P''_α *can* be defined by α-recursion.[31] But the whole *sequence* $\mathscr{P}_{\omega_n}$ (for $n = 1, 2, \ldots$) cannot even be *defined* in any particular $\mathscr{P}_{\omega_n}$, let alone in $\mathscr{P}_0$. Undefinability results are always more convincing than unprovability! More important, they avoid a natural *error* (e.g., by Herbrand [**7**], p. 231 l. 20–23 or myself, footnote 2 on p. 242 of [**13**]) of supposing that the theorems implicit in given notions (or, e.g., the finitist theorems) cannot be recursively enumerated; what is true is of course only that no such enumeration can be proved to be sound by means of the *particular* methods considered.

7. Relation to intuitionistic mathematics (as presented e.g., in section 5 of my other lecture). The most striking difference between the general intuitionistic notion of constructive proof and those considered here (that is, proofs implicit in the two sets of concepts of sections 3 and 4) is clearly this.

In intuitionistic mathematics a proposition is understood if we have *grasped* the possibilities of proving it (at least, by irredundant or 'normalized' methods). For the notions of proof here considered, not even purely universal statements formulated at the lowest level, say in P_0, are understood in this sense, because new theorems of this form appear all the way out to ε_0).[32]

In view of this observation the comparison between constructive and set theoretic methods in (a) on p. 212 of [**19**] should be modified as follows. We still make mechanical computations correspond to the hereditarily finite sets. But notions of proof implicit in such concepts as considered in the present paper correspond to ramified versions of the cumulative hierarchy up to ordinals implicit in the definition principles used for the ramification.[33] Intuitionistic proofs correspond then to the cumulative hierarchy itself. Specifically, just as there is no set of 'all' sets, so we have no grasp of 'all' proofs or 'all' constructions; but just as for any given set there is a set of all its subsets, so for any given construction we have a grasp of proofs about it (for more detail, see the discussion of grasped domains in my other lecture).[34]

Certainly there is something depressing about the comparison. After all, the current search for axioms of infinity is very naturally thought of as: looking for the ordinals implicit in the power set operation; and why should the problem mentioned in the *digression* at the end of section 3 be any easier? Or, again, in 1908 Zermelo [**33**] gave a discussion of the notion of *set* and some important properties, his axioms; but it was only 22 years later, in [**34**], that this great logician was really able to say clearly what notion he was talking about (incidentally, with very little help from the many pages of 'technical' papers that had appeared in the intervening years). Is there anything to encourage us?

Well, since the question assumes the comparison, let's also assume it in the answer! Then, trivially, we start where the pioneers in set theory left off. A quite different point is that here we want to know about constructions which in turn refer only to our own constructions and reflections on this process. I still don't see (cf. **[17]**, p. 267, 1, 18–19) any guarantee for easy (self) knowledge; but it seems reasonable to take a chance.

TECHNICAL NOTES

I. Background on ordinals. The purpose of this note is to summarize the most important *familiar* distinctions both in (a) set theoretic and (b) intuitionistic mathematics.

(a). *Set theory.* The notion of *transfinite iteration* is used in the analysis of the cumulative hierarchy itself (which is the principal interpretation of current formal set theories [**34**]). It is therefore, perhaps, not too surprising that we can 'recapture' quite faithfully this notion in terms of the notions of set theory itself.

Case 1: ordinals *built up* by the process of forming *successors* σ (of any given ordinal) and the supremum σ' of a ***set*** of ordinals. Any building up process induces a (partial) ordering, say $<$, where $x < y$ if x occurs at a stage in the process of building up y. To speak of a 'building up', clearly (i) $\sigma x \neq y$ for all $y \leqslant x$; and to speak of the supremum $\sigma' x$ (whose construction involves only the elements of the set x of ordinals), (ii) if $y < \sigma' x$, for some (ordinal) $u \in x$ we must have $y < u$. It is natural, to satisfy (i), to form σx by operating on the *set* $\{y: y < x\}$ (for the relation $<$ to be constructed!); but it is not altogether obvious that there is a uniform way of defining σ which ensures (i); von Neumann discovered

$$\sigma x = x \cup \{x\} \ (\neq x);$$

it is, in fact, the successor operation forced upon one if $<$ *is to be membership.* To satisfy (ii), one puts

$$\sigma' x = \bigcup x$$

if one wants the supremum of a set with a largest element z to be z, and

$$\sigma' x = \bigcup \{\sigma y: y \in x\}$$

if one wants it to be σz. (If x has no largest element the two definitions are equivalent.) Note that (iii) if x and x' are *equivalent* in the sense that

$$\forall u \exists v[u \in x \to (v \in x' \wedge u < v)], \quad \forall v \exists u[v \in x' \to (u \in x \wedge v < u)]$$

then $\sigma' x$ and $\sigma' x'$ are actually identical.

A critical point here is that σx is of *higher type* than x. There is certainly no apparent way of getting 'uniform' (e.g., set theoretically definable) σ and σ', and $<$, satisfying (i)–(iii) which stay at some restricted type; and it is consistent (with the usual set theoretic principles) to assume that there is none.

Case 2: ordinals treated as *order types* satisfying some condition of *well foundedness* such as

(i). The least element principle.

(ii). The principle of proof by transfinite induction, that is for each formula Fx with free variable x (and not containing y)

$$\forall x[(\forall y < x)Fy \rightarrow Fx] \rightarrow \forall x Fx$$ [35].

(iii). Finiteness of descending sequences (from ω into the field of $<$). Clearly, the ordering built up in case 1, satisfies (i)–(iii). The converse involves a quite independent principle.[36] In short, the remark on p. 493 on different notions of set theoretic ordinal was justified.

(b). *Intuitionistic mathematics*. Though the basic distinctions which arise here are remarkably similar to the set theoretic case, the proper emphasis is different. (I use **[8]** as a convenient reference.)

Case 1: ordinals *built up* by the process of forming successors and suprema of ω-sequences.[37] These were originally introduced by Brouwer by means of higher type operations, indeed by use of *species*, but as observed in **[8]**, they can be reduced in an obvious sense to constructive orderings of the natural numbers.[38] Each of these orderings has a constructive characteristic function, a constructive successor and constructive so called fundamental sequences.

Case 2: ordinals treated as *order types*; it will also be important to distinguish between *decidable order types* (with a decidable characteristic function and decidable field) and *general* order types (determined by a species, that is a relation which is in general undecidable, but which can be proved to be a partial ordering[39]).

Here the distinctions corresponding to (i)–(iii) in (a) are more fundamental. Thus (i) is useless, and (ii) is, for decidable $<$, stronger than (iii) if only *constructive* descending sequences are meant since formulae F define, in general, species which simply do not have a constructive characteristic function. Brouwer introduced

(iii′). all descending *freely chosen* sequences are finite.

Brouwer's socalled *bar theorem* asserts, for *decidable*[40] $<$ satisfying (iii′), that $<$ can be mapped by a constructive function in to an ordinal built up as in case 1, preserving order, and hence satisfies (ii). It is evident that (iii') alone does not ensure such a mapping *onto* an ordinal of Case 1, because the successor need not be constructive.

II. Primitive recursive arithmetic: PRA. For a description see, e.g., Hilbert-Bernays, vol. 1. The purpose of this note is to consider whether PRA corresponds to a philosophically[41] *significant* notion of proof. Its immediate appeal (established by the empirical fact that people take to it) shows of course that it corresponds to the *immediately evident* part of such a notion and *not*, for instance, to *all* that is implicit in some given concepts.

1. In terms of the present paper, a plausible analysis is this. PRA corresponds to the *principles of proof implicit in ω-iteration and specific basic functions* (that is, in contrast to section 3, the notion of ω-sequence is not assumed to be understood; only some concatenation operations). Since, as is well known, ω^ω is the limit of the 'provable ordinals' of PRA the critical point is to discover the ordinals implicit in the concepts above. Let $\tau\alpha$ be the limit of the ordinals built up at stage α of our reflection process. Since we apply ω-iteration only to specific configurations, not to *any* configuration, we have, for $^+$ denoting the successor (as in § 2),

$$\tau\alpha^+ = \tau\alpha+\omega \text{ with } \tau 1 = \omega.$$

Assuming the formation of unions (which needs further analysis) we have $\tau\alpha = \omega \cdot \alpha$ (α copies of ω). Clearly ω^ω is inaccessible, since, for $\alpha < \omega^\omega$, also $\omega \cdot \alpha < \omega^\omega$.

2. The only serious[42] attempt in the literature to find philosophical significance for PRA seems to be Tait's discussion in **[31]**. Its central point seems to be that the evidence of each proof considered has, in some essential way, a strictly *finite* character. As it stands the analysis in **[31]** is unconvincing[43] since the understanding of any *one* rule goes beyond this. And using a formalism containing only constants for rules, that is, not *showing* variable arguments, does not alter this fact.

3. *Finitist proof* (finiter Beweis), as described in the introduction to volume 1 of Hilbert-Bernays. (As noted in several places, Hilbert's *own* publications are not consistent, in fact, his aims in metamathematics were not.[44]) This description seems to indicate a fairly well defined area of mathematics, which uses ω-iteration only of the *particular* construction of the number series by concatenation operations, and so, by (1), PRA may indeed correspond to the notion intended there.

NOTES

1. More technical defects which have spoilt proof theory for a long time, are due to the following 'dilemma'. Formal systems which codify actual reasoning well, such as (subsystems of) classical analysis or set theory do not lend themselves to proof theoretic analysis without *ad hoc* tricks. Those systems which do, are often formal theories of hierarchies such as ramified analysis in **[24]**; usually hopelessly removed from actual practice. Evidently the rational step (cf., e.g., **[18]**, p. 345, 1.17–19) is to use an auxiliary model theoretic reduction of 'natural' to 'artificial' systems which preserves a large class of theorems; beautiful applications of this procedure are in papers by Feferman **[5]** and Friedman **[6]**. Surely, one reason for the failure of using this method is sheer ignorance: either of the model theory involved or of the fact (cf. note II of **[18]** for details) that these reductions generally provide finitist proofs of conservative extension results. But perhaps a deeper, if unconscious, obstacle is the philosophical view that 'nothing is gained' by the use of transcendental (model theoretic) methods even as far as intelligibility is concerned. By accepting instead of testing this view its adherents make sure that indeed nothing is gained from their (non-existing) knowledge of transcendental notions!

2. The reader familiar with mathematical *practice* will find there related problems in making *objective* the choice between alternative notions and definitions, for instance the separation between a *structure-mère* and obviously minor variants. Equally important, the crude chase after 'bigger ordinals' has its parallel in the vulgar idea 'continuous functions are *better* than polynomials (say in finite fields!) because there are more of them'. Somebody, I think rightly, said about ordinals in proof theory: It's not how large you make them, it's how you make them large. Having recognized the general nature of the project, we are faced with a further difficulty which also has its parallel in 'ordinary' axiomatic mathematics: though, perhaps surprisingly, *few* structures (in algebra or proof theory: orderings together with suitable ordinal functions) turn out to be basic, recondite considerations and delicate distinctions may be needed to discover them.

3. Another familiar axiomatic analysis distinguishing between algebraic and analytic methods goes back to Sturm's famous work. His own purpose in giving an *algebraic* proof of his theorem (valid, as we should say, for all real closed fields) was to avoid *continuity* considerations which, with his background, were associated with dubious infinitesimals. In other words, his principal interest was of course not any extra generality; he wanted theorems about real numbers, but using only those methods of proof which he could see to be valid.

Digression. Paradoxically, that is, despite its heterodox presentation, the paper of Yesenin–Volpin **[32]** seems dominated by the preoccupation of current axiomatic mathematics here discussed, namely to analyze distinctions between notions of proof in terms of validity for different kinds of objects, for instance different 'number series'. Whatever (alleged) ambiguities or weaknesses the usual concept of natural number may have, surely none of the various different 'number series' of which Yessenin-Volpin talks, is any clearer! (The same applies of course to non-standard models.) Putting it bluntly, the critique of the usual concept serves, consciously or unconciously, as a kind of diversionary tactic, drawing attention away from the weakness of the new concepts. Even worse (in my opinion), quite basic questions raised by the new concepts make perfectly good sense even if the usual concept is used. First, there is the question to what extent our notion of *set* is derived from the notion of finite set; and hence (presumably) the distinction between finite and infinite set is derived from the distinction between small and large numbers. Second, there is the question of a coherent theory of this distinction, in particular of the *logical laws* obeyed by propositions involving the concept of *large* and *small* number. Clearly, the law of the excluded middle does not apply! But isn't it one of the more vulgar errors to suppose that therefore intuitionistic logic applies?

4. Psychologically, my original formulation makes *some* sense. It separates proofs involving a, possibly complicated, combination of notions actually named in T, from proofs making essential use of novel definitions. Needless to say there is another *kind* of reasoning which has some psychological interest and which *may* lend itself to rather crude formal characterizations: what is *immediately* clear or evident. (Any theory on the teaching of, say, some elementary part of mathematics to children, involves, implicitly or explicitly, ideas on the question above.) Though this matter is probably of limited *logical* interest, it seems plausible that the apparatus of mathematical logic may be useful for (stating psychological) theories about it.

5. Before Gödel's decisive results the following *plausibility* considerations were valid. First, given any structure, say arithmetic, there are, trivially, facts *about* this structure, which can only be stated by means of notions that are not *prima facie* connected with it (e.g., the relation between the structure and quite 'different' notions). Second experience had shown that certain facts can be proved *intelligibly* only by use of extraneous notions (e.g., replacing familiar functions of analytic number theory by means of rational approximations produces unintelligible constructions). These considerations made it plausible that other facts about the structure could not be proved (convincingly) at all without use of properties of such notions.

6. I do not know any systematic exposition of the current ideas for analyzing theoretically the nature of problems in number theory, but found Swinnerton-Dyer's remarks **[27]** very congenial. As to the (heuristic) value of the old questions it is hard to say whether or not it is supported by experience in number theory. Obviously, the illiterate formulation mentioned early on is repulsive to a thoughtful person; but the people concerned are ignorant of the logic which may be needed for a more satisfactory formulation, and therefore in no position to judge the matter.

7. This principle of induction is, classically, equivalent to the socalled: least-element-principle (LEP)

$$\forall X\{(\exists x(x \in X) \rightarrow \exists x[x \in X \wedge (\forall y < x) \neg (y \in X)]\}.$$

This formulation is not useful, intuitionistically; more important, the principle of induction is immediately *evident* from the build-up of the integers, while LEP is derived.

8. Take a primitive recursive An, for which we don't know whether $\forall x Ax$ holds. Our

ordering is according to magnitude for $\{\langle x, y\rangle : x \leqq n \wedge y \leqq n\}$ if $(\forall x < n)Ax$; if n_0 is the least x for which $\neg Ax$ holds, we put n_0^+ first, and the usual ordering for $\{\langle x, y\rangle$: $x \neq n_0^+, y \neq n_0^+\}$. (A first element is *given* with the building-up process.)

9. For reference below two points should be noticed. First, since the variables X and f occur purely universally in assertions of well-foundedness, formally they may be replaced by *free* variables; hence, if well-defined ranges for the variables x, y and n are understood, these assertions correspond to (assertions expressed by) free variable formulae in, say, primitive recursive arithmetic when the latter are interpreted *without* assuming a well-defined set of all natural numbers. Second, if no definite ranges are assumed for, say, x and y, we have a completely quantifier free *rule*: suppose, for some specific mapping τ of the ordering into itself, we have derived: $(\tau x < x \rightarrow \tau x \in X) \rightarrow x \in X$, i.e., we have $\tau x \in X \rightarrow x \in X$ and $(\neg \tau x < x) \rightarrow x \in X$; then we infer: $x \in X$. Naturally this 'reduction' is of interest only if we have given a suitable (non-classical) interpretation to free variable formulae.

10. Since the early days of logic it has been clear that a *stronger*, or more general statement can often be formulated in a more elementary way! Thus, as Hilbert-Bernays, vol. 2, emphasize, implications $\forall x Ax \rightarrow \forall y By$ (with primitive recursive A and B) are not finitistically meaningful; for given $\tau : A(\tau y) \rightarrow By$, with free variable y, is. Also, in the language of first order predicate logic we cannot characterize say the field of rationals (and hence not prove results about *it*). But we *can* express the notion of formally real field, prove general results about the latter, and 'thus' results about the field of rationals.

11. For an example, see **[18]**, p. 336, also in connection with note 9 above. Roughly speaking (or precisely in terms of the next subsection), if an ordering α is built up by the processes here considered, so is 2^α; but if (under minimal assumptions on finitistically decidable sets X in the example mentioned) the induction rule of note 9 has been justified for α, it does not necessarily hold for 2^α; for other examples, see **[4]**, p. 134.

12. We do not go here into the relations between (i) our way of expressing the build-up of the given ordering and (ii) the principles of proof by induction and definition by recursion (or the relations between the latter, cf. **[15]**). Formally, the simplest and, possibly, most satisfactory way of expressing the relation is by means of an *inference rule*; but for an analysis of the nature of this inference some new idea should be used.

13. 'Extended' by use of the operations explicitly given (in accordance with the idea of regarding ordinals as algebraic structures). Note that for general orderings the mapping must be relative to given μ, μ' since the segment $\{x: x < \xi_1\}$ may permit an (order preserving) automorphism. Conversely multiplication by ω preserves non-existence of non-trivial automorphisms. For detail, see [3] and footnote 11 on p. 339 of **[18]**.

14. The corresponding orderings are unique up to isomorphism (built up from the functions involved in the algebraic structures associated with ω_n).

Correction. In several places, e.g. **[16]**, p. 164, 3.331, I have drawn attention to such *intrinsic* characterizations of the ordinals $< \varepsilon_0$, using as *one* of the functions: $\alpha \rightarrow \omega^\alpha$ without restriction on α. This is pointless, as observed earlier; what is reasonable, for each ω_n with $n = p+1$ say, is: $\alpha \rightarrow \omega^\alpha$ for $\alpha \leqq \omega_p$, and say: $\alpha \rightarrow \omega_p$ for other α, and this is indeed sufficient for the required isomorphism result.

15. By way of *illustration*, it may be useful to remember that all the functions and re-

cursion equations involved can be equally obtained for (suitable) orderings which are not well orderings at all, and if $|a|$ is not well ordered it makes no good sense to say that $|\exp_\omega a|$ has been 'built up' by *iterating* anything $|a|$ times! (The easiest way of getting such orderings is to consider non-standard models of arithmetic, with the formal definition, unique up to provable isomorphism, of the natural ε_0 ordering and the functions mentioned. Of course all this is *only* an illustration because here we take the notion of ω-iteration to be understood in its proper 'standard' sense.) Naturally such properties of ordinal functions *express* the intended fact, namely the possibility of building up the ordering by means of ω-iteration, only if one understands the latter process.

Correction. The misuse of *verifiable* in **[2]** pp. 284–286, e.g. 3.8, is evidently due to disregarding the facts just mentioned; the formal proof (even in the elementary system Q) that a given function *satisfies* equations having the *form* of definitions by recursion tells us very little, in general not even uniqueness (though for special types of equations it tells us uniqueness with respect to *certain* variations! cf. **[15]**).

16. As by-products we shall get formal counterparts of both intuitively obvious facts (e.g. that our orderings are well founded in a suitable sense) and somewhat surprising converses (e.g. that orderings which can be proved to be well founded by the principles considered can always be mapped by a function of our hierarchy in an order preserving way into one of our ω_n). Needless to say, detailed 'technical' refinements *can* have great philosophical value for establishing the limit ε_0 on a 'minimum' of hypotheses. Putting it crudely: the more detail we have for our ω_n the easier it is to show that there is no ε_0 with the same sort of detail! The idea here is this. Simple results on an intensional concept C need only few details, given by a crude homomorphic image R_C of C, (e.g. the order type R_O of a given ordering O). Later R_C is enriched by other (relevant) structure of C.

17. The reader will now see the force of the apparently innocent restriction (on p. 489) to basic concepts which are not too self reflexive.

18. In contrast to the preceding section, I shall here give a *sketch* only. The purpose is to draw attention to the *kind* of technical refinement that is significant (cf. note 16 above). The existing relevant work of Feferman and Schütte is so thorough that one expects to read off the additional information provided only one knows what to look for.

19. Thus we are not concerned with systems in which *all* objects are intended to be definitions (or, more precisely, intuitive rules or attributes) in contrast to, e.g., **[24]**, chapter VIII and XI or Krasner **[12]**. In particular, self application does not arise since we consider sets (or properties) of certain individuals, namely natural numbers. Formally speaking, little is gained at the present time by embedding, say, arithmetic in a theory of attributes: in contrast to set theory the general principles which we can assert about attributes are so weak that special existential axioms seem to be needed even for arithmetic; cf. **[14]** § 33. See also note 27, p. 511.

20. Specifically, the formulae are meant to define sets (of natural numbers) if they contain no free set variables and properties of sets, if they do; cf. note 9, p. 509. For the discussion below it is best, I think, to regard (finite) formulae of the ramified hierarchy as codes for infinite formulae built up from symbols for the basic concepts considered in this section.

21. It seems likely that the work of Feferman and Schütte 'contains' all the formal details needed (cf. note 18 above); the principal problem is conceptual: to formulate properly

just what details are needed. (Compare: sometimes quite elementary calculations in the theory of addition of integers generalize to all groups; the *main* discovery may then be the observation *that* they generalize; the calculations correspond to the formal proof theoretic details in the comparison.)

Digression. A different way of proceeding is to analyse the logical laws which are valid, in conjunction with the particular notions here assumed, for incompletely defined properties such as P. At the present time this is not promising; cf. note 19.

Correction. It is sometimes pointed out (e.g., **[25]**) that the proofs of well-foundedness only use intuitionistic logic. This is pointless for the *present* purpose (at least, without further analysis) since the intended, highly impredicative, interpretation of the intuitionistic logical operations (for which Heyting's rules are valid) has nothing to do with incompletely defined properties; cf. end of note 3.

22. In footnote 8 of **[1]** Brouwer stresses that proofs are to be conceived as transfinite iterations of basic steps. Prof. van Heijenoort has drawn my attention to Zermelo's papers **[35]** and **[36]**, which also insist on the infinitistic character of proofs, see particularly **[36]**, p. 145 top. What is simply thoughtless is the negative attitude towards Gödel's incompleteness theorems which seems to go with this insight into the character of proofs (e.g. **[35]**, p. 87, but not repeated in **[36]**). First of all, properly interpreted, Gödel's theorems can be used to *support* this insight, just as they are used to refute Hilbert's *assumption* that finite formal derivations reflect faithfully the structure of mathematical reasoning. Second, from a practical point of view, formal systems may be a very good description of what people are likely to prove.

23. For a description, see e.g. **[15]** or, in more detail, **[29]**. The choice of $\omega^{\omega\alpha}$ instead of say α is technical; it ensures that P_α is *properly* included in $P_{\alpha+1}$.

24. Just as consistency is the 'least' one expects. (Incidentally I do not know if, for $P''_{\alpha+1}$ consisting of P''_α together with the sentence asserting the consistency of P''_α, $\bigcup\{P''_\alpha : \alpha < \varepsilon_0\}$ is the primitive recursive part of $\bigcup\{P_\alpha : \alpha < \varepsilon_0\}$.)

25. Gödel has stressed this point in conversation; indeed the obviously *finitist* character of this addition.

Correction. In **[14]**, p. 295, I say it would be 'desirable' to do so without being in the least clear on the point, in fact the formal rules (i) and (ii) which I set up in order to avoid the use of such variables are quite unsatisfactory; cf. **[18]**, p. 336. Tait **[30]**, p. 175, last 4 lines, rejects the use of such variables out of hand.

26. But omitting the rule for introducing function symbols; they are quite pointless, in the presence of an existential quantifier.

27. Roughly, arithmetic relations correspond to rudimentary ones (and it would perhaps be of interest to investigate the correspondence). Provably definite properties of sets here correspond to provably recursive ones in (a). One difference between Feferman's unramified hierarchies and (iv) is that he also considers theorems which are *not* Σ^1_1; for such theorems we do not get an unambiguous correspondence to the ramified hierarchy but only 'interpretations'; naturally since there are logical theorems $\exists X A(X)$, for $A \notin \Sigma^1_1$, such that no set in the ramified hierarchy can be proved to satisfy A (when the quantifiers in A range over all sets), cf. **[18]**, p. 349, last line. However, certain striking results do involve arbitrary formulae; transfinite induction can be proved for all formulae on any or-

dinal (in sense (i) of Section 4) [3] though not every formula defines a set; all (provably) definite formulae are equivalent to Δ_1^1-formulae [4] while only the converse is obvious. The significance of these formal results for the particular notions of section 4 remains to be analyzed.

Digression. The provably *definite properties* were not introduced *ad hoc*, but correspond to a quite central aim, already formulated (informally) by Poincaré: to look for invariant (sometimes called: extensionally definite) definitions, that is formulae which define a definite object so to speak 'before' one has made up one's mind on possible extensions of a given universe; and this idea is formulated in terms of extensions of a given model (only very general axiomatic conditions being imposed on these extensions). Now though it is clear that Krasner's interests [12] in 'tests' go in the same direction, it is possible that his notion is actually a bit different from invariance in the sense above. As explained above in note 19, Krasner's notion is not promising if one is principally concerned with sets of integers. In any case, at the present time it does not compete with the notion of invariance which (i) is quite precise, (ii) has been thoroughly investigated, (iii) has been found to have very satisfactory closure properties and (iv) wide generalizations in model theoretic generalizations of recursion theory.

Correction. While, clearly, definitions implicit in the notions of Section 4 must be provably definite in a suitable hierarchy satisfying the autonomy condition used, it is not apparent that Poincaré's aim requires such autonomy. So, without further analysis, Feferman's results [4] on provably definite formulae should be regarded as elegant *stability properties* of his unramified systems, and the latter as a kind of metatheory for the ramified hierarchy.

28. *Correction.* This presents a change of view; when the term 'autonomous progression' was introduced, it was thought that the *formal machinery* of say P''_{ω_n} was needed in an essential way to obtain the ordinal ω_{n+1}. In the system [16], p. 172, a symbol O is indeed added to the language to express: can (be proved to) be reached by ω-iteration. However, it is treated as a pseudo property and the relevant result 3.422 uses nothing of the formal machinery.

29. Specifically, a suitable term τ in P''_{ω_n} for the natural ordering $<$ of ω_{n+1}, in the notation of section 5a(iii).

30. 'Primitive recursive in' is here taken as a translation of 'read straight off'.

31. The reader should recall an analogous (and, I believe, much neglected) situation in the theory of cut free *infinite* proof figures. If we are allowed to infer $\exists x Ax$ only from At for some term t, cut free derivations corresponding to formal first order number theory cannot in general be defined primitive recursively; if $\exists x Ax$ is inferred from $At \vee \exists x Ax$, they can. Put in present terms, proof figures using the latter formal rule conceal the steps involved in understanding the formal derivation as a proof.

Correction. In [16], p. 165, 3.3321, I had in mind the formal fact associated with the two rules; my observation was a prize example of pointlessness since I did not realize any significance in the formal fact.

32. In a very strict sense, not even *numerical* statements are understood in this sense, because we can't even define the sequence $\mathscr{P}_\alpha$: $\alpha < \varepsilon_0$. However, a consistency *assumption* is enough to justify a particular definition of irredundant proof, namely: computation in the $\mathscr{P}_\alpha$ in which the symbols used first occur.

Digression. It seems to me that the following mathematical *problem* may be of some interest. Let us use the standard definition of the intuitionistic logical operations *relativized* to proofs (and functions) in one of our autonomous progressions of *formal* theories; in this case decidability of the proof predicate is of course unproblematic. *What are the resulting formal logical laws? Does cut play a special role? Are there reasonable variants of such relativizations?* (These questions belong to the *theory of hereditarily formalizable proofs.*)

33. In Gödel's constructible hierarchy, as he repeatedly emphasized, there is no connection between the definition principles (first order quantification) and the ordinals used. Consequently, with 'definitions' in place of 'proofs' there is, e.g., an obvious meaning of *irredundant definition* of a set of integers for which all sets of integers in the hierarchy can be defined *before* a certain ordinal, the first constructibly uncountable one. But it seems far fetched to regard it as implicit in the definition principle.

34. The fact that, as pointed out in my other paper, certain very elementary proofs are evidently applicable without restriction to grasped domains, corresponds to such elementary set theoretic operations as the boolean operations which evidently apply without careful consideration of what objects sets are.

Digression. It cannot be stressed too much that Heyting's interpretation of the logical operations (from which the presentation in my other paper is derived) *is* abstract and problematic. This fact may not be quite irrelevant to Brouwer's notorious objections to Heyting's formalization. Whatever Brouwer's conscious reasons may have been, he may well have had doubts about *what* exactly is asserted in general logical laws. It seems quite absurd to suppose that he couldn't have made up for himself all the well-known bromides about the 'innocence' of formalization (how it 'clarifies' matters, or helps 'communication'). In addition, he would have been right in expecting popular misinterpretation of the *significance* of Heyting's particular rules since, at the time, there was no indication at all that they were complete for the intended meaning; in this connection, see note I of my other paper.

35. (i) and (ii) are equivalent in classical, but not in intuitionistic *logic*. In *axiomatic* set theory, or, more explicitly, in ramified set theories where not every definable property has an extension, (ii) may be stronger than

$$\forall z\{\forall x[(\forall y < x)(y \in z) \to x \in z] \to \forall x(x \in z)\}.$$

36. Precisely, while the derivation of (i) for von Neumann's orderings or the equivalence in note 35 above holds for *every* level of the cumulative hierarchy, the converse is an *existential* theorem on the number of levels to be used. (The replacement axiom is a familiar *sufficient* condition for the converse, that is for the existence of a von Neumann ordering isomorphic to any given well-founded ordering.)

37. In **[16]**, 2.8, p. 147–148 (cf. 2.812) also suprema of longer sequences are considered (but given by constructive operations).

38. In *contrast* to the set theoretic case 1, I know no way, even by use of higher types, of satisfying condition (iii) in (a) above.

39. Evidently, if it can be proved to be a total ordering in the sense $\forall x \forall y(x < y \lor x = y \lor y < x)$ and to have a decidable field, then $<$ is decidable too.

40. Using α for choice sequences, $\forall \alpha \exists n \neg (\alpha n^+ < \alpha n)$ does not in general ensure the exis-

tence of an *extensional* functional, say N, such that $\forall\alpha \neg [\alpha(N\alpha)^+] < \alpha(N\alpha)$, where $n^+ = n+1$. However, an extensional N can be obtained for decidable $<$ by the device in the remark at the end of Technical Note III in my other paper, since for such $<$

$$\forall\alpha\exists n \neg (\alpha n^+ < \alpha n) \rightarrow \forall\alpha\exists! n[\neg (\alpha n^+ < \alpha n) \wedge (\forall m \prec n)(\alpha m^+ < \alpha m)],$$

where $\prec$ denotes order of magnitude. For more detail, see the discussion of **BI** and **BI**! in technical note IV of my other lecture.

Digression (cf. [37]). For $<$ with a possibly *undecidable* field F, the situation is less neat; (iii′): $\forall\alpha\exists n \neg (\alpha n^+ < \alpha n)$, called WF_1 in [37], is too strong. Specifically, our (ii) (transfinite induction) does not imply WF_1 nor even WF_2: $\forall\alpha\exists n \neg (\forall m \prec n)(\alpha m^+ < \alpha n)$ by [37], pp. 333, 335 resp. In any case, $WF_1 \rightarrow \forall x \forall y [\neg(x < y) \vee \neg(y < x)]$ (by taking $\alpha(2p) = x$, $\alpha(2p+1) = y$) and so $<$ cannot be 'too' undecidable.

Correction. While treating WF_3 and WF_4, which are intuitionistically useless by [37] p. 334, [37] omits the further classical equivalent

$$\forall\alpha[\forall n \in F) \rightarrow \exists n \neg (\alpha n^+ < \alpha n)]$$

and the (related) extended bar theorem of [17], p. 249.

41. Mathematically speaking, there are weak subsystems of PRA which seem to be equally interesting; for instance the rudimentary arithmetic of Smullyan or the remarkable applications of Kalmar's elementary functions by Rabin [22]; cf. also the occurrence of this class of functions for certain notions of complexity of computations [23].

42. When describing the notion of combinatorial proof in [19], App. II B, on p. 197, l. 11, I, inadvertently, slipped in a parenthetical restriction (to a finite number of rules) which, taken literally (cf., ibid., p. 214, l. —7), would not allow us to go beyond PRA. But for the notion intended in [19], App. II B, the restriction is simply not justified (or else the proof of validity of the system $\mathscr{S}_C$ is not correct as it stands!)

43. I may be unduly skeptical because some (peripheral?) parts of the analysis are not thought out at all. For instance, Tait refers to [9] as a source concerning Hilbert's own notion of finitist proof, goes on to say 'it is difficult perhaps to determine what Hilbert really had in mind' and argues that Ackermann's enumeration of the primitive resursive functions is not finitist. But whatever else may be in doubt, Hilbert's own notion as *used in* [9] certainly includes Ackermann's function since it is explicitly mentioned! The argument that non-trivial mathematics can be done in PRA is weak in view of note 41 above. Probably Tait has simply overstated a perfectly legitimate point. Also, as is constantly done in foundations to prepare the way for highly problematic principles (e.g. full set theory), one is tempted to draw a very *narrow* line (mechanical or formal derivations for the strict formalist) beyond which everything is 'much of a muchness'. Tait's particular concern is the use of well-founded *undecidable* species (of a certain sort); cf. note 40.

44. Compare the quotation from the year 1922 given in the last paragraph of the introduction above with ([10], p. 180 from 1923): 'results of usual mathematics... not absolute truths, ... only those of proof theory'. It would perhaps be natural to try and reconcile these views by supposing that Hilbert believed that the reliability of finitist mathematics *consists* in being *anschaulich* (visualizable in its *entirety*). But Bernays has cast coubt on this by drawing attention to [10], pp. 162–163. Of course these inconsistencies are not surprising because (as a matter of experience) in *philosophical* matters often a major advance is needed to produce as much as a semblance of coherence!

REFERENCES

[1] L. J. Brouwer, Über Definitionsbereiche von Funktionen, *Math. Ann.* **47** (1927) 60–75.

[2] S. Feferman, Transfinite recursive progressions of axiomatic theories, *J. Symb. Logic* **27** (1962) 259–316.

[3] S. Feferman, Systems of predicative analysis II, *J. Symb. Logic* **33** (1968) 193–220.

[4] S. Feferman, Autonomous transfinite progressions and the extent of predicative mathematics, in *Logic, methodology and philosophy of science*, North-Holland, Amsterdam (1968) 121–135.

[5] S. Feferman, Formal theories for transfinite iterations of generalized inductive definitions and some subsystems of analysis, these proceedings, 303–326.

[6] H. Friedman, Iterated inductive definitions and Σ_2^1–AC, these proceedings, 435–442.

[7] J. Herbrand, *Ecrits logiques*, ed. J. van Heijenoort, Paris (1968).

[8] Al Heyting, Infinitistic methods from a finitist point of view, in *Infinitistic methods*, Warsaw (1961) 185–192.

[9] D. Hilbert, Über das Unendliche, *Math. Ann.* **95** (1925) 161–190.

[10] D. Hilbert, *Gesammelte Abhandlungen* **3**, Berlin (1935).

[11] A. E. Ingham, *The distribution of prime numbers*, Cambridge, 1932.

[12] M. Krasner, Théorie de la définition, *J. Math. Pures et Appliquées* **37** (1958) 53–101 and **39** (1957) 325–357.

[13] G. Kreisel, On the interpretation of non-finitist proofs, *J. Symb. Logic* **16** (1951) 241–267.

[14] G. Kreisel, Ordinal logics and the characterization of informal notions of proof, in *Proc. Intern. congress of mathematicians*, Edinburgh (1958) 289–299.

[15] G. Kreisel, Proof by transfinite induction and definition by transfinite recursion in quantifier-free system, *J. Symb. Logic* **24** (1959) 322–323.

[16] G. Kreisel, Mathematical logic, in *Lectures on modern mathematics III*, ed. Saaty, New York (1965) 95–195.

[17] G. Kreisel, Mathematical logic: what has it done for the philosophy of mathematics, in *Bertrand Russell: Philosopher of the century*, London (1967) 201–272.

[18] G. Kreisel, Survey of proof theory, *J. Symb. Logic* **33** (1968) 321–388.*

[19] G. Kreisel and J. L. Krivine, *Elements of mathematical logic (model theory)*, Amsterdam (1967).

[20] J. R. Myhill, A system which can define its own truth, *Fund. Math.* **37** (1950) 190–192.

[21] D. Prawitz, Some results for intuitionistic logic with second order quantification rules, these proceedings, 259–269.

[22] M. O. Rabin, Decidability of second order theories and automata on infinite trees, *Bull. Am. Math. Soc.* **74** (1968) 1025–1029.

[23] R. W. Ritchie, Classes of predictably computable functions, *Trans. Am. Math. Soc.* **106** (1963) 139–173.

[24] K. Schütte, *Beweistheorie*, Berlin (1960).

[25] K. Schütte, Predicative well-orderings, in *Formal systems and recursive functions*, eds. Dummett and Crossley, Amsterdam (1965) 279–302.

[26] J. C. Shepherdson, Non-standard models for fragments of number theory, in *The theory of models*, Amsterdam (1965) 342–358.